KIPLING

A Selection of His Stories and Poems

VOLUME I

KIPLING

A Selection of His Stories and Poems

BY JOHN BEECROFT

ILLUSTRATED BY RICHARD M. POWERS

Doubleday & Company, Inc., Garden City, N. Y.

Library of Congress Catalog Card Number: 56-6647

CONTENTS

VOLUME I

INTRODUCTION

§ I HAVE always envied those friends who owned a complete set of Kipling. What a great treasury of stories, what excitement of living in an exotic world Kipling gave to those who knew him. Few authors have had the popularity Rudyard Kipling has had since his twenty-fourth year until today, almost a century after his birth. His writings have been in and out of fashion, but he always captured the interest of readers and held their attention and affection. Almost everyone has a favorite Kipling story or poem and has been loyal to his preference over the years. Other authors of his period have had their day; Kipling has always had his audience.

Rudyard Kipling (the name Rudyard was the name of a lake where his parents first met) was born in the very late days of December 1865, in Bombay, India, where his father was curator of a museum. Brought up with native servants, as a child he spoke Hindustani better than English. The Kipling family was from Yorkshire. His mother's family were Scots from the north of Ireland. Both his grandfathers were Methodist ministers—though Kipling was baptized in the Church of England. Through his mother he was related to Sir Ambrose Poynter, Sir Edward Burne-Jones and the Baldwin family, whose son, his cousin, became Prime Minister and was later created Earl Baldwin of Bewdley.

When Kipling was a young boy, not yet six years old, he was brought to England and boarded with a family where his parents expected he would be well taken care of. The brutal treatment he received there marked his entire life. For five years he suffered uncomplainingly until a breakdown brought his mother from India, and she put him in the United Services College at Westward Ho! in Devonshire. Kipling loved the school and those years he spent there gave him a security of mind and a happy memory of companionship that influenced much of his later writing.

vii

At seventeen he went back to India to take a job on a newspaper—*The Civil and Military Gazette* in Lahore. There he "never worked less than ten hours a day and seldom more than fifteen." Kipling had begun writing while in school, and he was well able to supply fillers for the paper. These sketches, tales and poems were later collected in his *Plain Tales from the Hills*, a book which was an immediate success, and is still one of his most popular works, while the poems became the lasting favorite, *Departmental Ditties*. For five years he worked at Lahore, spending a part of the hot seasons at Simla, the setting of many of his stories. Two more years were spent at Allahabad on the *Pioneer*, which gave him a chance to know other sections of India and gave him time to write the longer stories, for there again the paper needed fillers and, as Kipling said, "Why buy Bret Harte when I was prepared to supply home-grown fiction on the hoof? And I did." From these fillers came some of his most famous stories, later collected into *Soldiers Three* and *Wee Willie Winkie*. After seven years in India, Kipling sold the rights to his books for about $1250. He was given six months' salary "in lieu of notice" and took off for England by way of America.

In 1889, Kipling arrived in London. Though not yet twenty-five years old, he already had a famous name, but not too much money. At this point, in London, he wrote some of his best stories, including *Without Benefit of Clergy*, which is considered by many to be his finest short story, and from then on had little to worry about financially. He could always make money by his writing.

Though Kipling has been considered the incarnation of the British imperialist, his connections through his adult life were close with Americans. Kipling has been influenced and had admiration for the American writers of his period—Ralph Waldo Emerson, Mark Twain, Bret Harte, Edgar Allan Poe and to some extent Walt Whitman. From Emerson he adopted the style of writing a preface in verse for his prose pieces. Edmonia Hill, the American wife of a government meteorologist whom he met in Allahabad, played an important part in his life for many years. When Kipling left India it was in company with Professor and Mrs. Hill, who were returning to her home in Pennsylvania, where Kipling visited them. This visit is described in *From Sea to Sea*.

Kipling married Caroline, the sister of an American friend, Wolcott Balestier, to whom he was devoted. Caroline Balestier became his wife at All Souls', Langham Place, in London. Henry James, the famous expatriate American novelist, gave the bride away. Their honeymoon, which began two days later, was a trip around the world. At Yokohama, Kipling found that the bank he had trusted had closed its doors. They were almost penniless, but cashing in their unused travel tickets, they managed to reach Vermont, where Mrs. Kipling's family lived.

In Vermont, Kipling almost achieved happiness. The only place they could find to live was a workman's house, Bliss Cottage, near Brattleboro, which they rented for ten dollars a month. There was not adequate heating

for the Vermont winter, yet living through "with snow level high with window sill," he wrote one of his finest books, *The Jungle Book*, in which, Maugham says, "his great and varied gifts found their most brilliant expression"; there, also, was nurtured the germ of a story in which Kipling found "a vague notion of an Irish boy born in India and mixed up with native life." This was to be *Kim*—his greatest book. The Kiplings decided to live in Vermont and built a house which they called Naulahka, but after four years returned to England.

Shortly after the Kiplings were settled in England, Kipling wrote *Recessional*, which was the great poem of Victoria's Diamond Jubilee in 1897. In *The Life of Rudyard Kipling*, C. E. Carrington tells how it was another American friend of the Kiplings, Mrs. Charles Eliot Norton, who rescued this poem from the wastebasket and persuaded Kipling to allow its publication. Along with *If*, it is one of his most loved poems. In the same year of *Recessional*, Kipling's only son, John, was born. There were already two daughters, Josephine and Elsie, who were born during the American period. Kipling's devotion to his children produced two of his most loved books, *Just So Stories* and *Puck of Pook's Hill*. These have become classics in our language, adored by grownups and children alike.

The later years were steadily productive, though Kipling became more and more involved in affairs of the Empire. Despite the fact he was never named poet laureate, it was Kipling who gave the English people the poetry they loved. He knew the great men of his time and was awarded many honors. In 1907, he was given the Nobel Prize for Literature, being the first writer of his nation to be so honored. He received many academic degrees and was repeatedly offered a knighthood and orders which he consistently refused. When he died in 1936, the whole world mourned.

Somerset Maugham says that Kipling is ". . . our greatest story writer. I can't believe he will ever be equalled. I am sure he can never be excelled." In this two-volume collection of his works, I have gathered much of the best writing Kipling produced. I need no longer regret not having a shelfful of his books when I feel like reading Kipling and enjoying again an old favorite.

JOHN BEECROFT

Conway, Massachusetts
December 30, 1955

KIM

KIM

CHAPTER I

'Oh ye who tread the Narrow Way
By Tophet-flare to Judgment Day,
Be gentle when the heathen pray
To Buddha at Kamakura!'

HE SAT, in defiance of municipal orders, astride the gun Zam-Zammah on her brick platform opposite the old Ajaib-Gher—the Wonder House, as the natives call the Lahore Museum. Who hold Zam-Zammah, that 'fire-breathing dragon,' hold the Punjab, for the great green-bronze piece is always first of the conqueror's loot.

There was some justification for Kim,—he had kicked Lala Dinanath's boy off the trunnions,—since the English held the Punjab and Kim was English. Though he was burned black as any native; though he spoke the vernacular by preference, and his mother-tongue in a clipped uncertain singsong; though he consorted on terms of perfect equality with the small boys of the bazar; Kim was white—a poor white of the very poorest. The half-caste woman who looked after him (she smoked opium, and pretended to keep a second-hand furniture shop by the square where the cheap cabs wait) told the missionaries that she was Kim's mother's sister; but his mother had been nursemaid in a colonel's family and had married Kimball O'Hara, a young colour-sergeant of the Mavericks, an Irish regiment. He afterwards took a post on the Sind, Punjab, and Delhi railway, and his regiment went home without him. The wife died of cholera in Ferozepore, and O'Hara fell to drink and loafing up and down the line with the keen-eyed three-year-old baby. Societies and chaplains, anxious for the child, tried to catch him, but O'Hara drifted away, till he came across the woman who took opium and learned the taste from her, and died as poor whites die in India. His estate at death consisted of three papers—one he called his 'ne varietur' because those words were written below his signature thereon, and another his 'clearance-certificate.' The third was Kim's birth-certificate. Those things, he was used to say, in his glorious opium-hours, would yet make little Kimball a man. On no account was Kim to part with them, for they be-

longed to a great piece of magic—such magic as men practised over yonder behind the Museum, in the big blue and white Jadoo-Gher—the Magic House, as we name the Masonic Lodge. It would, he said, all come right some day, and Kim's horn would be exalted between pillars—monstrous pillars—of beauty and strength. The Colonel himself, riding on a horse, at the head of the finest regiment in the world, would attend to Kim,—little Kim that should have been better off than his father. Nine hundred first-class devils, whose god was a Red Bull on a green field, would attend to Kim, if they had not forgotten O'Hara—poor O'Hara that was gangforeman on the Ferozepore line. Then he would weep bitterly in the broken rush chair on the veranda. So it came about after his death that the woman sewed parchment, paper, and birth-certificate into a leather amulet-case which she strung round Kim's neck.

'And some day,' she said, confusedly remembering O'Hara's prophecies, 'there will come for you a great Red Bull on a green field, and the Colonel riding on his tall horse, yes, and '—dropping into English—'nine hundred devils.'

'Ah,' said Kim, 'I shall remember. A Red Bull and a Colonel on a horse will come, but first, my father said, will come the two men making ready the ground for these matters. That is how, my father said, they always did; and it is always so when men work magic.'

If the woman had sent Kim up to the local Jadoo-Gher with those papers, he would, of course, have been taken over by the Provincial Lodge and sent to the Masonic Orphanage in the Hills; but what she had heard of magic she distrusted. Kim, too, held views of his own. As he reached the years of indiscretion, he learned to avoid missionaries and white men of serious aspect who asked who he was, and what he did. For Kim did nothing with an immense success. True, he knew the wonderful walled city of Lahore from the Delhi Gate to the outer Fort Ditch; was hand in glove with men who led lives stranger than anything Haroun al Raschid dreamed of; and he lived in a life wild as that of the Arabian Nights, but missionaries and secretaries of charitable societies could not see the beauty of it. His nickname through the wards was 'Little Friend of all the World'; and very often, being lithe and inconspicuous, he executed commissions by night on the crowded housetops for sleek and shiny young men of fashion. It was intrigue, of course,—he knew that much, as he had known all evil since he could speak,—but what he loved was the game for its own sake—the stealthy prowl through the dark gullies and lines, the crawl up a water-pipe, the sights and sounds of the women's world on the flat roofs, and the headlong flight from housetop to housetop under cover of the hot dark. Then there were holy men, ash-smeared faquirs by their brick shrines under the trees at the riverside, with whom he was quite familiar—greeting them as they returned from begging-tours, and, when no one was by, eating from the same dish. The woman who looked after him insisted with tears that he should wear European clothes—trousers, a shirt, and a battered hat. Kim found it easier to

slip into Hindu or Mohammedan garb when engaged on certain businesses. One of the young men of fashion—he who was found dead at the bottom of a well on the night of the earthquake—had once given him a complete suit of Hindu kit, the costume of a low-caste street boy, and Kim stored it in a secret place under some baulks in Nila Ram's timber-yard, beyond the Punjab High Court, where the fragrant deodar logs lie seasoning after they have driven down the Ravee. When there was business or frolic afoot, Kim would use his properties, returning at dawn to the veranda, all tired out from shouting at the heels of a marriage procession, or yelling at a Hindu festival. Sometimes there was food in the house, more often there was not, and then Kim went out again to eat with his native friends.

As he drummed his heels against Zam-Zammah he turned now and again from his king-of-the-castle game with little Chota Lal, and Abdullah the sweetmeat-seller's son, to make a rude remark to the native policeman on guard over rows of shoes at the Museum door. The big Punjabi grinned tolerantly: he knew Kim of old. So did the water-carrier, sluicing water on the dry road from his goat-skin bag. So did Jawahir Singh, the Museum carpenter, bent over new packing-cases. So did everybody in sight except the peasants from the country, hurrying up to the Wonder House to view the things that men made in their own Province and elsewhere. The Museum was given up to Indian arts and manufactures, and anybody who sought wisdom could ask the curator to explain.

'Off! Off! Let me up!' cried Abdullah, climbing up Zam-Zammah's wheel.

'Thy father was a pastry-cook, Thy mother stole the ghi,' sang Kim. 'All Mussalmans fell off Zam-Zammah long ago!'

'Let me up!' shrilled little Chota Lal in his gilt-embroidered cap. His father was worth perhaps half a million sterling, but India is the only democratic land in the world.

'The Hindus fell off Zam-Zammah too. The Mussalmans pushed them off. Thy father was a pastry-cook—'

He stopped; for there shuffled round the corner, from the roaring Motee Bazar, such a man as Kim, who thought he knew all castes, had never seen. He was nearly six feet high, dressed in fold upon fold of dingy stuff like horse-blanketing, and not one fold of it could Kim refer to any known trade or profession. At his belt hung a long open-work iron pencase and a wooden rosary such as holy men wear. On his head was a gigantic sort of tam-o'-shanter. His face was yellow and wrinkled, like that of Fook Shing, the Chinese bootmaker in the bazar. His eyes turned up at the corners and looked like little slits of onyx.

'Who is that?' said Kim to his companions.

'Perhaps it is a man,' said Abdullah, finger in mouth, staring.

'Without doubt,' returned Kim; 'but he is no man of India that I have ever seen.'

'A priest, perhaps,' said Chota Lal, spying the rosary. 'See! He goes

into the Wonder House!'

'Nay, nay,' said the policeman, shaking his head. 'I do not understand your talk.' The constable spoke Punjabi. 'Oh, Friend of all the World, what does he say?'

'Send him hither,' said Kim, dropping from Zam-Zammah, flourishing his bare heels. 'He is a foreigner, and thou art a buffalo.'

The man turned helplessly and drifted towards the boys. He was old, and his woollen gaberdine still reeked of the stinking artemisia of the mountain passes.

'O Children, what is that big house?' he said in very fair Urdu.

'The Ajaib-Gher, the Wonder House!' Kim gave him no title—such as Lala or Mian. He could not divine the man's creed.

'Ah! The Wonder House! Can any enter?'

'It is written above the door—all can enter.'

'Without payment?'

'I go in and out. I am no banker,' laughed Kim.

'Alas! I am an old man. I did not know.' Then, fingering his rosary, he half turned to the Museum.

'What is your caste? Where is your house? Have you come far?' Kim asked.

'I came by Kulu—from beyond the Kailas—but what know you? From the hills where'—he sighed—'the air and water are fresh and cool.'

'Aha! Khitai' (Chinaman), said Abdullah proudly. Fook Shing had once chased him out of his shop for spitting at the joss above the boots.

'Pahari?' (a hillman), said little Chota Lal.

'Aye, child—a hillman from hills thou'lt never see. Didst hear of Bhotiyal (Tibet)? I am no Khitai, but a Bhotiya (Tibetan), since you must know—a lama—or, say a guru in your tongue.'

'A guru from Tibet,' said Kim. 'I have not seen such a man. They be Hindus in Tibet, then?'

'We be followers of the Middle Way, living in peace in our lamas-series, and I go to see the Four Holy Places before I die. Now do you, who are children, know as much as I do who am old.' He smiled benignantly on the boys.

'Hast thou eaten?'

He fumbled in his bosom and drew forth a worn wooden begging-bowl. The boys nodded. All priests of their acquaintance begged.

'I do not wish to eat yet.' He turned his head like an old tortoise in the sunlight. 'Is it true that there are many images in the Wonder House of Lahore?' He repeated the last words as one making sure of an address.

'That is true,' said Abdullah. 'It is full of heathen buts. Thou also art an idolator.'

'Never mind him,' said Kim. 'That is the Government's house and there is no idolatry in it, but only a Sahib with a white beard. Come with me and I will show.'

'Strange priests eats boys,' whispered Chota Lal.

'And he is a stranger and a but-parast' (idolater), said Abdullah, the Mohammedan.

Kim laughed. 'He is new. Run to your mothers' laps, and be safe. Come!'

Kim clicked round the self-registering turnstile; the old man followed and halted amazed. In the entrance-hall stood the larger figures of the Greco-Buddhist sculptures done, savants know how long since, by forgotten workmen whose hands were feeling, and not unskilfully, for the mysteriously transmitted Grecian touch. There were hundreds of pieces, friezes of figures in relief, fragments of statues and slabs crowded with figures that had encrusted the brick walls of the Buddhist stupas and viharas of the North Country and now, dug up and labelled, made the pride of the Museum. In open-mouthed wonder the lama turned to this and that, and finally checked in rapt attention before a large alto-relief representing a coronation or apotheosis of the Lord Buddha. The Master was represented seated on a lotus the petals of which were so deeply undercut as to show almost detached. Round Him was an adoring hierarchy of kings, elders, and old-time Buddhas. Below were lotus-covered waters with fishes and water-birds. Two butterfly-winged dewas held a wreath over His head; above them another pair supported an umbrella surmounted by the jewelled headdress of the Bodhisat.

'The Lord! The Lord! It is Sakya Muni himself,' the lama half sobbed; and under his breath began the wonderful Buddhist invocation:—

'To Him the Way—the Law—Apart—
Whom Maya held beneath her heart
Ananda's Lord—the Bodhisat.

'And He is here! The Most Excellent Law is here also! My pilgrimage is well begun. And what work! What work!'

'Yonder is the Sahib,' said Kim, and dodged sideways among the cases of the arts and manufacture wing. A white-bearded Englishman was looking at the lama, who gravely turned and saluted him and after some fumbling drew forth a note-book and a scrap of paper.

'Yes, that is my name,' smiling at the clumsy, childish print.

'One of us who had made pilgrimage to the Holy Places—he is now Abbot of the Lung-Cho Monastery—gave it me,' stammered the lama. 'He spoke of these.' His lean hand moved tremulously round.

'Welcome, then, O lama from Tibet. Here be the images, and I am here'—he glanced at the lama's face—'to gather knowledge. Come to my office awhile.' The old man was trembling with excitement.

The office was but a little wooden cubicle partitioned off from the sculpture-lined gallery. Kim laid himself down, his ear against a crack in the heat-split cedar door, and, following his instinct, stretched out to listen and watch.

Most of the talk was altogether above his head. The lama, haltingly at first, spoke to the curator of his own lamassery, the Suchzen, opposite the Painted Rocks, four months' march away. The curator brought out a huge book of photos and showed him that very place, perched on its crag, overlooking the gigantic valley of many-hued strata.

' Ay, ay! ' The lama mounted a pair of horn-rimmed spectacles of Chinese work. ' Here is the little door through which we bring wood before winter. And thou—the English know of these things? He who is now Abbot of Lung-Cho told me, but I did not believe. The Lord—the Excellent One— He has honour here too? And His life is known? '

' It is all carven upon the stones. Come and see, if thou art rested.'

Out shuffled the lama to the main hall, and, the curator beside him, went through the collection with the reverence of a devotee and the appreciative instinct of a craftsman.

Incident by incident in the beautiful story he identified on the blurred stone, puzzled here and there by the unfamiliar Greek convention, but delighted as a child at each new trove. Where the sequence failed, as in the Annunciation, the curator supplied it from his mound of books—French and German, with photographs and reproductions.

Here was the devout Asita, the pendant of Simeon in the Christian story, holding the Holy Child on his knee while mother and father listened; and here were incidents in the legend of the cousin Devadatta. Here was the wicked woman who accused the Master of impurity, all confounded; here was the teaching in the Deer-park; the miracle that stunned the fire-worshippers; here was the Bodhisat in royal state as a prince; the miraculous birth; the death at Kusinagara, where the weak disciple fainted; while there were almost countless repetitions of the meditation under the Bodhi tree; and the adoration of the alms-bowl was everywhere. In a few minutes the curator saw that his guest was no mere bead-telling mendicant, but a scholar of parts. And they went at it all over again, the lama taking snuff, wiping his spectacles, and talking at railway speed in a bewildering mixture of Urdu and Tibetan. He had heard of the travels of the Chinese pilgrims, Fo-Hian and Hwen-Thiang, and was anxious to know if there was any translation of their record. He drew in his breath as he turned helplessly over the pages of Beal and Stanislas Julien. ' 'Tis all here. A treasure locked.' Then he composed himself reverently to listen to fragments, hastily rendered into Urdu. For the first time he heard of the labours of European scholars, who by the help of these and a hundred other documents have identified the Holy Places of Buddhism. Then he was shown a mighty map, spotted and traced with yellow. The brown finger followed the curator's pencil from point to point. Here was Kapilavastu, here the Middle Kingdom, and here Mahabodi, the Mecca of Buddhism; and here was Kusinagara, sad place of the Holy One's death. The old man bowed his head over the sheets in silence for a while, and the curator lit another pipe. Kim had fallen asleep. When he waked, the talk, still in spate, was more within his comprehension.

'And thus it was, O Fountain of Wisdom, that I decided to go to the Holy Places which His foot had trod—to the Birth-place, even to Kapila; then to Maha Bodhi, which is Buddh Gaya—to the Monastery—to the Deer-park—to the place of His death.'

The lama lowered his voice. 'And I come here alone. For five—seven—eighteen—forty years it was in my mind that the Old Law was not well followed; being overlaid, as thou knowest, with devildom, charms, and idolatry. Even as the child outside said but now. Aye, even as the child said, with but-parasti.'

'So it comes with all faiths.'

'Thinkest thou? The books of my lamassery I read, and they were dried pith; and the later ritual with which we of the Reformed Law have cumbered ourselves—that, too, had no worth to these old eyes. Even the followers of the Excellent One are at feud on feud with one another. It is all illusion. Ay, maya, illusion. But I have another desire '—the seamed yellow face drew within three inches of the curator, and the long forefinger nail tapped on the table. 'Your scholars, by these books, have followed the Blessed Feet in all their wanderings; but there are things which they have not sought out. I know nothing,—nothing do I know,—but I go to free myself from the Wheel of Things by a broad and open road.' He smiled with most simple triumph. 'As a pilgrim to the Holy Places I acquire merit. But there is more. Listen to a true thing. When our gracious Lord, being as yet a youth, sought a mate, men said, in His father's court, that He was too tender for marriage. Thou knowest?'

The curator nodded, wondering what would come next.

'So they made the triple trial of strength against all comers. And at the test of the Bow, our Lord first breaking that which they gave Him, called for such a bow as none might bend. Thou knowest?'

'It is written. I have read.'

'And, overshooting all other marks, the arrow passed far and far beyond sight. At the last it fell; and, where it touched earth, there broke out a stream which presently became a River, whose nature, by our Lord's beneficence, and that merit He acquired ere He freed himself, is that whoso bathes in it washes away all tint and speckle of sin.'

'So it is written,' said the curator sadly.

The lama drew a long breath. 'Where is that River? Fountain of Wisdom, where fell the arrow?'

'Alas, my brother, I do not know,' said the curator.

'Nay, if it please thee to forget—the one thing only that thou hast not told me. Surely thou must know? See, I am an old man! I ask with my head between thy feet, O Fountain of Wisdom. We know He drew the bow! We know the arrow fell! We know the stream gushed! Where, then, is the River? My dream told me to find it. So I came. I am here. But where is the River?'

'If I knew, think you I would not cry it aloud?'

'By it one attains freedom from the Wheel of Things,' the lama went

on, unheeding. 'The River of the Arrow! Think again! Some little stream,
may be—dried in the heats? But the Holy One would never so cheat an old
man.'

'I do not know. I do not know.'

The lama brought his thousand-wrinkled face once more a hands-
breadth from the Englishman's. 'I see thou dost not know. Not being of
the Law, the matter is hid from thee.'

'Ay—hidden—hidden.'

'We are both bound, thou and I, my brother. But I '—he rose with a
sweep of the soft thick drapery—'I go to cut myself free. Come also!'

'I am bound,' said the curator. 'But whither goest thou?'

'First to Kashi (Benares): where else? There I shall meet one of the
pure faith in a Jain temple of that city. He also is a Seeker in secret, and
from him haply I may learn. May be he will go with me to Buddh Gaya.
Thence north and west to Kapilavastu, and there will I seek for the River.
Nay, I will seek everywhere as I go—for the place is not known where the
arrow fell.'

'And how wilt thou go? It is a far cry to Delhi, and farther to Benares.'

'By road and the trains. From Pathankot, having left the Hills, I came
hither in a te-rain. It goes swiftly. At first I was amazed to see those tall poles
by the side of the road snatching up and snatching up their threads,'—he
illustrated the stoop and whirl of a telegraph-pole flashing past the train.
'But later, I was cramped and desired to walk, as I am used.'

'And thou art sure of thy road?' said the curator.

'Oh, for that one but asks a question and pays money, and the ap-
pointed persons despatch all to the appointed place. That much I knew in
my lamassery from sure report,' said the lama proudly.

'And when dost thou go?' The curator smiled at the mixture of old-
world piety and modern progress that is the note of India to-day.

'As soon as may be. I follow the places of His life till I come to the
River of the Arrow. There is, moreover, a written paper of the hours of the
trains that go south.'

'And for food?' Lamas, as a rule, have good store of money some-
where about them, but the curator wished to make sure.

'For the journey, I take up the Master's begging-bowl. Yes. Even as
He went so go I, forsaking the ease of my monastery. There was with me
when I left the hills a chela (disciple) who begged for me as the Rule de-
mands, but halting in Kulu awhile a fever took him and he died. I have now
no chela, but I will take the alms-bowl and thus enable the charitable to
acquire merit.' He nodded his head valiantly.

Learned doctors of a lamassery do not beg, but the lama was an enthusi-
ast in this quest.

'Be it so,' said the curator, smiling. 'Suffer me now to acquire merit.
We be craftsmen together, thou and I. Here is a new book of white English
paper: here be sharpened pencils two and three—thick and thin, all good

for a scribe. Now lend me thy spectacles.'

The curator looked through them. They were heavily scratched, but the power was almost exactly that of his own pair, which he slid into the lama's hand, saying: ' Try these.'

' A feather! A very feather upon the face! ' The old man turned his head delightedly and wrinkled up his nose. ' How scarcely do I feel them! How clearly do I see! '

' They be bilaur—crystal and will never scratch. May they help thee to thy River, for they are thine.'

' I will take them and the pencils and the white note-book,' said the lama, ' as a sign of friendship between priest and priest—and now '—he fumbled at his belt, detached the open iron-work pencase, and laid it on the curator's table. ' That is for a memory between thee and me—my pencase. It is something old—even as I am.'

It was a piece of ancient design, Chinese, of an iron that is not smelted these days; and the collector's heart in the curator's bosom had gone out to it from the first. For no persuasion would the lama resume his gift.

' When I return, having found the River, I will bring thee a written picture of the Padma Samthora—such as I used to make on silk at the lamassery. Yes—and of the Wheel of Life,' he chuckled, ' for we be crafts-men together, thou and I.'

The curator would have detained him: they are few in the world who still have the secret of the conventional brush-pen Buddhist pictures which are, as it were, half written and half drawn. But the lama strode out, head high in air, and pausing an instant before the great statue of a Bodhisat in meditation, brushed through the turnstiles.

Kim followed like a shadow. What he had overheard excited him wildly. This man was entirely new to all his experience, and he meant to investigate further: precisely as he would have investigated a new building or a strange festival in Lahore city. The lama was his trove, and he purposed to take pos-session. Kim's mother had been Irish too.

The old man halted by Zam-Zammah and looked round till his eye fell on Kim. The inspiration of his pilgrimage had left him for a while, and he felt old, forlorn, and very empty.

' Do not sit under that gun,' said the policeman loftily.

' Huh! Owl! ' was Kim's retort on the lama's behalf. ' Sit under that gun if it please thee. When didst thou steal the milk-woman's slippers, Dunnoo? '

That was an utterly unfounded charge sprung on the spur of the mo-ment, but it silenced Dunnoo, who knew that Kim's clear yell could call up legions of bad bazar boys if need arose.

' And whom didst thou worship within? ' said Kim affably, squatting in the shade beside the lama.

' I worshipped none, child. I bowed before the Excellent Law.'

Kim accepted this new god without emotion. He knew already a few score.

'And what dost thou do?'

'I beg. I remember now it is long since I have eaten or drunk. What is the custom of charity in this town? In silence, as we do of Tibet, or speaking aloud?'

'Those who beg in silence starve in silence,' said Kim, quoting a native proverb. The lama tried to rise, but sank back again, sighing for his disciple, dead in faraway Kulu. Kim watched—head to one side, considering and interested.

'Give me the bowl. I know the people of this city—all who are charitable. Give, and I will bring it back filled.'

Simply as a child the old man handed him the bowl.

'Rest thou. I know the people.'

He trotted off to the open shop of a kunjri, a low-caste vegetable-seller, which lay opposite the belt-tramway line down the Motee Bazar. She knew Kim of old.

'Oho, hast thou turned yogi with thy begging-bowl?' she cried.

'Nay,' said Kim proudly. 'There is a new priest in the city—a man such as I have never seen.'

'Old priest—young tiger,' said the woman angrily. 'I am tired of new priests! They settle on our wares like flies. Is the father of my son a well of charity to give to all who ask?'

'No,' said Kim. 'Thy man is rather yagi (bad-tempered) than yogi (a holy man). But this priest is new. The Sahib in the Wonder House has talked to him like a brother. O my mother, fill me this bowl. He waits.'

'That bowl indeed! That cow-bellied basket! Thou hast as much grace as the holy bull of Shiv. He has taken the best of a basket of onions already, this morn; and forsooth, I must fill thy bowl. He comes here again.'

The huge, mouse-coloured Brahminee bull of the ward was shouldering his way through the many-coloured crowd, a stolen plantain hanging out of his mouth. He headed straight for the shop, well knowing his privileges as a sacred beast, lowered his head, and puffed heavily along the line of baskets ere making his choice. Up flew Kim's hard little heel and caught him on his moist blue nose. He snorted indignantly, and walked away across the tram rails, his hump quivering with rage.

'See! I have saved more than the bowl will cost thrice over. Now, mother, a little rice and some dried fish atop—yes, and some vegetable curry.'

A growl came out of the back of the shop, where a man lay.

'He drove away the bull,' said the woman in an undertone. 'It is good to give to the poor.' She took the bowl and returned it full of hot rice.

'But my yogi is not a cow,' said Kim gravely, making a hole with his fingers in the top of the mound. 'A little curry is good, and a fried cake, and a morsel of conserve would please him, I think.'

'It is a hole as big as thy head,' said the woman fretfully. But she filled

it, none the less, with good, steaming vegetable curry, clapped a dried cake atop, and a morsel of clarified butter on the cake, dabbed a lump of sour tamarind conserve at the side; and Kim looked at the load lovingly.

'That is good. When I am in the bazar the bull shall not come to this house. He is a bold beggarman.'

'And thou?' laughed the woman. 'But speak well of bulls. Hast thou not told me that some day a Red Bull will come out of a field to help thee? Now hold all straight and ask for the holy man's blessing upon me. Perhaps,

too, he knows a cure for my daughter's sore eyes. Ask him that also, O thou Little Friend of all the World.'

But Kim had danced off ere the end of the sentence, dodging pariah dogs and hungry acquaintances.

'Thus do we beg who know the way of it,' said he proudly to the lama, who opened his eyes at the contents of the bowl. 'Eat now and—I will eat with thee. Ohe bhistie!' he called to the water-carrier, sluicing the crotons by the Museum. 'Give water here. We men are thirsty.'

'We men!' said the bhistie, laughing. 'Is one skinful enough for such a pair? Drink then, in the name of the Compassionate.'

He loosed a thin stream into Kim's hands, who drank native fashion;

but the lama must needs pull out a cup from his inexhaustible upper draperies and drink ceremonially.

'Pardesi' (a foreigner), Kim explained, as the old man delivered in an unknown tongue what was evidently a blessing.

They ate together in great content, clearing the beggar's bowl. Then the lama took snuff from a portentous wooden snuff-gourd, fingered his rosary awhile, and so dropped into the easy sleep of age, as the shadow of Zam-Zammah grew long.

Kim loafed over to the nearest tobacco-seller, a rather lively young Mohemmedan woman, and begged a rank cigar of the brand that they sell to students of the Punjab University who copy English customs. Then he smoked and thought, knees to chin, under the belly of the gun, and the outcome of his thoughts was a sudden and stealthy departure in the direction of Nila Ram's timber-yard.

The lama did not wake till the evening life of the city had begun with lamp-lighting and the return of white-robed clerks and subordinates from the Government offices. He stared dizzily in all directions, but none looked at him save a Hindu urchin in a dirty turban and Isabella-coloured clothes. Suddenly he bowed his head on his knees and wailed.

'What is this?' said the boy, standing before him. 'Hast thou been robbed?'

'It is my new chela (my disciple) that is gone away from me, and I know not where he is.'

'And what like of man was thy disciple?'

'It was a boy who came to me in place of him who died, on account of the merit which I had gained when I bowed before the Law within there.' He pointed toward the Museum. 'He came upon me to show me a road which I had lost. He led me into the Wonder House, and by his talk emboldened to speak to the Keeper of the Images, so that I was cheered and made strong. And when I was faint with hunger he begged for me, as would a chela for his teacher. Suddenly was he sent. Suddenly has he gone away. It was in my mind to have taught him the Law upon the road to Benares.'

Kim stood amazed at this, because he had overheard the talk in the Museum, and knew that the old man was speaking the truth, which is a thing a native on the road seldom presents to a stranger.

'But I see now that he was but sent for a purpose. By this I know that I shall find a certain River for which I seek.'

'The River of the Arrow?' said Kim, with a superior smile.

'Is this yet another Sending?' cried the lama. 'To none have I spoken of my search, save to the Priest of the Images. Who art thou?'

'Thy chela,' said Kim simply, sitting on his heels. 'I have never seen any one like to thee in all this my life. I go with thee to Benares. And, too, I think that so old a man as thou, speaking the truth to chance-met people at dusk, is in great need of a disciple."

'But the River—the River of the Arrow?'

' Oh, that I heard when thou wast speaking to the Englishman. I lay against the door.'

The lama sighed. ' I thought thou hadst been a guide permitted. Such things fall sometimes—but I am not worthy. Thou dost not, then, know of the River? '

' Not I.' Kim laughed uneasily. ' I go to look for—for a bull—a Red Bull on a green field who shall help me.' Boylike, if an acquaintance had a scheme, Kim was quite ready with one of his own; and, boylike, he had really thought for as much as twenty minutes at a time of his father's prophecy.

' To what, child? ' said the lama.

' God knows, but so my father told me. I heard thy talk in the Wonder House of all those new strange places in the Hills, and if one so old and so little—so used to truth-telling—may go out for the small matter of a river, it seemed to me that I too must go a-travelling. If it is our fate to find those things we shall find them—thou, thy River; and I, my Bull, and the strong Pillars and some other matters that I forget.'

' It is not pillars but a Wheel from which I would be free,' said the lama.

' That is all one. Perhaps they will make me a king,' said Kim, serenely prepared for anything.

' I will teach thee other and better desires upon the road,' the lama replied in the voice of authority. ' Let us go to Benares.'

' Not by night. Thieves are abroad. Wait till the day.'

' But there is no place to sleep.' The old man was used to the order of his monastery, and though he slept on the ground, as the Rule decrees, preferred a decency in these things.

' We shall get good lodging at the Kashmir Serai,' said Kim, laughing at his perplexity. ' I have a friend there. Come! '

The hot and crowded bazars blazed with light as they made their way through the press of all the races in Upper India, and the lama mooned through it like a man in a dream. It was his first experience of a large manufacturing city, and the crowded tram-car with its continually squealing brakes frightened him. Half pushed, half towed, he arrived at the high gate of the Kashmir Serai: that huge open square over against the railway station, surrounded with arched cloisters where the camel and horse caravans put up on their return from Central Asia. Here were all manner of Northern folk, tending tethered ponies and kneeling camels; loading and unloading bales and bundles; drawing water for the evening meal at the creaking well-windlasses; piling grass before the shrieking, wild-eyed stallions; cuffing the surly caravan dogs; paying off camel-drivers; taking on new grooms; swearing, shouting, arguing, and chaffering in the packed square. The cloisters, reached by three or four masonry steps, made a haven of refuge around this turbulent sea. Most of them were rented to traders, as we rent the arches of a viaduct; the space between pillar and pillar being bricked or boarded off into rooms,

which were guarded by heavy wooden doors and cumbrous native padlocks. Locked doors showed that the owner was away, and a few rude—sometimes very rude—chalk or paint scratches told where he had gone. Thus: ' Lutuf Ullah is gone to Kurdistan.' Below, in coarse verse: ' O Allah, who sufferest lice to live on the coat of a Kabuli, why hast thou allowed this louse Lutuf to live so long? '

Kim, fending the lama between excited men and excited beasts, sidled along the cloisters to the far end, nearest the railway station, where Mahbub Ali, the horsetrader, lived when he came in from that mysterious land beyond the Passes of the North.

Kim had had many dealings with Mahbub in his little life,—especially between his tenth and his thirteenth year,—and the big burly Afghan, his beard dyed scarlet with lime (for he was elderly and did not wish his gray hairs to show), knew the boy's value as a gossip. Sometimes he would tell Kim to watch a man who had nothing whatever to do with horses: to follow him for one whole day and report every soul with whom he talked. Kim would deliver himself of his tale at evening, and Mahbub would listen without a word or gesture. It was intrigue of some kind, Kim knew; but its worth lay in saying nothing whatever to any one except Mahbub, who gave him beautiful meals all hot from the cookshop at the head of the serai, and once as much as eight annas in money.

' He is here,' said Kim, hitting a bad-tempered camel on the nose. ' Ohe, Mahbub Ali! ' He halted at a dark arch and slipped behind the bewildered lama.

The horse-trader, his deep, embroidered Bokhariot belt unloosed, was lying on a pair of silk carpet saddle-bags, pulling lazily at an immense silver hookah. He turned his head very slightly at the cry; and seeing only the tall silent figure, chuckled in his deep chest.

' Allah! A lama! A Red Lama! It is far from Lahore to the Passes. What dost thou do here? '

The lama held out the begging-bowl mechanically.

' God's curse on all unbelievers! ' said Mahbub. ' I do not give to a lousy Tibetan; but ask my Baltis over yonder behind the camels. They may value your blessings. Oh, horse-boys, here is a countryman of yours. See if he be hungry.'

A shaven, crouching Balti, who had come down with the horses, and who was nominally some sort of degraded Buddhist, fawned upon the priest, and in thick gutturals besought the Holy One to sit at the horse-boys' fire.

' Go! ' said Kim, pushing him lightly, and the lama strode away, leaving Kim at the edge of the cloister.

' Go! ' said Mahbub Ali, returning to his hookah. ' Little Hindu, run away. God's curse on all unbelievers! Beg from those of my tail who are of thy faith.'

' Maharaj,' whined Kim, using the Hindu form of address, and thoroughly enjoying the situation; ' my father is dead—my mother is dead— my stomach is empty.'

'Beg from my men among the horses, I say. There must be some Hindus in my tail.'

'Oh, Mahbub Ali, but am I a Hindu?' said Kim in English.

The trader gave no sign of astonishment, but looked under shaggy eyebrows.

'Little Friend of all the World,' said he, 'what is this?'

'Nothing. I am now that holy man's disciple; and we go a pilgrimage together—to Benares, he says. He is quite mad, and I am tired of Lahore city. I wish new air and water.'

'But for whom dost thou work? Why come to me?' The voice was harsh with suspicion.

'To whom else should I come? I have no money. It is not good to go about without money. Thou wilt sell many horses to the officers. They are very fine horses, these new ones: I have seen them. Give me a rupee, Mahbub Ali, and when I come to my wealth I will give thee a bond and pay.'

'Um,' said Mahbub Ali, thinking swiftly. 'Thou hast never before lied to me. Call that lama—stand back in the dark.'

'Oh, our tales will agree,' said Kim laughing.

'We go to Benares,' said the lama, as soon as he understood the drift of Mahbub Ali's questions. 'The boy and I. I go to seek for a certain River.'

'Maybe—but the boy?'

'He is my disciple. He was sent, I think, to guide me to that River. Sitting under a gun was I when he came suddenly. Such things have befallen the fortunate to whom guidance was allowed. But I remember now, he said he was of this world—a Hindu.'

'And his name?'

'That I did not ask. Is he not my disciple?'

'His country—his face—his village? Mussalman—Sikh—Hindu—Jain—low caste or high?'

'Why should I ask? There is neither high nor low in the Middle Way. If he is my chela—does—will—can any one take him from me? for, look you, without him I shall not find my River.' He wagged his head solemnly.

'None shall take him from thee. Go, sit among my Baltis,' said Mahbub Ali, and the lama drifted off, soothed by the promise.

'Is he not quite mad?' said Kim, coming forward to the light again. 'Why should I lie to thee, Hajji?'

Mahbub puffed his hookah in silence. Then he began, almost whispering: 'Umballa is on the road to Benares—if indeed ye two go there.'

'Tck! Tck! I tell thee he does not know how to lie—as we two know.'

'And if thou wilt carry a message for me as far as Umballa, I will give thee money. It concerns a horse—a white stallion which I have sold to an officer upon the last time I returned from the Passes. But then—stand nearer and hold up hands as begging—the pedigree of the white stallion was not fully established, and that officer, who is now at Umballa, bade me make it clear.' (Mahbub here described the horse and the appearance of the

officer.) ' So the message to that officer will be: " The pedigree of the white stallion is fully established." By this will he know that thou comest from me. He will then say " What proof hast thou? " and thou wilt answer: " Mahbub Ali has given me the proof." '

' And all for the sake of a white stallion,' said Kim, with a giggle, his eyes aflame.

' That pedigree I will give thee now—in my own fashion—and some hard words as well.' A shadow passed behind Kim, and a feeding camel. Mahbub Ali raised his voice.

' Allah! Art thou the only beggar in the city? Thy mother is dead. Thy father is dead. So is it with all of them. Well, well— ' he turned as feeling on the floor beside him and tossed a flap of soft, greasy Mussalman bread to the boy. ' Go and lie among my horse-boys for to-night—thou and the lama. To-morrow I may give thee service.'

Kim slunk away, his teeth in the bread, and, as he expected, he found a small wad of folded tissue-paper wrapped in oil-skin, with three silver rupees—enormous largesse. He smiled and thrust money and paper into his leather amulet-case. The lama, sumptuously fed by Mahbub's Baltis, was already asleep in a corner of one of the stalls. Kim lay down beside him and laughed. He knew he had rendered a service to Mahbub Ali, and not for one little minute did he believe the tale of the stallion's pedigree.

But Kim did not suspect that Mahbub Ali, known as one of the best horse-dealers in the Punjab, a wealthy and enterprising trader, whose caravans penetrated far and far into the Back of Beyond, was registered in one of the locked books of the Indian Survey Department as C.25.1B. Twice or thrice yearly C.25 would send in a little story, badly told but most interesting, and generally—it was checked by the statements of R.17 and M.4—quite true. It concerned all manner of out-of-the-way mountain principalities, explorers of nationalities other than English, and the gun-trade—was, in brief, a small portion of that vast mass of ' information received ' on which the Indian Government acts. But, recently, five confederated Kings, who had no business to confederate, had been informed by a kindly Northern Power that there was a leakage of news from their territories into British India. So those Kings' prime ministers were seriously annoyed and took steps, after the Oriental fashion. They suspected, among many others, the bullying red-bearded horse-dealer whose caravans ploughed through their fastnesses belly deep in snow. At least, his caravan that season had been ambushed and shot at twice on the way down, when Mahbub's men accounted for three strange ruffians who might, or might not, have been hired for the job. Therefore Mahbub had avoided halting at the insalubrious city of Peshawur, and had come through without stop to Lahore, where, knowing his country-people, he anticipated curious developments.

And there was that on Mahbub Ali which he did not wish to keep an hour longer than was necessary—a wad of closely folded tissue-paper, wrapped in oil-skin—an impersonal, unaddressed statement, with five mi-

croscopic pin-holes in one corner, that most scandalously betrayed the five confederated Kings, the sympathetic Northern Power, a Hindu banker in Peshawur, a firm of gun-makers in Belgium, and an important, semi-independent Mohammedan ruler to the south. This last was R.17's work, which Mahbub had picked up beyond the Dora Pass and was carrying in for R.17, who, owing to circumstances over which he had no control, could not leave his post of observation. Dynamite was milky and innocuous beside that report of C.25; and even an Oriental, with an Oriental's views of the value of time, could see that the sooner it was in the proper hands the better. Mahbub had no particular desire to die by violence, because two or three family blood-feuds across the border hung unfinished on his hands, and when these scores were cleared he intended to settle down as a more or less virtuous citizen. He had never passed the serai gate since his arrival two days ago, but had been ostentatious in sending telegrams to Bombay, where he banked some of his money; to Delhi, where a sub-partner of his own clan was selling horses to the agent of a Rajputana state; and to Umballa, where an Englishman was excitedly demanding the pedigree of a white stallion. The public letter-writer, who knew English, composed excellent telegrams, such as:— ' Creighton, Laurel Bank, Umballa.—Horse is Arabian as already advised. Sorrowful delayed-pedigree which am translating.' And later to the same address: ' Much sorrowful delay. Will forward pedigree.' To this sub-partner at Delhi he wired: ' Lutuf Ullah.—Have wired two thousand rupees your credit Luchman Narain's bank.' This was entirely in the way of trade, but every one of those telegrams was discussed and re-discussed, by parties who conceived themselves to be interested, before they went over to the railway station in charge of a foolish Balti, who allowed all sorts of people to read them on the road.

When, in Mahbub's own picturesque language, he had muddied the wells of inquiry with the stick of precaution, Kim had dropped on him, sent from heaven; and, being as prompt as he was unscrupulous, Mahbub Ali, used to taking all sorts of gusty chances, pressed him into service on the spot.

A wandering lama with a low-caste boy-servant might attract a moment's interest as they wandered about India, the land of pilgrims; but no one would suspect them or, what was more to the point, rob.

He called for a new light-ball to his hookah, and considered the case. If the worst came to the worst, and the boy came to harm, the paper would incriminate nobody. And he would go up to Umballa leisurely and—at a certain risk of exciting fresh suspicion—repeat his tale by word of mouth to the people concerned.

But R.17's report was the kernel of the whole affair, and it would be distinctly inconvenient if that failed to come to hand. However, God was great, and Mahbub Ali felt he had done all he could for the time being. Kim was the one soul in the world who had never told him a lie. That would have been a fatal blot on Kim's character if Mahbub had not known that

to others, for his own ends or Mahbub's business, Kim could lie like an Oriental.

Then Mahbub Ali rolled across the serai to the Gate of the Harpies who paint their eyes and trap the stranger, and was at some pains to call on the one girl who, he had reason to believe, was a particular friend of a smooth-faced Kashmiri pundit who had waylaid his simple Balti in the matter of the telegrams. It was an utterly foolish thing to do; because they fell to drinking perfumed brandy against the Law of the Prophet, and Mahbub grew wonderfully drunk, and the gates of his mouth were loosened, and he pursued the Flower of Delight with the feet of intoxication till he fell flat among the cushions, where the Flower of Delight, aided by a smooth-faced Kashmiri pundit, searched him from head to foot most thoroughly.

About the same hour Kim heard soft feet in Mahbub's deserted stall. The horse-trader, curiously enough, had left his door unlocked, and his men were busy celebrating their return to India with a whole sheep of Mahbub's bounty. A sleek young gentleman from Delhi, armed with a bunch of keys

which the Flower had unshackled from the senseless one's belt, went through every single box, bundle, mat, and saddle-bag in Mahbub's possession even more systematically than the Flower and the pundit were searching the owner.

'And I think,' said the Flower scornfully an hour later, one rounded elbow on the snoring carcase, 'that he is no more than a pig of an Afghan horse-dealer, with no thought except women and horses. Moreover, he may have sent it away by now—if ever there were such a thing.'

'Nay—in a matter touching Five Kings it would be next his black heart,' said the pundit. 'Was there nothing?'

The Delhi man laughed and resettled his turban as he entered. 'I searched between the soles of his slippers as the Flower searched his clothes. This is not the man but another. I leave little unseen.'

'They did not say he was the very man,' said the pundit thoughtfully. 'They said, "Look if he be the man, since our councils are troubled."'

'That North country is full of horse-dealers as an old coat of lice. There is Sikandar Khan, Nur Ali Beg, and Farrukh Shah—all heads of Kafilas—who deal there,' said the Flower.

'They have not yet come in,' said the pundit. 'Thou must ensnare them later.'

'Phew!' said the Flower with deep disgust, rolling Mahbub's head from her lap. 'I earn my money. Farrukh Shah is a bear, Ali Beg a swashbuckler, and old Sikandar Khan—yaie! Go! I sleep now. This swine will not stir till dawn.'

When Mahbub woke, the Flower talked to him severely on the sin of drunkenness. Asiatics do not wink when they have outmanœuvred an enemy, but as Mahbub Ali cleared his throat, tightened his belt, and staggered forth under the early morning stars, he came very near to it.

'What a colt's trick,' said he to himself. 'As if every girl in Peshawur did not use it! But 'twas prettily done. Now God He knows how many more there be upon the road who have orders to test me—perhaps with

the knife. So it stands that the boy must go to Umballa—and by rail—for the writing is something urgent. I abide here, following the Flower and drinking wine as an Afghan coper should.'

He halted at the stall next but one to his own. His men lay there heavy with sleep. There was no sign of Kim or the lama.

'Up! ' He stirred a sleeper. 'Whither went those who lay here last even—the lama and the boy? Is aught missing? '

'Nay,' grunted the man; 'the old madman rose at second cock-crow saying he would go to Benares, and the young one led him away.'

'The curse of Allah on all unbelievers,' said Mahbub heartily, and climbed into his own stall, growling in his beard.

But it was Kim who had wakened the lama—Kim with one eye laid against a knot-hole in the planking, who had seen the Delhi man's search through the boxes. This was no common thief that turned over letters, bills, and saddles—no mere burglar who ran a little knife sideways into the soles of Mahbub's slippers, or picked the seams of the saddle-bags so deftly. At first Kim had been minded to give the alarm—the long-drawn ' cho-or—choor! ' (thief! thief!) that sets the serai ablaze of nights; but he looked more carefully, and, hand on amulet, drew his own conclusions.

' It must be the pedigree of that made-up horse-lie,' said he, ' the thing that I carry to Umballa. Better that we go now. Those who search bags with knives may presently search bellies with knives. Surely there is a woman behind this. Hai! Hai! ' in a whisper to the light-sleeping old man. ' Come. It is time—time to go to Benares.'

The lama rose obediently, and they passed out of the serai like shadows.

CHAPTER II

'For whoso will, from Pride released,
 Contemning neither creed nor priest,
 May hear the Soul of all the East
 About him at Kamakura.'

They entered the fort-like railway station, black in the end of night; the electrics sizzling over the goods yard where they handle the heavy Northern grain-traffic.

' This is the work of devils! ' said the lama, recoiling from the hollow echoing darkness, the glimmer of rails between the masonry platforms, and the maze of girders above. He stood in a gigantic stone hall paved, it seemed, with the sheeted dead—third-class passengers who had taken their tickets overnight and were sleeping in the waiting-rooms. All hours of the twenty-four are alike to Orientals, and their passenger traffic is regulated accordingly.

' This is where the fire-carriages come. One stands behinds that hole '—

Kim pointed to the ticket-office—'who will give thee a paper to take thee to Umballa.'

'But we go to Benares,' he replied petulantly.

'All one. Benares then. Quick: she comes!'

'Take thou the purse.'

The lama, not so well used to trains as he had pretended, started as the 3.25 a. m. south bound roared in. The sleepers sprang to life, and the station filled with clamour and shoutings, cries of water and sweetmeat vendors, shouts of native policemen, and shrill yells of women gathering up their baskets, their families, and their hubands.

'It is the train—only the te-rain. It will come here. Wait!' Amazed at the lama's immense simplicity (he had handed him a small bag full of rupees), Kim asked and paid for a ticket to Umballa. A sleepy clerk gruntcd and flung out a ticket to the next station, just six miles distant.

'Nay,' said Kim, scanning it with a grin. 'This may serve for farmers, but I live in the city of Lahore. It was cleverly done, babu. Now give the ticket to Umballa.'

The babu scowled and dealt the proper ticket.

'Now another to Amritzar,' said Kim, who had no notion of spending Mahbub Ali's money on anything so crude as a paid ride to Umballa. 'The price is so much. The small money in return is just so much. I know the ways of the te-rain. . . . Never did yogi need chela as thou dost,' he went on merrily to the bewildered lama. 'They would have flung thee out at Mian Mir but for me. This way! Come.' He returned the money, keeping only one anna in each rupee of the price of the Umballa ticket as his commission—the immemorial commission of Asia.

The lama jibbed at the open door of a crowded third-class carriage. 'Were it not better to walk?' said he weakly.

A burly Sikh artisan thrust forth his bearded head. 'Is he afraid? Do not be afraid. I remember the time when I was afraid of the te-rain. Enter! This thing is the work of the Government.'

'I do not fear,' said the lama. 'Have ye room within for two?'

'There is no room even for a mouse,' shrilled the wife of a well-to-do cultivator—a Hindu Jat from the rich Jullundur district. 'Our night trains are not as well looked after as the day ones, where the sexes are very strictly kept to separate carriages.'

'Oh, mother of my son, we can make space,' said the blue-turbaned husband. 'Pick up the child. It is a holy man, see'st thou?'

'And my lap full of seventy times seven bundles! Why not bid him sit on my knee, Shameless? But men are ever thus!' She looked round for approval. An Amritzar courtesan near the window sniffed behind her head drapery.

'Enter! Enter!' cried a fat Hindu money-lender, his folded account-book in a cloth under his arm. With an oily smirk: 'It is well to be kind to the poor.'

'Ay, at seven per cent a month with a mortgage on the unborn calf,' said a young Dogra soldier going south on leave; and they all laughed.

'Will it travel to Benares?' said the lama.

'Assuredly. Else why should we come? Enter, or we are left,' cried Kim.

'See!' shrilled the Amritzar girl. 'He has never entered a train. Oh see!'

'Nay, help,' said the cultivator, putting out a large brown hand and hauling him in. 'Thus is it done, father.'

'But—but—I sit on the floor. It is against the Rule to sit on a bench,' said the lama. 'Moreover, it cramps me.'

'I say,' began the money-lender, pursing his lips, 'that there is not one rule of right living which these te-rains do not cause us to break. We sit, for example, side by side with all castes and peoples.'

'Yea, and with most outrageously shameless ones,' said the wife, scowling at the Amritzar girl making eyes at the young sepoy.

'I said we might have gone by cart along the road,' said the husband, 'and thus have saved some money.'

'Yes—and spent twice over what we saved on food by the way. That was talked out ten thousand times.'

'Aye, by ten thousand tongues,' grunted he.

'The Gods help us poor women if we may not speak. Oho! He is of that sort which may not look at or reply to a woman.' For the lama, constrained by his Rule, took not the faintest notice of her. 'And his disciple is like him?'

'Nay, mother,' said Kim most promptly. 'Not when the woman is well-looking and above all charitable to the hungry.'

'A beggar's answer,' said the Sikh, laughing. 'Thou hast brought it on thyself, sister!' Kim's hands were crooked in supplication.

'And whither goest thou?' said the woman, handing him the half of a cake from a greasy package.

'Even to Benares.'

'Jugglers belike?' the young soldier suggested. 'Have ye any tricks to pass the time? Why does not that yellow man answer?'

'Because,' said Kim stoutly, 'he is holy, and thinks upon matters hidden from thee.'

'That may be well. We of the Loodhiana Sikhs,' he rolled it out sonorously, 'do not trouble our heads with doctrine. We fight.'

'My sister's brother's son is naik (corporal) in that regiment,' said the Sikh craftsman quietly. 'There are also some Dogra companies there.' The soldier glared, for a Dogra is of other caste than a Sikh, and the banker tittered.

'They are all one to me,' said the Amritzar girl.

'That we believe,' snorted the cultivator's wife malignantly.

'Nay, but all who serve the Sirkar with weapons in their hands are, as it were, one brotherhood. There is one brotherhood of the caste, but

beyond that again '—she looked round timidly—' the bond of the Pulton—the Regiment—eh? '

' My brother is in a Jat regiment,' said the cultivator. ' Dogras be good men.'

' Thy Sikhs at least were of that opinion,' said the soldier, with a scowl at the placid old man in the corner. ' Thy Sikhs thought so when our two companies came to help them at the Pirzai Kotal in the face of eight Afreedee standards on the ridge not three months gone.'

He told the story of a border action in which the Dogra companies of the Loodhiana Sikhs had acquitted themselves well. The Amritzar girl smiled; for she knew the tale was to win her approval.

' Alas! ' said the cultivator's wife at the end. ' So their villages were burnt and their little children made homeless? '

' They had marked our dead. They paid a great payment after we of the Sikhs had schooled them. So it was. Is this Amritzar? '

' Ay, and here they cut our tickets,' said the banker, fumbling at his belt.

The lamps were paling in the dawn when the half-caste guard came round. Ticket-collecting is a slow business in the East, where people secrete their tickets in all sorts of curious places. Kim produced his and was told to get out.

' But I go to Umballa,' he protested. ' I go with this holy man.'

' Thou canst go to Jehannum for aught I care. This ticket is only to Amritzar. Out! '

Kim burst into a flood of tears, protesting that the lama was his father and his mother, that he was the prop of the lama's declining years, and that the lama would die without his care. All the carriage bade the guard be merciful,—the banker was specially eloquent here,—but the guard hauled Kim on to the platform. The lama blinked, he could not overtake the situation and Kim lifted up his voice and wept outside the carriage window.

' I am very poor. My father is dead—my mother is dead. Oh, charitable ones, if I am left here, who shall tend that old man? '

' What—what is this? ' the lama repeated. ' He must go to Benares. He must come with me. He is my chela. If there is money to be paid— '

' Oh, be silent,' whispered Kim; ' are we Rajahs to throw away good silver when the world is so charitable? '

The Amritzar girl stepped out with her bundles, and it was on her that Kim kept his watchful eye. Ladies of that persuasion, he knew, were generous.

' A ticket—a little tikkut to Umballa—O Breaker of Hearts! ' She laughed. ' Hast thou no charity? '

' Does the holy man come from the North? '

' From far and far in the North he comes,' cried Kim. ' From among the hills.'

' There is snow among the pine trees in the North—in the hills there

is snow. My mother was from Kulu. Get thee a ticket. Ask him for a blessing.'

'Ten thousand blessings,' shrilled Kim. 'O Holy One, a woman has given us in charity so that I can come with thee—a woman with a golden heart. I run for the tikkut.'

The girl looked up at the lama, who had mechanically followed Kim to the platform. He bowed his head that he might not see her, and muttered in Tibetan as she passed on with the crowd.

'Light come—light go,' said the cultivator's wife viciously.

'She has acquired merit,' returned the lama. 'Beyond doubt it was a nun.'

'There be ten thousand such nuns in Amritzar alone. Return, old man, or the train may depart without thee,' cried the banker.

'Not only was it sufficient for the ticket, but for a little food also,' said Kim, leaping to his place. 'Now eat, Holy One. Look. Day comes! '

Golden, rose, saffron, and pink, the morning mists smoked away across the flat green levels. All the rich Punjab lay out in the splendour of the keen sun. The lama flinched a little as the telegraph-posts swung by.

'Great is the speed of the train,' said the banker, with a patronising grin. 'We have gone farther since Lahore than thou couldst walk in two days: at even, we shall enter Umballa.'

'And that is still far from Benares,' said the lama wearily, mumbling over the cakes that Kim offered. They all unloosed their bundles and made their morning meal. Then the banker, the cultivator, and the soldier prepared their pipes and wrapped the compartment in choking, acrid smoke, spitting and coughing and enjoying themselves. The Sikh and the cultivator's wife chewed pan; the lama took snuff and told his beads, while Kim, cross-legged, smiled over the comfort of a full stomach.

'What rivers have ye by Benares?' said the lama of a sudden to the carriage at large.

'We have Gunga,' returned the banker, when the little titter had subsided.

'What others? '

'What other than Gunga? '

'Nay, but in my mind was the thought of a certain River of healing.'

'That is Gunga. Who bathes in her is made clean and goes to the gods. Thrice have I made pilgrimage to Gunga.' He looked round proudly.

'There was need,' said the young sepoy drily, and the travellers' laugh turned against the banker.

'Clean—to return again to the Gods,' the lama muttered. 'And to go forth on the round of lives anew—still tied to the Wheel.' He shook his head testily. 'But maybe there is a mistake. Who, then, made Gunga in the beginning? '

'The Gods. Of what known faith art thou? ' the banker said, appalled.

'I follow the Law—the Most Excellent Law. So it was the Gods that made Gunga. What like of Gods were they? '

The carriage looked at him in amazement. It was inconceivable that any one should be ignorant of Gunga.

'What—what is thy God?' said the money-lender at last.

'Hear!' said the lama, shifting the rosary to his hand. 'Hear: for I speak of Him now! O people of Hind, listen!'

He began in Urdu the tale of the Lord Buddha, but, borne by his own thoughts, slid into Tibetan and long-droned texts from a Chinese book of the Buddha's life. The gentle, tolerant folk looked on reverently. All India is full of holy men stammering gospels in strange tongues; shaken and consumed in the fires of their own zeal; dreamers, babblers, and visionaries: as it has been from the beginning and will continue to the end.

'Um!' said the soldier of the Loodhina Sikhs. 'There was a Mohammedan regiment lay next to us at the Pirzai Kotal, and a priest of theirs,—he was, as I remember, a naik,—when the fit was on him, spake prophecies. But the mad all are in God's keeping. His officers overlooked much in that man.'

The lama fell back on Urdu, remembering that he was in a strange land. 'Hear the tale of the Arrow which our Lord loosed from the bow,' he said.

This was much more to their taste, and they listened curiously while he told it. 'Now, O people of Hind, I go to seek that River. Know ye aught that may guide me, for we be all men and women in evil case.'

'There is Gunga—and Gunga alone—who washes away sin,' ran the murmur round the carriage.

'Though past question we have good Gods Jullundurway,' said the cultivator's wife, looking out of window. 'See how they have blessed the crops.'

'To search every river in the Punjab is no small matter,' said her husband. 'For me, a stream that leaves good silt on my land suffices, and I thank Bhumia, the God of the Homestead.' He shrugged one knotted, bronzed shoulder.

'Think you our Lord came so far north?' said the lama, turning to Kim.

'It may be,' Kim replied soothingly, as he spat red pan-juice on the floor.

'The last of the Great Ones,' said the Sikh with authority, 'was Sikander Julkarn (Alexander the Great). He paved the streets of Jullundur and built a great tank near Umballa. That pavement holds to this day; and the tank is there also. I never heard of thy God.'

'Let thy hair grow long and talk Punjabi,' said the young soldier jestingly to Kim, quoting a Northern proverb. 'That is all that makes a Sikh.' But he did not say this very loud.

The lama sighed and shrank into himself, a dingy, shapeless mass. In the pauses of their talk they could hear the low droning—'Om mane pudme hum! Om mane pudme hum!'—and the thick click of the wooden rosary beads.

'It irks me,' he said at last. 'The speed and the clatter irk me. Moreover, my chela, I think that may be we have overpassed that River.'

'Peace, peace,' said Kim. 'Was not the River near Benares? We are yet far from the place.'

'But—if our Lord came north, it may be any one of these little ones that we have run across.'

'I do not know.'

'But thou wast sent to me—wast thou sent to me?—for the merit I had acquired over yonder at Suchzen. From beside the cannon didst thou come—bearing two faces—and two garbs.'

'Peace. One must not speak of these things here,' whispered Kim. 'There was but one of me. Think again and thou wilt remember. A boy—a Hindu boy—by the great green cannon.'

'But was there not also an Englishman with a white beard—holy—among images—who himself made more sure my assurance of the River of the Arrow?'

'He—we—went to the Ajaib-Gher in Lahore to pray before the gods there,' Kim explained to the openly listening company. 'And the Sahib of the Wonder House talked to him—yes, this is truth—as a brother. He is a very holy man, from far beyond the hills. Rest thou. In time we come to Umballa.'

'But my River—the River of my healing?'

'And then, if it please thee, we will go hunting for that River on foot. So that we miss nothing—not even a little rivulet in a field-side.'

'But thou hast a Search of thine own?' The lama—very pleased that he remembered so well—sat bolt upright.

'Ay,' said Kim, humouring him. The boy was entirely happy to be out chewing pan and seeing new people in the great good-tempered world.

'It was a Bull—a Red Bull that shall come and help thee—and carry thee—whither? I have forgotten. A Red Bull on a green field, was it not?'

'Nay, it will carry me nowhere,' said Kim. 'It is but a tale I told thee.'

'What is this?' The cultivator's wife leaned forward, her bracelets clinking on her arm. 'Do ye both dream dreams? A Red Bull on a green field, that shall carry thee to the Heavens—or what? Was it a vision? Did one make a prophecy? We have a Red Bull in our village behind Jullundur city, and he grazes by choice in the very greenest of our fields!'

'Give a woman an old wife's tale and a weaver-bird a leaf and a thread, they will weave wonderful things,' said the Sikh. 'All holy men dream dreams, and by following holy men their disciples attain that power.'

'A Red Bull on a green field, was it?' the lama repeated. 'In a former life it may be thou hast acquired merit, and the Bull will come to reward thee.'

'Nay—nay—it was but a tale one told to me—for a jest belike. But I will seek the Bull about Umballa, and thou canst look for thy River and rest from the clatter of the train.'

'It may be that the Bull knows—that he is sent to guide us both,' said the lama, hopefully as a child. Then to the company, indicating Kim: 'This one was sent to me but yesterday. He is not, I think, of this world.'

'Beggars a plenty have I met, and holy men to boot, but never such a yogi nor such a disciple,' said the woman.

Her husband touched his forehead lightly with one finger and smiled. But the next time the lama would eat they took care to give him their best.

And at last—tired, sleepy, and dusty—they reached Umballa City Station.

'We abide here upon a law-suit,' said the cultivator's wife to Kim. 'We lodge with my man's cousin's younger brother. There is room also in the courtyard for thy yogi and for thee. Will—will he give me a blessing?'

'O holy man! A woman with a heart of gold gives us lodging for the night. It is a kindly land, this land of the South. See how we have been helped since the dawn!'

The lama bowed his head in benediction.

'To fill my cousin's younger brother's house with wastrels—' the husband began, as he shouldered his heavy bamboo staff.

'Thy cousin's younger brother owes my father's cousin something yet on his daughter's marriage-feast,' said the woman crisply. 'Let him put their food to that account. The yogi will beg, I doubt not.'

'Ay, I beg for him,' said Kim, anxious only to get the lama under shelter for the night, that he might seek Mahbub Ali's Englishman and deliver himself of the white stallion's pedigree.

'Now,' said he, when the lama had come to an anchor in the inner courtyard of a decent Hindu house behind the cantonments, 'I go away for a while—to—to buy us victual in the bazar. Do not stray abroad till I return.'

'Thou wilt return? Thou wilt surely return?' The old man caught at his wrist. 'And thou wilt return in this very same shape? Is it too late to look to-night for the River?'

'Too late and too dark. Be comforted. Think how far thou art on the road—an hundred kos from Lahore already.'

'Yea—and farther from my monastery. Alas! It is a great and terrible world.'

Kim stole out and away, as unremarkable a figure as ever carried his own and a few score thousand other folk's fate slung round his neck. Mahbub Ali's directions left him little doubt of the house in which his Englishman lived; and a groom, bringing a dog-cart home from the Club, made him quite sure. It remained only to identify his man, and Kim slipped through the garden hedge and hid in a clump of plumed grass close to the veranda. The house blazed with lights, and servants moved about tables dressed with flowers, glass, and silver. Presently forth came an Englishman, dressed in black and white, humming a tune. It was too dark to see his face, so Kim, beggar-wise, tried an old experiment.

'Protector of the Poor!'

The man backed towards the voice.

'Mahbub Ali says——'

'Hah! What says Mahbub Ali?' He made no attempt to look for the speaker, and that showed Kim that he knew.

'The pedigree of the white stallion is fully established.'

'What proof is there?' The Englishman switched at the rose-hedge in the side of the drive.

'Mahbub Ali has given me this proof.' Kim flipped the wad of folded paper into the air, and it fell on the path beside the man, who put his foot on it as a gardener came round the corner. When the servant passed he picked it up, dropped a rupee,—Kim could hear the clink,—and strode into the house, never turning round. Swiftly Kim took up the money; but, for all his training, he was Irish enough by birth to reckon silver the least part of any game. What he desired was the visible effect of action; so, instead of slinking away, he lay close in the grass and wormed nearer to the house.

He saw—Indian bungalows are open through and through—the Englishman return to a small dressing-room, in a corner of the veranda, that was half-office, littered with papers and despatch-boxes, and sit down to study Mahbub Ali's message. His face, by the full ray of the kerosene lamp, changed and darkened, and Kim, used as every beggar must be to watching countenances, took good note.

'Will! Will, dear!' called a woman's voice. 'You ought to be in the drawing-room. They'll be here in a minute.'

The man still read intently.

'Will!' said the voice, five minutes later. 'He's come. I can hear the troopers in the drive.'

The man dashed out bareheaded as a big landau with four native troopers behind it halted at the veranda, and a tall, black-haired man, erect as an arrow, swung out, preceded by a young officer who laughed pleasantly.

Flat on his belly lay Kim, almost touching the high wheels. His man and the black stranger exchanged two sentences.

'Certainly, sir,' said the young officer promptly. 'Everything waits while a horse is concerned.'

'We shan't be more than twenty minutes,' said Kim's man. 'You can do the honours—keep 'em amused, and all that.'

'Tell one of the troopers to wait,' said the tall man, and they both passed into the dressing-room together as the landau rolled away. Kim saw their heads bent over Mahbub Ali's message, and heard the voices—one low and deferential, the other sharp and decisive.

'It isn't a question of weeks. It is a question of days—hours almost,' said the elder. 'I'd been expecting it for some time, but this'—he tapped Mahbub Ali's paper—'clenches it. Grogan's dining here to-night, isn't he?'

'Yes, sir, and Macklin too.'

'Very good. I'll speak to them myself. That matter will be referred to

the Council, of course, but this is a case where one is justified in assuming that we take action at once. Warn the Pindi and Peshawur brigades. It will disorganize all the summer reliefs, but we can't help that. This comes of not smashing them thoroughly the first time. Eight thousand should be enough.'

'What about artillery, sir?'

'I must consult Macklin.'

'Then it means war?'

'No. Punishment. When a man is bound by the action of his predecessor—'

'But C.25 may have lied.'

'He bears out the other's information. Practically, they showed their hand six months back. But Devenish would have it there was a chance of peace. Of course they used it to make themselves stronger. Send off those telegrams at once,—the new code, not the old,—mine and Wharton's. I don't think we need keep the ladies waiting any longer. We can settle the rest over the cigars. I thought it was coming. It's punishment—not war.'

As the trooper cantered off Kim crawled round to the back of the house, where, going on his Lahore experiences, he judged there would be food— and information. The kitchen was crowded with excited scullions, one of whom kicked him.

'Aie,' said Kim, feigning tears. 'I came only to wash dishes in return for a bellyful.'

'All Umballa is on the same errand. Get hence. They go in now with the soup. Think you that we who serve Creighton Sahib need strange scullions to help us through a big dinner?'

'It is a very big dinner,' said Kim, looking at the plates.

'Small wonder. The guest of honour is none other than the Jang-i-Lat Sahib' (the Commander-in-Chief).

'Ho!' said Kim, with the correct guttural note of wonder. He had learned what he wanted, and when the scullion turned he was gone.

'And all that trouble,' said he to himself, thinking as usual in Hindustanee, 'for a horse's pedigree! Mahbub Ali should have come to me to learn a little lying. Every time before that I have borne a message it concerned a woman. Now it is men. Better. The tall man said that they will loose a great army to punish some one—somewhere—the news goes to Pindi and Peshawur. There are also guns. Would I had crept nearer. It is big news!'

He returned to find the cultivator's cousin's younger brother discussing the family law-suit in all its bearings with the cultivator and his wife and a few friends, while the lama dozed. After the evening meal some one passed him a water-pipe; and Kim felt very much of a man as he pulled at the smooth cocoanut-shell, his legs spread abroad in the moonlight, his tongue clicking in remarks from time to time. His hosts were most polite; for the cultivator's wife had told them of his vision of the Red Bull, and of his probable descent from another world. Moreover, the lama was a great and

venerable curiosity. The family priest, an old, tolerant Sarsut Brahmin, dropped in later, and naturally started a theological argument to impress the family. By creed, of course, they were all on their priest's side, but the lama was the guest and the novelty. His gentle kindliness, and his impressive Chinese quotations, that sounded like spells, delighted them hugely; and in this sympathetic, simple air he expanded like the Bodhisat's own lotus, speaking of his life in the great hills of Suchzen, before, as he said, ' I rose up to seek enlightenment.'

Then it came out that in those worldly days he had been a master-hand at casting horoscopes and nativities; and the family priest led him on to describe his methods; each giving the planets names that the other could not understand, and pointing upwards as the big stars sailed across the dark. The children of the house tugged unrebuked at his rosary; and he clean forgot the Rule which forbids looking at women as he talked of enduring snows, landslips, blocked passes, the remote cliffs where men find sapphires and turquoise, and that wonderful upland road that leads at last into Great China itself.

' How thinkest thou of this one? ' said the cultivator aside to the priest.

' A holy man—a holy man indeed. His Gods are not the Gods, but his feet are upon the Way,' was the answer. ' And his methods of nativities, though that is beyond thee, are wise and sure.'

' Tell me,' said Kim lazily, ' whether I find my Red Bull on a green field, as was promised me.'

' What knowledge hast thou of thy birth-hour? ' the priest asked, swelling with importance.

' Between first and second cockcrow of the first night in May.'

' Of what year? '

' I do not know; but upon the hour that I cried first fell the great earthquake in Srinagur which is in Kashmir.' This Kim had from the woman who took care of him, and she again from Kimball O'Hara. The earthquake had been felt in India, and for long stood a leading date in the Punjab.

' Ali! ' said a woman excitedly. This seemed to make Kim's supernatural origin more certain. ' Was not such an one's daughter born then— '

' And her mother bore her husband four sons in four years—all likely boys,' cried the cultivator's wife, sitting outside the circle in the shadow.

' None reared in the knowledge,' said the family priest, ' forget how the planets stood in their Houses upon that night.' He began to draw in the dust of the courtyard. ' At least thou hast good claim to a half of the House of the Bull. How runs thy prophecy? '

' Upon a day,' said Kim, delighted at the sensation he was creating, ' I shall be made great by means of a Red Bull on a green field, but first there will enter two men making all things ready.'

' Yes: thus ever at the opening of a vision. A thick darkness that clears slowly; anon one enters with a broom making ready the place. Then begins the Sight. Two men—thou sayest? Ay, ay. The Sun, leaving the House of

the Bull, enters that of the Twins. Hence the two men of the prophecy. Let us now consider. Fetch me a twig, little one.'

He knitted his brows, scratched, smoothed out, and scratched again in the dust mysterious signs—to the wonder of all save the lama, who, with fine instinct, forbore to interfere.

At the end of half an hour he tossed the twig from him with a grunt.

' Hm. Thus say the stars. Within three days come the two men to make all things ready. After them follows the Bull; but the sign over against him is the sign of War and armed men.'

' There was indeed a man of the Loodhiana Sikhs in the carriage from Lahore,' said the cultivator's wife hopefully.

' Tck! Armed men—many hundreds. What concern hast thou with war? ' said the priest to Kim. ' Thine is a red and an angry sign of War to be loosed very soon.'

' None—none,' said the lama earnestly. ' We seek only peace and our River.'

Kim smiled, remembering what he had overheard in the dressing-room. Decidedly he was a favourite of the stars.

The priest brushed his foot over the rude horoscope. ' More than this I cannot see. In three days comes the Bull to thee, boy.'

' And my River, my River,' pleaded the lama. ' I had hoped his Bull would lead us both to the River.'

' Alas, for that wondrous River, my brother,' the priest replied. ' Such things are not common.'

Next morning, though they were pressed to stay, the lama insisted on departure. They gave Kim a large bundle of good food and nearly three annas in copper money for the needs of the road, and with many blessings watched the two go southward in the dawn.

' Pity it is that these and such as these could not be freed from the Wheel of Things,' said the lama.

' Nay, then would only evil people be left on the earth, and who would give us meat and shelter? ' quoth Kim, stepping merrily under his burden.

' Yonder is a small stream. Let us look,' said the lama, and he led from the white road across the fields; walking into a very hornets'-nest of pariah dogs.

CHAPTER III

'Yea, voice of every Soul that clung
To Life that strove from rung to rung
When Devadatta's rule was young,
The warm wind brings Kamakura.'

Behind them an angry farmer brandished a bamboo pole. He was a market-gardener, Arain by caste, growing vegetables and flowers for Umballa city, and well Kim knew the breed.

'Such an one,' said the lama, disregarding the dogs, 'is impolite to strangers, intemperate of speech and uncharitable. Be warned by his demeanour, my disciple.'

'Ho, shameless beggars!' shouted the farmer. 'Begone! Get hence!'

'We go,' the lama returned, with quiet dignity. 'We go from these unblessed fields.'

'Ah,' said Kim, sucking in his breath. 'If the next crop fails, thou canst only blame thy own tongue.'

The man shuffled uneasily in his slippers. 'The land is full of beggars,' he began, half apologetically.

'And by what sign didst thou know that we would beg from thee, O Mali?' said Kim tartly, using the name that a market-gardener least likes. 'All we sought was to look at that river beyond the field there.'

'River, forsooth!' the man snorted. 'What city do ye hail from not to know a canal-cut? It runs as straight as an arrow, and I pay for the water as though it were molten silver. There is a branch of a river beyond. But if ye need water I can give that—and milk.'

'Nay, we will go to the river,' said the lama, striding out.

'Milk and a meal,' the man stammered, as he looked at the strange tall figure. 'I—I would not draw evil upon myself—or my crops; but beggars are so many in these hard days.'

'Take notice,' the lama turned to Kim. 'He was led to speak harshly by the Red Mist of anger. That clearing from his eyes, he becomes courteous and of an affable heart. May his fields be blessed. Beware not to judge men too hastily, O farmer.'

'I have met holy ones who would have cursed thee from hearthstone to byre,' said Kim to the abashed man. 'Is he not wise and holy? I am his disciple.'

He cocked his nose in the air loftily and stepped across the narrow field-borders with great dignity.

'There is no pride,' said the lama, after a pause, 'there is no pride among such as follow the Middle Way.'

'But thou hast said he was low caste and discourteous.'

'Low caste I did not say, for how can that be which is not? Afterwards he amended his discourtesy, and I forgot the offense. Moreover, he is as we are, bound upon the Wheel of Things; but he does not tread the way of deliverance.' He halted at a little runlet among the fields, and considered the hoof-pitted bank.

'Now, how wilt thou know thy River?' said Kim, squatting in the shade of some tall sugar-cane.

'When I find it, an enlightenment will surely be given. This, I feel, is not the place. O littlest among the waters, if only thou couldst tell me where runs my River! But be thou blessed to make the fields bear!'

'Look! Look!' Kim sprang to his side and dragged him back. A yellow and brown streak glided from the purple rustling stems to the bank, stretched its neck to the water, drank, and lay still—a big cobra with fixed, lidless eyes.

'I have no stick—I have no stick,' said Kim. 'I will get one and break his back.'

'Why? He is upon the Wheel as we are—a life ascending or descending—very far from deliverance. Great evil must the soul have done that is cast into this shape.'

'I hate all snakes,' said Kim. No native training can quench the white man's horror of the Serpent.

'Let him live out his life.' The coiled thing hissed and half opened its hood. 'May thy release come soon, brother,' the lama continued placidly. 'Hast thou knowledge, by chance, of my River?'

'Never have I seen such a man as thou art,' Kim whispered, overwhelmed. 'Do the very snakes understand thy talk?'

'Who knows?' He passed within a foot of the cobra's poised head. It flattened itself among the dusty coils.

'Come thou!' he called over his shoulder.

'Not I,' said Kim. 'I go round.'

'Come. He does no hurt.'

Kim hesitated for a moment. The lama backed his order by some droned Chinese quotation which Kim took for a charm. He obeyed and bounded across the rivulet, and the snake, indeed, made no sign.

'Never have I seen such a man.' Kim wiped the sweat from his forehead. 'And now, whither go we?'

'That is for thee to say. I am old, and a stranger—far from my own place. But that the rel-carriage fills my head with noises of devil-drums I would go in it to Benares now. . . . Yet by so going we may miss the River. Let us find another river.'

Where the hard-worked soil gives three and even four crops a year—through patches of sugar-cane, tobacco, long white radishes, and nol-kol, all that day they strolled on, turning aside to every glimpse of water; rousing

village dogs and sleeping villages at noonday; the lama replying to the vollied questions with an unswerving simplicity. They sought a River—a River of miraculous healing. Had any one knowledge of such a stream? Sometimes men laughed, but more often heard the story out to the end and offered them a place in the shade, a drink of milk, and a meal. The women were always kind, and the little children as children are the world over, alternately shy and venturesome. Evening found them at rest under the village tree of a mud-walled, mud-roofed hamlet, talking to the headman as the cattle came in from the grazing-grounds and the women prepared the day's last meal. They had passed beyond the belt of market-gardens round hungry Umballa, and were among the mile-wide green of the staple crops.

He was a white-bearded and affable elder, used to entertaining strangers. He dragged out a string bedstead for the lama, set warm cooked food before him, prepared him a pipe, and, the evening ceremonies being finished in the village temple, sent for the village priest.

Kim told the older children tales of the size and beauty of Lahore, of railway travel, and such-like city things, while the men talked, slowly as their cattle chew the cud.

' I cannot fathom it,' said the headman at last to the priest. ' How readest thou this talk? ' The lama, his tale told, was silently telling his beads.

' He is a Seeker,' the priest answered. ' The land is full of such. Remember him who came only last month—the faquir with the tortoise? '

' Ay, but that man had right and reason, for Krishna Himself appeared in a vision promising him Paradise without the burning-pyre if he journeyed to Prayag. This man seeks no god who is within my knowledge.'

' Peace, he is old: he comes from far off, and he is mad,' the smooth-shaven priest replied. ' Hear me.' He turned to the lama. ' Three kos (six miles) to the westward runs the great road to Calcutta.'

' But I would go to Benares—to Benares.'

' And to Benares also. It crosses all streams on this side of Hind. Now my word to thee, Holy One, is rest here till to-morrow. Then take the road ' (it was the Grand Trunk Road he meant) ' and test each stream that it over-passes; for, as I understand, the virtue of thy River lies neither in one pool nor place, but throughout its length. Then, if thy gods will, be assured that thou wilt come upon thy freedom.'

' That is well said.' The lama was much impressed by the plan. ' We will begin to-morrow, and a blessing on thee for showing old feet such a near road.' A deep, sing-song Chinese half-chant closed the sentence. Even the priest was impressed, and the headman feared an evil spell: but none could look at the lama's simple, eager face and doubt him long.

' Seest thou my chela? ' he said, diving into his snuff-gourd with an important sniff. It was his duty to repay courtesy with courtesy.

' I see—and hear.' The headman rolled his eye where Kim was chatting to a girl in blue as she laid crackling thorns on a fire.

' He also has a Search of his own. No river, but a Bull. Yea, a Red Bull

on a green field will some day raise him to honour. He is, I think, not alto-
gether of this world. He was sent of a sudden to aid me in this search, and
his name is Friend of all the World.'

The priest smiled. ' Ho there, Friend of all the World,' he cried across
the sharp-smelling smoke, ' what art thou? '

' This Holy One's disciple,' said Kim.

' He says thou art a but ' (a spirit).

' Can buts eat? ' said Kim, with a twinkle. ' For I am hungry.'

' It is no jest,' cried the lama. ' A certain astrologer of that city whose
name I have forgotten— '

' That is no more than the city of Umballa where we slept last night,'
Kim whispered to the priest.

' Ay, Umballa was it? He cast a horoscope and declared that my chela
should find his desire within two days. But what said he of the meaning
of the stars, Friend of all the World? '

Kim cleared his throat and looked around at the village gray-beards.

' The meaning of my Star is War,' he replied pompously.

Somebody laughed at the little tattered figure strutting on the brickwork
plinth under the great tree. Where a native would have lain down, Kim's
white blood set him upon his feet.

' Ay, War,' he answered.

' That is a sure prophecy,' rumbled a deep voice. ' For there is always
war along the Border—as I know.'

It was an old, withered man, who had served the Government in the
days of the Mutiny as a native officer in a newly raised cavalry regiment.
The Government had given him a good holding in the village, and though
the demands of his sons, now gray-bearded officers on their own account, had
impoverished him, he was still a person of consequence. English officials—
Deputy Commissioners even—turned aside from the main road to visit him,
and on those occasions he dressed himself in the uniform of ancient days,
and stood up like a ramrod.

' But this shall be a great war—a war of eight thousand,' Kim's voice
shrilled across the quick-gathering crowd, astonishing himself.

' Redcoats or our own regiments? ' the old man snapped, as though he
were asking an equal. His tone made men respect Kim.

' Redcoats,' said Kim at a venture. ' Redcoats and guns.'

' But—but the astrologer said no word of this,' cried the lama, snuffing
prodigiously in his excitement.

' But I know. The word has come to me, who am this Holy One's
disciple. There will rise a war—a war of eight thousand redcoats. From Pindi
and Peshawur they will be drawn. This is sure.'

' The boy has heard bazar-talk,' said the priest.

' But he was always by my side,' said the lama. ' How should he know?
I did not know.'

' He will make a clever juggler when the old man is dead,' muttered

the priest to the headman. 'What new trick is this?'

'A sign. Give me a sign,' thundered the old soldier suddenly. 'If there were war my sons would have told me.'

'When all is ready, thy sons, doubt not, will be told. But it is a long road from thy sons to the man in whose hands these things lie.' Kim warmed to the game, for it reminded him of experiences in the letter-carrying line, when, for the sake of a few pice, he pretended to know more than he knew. But now he was playing for larger things—the sheer excitement and the sense of power. He drew a new breath and went on.

'Old man, give me a sign. Do underlings order the goings of eight thousand redcoats—with guns?'

'No.' Still the old man answered as though Kim were an equal.

'Dost thou know who He is then that gives the order?'

'I have seen Him.'

'To know again?'

'I have known Him since he was a lieutenant in the topkhana' (the Artillery).

'A tall man. A tall man with black hair, walking thus?' Kim took a few paces in a stiff, wooden style.

'Ay. But that any one may have seen.' The crowd were breathless-still through all this talk.

'That is true,' said Kim. 'But I will say more. Look now. First the great man walks thus. Then He thinks thus. (Kim drew a forefinger over his forehead and downwards till it came to rest by the angle of the jaw.) Anon He twitches his fingers thus. Anon He thrusts his hat under his left armpit.' Kim illustrated the motion and stood like a stork.

The old man groaned, inarticulate with amazement; and the crowd shivered.

'So—so—so. But what does He when He is about to give an order?'

'He rubs the skin at the back of his neck—thus. Then falls one finger on the table and He makes a small sniffing noise through his nose. Then He speaks, saying: "Loose such and such a regiment. Call out such guns."'

The old man rose stiffly and saluted.

'"For"'—Kim translated into the vernacular the clinching sentences he had heard in the dressing-room at Umballa—'"For," says He, "we should have done this long ago. It is not war—it is a chastisement. Snff!"'

'Enough. I believe. I have seen Him thus in the smoke of battles. Seen and heard. It is He!'

'I saw no smoke'—Kim's voice shifted to the rapt sing-song of the wayside fortune-teller. 'I saw this in darkness. First came a man to make things clear. Then came horsemen. Then came He, standing in a ring of light. The rest followed as I have said. Old man, have I spoken truth?'

'It is He. Past all doubt it is He.'

The crowd drew a long, quavering breath, staring alternately at the old man, still at attention, and ragged Kim against the purple twilight.

'Said I not—said I not he was from the other world?' cried the lama proudly. 'He is the Friend of all the World. He is the Friend of the Stars!'

'At least it does not concern us,' a man cried. 'O thou young sooth-sayer, if the gift abides with thee at all seasons, I have a red-spotted cow. She may be sister to thy Bull for aught I know—'

'Or I care,' said Kim. 'My Stars do not concern themselves with thy cattle.'

'Nay, but she is very sick,' a woman struck in. 'My man is a buffalo, or he would have chosen his words better. Tell me if she recover?'

Had Kim been at all an ordinary boy, he would have carried on the play; but one does not know Lahore city, and least of all the faquirs by the Taksali Gate, for thirteen years without also knowing human nature.

The priest looked at him sideways, something bitterly—a dry and blight-ing smile.

'Is there no priest then in the village? I thought I had seen a great one even now,' cried Kim.

'Ay—but—' the woman began.

'But thou and thy husband hoped to get the cow cured for a handful of thanks.' The shot told: they were notoriously the closest-fisted couple in the village. 'It is not well to cheat the temples. Give a young calf to thy own priest, and, unless thy gods are angry past recall, she will give milk within a month.'

'A master-beggar art thou,' purred the priest approvingly. 'Not the cunning of forty years could have done better. Surely thou hast made the old man rich?'

'A little flour, a little butter and a mouthful of cardamoms,' Kim re-torted, flushed with the praise, but still cautious—'does one grow rich on that? And, as thou canst see, he is mad. But it serves me while I learn the road at least.'

He knew what the faquirs of the Taksali Gate were like when they talked among themselves, and copied the very inflection of their lewd dis-ciples.

'Is his Search, then, truth or a cloak to other ends? It may be treasure.'

'He is mad—many times mad. There is nothing else.'

Here the old soldier hobbled up and asked if Kim would accept his hospitality for the night. The priest recommended him to do so, but insisted that the honour of entertaining the lama belonged to the temple—at which the lama smiled guilelessly. Kim glanced from one face to the other, and drew his own conclusions.

'Where is the money?' he whispered, beckoning the old man off into the darkness.

'In my bosom. Where else?'

'Give it me. Quietly and swiftly give it me.'

'But why? Here is no ticket to buy.'

'Am I thy chela, or am I not? Do I not safeguard thy old feet about

the ways? Give me the money and at dawn I will return it.' He slipped his
hand above the lama's girdle and brought away the purse.

'Be it so—be it so.' The old man nodded his head. 'This is a great
and terrible world. I never knew there were so many men alive in it.'

Next morning the priest was in a very bad temper, but the lama was
quite happy; and Kim had enjoyed a most interesting evening with the old
man, who brought out his cavalry sabre and, balancing it on his dry knees,
told tales of the Mutiny and young captains thirty years in their graves, till
Kim dropped off to sleep.

'Certainly the air of this country is good,' said the lama. 'I sleep lightly,
as do all old men; but last night I slept unwaking till broad day. Even now
I am heavy.'

'Drink a draught of hot milk,' said Kim, who had carried not a few
such remedies to opium-smokers of his acquaintance. 'It is time to take the
road again.'

'The long road that overpasses all the rivers of Hind,' said the lama
gaily. 'Let us go. But how thinkest thou, chela, to recompense these people,
and especially the priest, for their great kindness? Truly they are but-parast,
but in other lives, may be, they will receive enlightenment. A rupee to the
temple? The thing within is no more than stone and red paint, but the heart
of man we must acknowledge when and where it is good.'

'Holy One, hast thou ever taken the road alone?' Kim looked up
sharply, like the Indian crows so busy about the fields.

'Surely, child: from Kulu to Pathankot—from Kulu, where my first
chela died. When men were kind to us we made offerings, and all men were
well-disposed throughout all the Hills.'

'It is otherwise in Hind,' said Kim drily. 'Their gods are many-armed
and malignant. Let them alone.'

'I would set thee on thy road for a little, Friend of all the World—
thou and thy yellow man.' The old soldier ambled up the village street, all
shadowy in the dawn, on a gaunt, scissor-hocked pony. 'Last night broke
up the fountains of remembrance in my so-dried heart, and it was as a bless-
ing to me. Truly there is war abroad in the air. I smell it. See! I have brought
my sword.'

He sat long-legged on the little beast, with his big sword at his side,
—hand dropped on the pommel,—staring fiercely over the flat lands towards
the north. 'Tell me again how He showed in thy vision. Come up and sit
behind me. The beast will carry two.'

'I am this Holy One's disciple,' said Kim, as they cleared the village-
gate. The villagers seemed almost sorry to be rid of them, but the priest's
farewell was cold and distant. He had wasted some opium on a man who
carried no money.

'That is well spoken. I am not much used to holy men, but respect is
always good. There is no respect in these days—not even when a Commis-
sioner Sahib comes to see me. But why should one whose Star leads him to
war follow a holy man?'

'But he is a holy man,' said Kim earnestly. 'In truth, and in talk and in act, holy. He is not like the others. I have never seen such an one. We be not fortune-tellers, or jugglers, or beggars.'

'Thou art not, that I can see; but I do not know that other. He marches well, though.'

The first freshness of the day carried the lama forward with long, easy, camel-like strides. He was deep in meditation, mechanically clicking his rosary.

They followed the rutted and worn country road that wound across the flat between the great dark-green mango-groves, the line of the snow-capped Himalayas faint to the eastward. All India was at work in the fields, to the creaking of well-wheels, the shouting of ploughmen behind their cattle, and the clamour of the crows. Even the pony felt the good influence and almost broke into a trot as Kim laid a hand on the stirrup-leather.

'It repents me that I did not give a rupee to the shrine,' said the lama on the last bead of his eighty-one.

The old soldier growled in his beard, so that the lama for the first time was aware of him.

'Seekest thou the River also?' said he, turning.

'The day is new,' was the reply. 'What need of a river save to water at before sundown? I come to show thee a short lane to the Big Road.'

'That is a courtesy to be remembered, O man of good will; but why the sword?'

The old soldier looked as abashed as a child interrupted in his game of make-believe.

'The sword,' he said, fumbling it. 'Oh, that was a fancy of mine—an old man's fancy. Truly the police orders are that no man must bear weapons throughout Hind, but'—he cheered up and slapped the hilt—'all the con- stabeels hereabout know me.'

'It is not a good fancy,' said the lama. 'What profit to kill men?'

'Very little—as I know; but if evil men were not now and then slain it would not be a good world for weaponless dreamers. I do not speak with- out knowledge who have seen the land from Delhi south awash with blood.'

'What madness was that, then?'

'The Gods, who sent it for a plague, alone know. A madness ate into all the Army, and they turned against their officers. That was the first evil, but not past remedy if they had then held their hands. But they chose to kill the Sahibs' wives and children. Then came the Sahibs from over the sea and called them to most strict account.'

'Some such rumour, I believe, reached me once long ago. They called it the Black Year, as I remember.'

'What manner of life hast thou led, not to know The Year? A rumour indeed! All earth knew, and trembled.'

'Our earth never shook but once—upon the day that the Excellent One received Enlightenment.'

'Umph! I saw Delhi shake at least; and Delhi is the navel of the world.'

'So they turned against women and children? That was a bad deed, for which the punishment cannot be avoided.'

'Many strove to do so, but with very small profit. I was then in a regiment of cavalry. It broke. Of six hundred and eighty sabres stood fast to their salt—how many think you? Three. Of whom I was one.'

'The greater merit.'

'Merit! We did not consider it merit in those days. My people, my friends, my brothers fell from me. They said: "The time of the English is accomplished. Let each strike out a little holding for himself." But I had talked with the men of Sobraon, of Chillianwallah, of Moodkee and Ferozeshah. I said: "Abide a little and the wind turns. There is no blessing in this work." In those days I rode seventy miles with an English mem-sahib and her babe on my saddle-bow. (Wow! That was a horse fit for a man!) I placed them in safety, and back came I to my officer—the one that was not killed of our five. "Give me work," said I, "for I am an outcast among my own kin, and my cousin's blood is wet on my sabre." "Be content," said he. "There is great work forward. When this madness is over there is a recompense."'

'Ay, there is a recompense when the madness is over, surely?' the lama muttered half to himself.

'They did not hang medals in those days on all who by accident had heard a gun fired. No! In nineteen pitched battles was I; in six-and-forty skirmishes of horse; and in small affairs without number. Nine wounds I bear; a medal and four clasps and the medal of an Order, for my captains who are now generals, remembered me when the Kaiser-i-Hind had accomplished fifty years of her reign, and all the land rejoiced. They said: "Give him the order of Berittish India." I carry it upon my neck now. I have also my jaghir (holding) from the hands of the State—a free gift to me and mine. The men of the old days—they are now Commissioners—come riding to me through the crops,—high upon horses so that all the village sees,—and we talk out the old skirmishes, one dead man's name leading to another.'

'And after?' said the lama.

'Oh, afterwards they go away, but not before my village has seen.'

'And at the last what wilt thou do?'

'At the last I shall die.'

'And after?'

'Let the Gods order it. I have never pestered Them with prayers: I do not think They will pester me. Look you, I have noticed in my long life that those who eternally break in upon Those Above with complaints and reports and bellowings and weepings are presently sent for in haste, as our colonel used to send for slack-jawed down-country men who talked too much. No, I have never wearied the Gods. They will remember this, and give me a quiet place where I can drive my lance in the shade, and wait to welcome my sons: I have no less than three—ressaldar-majors all—in the regiments.'

'And they likewise, bound upon the Wheel, go forth from life to life—from despair to despair,' said the lama below his breath, 'hot, uneasy, snatching.'

'Ay,' the old soldier chuckled. 'Three ressaldar-majors in three regiments. Gamblers a little, but so am I. They must be well mounted; and one cannot take the horses as in the old days one took women. Well, well, my holding can pay for all. How thinkest thou? It is a well-watered strip, but my men cheat me. I do not know how to ask save at the lance's point. Ugh! I grow angry and I curse them, and they feign penitence, but behind my back I know they call me a toothless old ape.'

'Hast they never desired any other thing?'

'Yes—yes—a thousand times! A straight back and a close-clinging knee once more; a quick wrist and a keen eye; and the marrow that makes a man. Oh, the old days—the good days of my strength!'

'That strength is weakness.'

'It has turned so; but fifty years since I could have proved it otherwise,' the old soldier retorted, driving his stirrup-edge into the pony's lean flank.

'But I know a River of great healing.'

'I have drunk Gunga-water to the edge of dropsy. All she gave me was a flux, and no sort of strength.'

'It is not Gunga. The River that I know washes from all taint of sin. Ascending the far bank one is assured of Freedom. I do not know thy life, but thy face is the face of the honourable and courteous. Thou hast clung to thy Way, rendering fidelity when it was hard to give, in that Black Year of which I now remember other tales. Enter now upon the Middle Way, which is the path to Freedom. Hear the Most Excellent Law, and do not follow dreams.'

'Speak then, old man,' the soldier smiled, half saluting. 'We be all babblers at our age.'

The lama squatted under the shade of a mango, whose shadow played checkerwise over his face; the soldier sat stiffly on the pony; and Kim, making sure that there were no snakes, lay down in the crotch of the twisted roots.

There was a drowsy buzz of small life in hot sunshine, a cooing of doves, and a sleepy drone of well-wheels across the fields. Slowly and impressively the lama began. At the end of ten minutes the old soldier slid from his pony, to hear better as he said, and sat with the reins round his wrist. The lama's voice faltered—the periods lengthened. Kim was busy watching a gray squirrel. When the little scolding bunch of fur, close pressed to the branch, disappeared, preacher and audience were fast asleep, the old officer's strong-cut head pillowed on his arm, the lama's thrown back against the tree bole, where it showed like yellow ivory. A naked child toddled up, stared, and, moved by some quick impulse of reverence, made a solemn little obeisance before the lama—only the child was so short and fat that it toppled over sideways, and Kim laughed at the sprawling, chubby legs. The child, scared and indignant, yelled aloud.

'Hai! Hai!' said the soldier leaping to his feet. 'What is it? What orders? . . . It is . . . a child! I dreamed it was an alarm. Little one— little one—do not cry. Have I slept? That was discourteous indeed!'

'I fear! I am afraid!' roared the child.

'What is it to fear? Two old men and a boy? How wilt thou ever make a soldier, Princeling?'

The lama had waked too, but, taking no direct notice of the child, clicked his rosary.

'What is that?' said the child, stopping a yell midway. 'I have never seen such things. Give them me.'

'Aha,' said the lama, smiling, and trailing a loop of it on the grass:

> 'This is a handful of cardamoms,
> This is a lump of ghi:
> This is millet and chillies and rice,
> A supper for thee and me!'

The child shrieked with joy, and snatched at the dark, glancing beads.

'Oho!' said the old soldier. 'Whence had thou that song, despiser of this world?'

'I learned it in Pathankot—sitting on a door-step,' said the lama shyly. 'It is good to be kind to babes.'

'As I remember, before the sleep came on us, thou hadst told me that marriage and bearing were darkeners of the true light, stumbling-blocks upon the way. Do children drop from heaven in thy country? Is it the Way to sing them songs?'

'No man is all perfect,' said the lama gravely, recoiling the rosary. 'Run now to thy mother, little one.'

'Hear him!' said the soldier to Kim. 'He is ashamed for that he has made a child happy. There was a very good householder lost in thee, my brother. Hai, child!' He threw it a pice. 'Sweetmeats are always sweet.' And as the little figure capered away into the sunshine: 'They grow up and become men. Holy One, I grieve that I slept in the midst of thy preaching. Forgive me.'

'We be two old men,' said the lama. 'The fault is mine. I listened to thy talk of the world and its madness, and one fault led to the next.'

'Hear him! What harm do thy Gods suffer from play with a babe? And that song was very well sung. Let us go on and I will sing thee the song of Nikal Seyn before Delhi—the old song.'

And they fared out from the gloom of the mango tope, the old man's high, shrill voice ringing across the field, as wail by long-drawn wail he unfolded the story of Nikal Seyn (Nicholson)—the song that men sing in the Punjab to this day. Kim was delighted, and the lama listened with deep interest.

'Ahi! Nikal Seyn is dead—he died before Delhi! Lances of North take vengeance for Nikal Seyn.' He quavered it out to the end, marking the trills with the flat of his sword on the pony's rump.

' And now we come to the Big Road,' said he, after receiving the com-
pliments of Kim; for the lama was markedly silent. ' It is long since I have
ridden this way, but thy boy's talk stirred me. See, Holy One—the Great
Road which is the backbone of all Hind. For the most part it is shaded, as
here, with four lines of trees; the middle road—all hard—takes the quick
traffic. In the days before rail-carriages the Sahibs travelled up and down here
in hundreds. Now there are only country-carts and such like. Left and right
is the rougher road for the heavy carts—grain and cotton and timber, bhoosa,
lime and hides. A man goes in safety here—for at every few kos is a police-
station. The police are thieves and extortioners (I myself would patrol it
with cavalry—young recruits under a strong captain), but at least they do
not suffer any rivals. All castes and kinds of men move here. Look! Brahmins
and chumars, bankers and tinkers, barbers and bunnias, pilgrims and potters
—all the world going and coming. It is to me as a river from which I am
withdrawn like a log after a flood.'

And truly the Grand Trunk Road is a wonderful spectacle. It runs
straight, bearing without crowding India's traffic for fifteen hundred miles
—such a river of life as nowhere else exists in the world. They looked at
the green-arched, shade-flecked length of it, the white breadth speckled with
slow-pacing folk; and the two-roomed police-station opposite.

' Who bears arms against the law? ' a constable called out laughingly,
as he caught sight of the soldier's sword. ' Are not the police enough to
destroy evil-doers? '

' It was because of the police I bought it,' was the answer. ' Does all go
well in Hind? '

' Ressaldar Sahib, all goes well.'

' I am like an old tortoise, look you, who puts his head out from the
bank and draws it in again. Ay, this is the road of Hindustan. All men come
by this way. . . .'

' Son of a swine, is the soft part of the road meant for thee to scratch
thy back upon? Father of all the daughters of shame and husband of ten
thousand virtueless ones, thy mother was devoted to a devil, being led thereto
by her mother; thy aunts have never had a nose for seven generations! Thy
sister— What owl's folly told thee to draw thy carts across the road? A
broken wheel? Then take a broken head and put the two together at leisure! '

The voice and a venomous whip-cracking came out of a pillar of dust
fifty yards away, where a cart had broken down. A thin, high Kattiwar mare,
with eyes and nostrils aflame, rocketed out of the jam, snorting and wincing
as her rider bent her across the road in chase of a shouting man. He was
tall and gray-bearded, sitting the almost mad beast as a piece of her, and
scientifically lashing his victim between plunges.

The old man's face lit with pride. ' My child! ' said he briefly, and strove
to rein the pony's neck to a fitting arch.

' Am I to be beaten before the police? ' cried the carter. ' Justice! I will
have Justice— '

' Am I to be blocked by a shouting ape who upsets ten thousand sacks under a young horse's nose? That is the way to ruin a mare.'

' He speaks truth. He speaks truth. But she follows her man close,' said the old man. The carter ran under the wheels of his cart and thence threatened all sorts of vengeance.

' They are strong men, thy sons,' said the policeman serenely, picking his teeth.

The horseman delivered one last vicious cut with his whip and came on at a canter.

' My father! ' He reined back ten yards and dismounted.

The old man was off his pony in an instant, and they embraced as do father and son in the East.

CHAPTER IV

Good Luck, she is never a lady,
But the cursedest quean alive.
Tricksy, wincing, and jady—
Kittle to lead or drive.
Greet her—she's hailing a stranger!
Meet her—she's busking to leave!
Let her alone for a shrew to the bone
And the hussy comes plucking your sleeve!
　　　Largesse! Largesse, O Fortune!
　　　Give or hold at your will
　　　If I've no care for Fortune,
　　　Fortune must follow me still!

THE WISHING CAPS

Then, lowering their voices, they spoke together. Kim came to rest under a tree, but the lama tugged impatiently at his elbow.

' Let us go on. The River is not here.'

' Hai mai! Have we not walked enough for a little? Our River will not run away. Patience, and he will give us a dole.'

' That,' said the old soldier suddenly, ' is the Friend of the Stars. He brought me the news yesterday. Having seen the very man Himself, in a vision, giving orders for the war.'

' Hm! ' said his son, all deep in his broad chest. ' He came by a bazar-rumour and made profit of it.'

His father laughed. ' At least he did not ride to me begging for a new charger and the gods know how many rupees. Are thy brothers' regiments also under orders? '

' I do not know. I took leave and came swiftly to thee in case— '

' In case they ran before thee to beg. O gamblers and spendthrifts all!

But thou hast never yet ridden in a charge. A good horse is needed there, truly. A good follower and a good pony also for the marching. Let us see— let us see.' He thrummed on the pommel.

'This is no place to cast thy accounts in, my father. Let us go to thy house.'

'At least pay the boy then: I have no pice with me, and he brought auspicious news. Ho! Friend of all the World, a war is toward as thou hast said.'

'Nay, as I know, the war,' returned Kim composedly.

'Eh?' said the lama, fingering his beads, all eager for the road.

'My master does not trouble the Stars for hire. We brought the news —bear witness we brought the news, and now we go.' Kim half-crooked his hand at his side.

The son tossed a silver coin through the sunlight, grumbling something about beggars and jugglers. It was a four-anna piece, and would feed them well for some days. The lama, seeing the flash of the metal, droned a blessing.

'Go thy way, Friend of all the World,' piped the old soldier, wheeling his scrawny mount. 'For once in all my days I have met a true prophet— who was not in the Army.'

Father and son swung round together: the old man sitting as erect as the younger.

A Punjabi constable in yellow linen trousers slouched across the road. He had seen the money pass.

'Halt!' he cried in impressive English. 'Know ye not that there is a takkus of two annas a head, which is four annas, on those who enter the road from this side-road. It is the order of the Sirkar, and the money is spent for the planting of trees and the beautification of the ways.'

'And the bellies of the police,' said Kim, skipping out of arm's reach. 'Consider for a while, man with a mud head. Think you we came from the nearest pond like the frog, thy father-in-law. Hast thou ever heard the name of thy brother?'

'And who was he? Leave the boy alone,' cried a senior constable, immensely delighted, as he squatted down to smoke his pipe in the veranda.

'He took a label from a bottle of belaitee-pani (soda-water), and, affixing it to a bridge, collected taxes for a month from those who passed, saying that it was the Sirkar's order. Then came an Englishman and broke his head. Ah, brother, I am a town-crow, not a village-crow!'

The policeman drew back abashed, and Kim hooted at him all down the road.

'Was there ever such a disciple as I?' he cried merrily to the lama. 'All earth would have picked thy bones within ten mile of Lahore city if I had not guarded thee.'

'I consider in my own mind whether thou art a spirit, sometimes, or sometimes an evil imp,' said the lama, smiling slowly.

'I am thy chela.' Kim dropped into step at his side—that indescribable

gait of the long-distance tramp all the world over.

'Now let us walk,' muttered the lama, and to the click of his rosary they walked in silence mile upon mile. The lama, as usual, was deep in meditation, but Kim's bright eyes were open wide. This broad, smiling river of life, he considered, was a vast improvement on the cramped and crowded Lahore streets. There were new people and new sights at every stride—castes he knew and castes that were altogether out of his experience.

They met a troop of long-haired, strong-scented Sansis with baskets of lizards and other unclean food on their backs, their lean dogs sniffing at their heels. These people kept their own side of the road, moving at a quick, furtive jog-trot, and all other castes gave them ample room; for the Sansi is deep pollution. Behind them, walking wide and stiffly across the strong shadows, the memory of his leg-irons still on him, strode one newly released from the jail; his full stomach and shiny skin to prove that the Government fed its prisoners better than most honest men could feed themselves. Kim knew that walk well, and made broad jest of it as they passed. Then an Akali, a wild-eyed, wild-haired Sikh devotee in the blue-checked clothes of his faith, with polished-steel quoits glistening on the cone of his tall blue turban, stalked past, returning from a visit to one of the independent Sikh States, where he had been singing the ancient glories of the Khalsa to College-trained princelings in top-boots and white-cord breeches. Kim was careful not to irritate that man; for the Akali's temper is short and his arm quick. Here and there they met or were overtaken by the gaily dressed crowds of whole villages turning out to some local fair; the women, with their babes on their hips, walking behind the men, the older boys prancing on sticks of sugar-cane, dragging rude brass models of locomotives such as they sell for a halfpenny, or flashing the sun into the eyes of their betters from cheap toy mirrors. One could see at a glance what each had bought; and if there were any doubt it needed only to watch the wives comparing, brown arm against brown arm, the newly purchased dull glass bracelets that come from the North-West. These merry-makers stepped slowly, calling one to the other and stopping to haggle with sweetmeat-sellers, or to make a prayer before one of the wayside shrines—sometimes Hindu, sometimes Mussalman— which the low caste of both creeds share with beautiful impartiality. A solid line of blue, rising and falling like the back of a caterpillar in haste, would swing up through the quivering dust and trot past to a chorus of quick cackling. That was a gang of changars—the women who have taken all the embankments of all the Northern railways under their charge—a flat-footed, big-bosomed, strong-limbed, blue-petticoated clan of earth-carriers, hurrying north on news of a job, and wasting no time by the road. They belong to the caste whose men do not count, and they walked with squared elbows, swinging hips, and heads on high, as suits women who carry heavy weights. A little later a marriage procession would strike into the Grand Trunk with music and shoutings, and a smell of marigold and jasmine stronger even than the reek of the dust. One could see the bride's litter, a blur of red and

tinsel, staggering through the haze, while the bridegroom's bewreathed pony turned aside to snatch a mouthful from a passing fodder-cart. Then Kim would join the Kentish-fire of good wishes and bad jokes, wishing the couple a hundred sons and no daughters, as the saying is. Still more interesting and more to be shouted over it was when a strolling juggler with some half-trained monkeys, or a panting, feeble bear, or a woman who tied goats' horns to her feet, and with these danced on a slack-rope, set the horses to shying and the women to shrill, long-drawn quavers of amazement.

The lama never raised his eyes. He did not note the money-lender on his goose-rumped pony, hastening along to collect the cruel interest; or the long-shouting, deep-voiced little mob—still in military formation—of native soldiers on leave, rejoicing to be rid of their breeches and puttees, and saying the most outrageous things to the most respectable women in sight. Even the seller of Ganges-water he did not see, and Kim expected that he would at least buy a bottle of that precious stuff. He looked steadily at the ground, and strode as steadily hour after hour, his soul busied elsewhere. But Kim was in the seventh heaven of joy. The Grand Trunk at this point was built on an embankment to guard against winter floods from the foothills, so that one walked, as it were, a little above the country, along a stately corridor, seeing all India spread out to left and right. It was beautiful to behold the many-yoked grain and cotton waggons crawling over the country-roads: one could hear their axles, complaining a mile away, coming nearer, till with shouts and yells and bad words they climbed up the steep incline and plunged on to the hard main road, carter reviling carter. It was equally beautiful to watch the people, little clumps of red and blue and pink and white and saffron, turning aside to go to their own villages, dispersing and growing small by twos and threes across the level plain. Kim felt these things, though he could not give tongue to his feelings, and so contented himself with buying peeled sugar-cane and spitting the pith generously about his path. From time to time the lama took snuff, and at last Kim could endure the silence no longer.

'This is a good land—the land of the South!' said he. 'The air is good; the water is good. Eh?'

'And they are all bound upon the Wheel,' said the lama. 'Bound from life after life. To none of these has the Way been shown.' He shook himself back to this world.

'And now we have walked a weary way,' said Kim. 'Surely we shall soon come to a parao (a resting-place). Shall we stay there? Look, the sun is sloping.'

'Who will receive us this evening?'

'That is all one. This country is full of good folk. Besides,'—he sunk his voice beneath a whisper,—'we have money.'

The crowd thickened as they neared the resting-place which marked the end of their day's journey. A line of stalls selling very simple food and tobacco, a stack of firewood, a police-station, a well, a horse-trough, a few

trees, and, under them, some trampled ground dotted with the black ashes of old fires, are all that mark a parao on the Grand Trunk; if you except the beggars and the crows—both hungry.

By this time the sun was driving broad golden spokes through the lower branches of the mango trees; the parakeets and doves were coming home in their hundreds; the chattering, gray-backed Seven Sisters, talking over the day's adventures, walked back and forth in twos and threes almost under the feet of the travellers; and shufflings and scufflings in the branches showed that the bats were ready to go out on the night-picket. Swiftly the light gathered itself together, painted for an instant the faces and the cart-wheels and the bullocks' horns as red as blood. Then the night fell, changing the touch of the air, drawing a low, even haze, like a gossamer veil of blue, across the face of the country, and bringing out, keen and distinct, the smell of wood-smoke and cattle and the good scent of wheaten cakes cooked on ashes. The evening patrol hurried out of the police-station with important coughings and reiterated orders; and a live charcoal ball in the cup of a wayside carter's hookah glowed red while Kim's eye mechanically watched the last flicker of the sun on the brass tweezers.

The life of the parao was very like that of the Kashmir Serai on a small scale. Kim dived into the happy Asiatic disorder which, if you only allow time, will bring you everything that a simple man needs.

His wants were few, because, since the lama had no caste scruples, cooked food from the nearest stall would serve; but, for luxury's sake, Kim bought a handful of dung-cakes to build a fire. All about, coming and going round the little flames, men cried for oil, or grain, or sweetmeats, or tobacco, jostling one another while they waited their turn at the well; and under the men's voices you heard from halted, shuttered carts the high squeals and giggles of women whose faces should not be seen in public.

Nowadays, well-educated natives are of opinion that when their women-folk travel—and they visit a good deal—it is better to take them quickly by rail in a properly screened compartment; and that custom is spreading. But there are always those of the old rock who hold by the use of their forefathers; and, above all, there are always the old women,—more conservative than the men,—who toward the end of their days go a pilgrimage. They, being withered and undesirable, do not, under certain circumstances, object to unveiling. After their long seclusion, during which they have always been in business touch with a thousand outside interests, they love the bustle and stir of the open road, the gatherings at the shrines, and the infinite possibilities of gossip with like-minded dowagers. Very often it suits a long-suffering family that a strong-tongued, iron-willed old lady should disport herself about India in this fashion; for certainly pilgrimage is grateful to the Gods. So all about India, in the most remote places, as in the most public, you find some knot of grizzled servitors in nominal charge of an old lady who is more or less curtained and hid away in a bullock-cart. Such men are staid and discreet, and when a European or a high-caste native is near will

net their charge with most elaborate precautions; but in the ordinary haphazard chances of pilgrimage the precautions are not taken. The old lady is, after all, intensely human, and lives to look upon life.

Kim marked down a gaily ornamented ruth or family bullock-cart, with a broidered canopy of two domes, like a double-humped camel, which had just been drawn into the parao. Eight men made its retinue, and two of the eight were armed with rusty sabres—sure signs that they followed a person of distinction, for the common folk do not bear arms. An increasing cackle of complaints, orders, and jests, and what to a European would have been bad language, came from behind the curtains. Here was evidently a woman used to command.

Kim looked over the retinue critically. Half of them were thin-legged, gray-bearded Ooryas from down country. The other half were duffle-clad, felt-hatted hillmen of the North: and that mixture told its own tale, even if he had not overheard the incessant sparring between the two divisions. The old lady was going south on a visit—probably to a rich relative, most probably to a son-in-law, who had sent up an escort as a mark of respect. The hillmen would be of her own people—Kulu or Kangra folk. It was quite clear that she was not taking her daughter down to be wedded, or the curtains would have been laced home and the guard would have allowed no one near the cart. A merry and a high-spirited dame, thought Kim, balancing the dung-cake in one hand, the cooked food in the other, and piloting the lama with a nudging shoulder. Something might be made out of the meeting. The lama would give him no help, but, as a conscientious chela, Kim was delighted to beg for two.

He built his fire as close to the cart as he dared, waiting for one of the escort to order him away. The lama dropped wearily to the ground, much as a heavy fruit-eating bat cowers, and returned to his rosary.

'Stand farther off, beggar!' The order was shouted in broken Hindustanee by one of the hillmen.

'Huh! It is only a pahari' (a hillman), said Kim over his shoulder. 'Since when have the hill-asses owned all Hindustan?'

The retort was a swift and brilliant sketch of Kim's pedigree for three generations.

'Ah!' Kim's voice was sweeter than ever, as he broke the dung-cake into fit pieces. 'In my country we call that the beginning of love-talk.'

A harsh, thin cackle behind the curtains put the hillman on his mettle for a second shot.

'Not so bad—not so bad,' said Kim with calm. 'But have a care, my brother, lest we—we, I say—be minded to give a curse or so in return. And our curses have the knack of biting home.'

The Ooryas laughed; the hillman sprang forward threateningly; the lama suddenly raised his head, bringing his huge tam-o'-shanter cap into the full light of Kim's new-started fire.

'What is it?' said he.

The man halted as though struck to stone. 'I—I—am saved from a great sin,' he stammered.

'The foreigner has found him a priest at last,' whispered one of the Ooryas.

'Hai! Why is that beggar-brat not well beaten?' the old woman cried.

The hillman drew back to the cart and whispered something to the curtain. There was dead silence, then a muttering.

'This goes well,' thought Kim, pretending neither to see nor hear.

'When—when—he has eaten,'—the hillman fawned on Kim—'it—it is requested that the Holy One will do the honour to talk to one who would speak to him.'

'After he has eaten he will sleep,' Kim returned loftily. He could not quite see what new turn the game had taken, but stood resolute to profit by it. 'Now, I will get him his food.' The last sentence, spoken loudly, ended with a sigh as of faintness.

'I—I myself and the others of my people will look to that—if it is permitted.'

'It is permitted,' said Kim, more loftily than ever. 'Holy One, these people will bring us food.'

'The land is good. All the country of the South is good—a great and a terrible world,' mumbled the lama drowsily.

'Let him sleep,' said Kim, 'but look to it that we are well fed when he wakes. He is a very holy man.'

Again one of the Ooryas said something contemptuously.

'He is not a faquir. He is not a down-country beggar,' Kim went on severely, addressing the stars. 'He is the most holy of holy men. He is above all castes. I am his chela.'

'Come here!' said the flat thin voice behind the curtain; and Kim came, conscious that eyes he could not see were staring at him. One skinny brown finger heavy with rings lay on the edge of the cart, and the talk went this way:

'Who is that one?'

'An exceedingly holy one. He comes from far off. He comes from Tibet.'

'Where in Tibet?'

'From behind the snows—from a very far place. He knows the stars; he makes horoscopes; he reads nativities. But he does not do this for money. He does it for kindness and great charity. I am his disciple. I am called also the Friend of the Stars.'

'Thou art no hillman.'

'Ask him. He will tell thee I was sent to him from the stars to show him an end to his pilgrimage.'

'Humph! Consider, brat, that I am an old woman and not altogether a fool. Lamas I know, and to these I give reverence, but thou art no more a lawful chela than this my finger is the pole of this waggon. Thou art a casteless Hindu—a bold and unblushing beggar, attached, belike, to the Holy One for the sake of gain.'

'Do we not all work for gain?' Kim changed his tone promptly to match that altered voice. 'I have heard'—this was a bow drawn at a venture —'I have heard—'

'What hast thou heard?' she snapped, rapping with the finger.

'Nothing that I well remember, but some talk in the bazars, which is doubtless a lie, that even Rajahs—small hill Rajahs—'

'But none the less of good Rajput blood.'

'Assuredly of good blood. That these even sell the more comely of their womenfolk for gain. Down south they sell them—to zemindars and such-all of Oudh.'

If there be one thing in the world that the small hill Rajahs deny it is just this charge; but it happens to be one thing that the bazars believe, when they discuss the mysterious slave-traffics of India. The old lady explained to Kim, in a tense, indignant whisper, precisely what manner and fashion of malignant liar he was. Had Kim hinted this when she was a girl, he would have been pommelled to death that same evening by an elephant. This was perfectly true.

'Ahai! I am only a beggar's brat, as the Eye of Beauty has said,' he wailed in extravagant terror.

'Eye of Beauty, forsooth! Who am I that thou shouldst fling beggar-endearments at me?' And yet she laughed at the long-forgotten word. 'Forty years ago that might have been said, and not without truth. Ay, thirty years ago. But it is the fault of this gadding up and down Hind that a king's widow must jostle all the scum of the land, and be made a mock by beggars.'

'Great Queen,' said Kim promptly, for he heard her shaking with indignation, 'I am even what the Great Queen says I am; but none the less is my master holy. He has not yet heard the Great Queen's order that—'

'Order? I order a Holy One—a Teacher of the Law—to come and speak to a woman? Never!'

'Pity my stupidity. I thought it was given as an order—'

'It was not. It was a petition. Does this make all clear?'

A silver coin clicked on the edge of the cart. Kim took it and salaamed profoundly. The old lady recognized that, as the eyes and the ears of the lama, he was to be propitiated.

'I am but the Holy One's disciple. When he has eaten perhaps he will come.'

'Oh, villain and shameless rogue!' The jewelled forefinger shook itself at him reprovingly; but he could hear the old lady's chuckle.

'Nay, what is it?' he said, dropping into his most caressing and confidential tone—the one, he well knew, that few could resist. 'Is—is there any need of a son in thy family? Speak freely, for we priests—' That last was a direct plagiarism from a faquir by the Taksali Gate.

'We priests! Thou art not yet old enough to—' She checked the joke with another laugh. 'Believe me, now and again, we women, O priest, think of other matters than sons. Moreover, my daughter has borne her man-child.'

' Two arrows in the quiver are better than one; and three are better still.' Kim quoted the proverb with a meditative cough, looking discreetly earthward.

' True—oh, true. But perhaps that will come. Certainly those down-country Brahmins are utterly useless. I sent gifts and monies and gifts again to them and they prophesied.'

' Ah,' drawled Kim, with infinite contempt, ' they prophesied! ' A professional could have done no better.

' And it was not till I remembered my own Gods that my prayers were heard. I chose an auspicious hour, and—perhaps thy Holy One has heard of the Abbot of the Lung-Cho lamassery. It was to him I put the matter, and behold in the due time all came about as I desired. The Brahmin in the house of the father of my daughter's son has since said that it was through his prayers—which is a little error that I will explain to him when we reach our journey's end. And so afterwards I go to Buddh Gaya, to make shraddha for the father of my children.' ●

' Thither go we.'

' Doubly auspicious,' chirruped the old lady. ' A second son at least! '

' O Friend of all the World! ' The lama had waked, and, simply as a child bewildered in a strange bed, called for Kim.

' I come! I come, Holy One! ' He dashed to the fire, where he found the lama already surrounded by dishes of food, the hillmen visibly adoring him and the Southerners looking sourly.

' Go back! Withdraw! ' Kim cried. ' Do we eat publicly like dogs? ' They finished the meal in silence, each turned a little from the other, and Kim topped it with a native-made cigarette.

' Have I not said an hundred times that the South is a good land? Here is a virtuous and high-born widow of a Hill Rajah on pilgrimage, she says, to Buddh Gaya. She it is sends us those dishes; and when thou art well rested she would speak to thee.'

' Is this also thy work? ' The lama dipped deep into his snuff-gourd.

' Who else watched over thee since our wonderful journey began? ' Kim's eyes danced in his head as he blew the rank smoke through his nostrils and stretched him on the dusty ground. ' Have I failed to oversee thy comforts, Holy One? '

' A blessing on thee.' The lama inclined his solemn head. ' I have known many men in my so long life, and disciples not a few. But to none among men, if so be thou art woman-born, has my heart gone out as it has to thee—thoughtful, wise, and courteous, but something of a small imp.'

' And I have never seen such a priest as thou.' Kim considered the benevolent yellow face wrinkle by wrinkle. ' It is less than three days since we took road together, and it is as though it were a hundred years.'

' Perhaps in a former life it was permitted that I should have rendered thee some service. May be'—he smiled—' I freed thee from a trap; or, having caught thee on a hook in the days when I was not enlightened, cast thee back into the river.'

'May be,' said Kim quietly. He had heard this sort of speculation again and again, from the mouths of many whom the English would not consider imaginative. 'Now, as regards that woman in the bullock-cart, I think she needs a second son for her daughter.'

'That is no part of the Way,' sighed the lama. 'But at least she is from the Hills. Ah, the Hills, and the snow of the Hills! '

He rose and stalked to the cart. Kim would have given his ears to come too, but the lama did not invite him; and the few words he caught were in an unknown tongue, for they spoke some common speech of the mountains. The woman seemed to ask questions which the lama turned over in his mind before answering. Now and again he heard the sing-song cadence of a Chinese quotation. It was a strange picture that Kim watched between drooped eyelids. The lama, very straight and erect, the deep folds of his yellow clothing slashed with black in the light of the parao fires precisely as a knotted tree-trunk is slashed with the shadow of the long sun, addressed a tinsel and lacquered ruth which burned like a many-coloured jewel in the same uncertain light. The patterns on the gold-worked curtains ran up and down, melting and re-forming as the folds shook and quivered to the night wind; and when the talk grew more earnest the jewelled forefinger snapped out little sparks of light between the embroideries. Behind the cart was a wall of uncertain darkness speckled with little flames and alive with half-caught forms and faces and shadows. The voices of early evening had settled down to one soothing hum whose deepest note was the steady chumping of the bullocks above their chopped straw, and whose highest was the tinkle of a Bengali dancing-girl's sitar. Most men had eaten and pulled deep at their gurgling, grunting hookahs, which in full blast sound like bull-frogs.

At last the lama returned. A hillman walked behind him with a wadded cotton-quilt and spread it carefully by the fire.

'She deserves ten thousand grandchildren,' thought Kim. 'None the less, but for me, these gifts would not have come.'

'A virtuous woman—and a wise one.' The lama slackened off, joint by joint, like a slow camel. 'The world is full of charity to those who follow the Way.' He flung a fair half of the quilt over Kim.

'And what said she? ' Kim rolled up in his share of it.

'She asked me many questions and propounded many problems—the most of which were idle tales which she had heard from devil-serving priests who pretend to follow the Way. Some I answered, and some I said were foolish. Many wear the Robe, but few keep the Way.'

'True. That is true.' Kim used the thoughtful, conciliatory tone of those who wish to draw confidences.

'But by her lights she is most right-minded. She desires greatly that we should go with her to Buddh Gaya; her road being ours, as I understand, for many days' journey to the southward.'

'And? '

'Patience a little. To this I said that my Search came before all things.

She had heard many foolish legends, but this great truth of my River she had never heard. Such are the priests of the lower hills! She knew the Abbot of Lung-Cho, but she did not know of my River—nor the tale of the Arrow.'

'And?'

'I spoke therefore of the Search, and of the Way, and of matters that were profitable; she desiring only that I should accompany her and make prayer for a second son.'

'Aha! "We women" do not think of anything save children,' said Kim sleepily.

'Now, since our roads run together for a while, I do not see that we in any way depart from our Search if so be we accompany her—at least as far as—I have forgotten the name of the city.'

'Ohe!' said Kim, turning and speaking in a sharp whisper to one of the Ooryas a few yards away. 'Where is your master's house?'

'A little behind Saharunpore, among the fruit gardens.' He named the village.

'That was the place,' said the lama. 'So far, at least, we can go with her.'

'Flies go to carrion,' said the Oorya, in an abstracted voice.

'For the sick cow a crow; for the sick man a Brahmin.' Kim breathed the proverb impersonally to the shadow-tops of the trees overhead.

The Oorya grunted and held his peace.

'So then we go with her, Holy One?'

'Is there any reason against? I can still step aside and try all the rivers that the road overpasses. She desires that I should come. She very greatly desires it.'

Kim stifled a laugh in the quilt. When once that imperious old lady had recovered from her natural awe of a lama he thought it probable that she would be worth listening to.

He was nearly asleep when the lama suddenly quoted a proverb: 'The husbands of the talkative have a great reward hereafter.' Then Kim heard him snuff thrice, and dozed off, still laughing.

The diamond-bright dawn woke men and crows and bullocks together. Kim sat up and yawned, shook himself, and thrilled with delight. This was seeing the world in real truth; this was life as he would have it—bustling and shouting, the buckling of belts, and beating of bullocks and creaking of wheels, lighting of fires and cooking of food, and new sights at every turn of the approving eye. The morning mist swept off in a whorl of silver, the parrots shot away to some distant river in shrieking green hosts: all the well-wheels within earshot went to work. India was awake, and Kim was in the middle of it, more awake and more excited than any one, chewing on a twig that he would presently use as a toothbrush; for he borrowed right- and left-handedly from all the customs of the country he knew and loved. There was no need to worry about food—no need to spend a cowrie at the crowded stalls. He was the disciple of a holy man annexed by a strong-willed old

lady. All things would be prepared for them, and when they were respect-
fully invited so to do they would sit and eat. For the rest,—Kim giggled
here as he cleaned his teeth,—his hostess would rather heighten the enjoy-
ment of the road. He inspected her bullocks critically, as they came up
grunting and blowing under the yokes. If they went too fast—it was not
likely—there would be a pleasant seat for himself along the pole; the lama
would sit beside the driver. The escort, of course, would walk. The old lady,
equally of course, would talk a great deal, and by what he had heard that
conversation would not lack salt. She was already ordering, haranguing, re-
buking, and, it must be said, cursing her servants for delays.

' Get her her pipe. In the name of the Gods, get her her pipe and
stop her ill-omened mouth,' cried an Oorya, tying up his shapeless bundles
of bedding. ' She and the parrots are alike. They screech in the dawn.'

' The lead-bullocks! Hai! Look to the lead-bullocks! ' They were backing
and wheeling as a grain-cart's axle caught them by the horns. ' Son of an
owl, where dost thou go? ' This to the grinning carter.

' Ai! Yai! Yai! That within there is the Queen of Delhi going to pray
for a son,' the man called back over his high load. ' Room for the Queen
of Delhi and her prime minister the gray monkey climbing up his own
sword! ' Another cart loaded with bark for a down-country tannery followed
close behind, and its driver added a few compliments as the ruth-bullocks
backed and backed again.

From behind the shaking curtains came one volley of invective. It did
not last long, but in kind and quality, in blistering, biting appropriateness,
it was beyond anything that even Kim had heard. He could see the carter's
bare chest collapse with amazement, as the man salaamed reverently to the
voice, leaped from the pole, and helped the escort haul their volcano on to
the main road. Here the voice told him truthfully what sort of wife he had
wedded, and what she was doing in his absence.

' Oh, shabash! ' murmured Kim, unable to contain himself, as the man
slunk away.

' Well done, indeed? It is a shame and a scandal that a poor woman
may not go to make prayer to her gods except she be jostled and insulted by
all the refuse of Hindustan—that she must eat gali (abuse) as men eat ghi.
But I have yet a wag left to my tongue—a word or two well spoken that
serves the occasion. And still am I without my tobacco! Who is the one-eyed
and luckless son of shame that has not yet prepared my pipe? '

It was hastily thrust in by a hillman, and a trickle of thick smoke from
each corner of the curtains showed that peace was restored.

If Kim had walked proudly the day before, disciple of a holy man, to-day
he paced with tenfold pride in the train of a semi-royal procession, with a
recognised place under the patronage of an old lady of charming manners
and infinite resource. The escort, their heads tied up native fashion, fell
in on either side the cart, shuffling enormous clouds of dust.

The lama and Kim walked a little to one side; Kim chewing his stick

of sugar-cane, and making way for no one under the status of a priest. They could hear the old lady's tongue clack as steadily as a rice-husker. She bade the escort tell her what was going on on the road; and so soon as they were clear of the parao she flung back the curtains and peered out, her veil a third across her face. Her men did not eye her directly when she addressed them, and thus the proprieties were more or less observed.

A dark, sallowish District Superintendent of Police, faultlessly uni-formed, an Englishman, trotted by on a tired horse, and, seeing from her retinue what manner of person she was, chaffed her.

'O mother,' he cried, 'do they do this in the zenanas? Suppose an Englishman came by and saw that thou hadst no nose?'

'What?' she shrilled back. 'Thy own mother has no nose? Why say so, then, on the open road?'

It was a fair counter. The Englishman thew up his hand with the gesture of a man hit at sword-play. She laughed and nodded.

'Is this a face to tempt virtue aside?' She withdrew all her veil and stared at him.

It was by no means lovely, but as the man gathered up his reins he called it a Moon of Paradise, a Disturber of Integrity, and a few other fan-tastic epithets which doubled her up with mirth.

'That is a nut-cut' (rogue), she said. 'All police-constables are nut-cuts; but the police-wallahs are the worst. Hai, my son, thou hast never learned all that since thou camest from Belait (Europe). Who suckled thee?'

'A pahareen—a hillwoman of Dalhousie, my mother. Keep thy beauty under a shade—O Dispenser of Delights,' and he was gone.

'These be the sort'—she took a fine judicial tone, and stuffed her mouth with pan. 'These be the sort to oversee justice. They know the land and the customs of the land. The others, all new from Europe, suckled by white women and learning our tongues from books, are worse than the pestilence. They do harm to Kings.' Then she told a long, long tale to the world at large, of an ignorant young policeman who had disturbed some small Hill Rajah, a ninth cousin of her own, in the matter of a trivial land-case, winding up with a quotation from a work by no means devotional.

Then her mood changed, and she bade one of the escort ask whether the lama would walk alongside and discuss matters of religion. So Kim dropped back into the dust and returned to his sugar-cane. For an hour or more the lama's tam-o'-shanter showed like a moon through the haze; and, from all he heard, Kim gathered that the old woman wept. One of the Ooryas half apologised for his rudeness overnight, saying that he had never known his mistress of so bland a temper, and he ascribed it to the presence of the strange priest. Personally, he believed in Brahmins, though, like all natives, he was acutely aware of their cunning and their greed. Still, when Brahmins but irritated with begging demands the mother of his master's wife, and when she sent them away so angry that they cursed the whole

retinue (which was the real reason of the second off-side bullock going lame, and of the pole breaking the night before), he was prepared to accept any priest of any other denomination in or out of India. To this Kim assented with wise nods, and bade the Oorya observe that the lama took no money, and that the cost of his and Kim's food would be repaid a hundred times in the good luck that would attend the caravan henceforward. He also told stories of Lahore city, and sang a song or two which made the escort laugh. As a town-mouse well acquainted with the latest songs by the most fashionable composers,—they are women for the most part,—Kim had a distinct advantage over men from a little fruit-village behind Saharunpore, but he let that advantage be inferred.

At noon they turned aside to eat, and the meal was good, plentiful, and well served on plates of clean leaves, in decency, out of drift of the dust. They gave the scraps to certain beggars, that all requirements might be fulfilled, and sat down to a long, luxurious smoke. The old lady had retreated behind her curtains, but mixed most freely in the talk, her servants arguing with and contradicting her as servants do throughout the East. She compared the cool and the pines of the Kangra and Kulu hills with the dust and the mangoes of the South; she told a tale of some old local Gods at the edge of her husband's territory; she roundly abused the tobacco which she was then smoking, reviled all Brahmins, and speculated without reserve on the coming of many grandsons.

CHAPTER V

Here come I to my own again—
Fed, forgiven, and known again—
Claimed by bone of my bone again,
 And sib to flesh of my flesh!
The fatted calf is dressed for me,
But the husks have greater zest for me . . .
I think my pigs will be best for me,
 So I'm off to the styes afresh.

THE PRODIGAL SON

Once more the lazy, string-tied, shuffling procession got under way, and she slept till they reached the next halting-stage. It was a very short march, and time lacked an hour to sundown, so Kim cast about for means of amusement.

'But why not sit and rest?' said one of the escort. 'Only the devils and the English walk to and fro without reason.'

'Never make friends with the Devil, a monkey, or a boy. No man knows what they will do next,' said his fellow.

Kim turned a scornful back—he did not want to hear the old story how the Devil played with the boys and repented of it—and walked idly across country.

The lama strode after him. All that day, whenever they passed a stream, he had turned aside to look at it, but in no case had he received any warning that he had found his River. Insensibly too the comfort of speaking to some one in a reasonable tongue, and of being properly considered and respected as her spiritual adviser by a well-born woman, had weaned his thoughts a little from the Search. And further, he was prepared to spend serene years in his quest; having nothing of the white man's impatience, but a great faith.

' Where goest thou? ' he called after Kim.

' No whither—it was a small march, and all this '—Kim waved his hands abroad—' is new to me.'

' She is beyond question a wise and a discerning woman. But it is hard to meditate when— '

' All women are thus.' Kim spoke as might have Solomon.

' Before the lamassery was a broad platform,' the lama muttered, looping up the well-worn rosary, ' of stone. On that I have left the marks of my feet—pacing to and fro with these.'

He clicked the beads, and began the ' Om mane pudme hum ' of his devotion; grateful for the cool, the quiet, and the absence of dust.

One thing after another drew Kim's idle eye across the plain. There was no purpose in his wanderings, except that the build of the huts near by seemed new, and he wished to investigate.

They came out on a broad tract of grazing-ground, brown and purple in the afternoon light, with a heavy clump of mangoes in the centre. It struck Kim as curious that no shrine stood in so eligible a spot: the boy was observing as any priest for these things. Far across the plain walked side by side four men, made small by the distance. He looked intently under his curved palms and caught the sheen of brass.

' Soldiers. White soldiers! ' said he. ' Let us see.'

' It is always soldiers when thou and I go out alone together. But I have never seen the white soldiers.'

' They do no harm except when they are drunk. Keep behind this tree.'

They stepped behind the thick trunks in the cool dark of the mango-tope. Two little figures halted; the other two came forward uncertainly. They were the advance-party of a regiment on the march, sent out, as usual, to mark the camp. They bore five-foot sticks with fluttering flags, and called to each other as they spread over the flat earth.

At last they entered the mango-grove, walking heavily.

' It's here or hereabouts—officers' tents under the trees, I take it, an' the rest of us can stay outside. Have they marked out for the baggage-waggons behind? '

They cried again to their comrades in the distance, and the rough answer came back faint and mellowed.

'Shove the flag in here, then,' said one.

'What do they prepare?' said the lama, wonder-struck. 'This is a great and terrible world. What is the device on the flag?'

A soldier thrust a stave within a few feet of them, grunted discontentedly, pulled it up again, conferred with his companion, who looked up and down the shaded cave of greenery, and returned it.

Kim stared with all his eyes, his breath coming short and sharp between his teeth. The soldiers stamped off into the sunshine.

'O Holy One,' he gasped, 'my horoscope! The drawing in the dust by the priest at Umballa! Remember what he said. First come two—ferashes—to make all things ready—in a dark place, as it is always at the beginning of a vision.'

'But this is not vision,' said the lama. 'It is the world's Illusion, and no more.'

'And after them comes the Bull—the Red Bull on the green field. Look! It is he!'

He pointed to the flag that was snap-snapping in the evening breeze not ten feet away. It was no more than an ordinary camp marking-flag; but the regiment, always punctilious in matters of millinery, had charged it with the regimental device, the Red Bull, which is the crest of the Mavericks—the great Red Bull on a background of Irish green.

'I see, and now I remember,' said the lama. 'Certainly it is thy Bull. Certainly, also, the two men came to make all ready.'

'They are soldiers—white soldiers. What said the priest? "The sign over against the Bull is the sign of War and armed men." Holy One, this thing touches my Search.'

'True. It is true.' The lama stared fixedly at the device that flamed like a ruby in the dusk. 'The priest at Umballa said that thine was the sign of War.'

'What is to do now?'

'Wait. Let us wait.'

'Even now the darkness clears,' said Kim. It was only natural that the descending sun should at last strike through the tree-trunks, across the grove, filling it with mealy gold light for a few minutes; but to Kim it was crown of the Umballa Brahmin's prophecy.

'Hark!' said the lama. 'One beats a drum—far off!'

At first the sound, carrying diluted through the still air, resembled the beating of an artery in the head. Soon a sharpness was added.

'Ah! The music,' Kim explained. He knew the sound of a regimental band, but it amazed the lama.

At the far end of the plain a heavy, dusty column crawled in sight. Then the wind brought the tune:—

> 'We crave your condescension
> To tell you what we know
> Of marching in the Mulligan Guards
> To Sligo Port below.'

Here broke in the shrill-tongued fifes:—

> 'We shouldered arms,
> We marched—we marched away
> From Phœnix Park
> We marched to Dublin Bay.
> The drums and the fifes,
> Oh, sweetly they did play,
> As we marched—marched—marched—with the Mulligan Guards!'

It was the band of the Mavericks playing the regiment to camp; for the men were route-marching with their baggage. The rippling column swung into the level—carts behind it—divided left and right, ran about like an ant-hill, and . . .

'But this is sorcery!' said the lama.

The plain dotted itself with tents that seemed to rise, all spread, from the carts. Another rush of men invaded the grove, pitched a huge tent in silence, ran up yet eight or nine more by the side of it, unearthed cooking-pots, pans, and bundles, which were taken possession of by a crowd of native servants; and behold the mango-tope turned into an orderly town as they watched!

'Let us go,' said the lama, sinking back afraid, as the fires twinkled and white officers with jingling swords stalked into the mess-tent.

'Stand back in the shadow. No one can see beyond the light of a fire,' said Kim, his eyes still on the flag. He had never before watched the routine of a seasoned regiment pitching camp in thirty minutes.

'Look! look! look!' clucked the lama. 'Yonder comes a priest.'

It was Bennett, the Church of England chaplain of the regiment, limping in dusty black. One of his flock had made some rude remarks about the chaplain's mettle; and to abash him Bennett had marched step by step with the men that day. The black dress, gold cross on the watch-chain, the hairless face, and the soft, black wide-awake hat would have marked him as a holy man anywhere in all India. He dropped into a camp-chair by the door of the mess-tent and slid off his boots. Three or four officers gathered round him, laughing and joking over his exploit.

'The talk of white men is wholly lacking in dignity,' said the lama, who judged only by tone. 'But I have considered the countenance of that priest, and I think he is learned. Is it likely that he will understand our talk? I would talk to him of my Search.'

'Never speak to a white man till he is fed,' said Kim, quoting a well-known proverb. 'They will eat now, and—and I do not think they are good to beg from. Let us go back to the resting-place. After we have eaten we will come again. It certainly was a Red Bull—my Red Bull.'

They were both noticeably absent-minded when the old lady's retinue set their meal before them; so none broke their reserve, for it is not lucky to annoy guests.

'Now,' said Kim, picking his teeth, 'we will return to that place; but thou, O Holy One, must wait a little way off, because thy feet are heavier than mine and I am anxious to see more of that Red Bull.'

'But how canst thou understand the talk? Walk slowly. The road is dark,' the lama replied uneasily.

Kim put the question aside. 'I marked a place near to the trees,' said he, 'where thou canst sit till I call. Nay,' as the lama made some sort of protest, 'remember this is my Search—the Search for my Red Bull. The sign in the Stars was not for thee. I know a little of the customs of white soldiers, and I always desire to see some new things.'

'What dost thou not know of this world?' The lama squatted obediently in a little hollow of the ground not a hundred yards from the hump of the mango trees dark against the star-powdered sky.

'Stay till I call.' Kim flitted into the dusk. He knew that in all probability there would be sentries round the camp, and smiled to himself as he heard the thick boots of one. A boy who can dodge over the roofs of Lahore city on a moonlight night, using every little patch and corner of darkness to discomfit his pursuer, is not likely to be checked by a line of well-trained soldiers. He paid them the compliment of crawling between a couple, and, running and halting, crouching and dropping flat, worked his way toward the lighted mess-tent where, close pressed behind the mango tree, he waited till some chance word should give him a returnable lead.

The one thing in his mind now was further information as to the Red Bull. For aught he knew, and Kim's limitations were as curious and sudden as his expansions, the men, the nine hundred thorough devils of his father's prophecy, might pray to the beast after dark, as Hindus pray to the Holy Cow. That at least would be entirely right and logical, and the Padre with the gold cross would be therefore the man to consult in the matter. On the other hand, remembering sober-faced padres whom he had avoided in Lahore city, the priest might be an inquisitive nuisance who would bid him learn. But had it not been proven at Umballa that his sign in the high heavens portended war and armed men? Was he not the Friend of the Stars as well as of all the world, crammed to the teeth with dreadful secrets? Lastly,—and firstly as the undercurrent of all his quick thoughts,—this adventure, though he did not know the English word, was a stupendous lark—a delightful continuation of his old flights across the housetops, as well as the fulfilment of sublime prophecy. He lay belly-flat and wriggled towards the mest-tent door, a hand on the amulet round his neck.

It was as he suspected. The Sahibs prayed to their God; for in the centre of the mess-table—its sole ornament when they were on the line of march—stood a golden bull fashioned from old-time loot of the Summer Palace at Pekin—a red-gold bull with lowered head, ramping upon a field of Irish green. To him the Sahibs held out their glasses and cried aloud confusedly.

Now the Reverend Arthur Bennett always left mess after that toast,

and being rather tired by his march his movements were more abrupt than
usual. Kim, with slightly raised head, was still staring at his totem on the
table, when the chaplain stepped on his right shoulder-blade. Kim flinched
under the leather, and, rolling sideways, brought down the chaplain, who,
ever a man of action, caught him by the throat and nearly choked the life
out of him. Kim then kicked him desperately in the stomach. Mr. Bennett
gasped and doubled up but without relaxing his grip, rolled over again, and
silently hauled Kim to his own tent. The Mavericks were incurable practical
jokers; and it occurred to the Englishman that silence was best till he had
made complete inquiry.

'Why, it's a boy!' he said, as he drew his prize under the light of the
tent-pole lantern, then shaking him severely cried: 'What were you doing?
You're a thief. Choor? Mallum?' His Hindustanee was very limited, and
the ruffled and disgusted Kim intended to keep to the character laid down
for him. As he recovered his breath he was inventing a beautifully plausible
tale of his relations to some mess-scullion, and at the same time keeping a
keen eye on and a little under the chaplain's left armpit. The chance came;
he ducked for the doorway, but a long arm shot out and clutched at his
neck, snapping the amulet string and closing on the amulet.

'Give it me. O give it me. Is it lost? Give me the papers.'

The words were in English—the tinny, saw-cut English of the native-
bred, and the chaplain jumped.

'A scapular,' said he, opening his hand. 'No, some sort of heathen
charm. Why—why, do you speak English? Little boys who steal are beaten.
You know that?'

'I do not—I did not steal.' Kim danced in agony like a terrier at a
lifted stick. 'O give it me. It is my charm. Do not thieve it from me.'

The chaplain took no heed, but, going to the tent door, called aloud.
A fattish, clean-shaven man appeared.

'I want your advice, Father Victor,' said Bennett. 'I found this boy in
the dark outside the mess-tent. Ordinarily, I should have chastised him and
let him go, because I believe him to be a thief. But it seems he talks English,
and he attaches some sort of value to a charm round his neck. I thought
perhaps you might help me.'

Between himself and the Roman Catholic chaplain of the Irish con-
tingent lay, as Bennett believed, an unbridgeable gulf, but it was noticeable
that whenever the Church of England dealt with a human problem she was
likely to call in the Church of Rome. Bennett's official abhorrence of the
Scarlet Woman and all her ways was only equalled by his private respect for
Father Victor.

'A thief talking English is it? Let's look at his charm. No, it's not a
scapular, Bennett.' He held out his hand.

'But have we any right to open it? A sound whipping—'

'I did not thieve,' protested Kim. 'You have hit me kicks all over my
body. Now give me my charm and I will go away.'

'Not quite so fast; we'll look first,' said Father Victor, leisurely rolling out poor Kimball O'Hara's 'ne varietur' parchment, his clearance-certificate, and Kim's baptismal certificate. On this last O'Hara—with some confused idea that he was doing wonders for his son—had scrawled scores of times: 'Look after the boy. Please look after the boy,'—signing his name and regimental number in full.

'Powers of Darkness below!' said Father Victor, passing all over to Mr. Bennett. 'Do you know what these things are?'

'Yes,' said Kim. 'They are mine, and I want to go away.'

'I do not quite understand,' said Mr. Bennett. 'He probably brought them on purpose. It may be a begging trick of some kind.'

'I never saw a beggar less anxious to stay with his company, then. There's the makings of a gay mystery here. Ye believe in Providence, Bennett?'

'I hope so.'

'Well, I belive in miracles, so it comes to the same thing. Powers of Darkness! Kimball O'Hara! And his son! But then he's a native, and I saw Kimball married myself to Annie Shott. How long have you had these things, boy?'

'Ever since I was a little baby.' Father Victor stepped forward quickly and opened the front of Kim's upper garment. 'You see, Bennett, he's not very black. What's your name?'

'Kim.'

'Or Kimball?'

'Perhaps. Will you let me go away?'

'What else?'

'They call me Kim Rishti ke. That is Kim of the Rishti.'

'What is that—"Rishti"?'

'Eye-rishti—that was the regiment—my father's.'

'Irish, oh I see.'

'Yess. That was how my father told me. My father, he has lived.'

'Has lived where?'

'Has lived. Of course he is dead—gone-out.'

'Oh. That's your abrupt way of putting it, is it?'

Bennett interrupted. 'It is possible I have done the boy an injustice. He is certainly white, though evidently neglected. I am sure I must have bruised him. I do not think spirits—'

'Get him a glass of sherry, then, and let him squat on the cot. Now, Kim,' continued Father Victor, 'no one is going to hurt you. Drink that down and tell us about yourself. The truth, if you've no objection.'

Kim coughed a little as he put down the empty glass, and considered. This seemed a time for caution and fancy. Small boys who prowl about camps are generally turned out after a whipping. But he had received no stripes; the amulet was evidently working in his favour, and it looked as though the Umballa horoscope and the few words that he could remember

of his father's maunderings fitted in most miraculously. Else why did the fat padre seem so impressed, and why the glass of hot yellow wine from the lean one?

'My father, he is dead in Lahore city since I was very little. The woman, she kept kabarri-shop near where the hire-carriages are.' Kim began with a plunge, not quite sure how far the truth would serve him.

'Your mother?'

'No'—with a gesture of disgust. 'She went out when I was born. My father, he got these papers from the Jadoo-Gher—what do you call that?' (Bennett nodded) 'because he was in—good-standing. What do you call that?' (again Bennett nodded). 'My father told me that. He said too, and also the Brahmin who made the drawing in the dust at Umballa two days ago, he said, that I shall find a Red Bull on a green field and that the Bull shall help me.'

'A phenomenal little liar,' muttered Bennett.

'Powers of Darkness below, what a country!' murmured Father Victor. 'Go on, Kim.'

'I did not thieve. Besides, I am just now disciple of a very holy man. He is sitting outside. We saw two men come with flags, making the place ready. That is always so in a dream, or on account of a—a—prophecy. So I knew it was come true. I saw the Red Bull on the green field, and my father he said: "Nine hundred pukka devils and the Colonel riding on a horse will look after you when you find the Red Bull!" I did not know what to do when I saw the Bull, but I went away and I came again when it was dark. I wanted to see the Bull again, and I saw the Bull again with the—the Sahibs praying to it. I think the Bull shall help me. The holy man said so too. He is sitting outside. Will you hurt him, if I call him a shout now? He is very holy. He can witness to all the things I say, and he knows I am not a thief.'

'"Officers praying to a bull!" What in the world do you make of that?' said Bennett. '"Disciple of a holy man!" Is the boy mad?'

'It's O'Hara's boy, sure enough. O'Hara's boy leagued with all the Powers of Darkness. It's very much what his father would have done—if he was drunk. We'd better invite the holy man. He may know something.'

'He does not know anything,' said Kim. 'I will show you him if you come. He is my master. Then afterwards we can go.'

'Powers of Darkness!' was all that Father Victor could say, as Bennett marched off, with a firm hand on Kim's shoulder.

They found the lama where he had dropped.

'The Search is at an end for me,' shouted Kim in the vernacular. 'I have found the Bull, but God knows what comes next. They will not hurt you. Come to the fat priest's tent with this thin man and see the end. It is all new, and they cannot talk Hindi. They are only uncurried donkeys.'

'Then it is not well to make a jest of their ignorance,' the lama returned. 'I am glad if thou art rejoiced, chela.'

Dignified and unsuspicious, he strode into the little tent, saluted the Churches as a Churchman, and sat down by the open charcoal brazier. The yellow lining of the tent reflected in the lamplight made his face red-gold.

Bennett looked at him with the triple-ringed uninterest of the creed that lumps nine-tenths of the world under the title of ' heathen.'

' And what was the end of the search? What gift has the Red Bull brought? ' The lama addressed himself to Kim.

' He says, " What are you going to do? " ' Bennett was staring uneasily at Father Victor, and Kim, for his own ends, took upon himself the office of interpreter.

' I do not see what concern this faquir has with the boy, who is probably his dupe or his confederate,' Bennett began. ' We cannot allow an English boy— Assuming that he is the son of a Mason, the sooner he goes to the Masonic Orphanage the better.'

' Ah! That's your opinion as Secretary to the Regimental Lodge,' said Father Victor; ' but we might as well tell the old man what we are going to do. He doesn't look like a villain.'

' My experience is that one can never fathom the Oriental mind. Now, Kimball, I wish you to tell this man what I say—word for word.'

Kim gathered the import of the next few sentences and began thus:

' Holy One, the thin fool who looks like a camel says that I am the son of a Sahib.'

' But how? '

' Oh, it is true. I knew it since my birth, but he could only find it out by rending the amulet from my neck and reading all the papers. He thinks that once a Sahib is always a Sahib, and between the two of them they purpose to keep me in this regiment or to send me to a madrissah (a school). It has happened before. I have always avoided it. The fat fool is of one mind and the camel-like one of another. But that is no odds. I may spend one night here and perhaps the next. It has happened before. Then I will run away and return to thee.'

' But tell them that thou art my chela. Tell them how thou didst come to me when I was faint and bewildered. Tell them of our Search, and they will surely let thee go now.'

' I have already told them. They laugh, and they talk of the Police.'

' What are you saying? ' asked Mr. Bennett.

' Oah. He only says that if you do not let me go it will stop him in his business—his ur-gent private affairs.' This last was a reminiscence of some talk with a Eurasian clerk in the Canal Department, but it only drew a smile, which nettled him. ' And if you did know what his business was you would not be in such a beastly hurry to interfere.'

' What is it then? ' said Father Victor, not without feeling, as he watched the lama's face.

' There is a River in this country which he wishes to find so verree much. It was put out by an Arrow which— ' Kim tapped his foot impa-

tiently as he translated in his own mind from the vernacular to his clumsy English. ' Oah, it was made by our Lord God Buddha, you know, and if you wash there you are washed away from all your sins and made as white as cotton-wool.' (Kim had heard mission-talk in his time.) ' I am his disciple, and we must find that River. It is so verree valuable to us.'

' Say that again,' said Bennett. Kim obeyed, with amplifications.

' But this is gross blasphemy! ' cried the Church of England.

' Tck! Tck! ' said Father Victor sympathetically. ' I'd give a good deal to be able to talk the vernacular. A river that washes away sin! And how long have you two been looking for it? '

' Oh, many days. Now we wish to go away and look for it again. It is not here, you see.'

' I see,' said Father Victor gravely. ' But he can't go on in that old man's company. It would be different, Kim, if you were not a soldier's son. Tell him that the regiment will take care of you and make you as good a man as your—as good a man as can be. Tell him that if he believes in miracles he must believe that— '

' There is no need to play on his credulity,' Bennett interrupted.

' I'm doing no such thing. He must believe that the boy's coming here —to his own regiment—in search of his Red Bull is in the nature of a miracle. Consider the chances against it, Bennett. This one boy in all India, and our regiment of all others on the line o' march for him to meet with! It's predestined on the face of it. Yes, tell him it's Kismet. Kismet, mallum? ' (Fate! Do you understand?)

He turned towards the lama, to whom he might as well have talked of Mesopotamia.

' They say,'—the old man's eye lighted at Kim's speech,—' they say that the meaning of my horoscope is now accomplished, and that being led back—though as thou knowest I went out of curiosity—to these people and their Red Bull I must needs go to a madrissah and be turned into a Sahib. Now I make pretence of agreement, for at the worst it will be but a few meals eaten away from thee. Then I will slip away and follow down the road to Saharunpore. Therefore, Holy One, keep with that Kulu woman—on no account stray far from her cart till I come again. Past question, my sign is of War and of armed men. See how they have given me wine to drink and set me upon a bed of honour! My father must have been some great person. So if they raise me to honour among them, good. If not, good again. However it goes, I will run back to thee when I am tired. But stay with the Rajputni, or I shall miss thy feet. . . . Oah yess,' said the boy, ' I have told him everything you tell me to say.'

' And I cannot see any need why he should wait,' said Bennett, feeling in his trouser-pocket. ' We can investigate the details later—and I will give him a ru— '

' Give him time. May be he's fond of the lad,' said Father Victor, half-arresting the clergyman's motion.

The lama dragged forth his rosary and pulled his huge hat-brim over his eyes.

'What can he want now?'

'He says'—Kim put up one hand. 'He says: Be quiet. He wants to speak to me by himself. You see you do not know one little word of what he says, and I think if you talk he will perhaps give you very bad curses. When he takes those beads like that, you see he always wants to be quiett.'

The two Englishmen sat overwhelmed, but there was a look in Bennett's eye that promised ill for Kim when he should be relaxed to the religious arm.

'A Sahib and the son of a Sahib—' The lama's voice was harsh with pain. 'But no white man knows the land and the customs of the land as thou knowest. How comes it this is true?'

'What matter, Holy One: but remember it is only for a night or two. Remember, I can change swiftly. It will be as it was when I first spoke to thee under Zam-Zammah the great gun—'

'As a boy in the dress of white men—when I first went to the Wonder House. And a second time thou wast a Hindu. What shall the third incarnation be?' He chuckled drearily. 'Ah, chela, thou hast done a wrong to an old man because my heart went out to thee.'

'And mine to thee. But how could I know that the Red Bull would bring me to this business?'

The lama covered his face afresh, and nervously rattled the rosary. Kim squatted beside him and laid hold upon a fold of his clothing.

'Now it is understood that the boy is a Sahib?' he went on in a muffled tone. 'Such a Sahib as was he who kept the images in the Wonder House.' The lama's experience of white men was limited. He seemed to be repeating a lesson. 'So then it is not seemly that he should do other than as the Sahibs do. He must go back to his own people.'

'For a day and a night and a day,' Kim pleaded.

'No, ye don't!' Father Victor saw Kim edging towards the door, and interposed a strong leg.

'I do not understand the customs of white men. The Priest of the Images in the Wonder House in Lahore was more courteous than the thin one here. This boy will be taken from me. They will make a Sahib of my disciple? Woe to me, how shall I find my River? Have they no disciples? Ask.'

'He says he is very sorry that he cannot find the River now any more. He says, Why have you no disciples, and stop bothering him? He wants to be washed of his sins.'

Neither Bennett nor Father Victor found any answer ready.

Said Kim in English, distressed for the lama's agony: 'I think if you will let me go now we will walk away quietly and not steal. We will look for that River like before I was caught. I wish I did not come here to find the Red Bull and all that sort of thing. I do not want it.'

'It's the very best day's work you ever did for yourself, young man,' said Bennett.

'Good heavens, I don't know how to console him,' said Father Victor, watching the lama intently. 'He can't take the boy away with him, and yet he's a good man—I'm sure he's a good man. Bennett, if you give him that rupee he'll curse you root and branch!'

They listened to each other's breathing—three—five full minutes. Then the lama raised his head, and looked forth across them into space and emptiness.

'And I am a follower of the Way,' he said bitterly. 'The sin is mine and the punishment is mine. I made believe to myself—for now I see it was but make-belief—that thou wast sent to me to aid in the Search. So my heart went out to thee for thy charity and thy courtesy and the wisdom of thy little years. But those who follow the Way must permit not the fire of any desire or attachment, for that is all illusion. As says . . .' He quoted an old, old Chinese text, backed it with another, and reinforced these with a third. 'I stepped aside from the Way, my chela. It was no fault of thine. I delighted in the sight of life, the new people upon the roads, and in thy joy at seeing these things. I was pleased with thee who should have considered my Search and my Search alone. Now I am sorrowful because thou art taken away and my River is far from me. It is the Law which I have broken!'

'Powers of Darkness below!' said Father Victor, who, wise in the confessional, heard the pain in every sentence.

'I see now that the sign of the Red Bull was a sign for me as well as for thee. All Desire is red—and evil. I will do penance and find my River alone.'

'At least go back to the Kulu woman,' said Kim, 'otherwise thou wilt be lost upon the roads. She will feed thee till I run back to thee.'

The lama waved a hand to show that the matter was finally settled in his mind.

'Now,'—his tone altered as he turned to Kim,—'what will they do with thee? At least I may, acquiring merit, wipe out past ill.'

'Make me a Sahib—so they think. The day after to-morrow I return. Do not grieve.'

'Of what sort? Such an one as this or that man?' He pointed to Father Victor. 'Such an one as those I saw this evening—men wearing swords and stamping heavily?'

'May be.'

'That is not well. These men follow desire and come to emptiness. Thou must not be of their sort.'

'The Umballa priest said that my Star was War,' Kim interjected. 'I will ask these fools—but there is truly no need. I will run away this night, for all I wanted to see the new things.'

Kim put two or three questions in English to Father Victor, translating the replies to the lama.

Then: ' He says, " You take him from me and you cannot say what you will make him." He says, " Tell me before I go, for it is not a small thing to make a child." '

' You will be sent to a school. Later on, we shall see. Kimball, I suppose you'd like to be a soldier? '

' Gorah-log (white-folk). No-ah! No-ah! ' Kim shook his head violently. There was nothing in his composition to which drill and routine appealed. ' I will not be a soldier.'

' You will be what you're told to be,' said Bennett; ' and you should be grateful that we're going to help you.'

Kim smiled compassionately. If these men lay under the delusion that he would do anything that he did not fancy, so much the better.

Another long silence followed. Bennett fidgeted with impatience, and suggested calling a sentry to evict the faquir.

' Do they give or sell learning among the Sahibs? Ask them,' said the lama, and Kim interpreted.

' They say that money is paid to the teacher—but that money the regiment will give. . . . What need? It is only for a night.'

' And—the more money is paid the better learning is given? ' The lama disregarded Kim's plans for an early flight. ' It is no wrong to pay for learning; to help the ignorant to wisdom is always a merit.' The rosary clicked furiously as an abacus. Then he faced his oppressors.

' Ask them for how much money do they give a wise and suitable teaching? and in what city is that teaching given? '

' Well,' said Father Victor in English, when Kim had translated, ' that depends. The regiment would pay for you all the time you are at the Military Orphanage; or you might go on the Punjab Masonic Orphanage's list (not that he or you 'ud understand what that means); but the best schooling a boy can get in India is, of course, at St. Xavier's in Partibus at Lucknow.' This took some time to interpret, for Bennett wished to cut it short.

' He wants to know how much? ' said Kim placidly.

' Two or three hundred rupees a year.' Father Victor was long past any sense of amazement. Bennett, impatient, did not understand.

' He says: " Write that name and the money upon a paper and give it him." And he says you must write your name below, because he is going to write a letter in some days to you. He says you are a good man. He says the other man is a fool. He is going away.'

The lama rose suddenly. ' I follow my Search,' he cried, and was gone.

' He'll run slap into the sentries,' cried Father Victor, jumping up as the lama stalked out; ' but I can't leave the boy.' Kim made swift motion to follow, but checked himself. There was no sound of challenge outside. The lama had disappeared.

Kim settled himself composedly on the chaplain's cot. At least the lama had promised that he would stay with the Rajput woman from Kulu, and the rest was of the smallest importance. It pleased him that the two

padres were so evidently excited. They talked long in undertones, Father Victor urging some scheme on Mr. Bennett, who seemed incredulous. All this was very new and fascinating, but Kim felt sleepy. They called men into the tent—one of them certainly was the Colonel, as his father had prophesied—and they asked him an infinity of questions, chiefly about the woman who looked after him, all of which Kim answered truthfully. They did not seem to think the woman a good guardian.

After all, this was the newest of his experiences. Sooner or later, if he chose, he could escape into great, gray, formless India, beyond tents and padres and colonels. Meantime, if the Sahibs were to be impressed, he would do his best to impress them. He too was a white man.

After much talk that he could not comprehend, they handed him over to a sergeant, who had strict instructions not to let him escape. The regiment would go on to Umballa, and Kim would be sent up, partly at the expense of the Lodge and in part by subscription, to a place called Sanawar.

'It's miraculous past all whooping, Colonel,' said Father Victor, when he had talked without a break for ten minutes. 'His Buddhist friend has levanted after taking my name and address. I can't quite make out whether he'll pay for the boy's education or whether he is preparing some sort of witchcraft on his own account.' Then to Kim: 'You'll live to be grateful to your friend the Red Bull yet. We'll make a man of you at Sanawar—even at the price o' making you a Protestant.'

'Certainly—most certainly,' said Bennett.

'But you will not go to Sanawar,' said Kim.

'But we will go to Sanawar, little man. That's the order of the Commander-in-Chief, who's a trifle more important than O'Hara's son.'

'You will not go to Sanawar. You will go to thee war.'

There was a shout of laughter from the full tent.

'When you know your own regiment a trifle better you won't confuse the line of march with line of battle, Kim. We hope to go to " thee war " sometime.'

'Oah, I know all thatt.' Kim drew his bow again at a venture. If they were going to the war, at least they did not know what he knew of the talk in the veranda at Umballa.

'I know you are not at thee war now; but I tell you that as soon as you get to Umballa you will be sent to the war—the new war. It is a war of eight thousand men, besides the guns.'

'That's explicit. D'you add prophecy to your other gifts? Take him along, Sergeant. Take up a suit for him from the Drums, an' take care he doesn't slip through your fingers. Who says the age of miracles is gone by? I think I'll go to bed. My poor mind's weakening.'

At the far end of the camp, silent as a wild animal, an hour later sat Kim, newly washed all over, in a horrible stuff suit that rasped his arms and legs.

'A most amazin' young bird,' said the Sergeant. 'He turns up in charge

of a yellow-headed buck-Brahmin priest, with his father's Lodge certificates round his neck, talkin' God knows what all of a red bull. The buck-Brahmin evaporates without explanations, an' the bhoy sets cross-legged on the chaplain's bed prophesyin' bloody war to the men at large. Injia's a wild land for a God-fearin' man. I'll just tie his leg to the tent-pole in case he'll go through the roof. What did ye say about the war? '

'Eight thousand men, besides guns,' said Kim. 'Very soon you will see.'

'You're a consolin' little imp. Lie down between the Drums an' go to bye-bye. Those two boys beside ye will watch your slumbers.'

CHAPTER VI

Now I remember comrades—
 Old playmates on new seas—
Whenas we traded orpiment
 Among the savages.
Ten thousand leagues to southward,
 And thirty years removed—
They knew not noble Valdez,
 But me they knew and loved.
 Song of Diego Valdez

Very early in the morning the white tents came down and disappeared as the Mavericks took a side road to Umballa. It did not skirt the resting-place, and Kim, trudging beside a baggage-cart under fire of comments from soldiers' wives, was not so confident as over-night. He discovered that he was closely watched—Father Victor on the one side, and Mr. Bennett on the other.

In the forenoon the column checked. A camel-orderly handed the Colonel a letter. He read it, and spoke to a major. Half a mile in the rear, Kim heard a hoarse and joyful clamour rolling down on him through the thick dust. Then some one beat him on the back, crying: 'Tell us how ye knew, ye little limb of Satan? Father dear, see if ye can make him tell.'

A pony ranged alongside, and he was hauled on to the priest's saddle-bow.

'Now, my son, your prophecy of last night has come true. Our orders are to entrain at Umballa for the front to-morrow.'

'What is thatt? ' said Kim, for 'front' and 'entrain' were newish words to him.

'We are going to " thee war," as you called it.'

'Of course you are going to thee war. I said last night.'

'Ye did; but, Powers o' Darkness, how did ye know? '

Kim's eyes sparkled. He shut his lips, nodded his head, and looked unspeakable things. The chaplain moved on through the dust, and privates, sergeants, and subalterns called one another's attention to the boy. The Colonel, at the head of the column, stared at him curiously. ' It was probably some bazar rumour,' he said; ' but even then— ' He referred to the paper in his hand. ' Hang it all, the thing was only decided within the last forty-eight hours.'

' Are there many more like you in India? ' said Father Victor, ' or are you by way o' being a lusus naturæ? '

' Now I have told you,' said the boy, ' will you let me go back to my old man? If he has not stayed with that woman from Kulu, I am afraid he will die.'

' By what I saw of him he's as well able to take care of himself as you. No. Ye've brought us luck, an' we're goin' to make a man of you. I'll take ye back to your baggage-cart and ye'll come to me this evening.'

For the rest of the day Kim found himself an object of distinguished consideration among a few hundred white men. The story of his appearance in camp, the discovery of his parentage, and his prophecy, had lost nothing in the telling. A big, shapeless white woman on a pile of bedding asked him mysteriously whether he thought her husband would come back from the war. Kim reflected gravely, and said that he would, and the woman gave him food. In many respects, this big procession that played music at intervals—this crowd that talked and laughed so easily—resembled a festival in Lahore city. So far, there was no sign of hard work, and he resolved to lend the spectacle his patronage. At evening there came out to meet them bands of music, and played the Mavericks into camp near Umballa railway station. That was an interesting night. Men of other regiments came to visit the Mavericks. The Mavericks went visiting on their own account. Their pickets hurried forth to bring them back, met pickets of strange regiments on the same duty; and, after a while, the bugles blew madly for more pickets with officers to control the tumult. The Mavericks had a reputation for liveliness to live up to. But they fell in on the platform next morning in perfect shape and condition; and Kim, left behind with the sick, women, and boys, found himself shouting farewells excitedly as the trains drew away. Life as a Sahib was amusing so far; but he touched it with a cautious hand. Then they marched him back in charge of a drummer-boy to empty, lime-washed barracks, whose floors were covered with rubbish and string and paper, and whose ceilings gave back his lonely footfall. Native fashion, he curled himself up on a stripped cot and went to sleep. An angry man stumped down the veranda, woke him up, and said he was a schoolmaster. This was enough for Kim, and he retired into his shell. He could just puzzle out the various English Police notices in Lahore city, because they affected his comfort; and among the many guests of the woman who looked after him had been a queer German who painted scenery for the Parsee travelling theatre. He told Kim that he had been ' on the barricades in Forty-eight,' and there-

fore—at least that was how it struck Kim—he would teach the boy to write in return for food. Kim had been kicked as far as single letters, but did not think well of them.

'I do not know anything. Go away!' said Kim, scenting evil. Hereupon the man caught him by the ear, dragged him to a room in a far-off wing where a dozen drummer-boys were sitting on forms, and told him to be still if he could do nothing else. This he managed very successfully. The man explained something or other with white lines on a black board for at least half an hour, and Kim continued his interrupted nap. He much disapproved of the present aspect of affairs, for this was the very school and discipline he had spent two-thirds of his young life in avoiding. Suddenly a beautiful idea occurred to him, and he wondered that he had not thought of it before.

The man dismissed them, and first to spring through the veranda into the open sunshine was Kim.

''Ere you! 'Alt! Stop!' said a high voice at his heels. 'I've got to look after you. My orders are not to let you out of my sight. Where are you goin'?'

It was the drummer-boy who had been hanging round him all the forenoon—a fat and freckled person of about fourteen, and Kim loathed him from the soles of his boots to his cap-ribbons.

'To the bazar—to get sweets—for you,' said Kim, after thought.

'Well, the bazar's out o' bounds. If we go there we'll get a dressing-down. You come back.'

'How near can we go?' Kim did not know what bounds meant, but he wished to be polite—for the present.

''Ow near? 'Ow far, you mean? We can go as far as that tree down the road.'

'Then I will go there.'

'All right. I ain't goin'. It's too 'ot. I can watch you from 'ere. It's no good runnin' away. If you did, they'd spot you by your clothes. That's regimental stuff you're wearin'. There ain't a picket in Umballa wouldn't 'ead you back quicker than you started out.'

This did not impress Kim as much as the knowledge that his raiment would tire him out if he tried to run. He slouched to the tree at the corner of a bare road leading towards the bazar, and eyed the natives passing. Most of them were barrack-servants of the lowest caste. Kim hailed a sweeper, who promptly retorted with a piece of unnecessary insolence, in the natural belief that the European boy could not follow. The low, quick answer undeceived him. Kim put his fettered soul into it, thankful for the late chance to abuse somebody in the tongue he knew best. 'And now, go to the nearest letter-writer in the bazar and tell him to come here. I would write a letter.'

'But—but what manner of white man's son art thou, to need a bazar letter-writer? Is there not a schoolmaster in the barracks?'

'Ay; and Hell is full of the same sort. Do my order, you—you Od! Thy

mother was married under a basket! Servant of Lal Beg' (Kim knew the god of the sweepers), 'run on my business or we will talk again.'

The sweeper shuffled off in haste. ' There is a white boy by the barracks waiting under a tree who is not a white boy,' he stammered to the first bazar letter-writer he came across. ' He needs thee.'

' Will he pay? ' said that spruce scribe, gathering up his desk and pens and sealing-wax all in order.

' I do not know. He is not like other boys. Go and see. It is well worth.'

Kim danced with impatience when the slim young Kayeth hove in sight. As soon as his voice could carry he cursed him volubly.

' First I will take my pay,' the letter-writer said. ' Bad words have made the price higher. But who art thou, dressed in that fashion, to speak in this fashion? '

' Aha! That is in the letter which thou shalt write. Never was such a tale. But I am in no haste. Another writer will serve me. Umballa city is as full of them as is Lahore.'

' Four annas,' said the writer, sitting down and spreading his cloth in the shade of a deserted barrack-wing.

Mechanically Kim squatted beside him,—squatted as only the natives can,—in spite of the abominable clinging trousers.

The writer regarded him sideways.

' That is the price to ask of Sahibs,' said Kim. ' Now fix me a true one.'

' An anna and a half. How do I know, having written the letter, that thou wilt not run away? '

' I must not go beyond this tree, and there is also the stamp to be considered.'

' I get no commission on the price of the stamp. Once more, what manner of white boy art thou? '

' That shall be said in the letter, which is to Mahbub Ali, the horse-dealer in the Kashmir Serai, at Lahore. He is my friend.'

' Wonder on wonder! ' murmured the letter-writer, dipping a reed in the inkstand. ' To be written in Hindi? '

' Assuredly. To Mahbub Ali then. Begin! " I have come down with the old man as far as Umballa in the train. At Umballa I carried the news of the bay mare's pedigree." ' After what he had seen in the garden, he was not going to write of white stallions.

' Slower a little. What has a bay mare to do. . . . Is it Mahbub Ali the great dealer? '

' Who else? I have been in his service. Take more ink. Again. " As the order was, so I did it. We then went on foot towards Benares, but on the third day we found a certain regiment." Is that down? '

' Ay, " pulton," ' murmured the writer, all ears.

' " I went into their camp and was caught, and by means of the charm about my neck, which thou knowest, it was established that I was the son of some man in the regiment: according to the prophecy of the Red Bull,

which thou knowest was common talk of our bazar." ' Kim waited for this shaft to sink into the letter-writer's heart, cleared his throat, and continued: ' " A priest clothed me and gave me a new name. . . . One priest, however, was a fool. The clothes are very heavy, but I am a Sahib and my heart is heavy too. They send me to a school and beat me. I do not like the air and water here. Come then and help me, Mahbub Ali, or send me some money, for I have not sufficient to pay the writer who writes this." '

' " Who writes this." It is my own fault that I was tricked. Thou art as clever as Husain Bux that forged the Treasury stamps at Nucklao. But what a tale! What a tale! Is it true by any chance? '

' It does not profit to tell lies to Mahbub Ali. It is better to help his friends by lending them a stamp. When the money comes I will repay.'

The writer grunted doubtfully, but took a stamp out of his desk, sealed the letter, handed it over to Kim, and departed. Mahbub Ali's was a name of power in Umballa.

' That is the way to win a good account with the Gods,' Kim shouted after him.

' Pay me twice over when the money comes,' the man cried over his shoulder.

' What was you bukkin' to that nigger about? ' said the drummer-boy when Kim returned to the veranda. ' I was watchin' you.'

' I was only talkin' to him.'

' You talk the same as a nigger, don't you? '

' No-ah! No-ah! I onlee speak a little. What shall we do now? '

' The bugles 'ill go for dinner in arf a minute. My Gawd! I wish I'd gone up to the front with the regiment. It's awful doin' nothin' but school down 'ere. Don't you 'ate it? '

' Oah yess! '

' I'd run away if I knew where to go to, but, as the men say, in this bloomin' Injia you're only a prisoner at large. You can't desert without bein' took back at once. I'm fair sick of it.'

' You have been in Be—England? '

' W'y, I only come out last troopin' season with my mother. I should think I 'ave been in England. What a ignorant little beggar you are. You was brought up in the gutter, wasn't you? '

' Oah yess. Tell me something about England. My father he came from there.'

Though he would not say so, Kim of course disbelieved every word the drummer-boy spoke about the Liverpool suburb which was his England. It passed the heavy time till dinner—a most unappetising meal served to the boys and a few invalids in a corner of a barrack-room. But that he had written to Mahbub Ali, Kim would have been almost depressed. The indifference of native crowds he was used to; but this strong loneliness among white men preyed on him. He was grateful when, in the course of the afternoon, a big soldier took him over to Father Victor, who lived in another wing

across another dusty parade-ground. The priest was reading an English letter written in purple ink. He looked at Kim more curiously than ever.

' An' how do you like it, my son, as far as you've gone? Not much, eh? It must be hard—very hard on a wild animal. Listen now. I've an amazin' epistle from your friend.'

' Where is he? Is he well? Oah! If he knows to write me letters, it is all right.'

' You're fond of him then? '

' Of course I am fond of him. He was fond of me.'

' It seems so by the look of this. He can't write English, can he? '

' Oah no. Not that I know, but of course he found a letter-writer who can write English verree well, and so he wrote. I do hope you understand.'

' That accounts for it. D'you know anything about his money affairs? ' Kim's face showed that he did not.

' How can I tell? '

' That's what I'm askin'. Now listen if you can make head or tail o' this. We'll skip the first part. . . . It's written from Jagadhir Road. . . . " Sitting on wayside in grave meditation, trusting to be favoured with your Honour's applause of present step, which recommend your Honour to execute for Almighty God's sake. Education is greatest blessing if of best sorts. Otherwise no earthly use." Faith, the old man's hit the bull's-eye that time! " If your Honour condescending giving my boy best educations Xavier " (I suppose that's St. Xavier in Partibus) " in terms of our conversation dated in your tent 15th instant " (a business-like touch there!) " then Almighty God blessing your Honour's succeedings to third an' fourth generation and " —now listen!—" confide in your Honour's humble servant for adequate remuneration per hoondie per annum three hundred rupees a year to one expensive education St. Xavier, Lucknow, and allow small time to forward same per hoondie sent to any part of India as your Honour shall address yourself. This servant of your Honour has presently no place to lay crown of his head, but going to Benares by train on account of persecution of old woman talking so much and unanxious residing Saharunpore in any domestic capacity." Now what in the world does that mean? '

' She has asked him to be puro—her clergyman—at Saharunpore, I think. He would not do that on account of his River. She did talk.'

' It's clear to you, is it? It beats me altogether. " So going to Benares, where will find address and forward rupees for boy who is apple of eye, and for Almighty God's sake execute this education, and your petitioner as in duty bound shall ever awfully pray. Written by Sobrao Satai, Failed Entrance Allahabad University, for Venerable Teshoo Lama the priest of Suchzen looking for a River, address care of Tirthankers' Temple, Benares. P.M.— Please note boy is apple of eye, and rupees shall be sent per hoondie three hundred per annum. For God Almighty's sake." Now, is that ravin' lunacy or a business proposition? I ask you, because I'm fairly at my wits' end.'

' He says he will give me three hundred rupees a year, so he will give me them.'

' Oh, that's the way you look at it, is it? '

' Of course. If he says so! '

The priest whistled; then he addressed Kim as an equal.

' I don't believe it; but we'll see. You were goin' off to-day to the Military Orphanage at Sanawar, where the regiment would keep you till you were old enough to enlist. Ye'd be brought up to the Church of England. Bennett arranged for that. On the other hand, if ye go to St. Xavier's ye'll get a better education an'—an' can have the religion. D'ye see my dilemma? '

Kim saw nothing save a vision of the lama going south in a train with none to beg for him.

' Like most people, I'm going to temporise. If your friend sends the money from Benares—Powers of Darkness below, where's a street-beggar to raise three hundred rupees?—ye'll go down to Lucknow and I'll pay your fare, because I can't touch the subscription money if I intend, as I do, to make ye a Catholic. If he doesn't, ye'll go to the Military Orphanage at the regiment's expense. I'll allow him three days' grace, though I don't believe it at all. Even then, if he fails in his payments later on . . . but it's beyond me. We can only walk one step at a time in this world, praise God! An' they sent Bennett to the front an' left me behind. Bennett can't expect anything.'

' Oah yess,' said Kim vaguely.

The priest leaned forward. ' I'd give a month's pay to find what's goin' on inside that little round head of yours.'

' There is nothing,' said Kim, and scratched it. He was wondering whether Mahbub Ali would send him as much as a whole rupee. Then he could pay the letter-writer and write letters to the lama at Benares. Perhaps Mahbub Ali would visit him next time he came south with horses. Surely he must know that Kim's delivery of the letter to the officer at Umballa had caused the great war which the men and boys had discussed so loudly over the barrack dinner-tables. But if Mahbub Ali did not know this, it would be very unsafe to tell him so. Mahbub Ali was hard upon boys who knew, or thought they knew, too much.

' Well, till I get further news '—Father Victor's voice interrupted the reverie—' ye can run along and play with the other boys. They'll teach ye something—but I don't think ye'll like it.'

The day dragged to its weary end. When he wished to sleep he was instructed how to fold up his clothes and set out his boots; the other boys deriding. Bugles waked him in the dawn; the schoolmaster caught him after breakfast, thrust a page of meaningless characters under his nose, gave them senseless names, and whacked him without reason. Kim meditated poisoning him with opium borrowed from a barrack-sweeper, but reflected that, as they all ate at one table in public (this was peculiarly revolting to Kim, who preferred to turn his back on the world at his meals), the stroke might be dangerous. Then he attempted running off to the village where the priest had tried to drug the lama—the village where the old soldier lived. But far-seeing sentries at every exit headed back the little scarlet figure. Trousers

and jacket crippled body and mind alike, so he abandoned the project and fell back, Oriental fashion, on time and chance. Three days of torment passed in the big, echoing white rooms. He walked out of afternoons under escort of the drummer-boy, and all he heard from his companion were the few useless words which seemed to make two-thirds of the white man's abuse. Kim knew and despised them all long ago. The boy resented his silence and lack of interest by beating him, as was only natural. He did not care for any of the bazars which were in bounds. He styled all natives ' niggers '; yet servants and sweepers called him abominable names to his face, and, misled by their deferential attitude, he never understood. This somewhat consoled Kim for the beatings.

On the morning of the fourth day a judgment overtook that drummer. They had gone out together towards Umballa race-course. He returned alone, weeping, with news that young O'Hara, to whom he had been doing nothing in particular, had hailed a scarlet-bearded nigger on horseback; that the nigger had then and there laid into him with a peculiarly adhesive quirt, picked up young O'Hara, and borne him off at full gallop. These tidings came to Father Victor, and he drew down his long upper lip. He was already sufficiently startled by a letter from the Temple of the Tirthankers at Benares, enclosing a native banker's note of hand for three hundred rupees, and an amazing prayer to ' Almighty God.' The lama would have been more annoyed than the priest had he known how the bazar letter-writer had translated his phrase ' to acquire merit.'

' Powers of Darkness below! ' Father Victor fumbled with the note. ' An' now he's off with another of his peep-o'-day friends. I don't know whether it will be a greater relief to me to get him back or to have him lost. He's beyond my comprehension. How the Divil—yes, He's the man I mean—can a street-beggar raise money to educate white boys? '

Three miles off, on Umballa race-course, Mahbub Ali, reining a gray Cabuli stallion with Kim in front of him, was saying:

' But, Little Friend of all the World, there is my honour and reputation to be considered. All the officer-sahibs in all the regiments, and all Umballa, know Mahbub Ali. Men saw me pick thee up and chastise that boy. We are seen now from far across this plain. How can I take thee away, or account for thy disappearing if I set thee down and let thee run off into the crops? They would put me in jail. Be patient. Once a Sahib, always a Sahib. When thou art a man—who knows—thou wilt be grateful to Mahbub Ali.'

' Take me beyond their sentries where I can change this red. Give me money and I will go to Benares and be with my lama again. I do not want to be a Sahib, and remember I did deliver that message.'

The stallion bounded wildly. Mahbub Ali had incautiously driven home the sharp-edged stirrup. (He was not the new sort of fluent horse-dealer who wears English boots and spurs.) Kim drew his own conclusions from that betrayal.

'That was a small matter. It lay on the straight road to Benares. I and the Sahib have by this time forgotten it. I send so many letters and messages to men who ask questions about horses, I cannot well remember one from the other. Was it some matter of a bay mare that Peters Sahib wished the pedigree of?'

Kim saw the trap at once. If he had said 'bay mare' Mahbub would have known by his very readiness to fall in with the amendment that the boy suspected something. Kim replied therefore:

'Bay mare? No. I do not forget my messages thus. It was a white stallion.'

'Ay, so it was. A white Arab stallion. But thou didst write bay mare to me.'

'Who cares to tell truth to a letter-writer?' Kim answered, feeling Mahbub's palm on his heart.

'Hi! Mahbub, you old villain, pull up!' cried a voice, and an Englishman raced alongside on a little polo-pony. 'I've been chasing you half over the country. That Cabuli of yours can go. For sale, I suppose?'

'I have some young stuff coming on made by Heaven for the delicate and difficult polo-game. He has no equal. He—'

'Plays polo and waits at table. Yes. We know all that. What the deuce have you got there?'

'A boy,' said Mahbub gravely. 'He was being beaten by another boy. His father was once a white soldier in the big war. The boy was a child in Lahore city. He played with my horses when he was a babe. Now I think they will make him a soldier. He has been newly caught by his father's regiment that went up to the war last week. But I do not think he wants to be a soldier. I take him for a ride. Tell me where thy barracks are and I will set thee there.'

'Let me go. I can find the barracks alone.'

'And if thou runnest away who will say it is not my fault?'

'He'll run back to his dinner. Where has he to run to?' the Englishman asked.

'He was born in the land. He has friends. He goes where he chooses. He is a chabuk sawai (a sharp chap). It needs only to change his clothing, and in a twinkling he would be a low-caste Hindu boy.'

'The deuce he would!' The Englishman looked critically at the boy as Mahbub headed towards the barracks. Kim ground his teeth. Mahbub was mocking him, as faithless Afghans will; for he went on:

'They will send him to a school and put heavy boots on his feet and swaddle him in these clothes. Then he will forget all he knows. Now which of the barracks is thine?'

Kim pointed—he could not speak—to Father Victor's wing, all staring white near by.

'Perhaps he will make a good soldier,' said Mahbub reflectively. 'He will make a good orderly at least. I sent him to deliver a message once from

Lahore. A message concerning the pedigree of a white stallion.'

Here was deadly insult on deadlier injury—and the Sahib to whom he had so craftily given that war-making letter heard it all. Kim beheld Mahbub Ali frying in flame for his treachery, but for himself he saw one long gray vista of barracks, schools, and barracks again. He gazed imploringly at the clear-cut face in which there was no glimmer of recognition; but even at this extremity it never occurred to him to throw himself on the white man's mercy or to denounce the Afghan. And Mahbub stared deliberately at the Englishman, who stared as deliberately at Kim, quivering and tongue-tied.

'My horse is well trained,' said the dealer. 'Others would have kicked, Sahib.'

'Ah,' said the Englishman at last, rubbing his pony's damp withers with his whip-butt. 'Who makes the boy a soldier?'

'He says the regiment that found him, and especially the padre-sahib of that regiment.'

'There is the padre!' Kim choked as bare-headed Father Victor sailed down upon them from the veranda.

'Powers o' Darkness below, O'Hara! How many more mixed friends do you keep in Asia?' he cried, as Kim slid down and stood helplessly before him.

'Good morning, Padre,' the Colonel said cheerily. 'I know you by reputation well enough. Meant to have come over and called before this. I'm Creighton.'

'Of the Ethnological Survey?' said Father Victor. The Colonel nodded. 'Faith I'm glad to meet ye then; an' I owe you some thanks for bringing back the boy.'

'No thanks to me, Padre. Besides, the boy wasn't going away. You don't know old Mahbub Ali'—the horse-dealer sat impassive in the sunlight. 'You will when you have been in the station a month. He sells us all our crocks. That boy is rather a curiosity. Can you tell me anything about him?'

'Can I tell you?' puffed Father Victor. 'You'll be the one man that could help me in my quandaries. Tell you! Powers o' Darkness, I'm bursting to tell some one who knows something o' the native!'

A groom came round the corner. Colonel Creighton raised his voice, speaking in Urdu. 'Very good, Mahbub Ali, but what is the use of telling me all those stories about the pony. Not one pie more than three hundred and fifty rupees will I give.'

'The Sahib is a little hot and angry after riding,' the horse-dealer returned, with the leer of a privileged jester. 'Presently, he will see my horse's points more clearly. I will wait till he has finished his talk with the padre. I will wait under that tree.'

'Confound you!' The Colonel laughed. 'That comes of looking at one of Mahbub's horses. He's a regular old leech, Padre. Wait then, if thou hast so much time to spare, Mahbub. Now I'm at your service, Padre. Where is the boy? Oh, he's gone off to collogue with Mahbub. Queer sort

of boy. Might I ask you to send my mare round under cover? '

He dropped into a chair which commanded a clear view of Kim and Mahbub Ali in conference beneath the tree. The padre went indoors for cheroots.

Creighton heard Kim say bitterly: ' Trust a Brahmin before a snake, and a snake before a harlot, and a harlot before an Afghan, Mahbub Ali.'

' That is all one,' the great red beard wagged solemnly. ' Children should not see a carpet on the loom till the pattern is made plain. Believe me, Friend of all the World, I do thee great service. They will not make a soldier of thee.'

' You crafty old sinner,' thought Creighton. ' But you're not far wrong. That boy mustn't be wasted if he is as advertised.'

' Excuse me half a minute,' cried the padre from within, ' but I'm gettin' the documents of the case.'

' If through me the favour of this bold and wise Colonel Sahib comes to thee, and thou art raised to honour, what thanks wilt thou give Mahbub Ali when thou art a man? '

' Nay, nay; I begged thee to let me take the road again, where I should have been safe; and thou hast sold me back to the English. What will they give thee for blood-money? '

' A cheerful young demon! ' The Colonel bit his cigar, and turned politely to Father Victor.

' What are the letters that the fat priest is waving before the Colonel? Stand behind the stallion as though looking at my bridle! ' said Mahbub Ali.

' A letter from my lama which he wrote from Jagadhir Road, saying that he will pay three hundred rupees by the year for my schooling.'

' Oho! Is old Red Hat of that sort? At which school? '

' God knows. I think in Nucklao.'

' Yes. There is a big school there for the sons of Sahibs—and half-Sahibs. I have seen it when I sell horses there. So the lama also loved the Friend of all the World? '

' Ay; and he did not tell lies, or return me to captivity.'

' Small wonder the padre does not know how to unravel the thread. How fast he talks to the Colonel Sahib.' Mahbub Ali chuckled. ' By Allah! ' —the keen eyes swept the veranda for an instant—' thy lama has sent what to me looks like a note of hand. I have had some small dealing in hoondies. The Colonel Sahib is looking at it.'

' What good is all this to me? ' said Kim wearily. ' Thou wilt go away, and they will return me to those empty rooms where there is no good place to sleep and where the boys beat me.'

' I do not think that. Have patience, child. All Pathans are not faithless —except in horseflesh.'

Five—ten—fifteen minutes passed, Father Victor talking energetically or asking questions which the Colonel answered.

' Now I've told you everything that I know about the boy from be-ginnin' to end; and it's a blessed relief to me. Did ye ever hear the like? '

'At any rate, the old man has sent the money. Gobind Sahai's notes of hand are good from here to China,' said the Colonel. 'The more one knows about natives the less can one say what they will or won't do.'

'That's consolin'—from the head of the Ethnological Survey. It's this mixture of Red Bulls and Rivers of Healing (poor heathen, God help him!) an' notes of hand and Masonic certificates. Are you a Mason, by any chance?'

'By Jove, I am, now I come to think of it. That's an additional reason,' said the Colonel absently.

'I'm glad ye see a reason in it. But as I said, it's the mixture o' things that's beyond me. An' his prophesyin' to our Colonel sitting on my bed with his little shimmy torn open showing his white skin; an' the prophecy comin' true! They'll cure all that nonsense at St. Xavier's, eh?'

'Sprinkle him with holy water,' the Colonel laughed.

'On my word, I fancy I ought to sometimes. But I'm hoping he'll be brought up as a good Catholic. All that troubles me is what'll happen if the old beggar-man—'

'Lama, lama, my dear sir; and some of them are gentlemen in their own country.'

'The lama, then, fails to pay next year. He's a fine business head to plan on the spur of the moment, but he's bound to die some day. An' takin' a heathen's money to give a child a Christian education—'

'But he said explicitly what he wanted. As soon as he knew the boy was white he seems to have made his arrangements accordingly. I'd give a month's pay to hear how he explained it all at the Tirthankers' Temple at Benares. Look here, Padre, I don't pretend to know much about natives, but if he says he'll pay, he'll pay—dead or alive. I mean his heirs will assume the debt. My advice to you is, send the boy down to Lucknow. If your Anglican chaplain thinks you've stolen a march on him—'

'Bad luck to Bennett! He was sent to the front instead o' me. Doughty certified me medically unfit. I'll excommunicate Doughty if he comes back alive! Surely Bennett ought to be content with—'

'Glory, leaving you the religion. Quite so! As a matter of fact I don't think Bennett will mind. Put the blame on me. I—er—strongly recommend sending the boy to St. Xavier's. He can go down on pass as a soldier's orphan, so the railway fare will be saved. You can buy him an outfit from the regimental subscription. The Lodge will be saved the expense of his education, and that will put the Lodge in a good temper. It's perfectly easy. I've got to go down to Lucknow next week. I'll look after the boy on the way—give him in charge of my servants, and so on.'

'You're a good man.'

'Not in the least. Don't make that mistake. The lama has sent us money for a definite end. We can't very well return it. We shall have to do as he says. Well, that's settled, isn't it? Shall we say that, Tuesday next, you'll hand him over to me at the night train south? That's only three days. He can't do much harm in three days.'

'It's a weight off my mind, but—this thing here?'—he waved the note of hand—'I don't know Gobind Sahai: or his bank, which may be a hole in a wall.'

'You've never been a subaltern in debt. I'll cash it if you like, and send you the vouchers in proper order.'

'But with all your own work too! It's askin'— '

'It's not the least trouble indeed. You see, as an ethnologist, the thing's very interesting to me. I'd like to make a note of it for some Government work that I'm doing. The transformation of a regimental badge like your Red Bull into a sort of fetish that the boy follows is very interesting.'

'But I can't thank you enough.'

'There's one thing you can do. All we Ethnological men are as jealous as jackdaws of one another's discoveries. They're of no interest to any one but ourselves, of course, but you know what book-collectors are like. Well, don't say a word, directly or indirectly, about the Asiatic side of the boy's character—his adventures and his prophecy, and so on. I'll worm them out of the boy later on and—you see?'

'I do. Ye'll make a wonderful account of it. Never a word will I say to any one till I see it in print.'

'Thank you. That goes straight to an ethnologist's heart. Well, I must be getting back to my breakfast. Good heavens! Old Mahbub here still?' He raised his voice, and the horse-dealer came out from under the shadow of the tree. 'Well, what is it?'

'As regards that young horse,' said Mahbub, 'I say that when a colt is born to be a polo-pony, closely following the ball without teaching—when such a colt knows the game by divination—then I say it is a great wrong to break that colt to a heavy cart, Sahib!'

'So do I say also, Mahbub. The colt will be entered for polo only. (These fellows think of nothing in the world but horses, Padre.) I'll see you to-morrow, Mahbub, if you've anything likely for sale.'

The dealer saluted, horseman fashion, with a sweep of the off hand. 'Be patient a little, Friend of all the World,' he whispered to the agonised Kim. 'Thy fortune is made. In a little while thou goest to Nucklao, and—here is something to pay the letter-writer. I shall see thee again, I think, many times,' and he cantered off down the road.

'Listen to me,' said the Colonel from the veranda, speaking in the vernacular. 'In three days thou wilt go with me to Lucknow, seeing and hearing new things all the while. Therefore sit still for three days and do not run away. Thou wilt go to school at Lucknow.'

'Shall I meet my Holy One there?' Kim whimpered.

'At least Lucknow is nearer to Benares than Umballa. It may be thou wilt go under my protection. Mahbub Ali knows this, and he will be angry if thou returnest to the road now. Remember—much has been told to me which I do not forget.'

'I will wait,' said Kim, 'but the boys will beat me.'

Then the bugles blew for dinner.

CHAPTER VII

Unto whose use the pregnant suns are poised
 With idiot moons and stars retracting stars?
Creep thou betweene—thy coming's all unnoised.
 Heaven hath her high, as earth her baser, wars.
Heir to these tumults, this affright, that fray
 (By Adam's, fathers', own, sin bound alway);
Peer up, draw out thy horoscope and say
 Which planet mends thy threadbare fate or mars!
<div align="right">Sir John Christie</div>

In the afternoon the red-faced schoolmaster told Kim that he had been 'struck off the strength,' which conveyed no meaning to him till he was ordered to go away and play. Then he ran to the bazar, and found the young letter-writer to whom he owed a stamp.

'Now I pay,' said Kim royally, 'and now I need another letter to be written.'

'Mahbub Ali is in Umballa,' said the writer jauntily. He was, by virtue of his office, a bureau of general misinformation.

'This is not to Mahbub, but to a priest. Take thy pen and write quickly. "To Teshoo Lama, the holy one from Bhotiyal seeking for a River, who is now in the Temple of the Tirthankers at Benares." Take more ink! "In three days I am to go down to Nucklao to the school at Nucklao. The name of the school is Xavier. I do not know where that school is, but it is at Nucklao." '

'But I know Nucklao,' the writer interrupted. 'I know the school.'

'Tell him where it is, and I give half an anna.'

The reed pen scratched busily. 'He cannot mistake.' The man lifted his head. 'Who watches us across the street?'

Kim looked up hurriedly and saw Colonel Creighton in tennis-flannels.

'Oh, that is some Sahib who knows the fat priest in the barracks. He is beckoning me.'

'What dost thou?' said the Colonel, when Kim trotted up.

'I—I am not running away. I send a letter to my Holy One at Benares.'

'I had not thought of that. Hast thou said that I take thee to Lucknow?'

'Nay, I have not. Read the letter, if there be a doubt.'

'Then why hast thou left out my name in writing to that Holy One?' The Colonel smiled a queer smile. Kim took his courage in both hands.

'It was said once to me that it is inexpedient to write the names of strangers concerned in any matter, because by the naming of names many good plans are brought to confusion.'

'Thou hast been well taught,' the Colonel replied, and Kim flushed. 'I have left my cheroot-case in the padre's veranda. Bring it to my house this even.'

'Where is the house?' said Kim. His quick wit told him that he was being tested in some fashion or another, and he stood on guard.

'Ask any one in the big bazar.' The Colonel walked on.

'He has forgotten his cheroot-case,' said Kim, returning. 'I must bring it to him this evening. That is all my letter except, thrice over, "Come to me! Come to me! Come to me!" Now I will pay for a stamp and put it in the post.' He rose to go, and as an afterthought asked, 'Who is that angry-faced Sahib who lost the cheroot-case?'

'Oh, he is only Creighton Sahib—a very foolish Sahib, who is a Colonel Sahib without a regiment.'

'What is his business?'

'God knows. He is always buying horses which he cannot ride, and asking riddles about the works of God—such as plants and stones and the customs of people. The dealers call him the father of fools, because he is so easily cheated about a horse. Mahbub Ali says he is madder than all other Sahibs.'

'Oh!' said Kim, and departed. His training had given him some small knowledge of character, and he argued that fools are not given information which leads to calling out eight thousand men, besides guns. The Commander-in-Chief of all India does not talk, as Kim had heard him talk, to fools. Nor would Mahbub Ali's tone have changed, as it did every time he mentioned the Colonel's name, if the Colonel had been a fool. Consequently —and this set Kim to skipping—there was a mystery somewhere, and Mahbub Ali probably spied for the Colonel much as Kim had spied for Mahbub. And, like the horse-dealer, the Colonel evidently respected people who did not show themselves to be too clever.

He rejoiced that he had not betrayed his knowledge of the Colonel's house; and when, on his return to barracks, he discovered that no cheroot-case had been left behind, he beamed with delight. Here was a man after his own heart—a tortuous and indirect person playing a hidden game. Well, if he could be a fool, so could Kim.

He showed nothing of his mind when Father Victor, for three long mornings, discoursed to him of an entirely new set of gods and godlings— notably of a goddess called Mary, who, he gathered, was one with Bibi Miriam of Mahbub Ali's theology. He betrayed no emotion when, after the lecture, Father Victor dragged him from shop to shop buying articles of outfit, nor when envious drummer-boys kicked him because he was going to a superior school did he complain, but awaited the play of circumstances with an interested soul. Father Victor, good man, took him to the station,

put him into an empty second-class next to Colonel Creighton's first, and
bade him farewell with genuine feeling.

'They'll make a man o' you, O'Hara, at St. Xavier's—a white man, an',
I hope, a good man. They know all about your comin', an' the Colonel
will see that ye're not lost or mislaid anywhere on the road. I've given you
a notion of religious matters,—at least I hope so,—and you'll remember,
when they ask you your religion, that you're a Cath'lic. Better say Roman
Cath'lic, tho' I'm not fond of the word.'

Kim lit a rank cigarette—he had been careful to buy a stock in the
bazar—and lay down to think. This solitary passage was very different from
that joyful down-journey in the third-class with the lama. 'Sahibs get little
pleasure of travel,' he reflected. 'Hai mai! I go from one place to another
as it might be a kick-ball. It is my kismet. No man can escape his kismet.
But I am to pray to Bibi Miriam and I am a Sahib'—he looked at his boots
ruefully. 'No; I am Kim. This is the great world, and I am only Kim. Who
is Kim?' He considered his own identity, a thing he had never done before,
till his head swam. He was one insignificant person in all this roaring whirl
of India, going southward to he knew not what fate.

Presently the Colonel sent for him, and talked for a long time. So far
as Kim could gather, he was to be diligent and enter the Survey of India
as a chain-man. If he were very good, and passed the proper examinations,
he would be earning thirty rupees a month at seventeen years old, and
Colonel Creighton would see that he found a suitable employment.

Kim pretended at first to understand perhaps one word in three of this
talk. Then the Colonel, seeing his mistake, turned to fluent and picturesque
Urdu and Kim was contented. No man could be a fool who knew the
language so intimately, who moved so gently and silently, and whose eyes
were so different from the dull fat eyes of other Sahibs.

'Yes, and thou must learn how to make pictures of roads and moun-
tains and rivers—to carry these pictures in thy eye till a suitable time comes
to set them upon paper. Perhaps some day, when thou art a chain-man,
I may say to thee when we are working together: "Go across those hills and
see what lies beyond." Then one will say: "There are bad people living
in those hills who will slay the chain-man if he be seen to look like a Sahib."
What then?'

Kim thought. Would it be safe to return the Colonel's lead?

'I would tell what that other man had said.'

'But if I answered: "I will give thee a hundred rupees for knowledge
of what is behind those hills—for a picture of a river and a little news of
what the people say in the villages there"?'

'How can I tell? I am only a boy. Wait till I am a man.' Then, seeing
the Colonel's brow clouded, he went on: 'But I think I should in a few
days earn the hundred rupees.'

'By what road?'

Kim shook his head resolutely. 'If I said how I would earn them,

another man might hear and forestall me. It is no good to sell knowledge for nothing.'

'Tell now.' The Colonel held up a rupee. Kim's hand half reached towards it, and dropped.

'Nay, Sahib; nay. I know the price that will be paid for the answer, but I do not know why the question is asked.'

'Take it for a gift, then,' said Creighton, tossing it over. 'There is a good spirit in thee. Do not let it be blunted at St. Xavier's. There are many boys there who despise the black men.'

'Their mothers were bazar-women,' said Kim. He knew well there is no hatred like that of the half-caste for his brother-in-law.

'True; but thou art a Sahib and the son of a Sahib. Therefore, do not at any time be led to contemn the black men. I have known boys newly entered into the service of the Government who feigned not to understand the talk or the customs of black men. Their pay was cut for ignorance. There is no sin so great as ignorance. Remember this.'

Several times in the course of the long twenty-four hours' run south did the Colonel send for Kim, always developing this latter text.

'We be all on one lead-rope, then,' said Kim at last, 'the Colonel, Mahbub Ali, and I—when I become a chain-man. He will use me as Mahbub Ali employed me, I think. That is good, if it allows me to return to the road again. This clothing grows no easier by wear.'

When they came to the crowded Lucknow station there was no sign of the lama. He swallowed his disappointment, while the Colonel bundled him into a ticca-garri with his neat belongings and despatched him alone to St. Xavier's.

'I do not say farewell, because we shall meet again,' he cried. 'Again, and many times, if thou art one of good spirit. But thou art not yet tried.'

'Not when I brought thee'—Kim actually dared to use the tum of equals—'a white stallion's pedigree that night?'

'Much is gained by forgetting, little brother,' said the Colonel, with a look that pierced through Kim's shoulder-blades as he scuttled into the carriage.

It took him nearly five minutes to recover. Then he sniffed the new air appreciatively. 'A rich city,' he said. 'Richer than Lahore. How good the bazars must be! Coachman, drive me a little through the bazars here.'

'My order is to take thee to the school.' The driver used the 'thou,' which is rudeness when applied to a white man. In the clearest and most fluent vernacular Kim pointed out his error, climbed on to the box-seat, and, perfect understanding established, drove for a couple of hours up and down, estimating, comparing, and enjoying. There is no city—except Bombay, the queen of all—more beautiful in her garish style than Lucknow, whether you see her from the bridge over the river, or from the top of the Imambara looking down on the gilt umbrellas of the Chutter Munzil, and the trees in which the town is bedded. Kings have adorned her with

fantastic buildings, endowed her with charities, crammed her with pen-
sioners, and drenched her with blood. She is the centre of all idleness, in-
trigue, and luxury, and shares with Delhi the claim to talk the only pure
Urdu.

' A fair city—a beautiful city.' The driver, as a Lucknow man, was
pleased with the compliment, and told Kim many astounding things where
an English guide would have talked of the Mutiny.

' Now we will go to the school,' said Kim at last. The great old school
of St. Xavier's in Partibus, block on block of low white buildings, stands
in vast grounds over against the Gumti River, at some distance from the city.

' What like of folk are they within? ' said Kim.

' Young Sahibs—all devils; but to speak truth, and I drive many of
them to and fro from the railway station, I have never seen one that had
in him the making of a more perfect devil than thou—this young Sahib
whom I am now driving.'

Naturally, for he was never trained to consider them in any way im-
proper, Kim had passed the time of day with one or two frivolous ladies
at upper windows in a certain street, and naturally, in the exchange of com-
pliments, had acquitted himself well. He was about to acknowledge the
driver's last insolence, when his eye—it was growing dusk—caught a figure
sitting by one of the white plaster gate-pillars in the long sweep of wall.

' Stop! ' he cried. ' Stay here! I do not go to the school at once.'

' But what is to pay me for this coming and recoming? ' said the driver
petulantly. ' Is the boy mad? Last time it was a dancing-girl. This time it is
a priest.'

Kim was in the road headlong, patting the dusty feet beneath the dirty
yellow robe.

' I have waited here a day and a half,' the lama's level voice began.
' Nay, I had a disciple with me. He that was my friend at the Temple of
the Tirthankers gave me a guide for this journey. I came from Benares in
the train, when thy letter was given me. Yes, I am well fed. I need nothing.'

' But why didst thou not stay with the Kulu woman, O Holy One? In
what way didst thou get to Benares? My heart has been heavy since we
parted.'

' The woman wearied me by constant flux of talk and requiring charms
for children. I separated myself from that company, permitting her to acquire
merit by gifts. She is at least a woman of open hands, and I made a promise
to return to her house if need arose. Then, perceiving myself alone in this
great and terrible world, I bethought me of the te-rain to Benares, where
I knew one abode in the Tirthankers' Temple who was a Seeker, even as I.'

' Ah! Thy River,' said Kim. ' I had forgotten the River.'

' So soon, my chela? I have never forgotten it; but when I had left thee
it seemed better that I should go to the temple and take counsel, for, look
you, India is very large, and it may be that wise men before us, some two
or three, have left a record of the place of our River. There is debate in

the Temple of the Tirthankers on this matter; some saying one thing, and some another. They are courteous folk.'

'So be it; but what dost thou do now?'

'I acquire merit in that I help thee, my chela, to wisdom. The priest of that body of men who serve the Red Bull wrote me that all should be as I desired for thee. I sent the money to suffice for one year, and then I came, as thou seest me, to watch for thee going up into the Gates of Learning. A day and a half have I waited—not because I was led by any affection towards thee—that is not part of the Way—but, as they said at the Tirthankers' Temple, because, money having been paid for learning, it was right that I should oversee the end of the matter. They resolved my doubts most clearly. I had a fear that, perhaps, I came because I wished to see thee—misguided by the red mist of affection. It is not so. . . . Moreover, I am troubled by a dream.'

'But surely, Holy One, thou hast not forgotten the Road and all that befell on it. Surely it was a little to see me that thou didst come?'

'The horses are cold, and it is past their feeding-time,' whined the driver.

'Go to Jehannum and abide there with thy reputationless aunt!' Kim snarled over his shoulder. 'I am all alone in this land; I know not where I go nor what shall befall me. My heart was in that letter I sent thee. Except for Mahbub Ali, and he is a Pathan, I have no friend save thee, Holy One. Do not altogether go away.'

'I have considered that also,' the lama replied, in a shaking voice. 'It is manifest that from time to time I shall acquire merit—if before that I have not found my River—by assuring myself that thy feet are set on wisdom. What they will teach thee I do not know, but the priest wrote me that no son of a Sahib in all India will be better taught than thou. So from time to time, therefore, I will come again. May be thou wilt be such a Sahib as he who gave me these spectacles'—the lama wiped them elaborately—'in the Wonder House at Lahore. That is my hope, for he was a Fountain of Wisdom—wiser than many abbots. . . . Again, may be thou wilt forget me and our meetings.'

'If I eat thy bread,' cried Kim passionately, 'how shall I ever forget thee?'

'No—no.' He put the boy aside. 'I must go back to Benares. From time to time, now that I know the customs of letter-writers in this land, I will send thee a letter, and from time to time I will come and see thee.'

'But whither shall I send my letters?' wailed Kim, clutching at the robe, all forgetful that he was a Sahib.

'To the Temple of the Tirthankers at Benares. That is the place I have chosen till I find my River. Do not weep; for, look you, all Desire is illusion and a new binding upon the Wheel. Go up to the Gates of Learning. Let me see thee go. . . . Dost thou love me? Then go, or my heart cracks. . . . I will come again. Surely I will come again.'

The lama watched the ticca-garri rumble into the compound, and strode off, snuffing between each long stride.

'The Gates of Learning' shut with a clang.

.

The country born and bred boy has his own manners and customs, which do not resemble those of any other land; and his teachers approach him by roads which an English master would not understand. Therefore, you would scarcely be interested in Kim's experiences as a St. Xavier's boy among two or three hundred precocious youths, most of whom had never seen the sea. He suffered the usual penalties for breaking out of bounds when there was cholera in the city. This was before he had learned to write fair English, and so was obliged to find a bazar letter-writer. He was, of course, indicted for smoking and for the use of abuse more full-flavoured than even St. Xavier's had ever heard. He learned to wash himself with the Levitical scrupulosity of the native-born, who in his heart considers the Englishman rather dirty. He played the usual tricks on the patient coolies pulling the punkahs in the sleeping-rooms where the boys thrashed through the hot nights telling tales till the dawn; and quietly he measured himself against his self-reliant mates.

They were sons of subordinate officials in the Railway, Telegraph, and Canal services; of warrant-officers sometimes retired and sometimes acting as commanders-in-chief to a feudatory Rajah's army; of captains of the Indian Marine, Government pensioners, planters, Presidency shopkeepers, and missionaries. A few were cadets of the old Eurasian houses that have taken strong root in Dhurrumtollah—Pereiras, De Souzas, and D'Silvas. Their parents could well have educated them in England, but they loved the school that had served their own youth, and generation followed sallow-hued generation at St. Xavier's. Their homes ranged from Howrah of the railway people to abandoned cantonments like Monghyr and Chunar; lost tea-gardens Shillong-way; villages where their fathers were large landholders in Oudh or the Deccan; Mission-stations a week from the nearest railway line; seaports a thousand miles south, facing the brazen Indian surf; and cinchona-plantations south of all. The mere story of their adventures, which to them were no adventures, on their road to and from school would have crisped a Western boy's hair. They were used to jogging off alone through a hundred miles of jungle, where there was always the delightful chance of being delayed by tigers; but they would no more have bathed in the English Channel in an English August than their brothers across the world would have lain still while a leopard snuffed at their palanquin. There were boys of fifteen who had spent a day and a half on an islet in the middle of a flooded river, taking charge, as by right, of a camp of frantic pilgrims returning from a shrine; there were seniors who had requisitioned a chance-met Rajah's elephant, in the name of St. Francis Xavier, when the rains once blotted out the cart-track that led to their father's estate, and had all but

lost the huge beast in a quicksand. There was a boy who, he said, and none doubted, had helped his father to beat off with rifles from the veranda a rush of Akas in the days when those head-hunters were bold against lonely plantations.

And every tale was told in the even, passionless voice of the native-born, mixed with quaint reflections, borrowed unconsciously from native foster-mothers, and turns of speech that showed they had been that instant translated from the vernacular. Kim watched, listened, and approved. This was not insipid, single-word talk of drummer-boys. It dealt with a life he knew and in part understood. The atmosphere suited him, and he throve by inches. They gave him a white drill suit as the weather warmed, and he rejoiced in the new-found bodily comforts as he rejoiced to use his sharpened mind over the tasks they set him. His quickness would have delighted an English master; but at St. Xavier's they know the first rush of minds developed by sun and surroundings, as well as they know the half-collapse that sets in at twenty-two or twenty-three.

None the less he remembered to hold himself lowly. When tales were told of hot nights, Kim did not sweep the board with his reminiscences; for St. Xavier's looks down on boys who ' go native altogether.' One must never forget that one is a Sahib, and that some day, when examinations are passed, one will command natives. Kim made a note of this, for he began to understand where examinations led.

Then came the holidays from August to October—the long holidays imposed by the heat and the rains. Kim was informed that he would go north to some station in the hills behind Umballa, where Father Victor would arrange for him.

' A barrack-school?' said Kim, who had asked many questions and thought more.

' Yes, I suppose so,' said the master. ' It will not do you any harm to keep you out of mischief. You can go up with young De Castro as far as Delhi.'

Kim considered it in every possible light. He had been diligent, even as the Colonel advised. A boy's holiday was his own property,—of so much the talk of his companions had advised him,—and a barrack-school would be torment after St. Xavier's. Moreover—this was magic worth anything else— he could write. In three months he had discovered how men can speak to each other without a third party, at the cost of half an anna and a little knowledge. No word had come from the lama, but there remained the Road. Kim yearned for the caress of soft mud squishing up between the toes, as his mouth watered for mutton stewed with butter and cabbages, for rice speckled with strong-scented cardamoms, for the saffron-tinted rice, garlic and onions, and the forbidden greasy sweetmeats of the bazars. They would feed him raw beef on a platter at the barrack-school, and he must smoke by stealth. But again, he was a Sahib and was at St. Xavier's, and that pig Mahbub Ali . . . No, he would not test Mahbub's hospitality—and yet . . .

He thought it out alone in the dormitory, and came to the conclusion he had been unjust to Mahbub.

The school was empty; nearly all the masters had gone away; Colonel Creighton's railway-pass lay in his hand, and Kim puffed himself that he had not spent Colonel Creighton's or Mahbub's money in riotous living. He was still lord of two rupees seven annas. His new bullock-trunk, marked ' K. O'H.,' and bedding-roll lay in the empty sleeping-room. ' Sahibs are always tied to their baggage,' said Kim, nodding at them. ' You will stay here.' He went out into the warm rain, smiling sinfully, and sought a certain house whose outside he had noted down some time before. . . .

' Arre! Dost thou know what manner of women we be in this quarter? O shame! '

' Was I born yesterday? ' Kim squatted native fashion on the cushions of that upper room. ' A little dye-stuff and three yards of cloth to help out a jest. Is it much to ask? '

' Who is she? Thou art full young, as Sahibs go, for this devilry.'

' Oh, she? She is the daughter of a certain schoolmaster of a regiment in the cantonments. He has beaten me twice because I went over their wall in these clothes. Now I would go as a gardener's boy. Old men are very jealous.'

' That is true. Hold thy face still while I dab on the juice.'

' Not too black, Naikan. I would not appear to her as a hubshi ' (nigger).

' Oh, love makes nought of these things. And how old is she? '

' Twelve years, I think,' said the shameless Kim. ' Spread it also on the breast. It may be her father will tear my clothes off me and if I am pie-bald— ' he laughed.

The girl worked busily, dabbing a twist of cloth into a little saucer of brown dye that holds longer than any walnut juice.

' Now send out and get me a cloth for the turban. Woe is me, my head is all unshaved! And he will surely knock off my turban.'

' I am not a barber, but I will make shift. Thou wast born to be a breaker of hearts! All this disguise for one evening? Remember, the stuff does not wash away.' She shook with laughter till her bracelets and anklets jingled. ' But who is to pay me for this? Huneefa herself could not have given thee better stuff.'

' Trust in the Gods, my sister,' said Kim gravely screwing his face round as the stain dried. ' Besides, hast thou ever helped to paint a Sahib thus before? '

' Never indeed. But a jest is not money.'

' It is worth much more.''

' Child, thou art beyond all dispute the most shameless son of Shaitan that I have ever known to take up a poor girl's time with this play, and then to say: " Is not the jest enough? " Thou wilt go very far in this world.' She gave the dancing-girls' salutation in mockery.

' All one. Make haste and rough-cut my head.' Kim shifted from foot

to foot, his eyes ablaze with mirth as he thought of the fat days before him. He gave the girl four annas, and ran down the stairs in the likeness of a low-caste Hindu boy—perfect in every detail. A cookshop was his next point of call, where he feasted in extravagance and greasy luxury.

On Lucknow station platform he watched young De Castro, all covered with prickly-heat, get into a second-class compartment. Kim patronised a third, and was the life and soul of it. He explained to the company that he was assistant to a juggler who had left him behind sick with fever, and that he would pick up his master at Umballa. As the occupants of the carriage changed, he varied this tale, or adorned it with all the shoots of a budding fancy, the more rampant for being held off native speech so long. In all India that night was no human being so joyful as Kim. At Umballa he got out and headed eastward, plashing over the sodden fields to the village where the old soldier lived.

About this time Colonel Creighton at Simla was advised from Lucknow by wire that young O'Hara had disappeared. Mahbub Ali was in town selling horses, and to him the Colonel confided the affair one morning cantering round Annandale race-course.

' Oh, that is nothing,' said the horse-dealer. ' Men are like horses. At certain times they need salt, and if that salt is not in the mangers they will lick it up from the earth. He has gone back to the Road again for a while. The madrissah wearied him. I knew it would. Another time, I will take him upon the Road myself. Do not be troubled, Creighton Sahib. It is as though a polo-pony, breaking loose, ran out to learn the game alone.'

' Then he is not dead, think you? '

' Fever might kill him. I do not fear for the boy otherwise. A monkey does not fall among trees.'

Next morning, on the same course, Mahbub's stallion ranged alongside the Colonel.

' It is as I had thought,' said the horse-dealer. ' He has come through Umballa at least, and there he has written a letter to me, having learned in the bazar that I was here.'

' Read,' said the Colonel, with a sigh of relief. It was absurd that a man of his position should take an interest in a little country-bred vagabond; but the Colonel remembered the conversation in the train, and often in the past few months had caught himself thinking of the queer, silent, self-possessed boy. His evasion, of course, was the height of insolence, but it argued some resource and nerve.

Mahbub's eyes twinkled as he reined out into the centre of the cramped little plain, where none could come near unseen.

' "The Friend of the Stars, who is the Friend of all the World— " '

' What is this? '

' A name we give him in Lahore city. " The Friend of all the World takes leave to go to his own places. He will come back upon the appointed day. Let the box and the bedding-roll be sent for; and if there has been a

fault, let the Hand of Friendship turn aside the Whip of Calamity." There is yet a little more, but—'

'No matter, read.'

' "Certain things are not known to those who eat with forks. It is better to eat with both hands for a while. Speak soft words to those who do not understand this that the return may be propitious." Now the manner in which that was cast is of course the work of the letter-writer, but see how wisely the boy has devised the matter of it so that no hint is given except to those who know!'

'Is this the Hand of Friendship to avert the Whip of Calamity?' laughed the Colonel.

'See how wise is the boy. He would go back to the Road again, as I said. Not knowing yet thy trade—'

'I am not quite sure of that,' the Colonel muttered.

'He turns to me to make a peace between you. Is he not wise? He says he will return. He is but perfecting his knowledge. Think, Sahib! He has been three months at the school. And he is not mouthed to that bit. For my part, I rejoice: the pony learns the game.'

'Ay, but another time he must not go alone.'

'Why? He went alone before he came under the Colonel Sahib's protection. When he comes to the Great Game he must go alone—alone, and at peril of his head. Then, if he spits, or sneezes, or sits down other than as the people do whom he watches, he may be slain. Why hinder him now? Remember how the Persians say: The jackal that lives in the wilds of Mazanderan can only be caught by the hounds of Mazanderan.'

'True. It is true, Mahbub Ali. And if he comes to no harm, I do not desire anything better. But it is great insolence on his part.'

'He does not tell me, even, whither he goes,' said Mahbub. 'He is no fool. When his time is accomplished he will come to me. It is time the healer of pearls took him in hand. He ripens too quickly—as Sahibs reckon.'

This prophecy was fulfilled to the letter a month later. Mahbub had gone down to Umballa to bring up a fresh consignment of horses, and Kim met him on the Kalka road at dusk riding alone, begged an alms of him, was sworn at, and replied in English. There was nobody within earshot to hear Mahbub's gasp of amazement.

'Oho! And where hast thou been?'

'Up and down—down and up.'

'Come under a tree, out of the wet, and tell.'

'I stayed for a while with an old man near Umballa; anon with a household of my acquaintance in Umballa. With one of these I went as far as Delhi to the southward. That is a wondrous city. Then I drove a bullock for a teli (an oilman) coming north; but I heard of a great feast forward in Puttiala, and thither went I in the company of a firework-maker. It was a great feast' (Kim rubbed his stomach). 'I saw Rajahs, and elephants with gold and silver trappings; and they lit all the fireworks at once, whereby

eleven men were killed, my firework-maker among them, and I was blown across a tent but took no harm. Then I came back to the rel with a Sikh horseman, to whom I was groom for my bread; and so here.'

' Shabash! ' said Mahbub Ali.

' But what does the Colonel Sahib say? I do not wish to be beaten.'

' The Hand of Friendship has averted the Whip of Calamity; but another time, when thou takest the Road it will be with me. This is too early.'

' Late enough for me. I have learned to read and to write English a little at the madrissah. I shall soon be altogether a Sahib.'

' Hear him! ' laughed Mahbub, looking at the little drenched figure dancing in the wet. ' Salaam—Sahib,' and he saluted ironically. ' Well, art tired of the Road, or wilt thou come on to Umballa with me and work back with the horses? '

' I come with thee, Mahbub Ali.'

CHAPTER VIII

' Something I owe to the soil that grew—
 More to the life that fed—
But most to Allah Who gave me two
 Separate sides to my head.

' I would go without shirts or shoes,
 Friends, tobacco or bread
Sooner than for an instant lose
 Either side of my head.'

' Then in God's Name take blue for red,' said Mahbub, alluding to the Hindu colour of Kim's disreputable turban.

Kim countered with the old proverb, ' I will change my faith and my bedding, but thou must pay for it.'

The dealer laughed till he nearly fell from his horse. At a shop on the outskirts of the city the change was made, and Kim stood up, externally at least, a Mohammedan.

Mahbub hired a room over against the railway station, sent for a cooked meal of the finest with almond-curd sweetmeats (balushai we call it) and fine-chopped Lucknow tobacco.

' This is better than some other meat that I ate with the Sikh,' said Kim, grinning as he squatted, ' and assuredly they give no such victuals at my madrissah.'

' I have a desire to hear of that same madrissah.' Mahbub stuffed himself with great boluses of spiced mutton fried in fat with cabbage and golden-

brown onions. 'But tell me first, altogether and truthfully, the manner of thy escape. For, O Friend of all the World,'—he loosed his cracking belt,— 'I do not think it is often that a Sahib and the son of a Sahib runs away from there.'

'How should they? They do not know the land. It was nothing,' said Kim, and began his tale. When he came to the disguisement and the interview with the girl in the bazar, Mahbub Ali's gravity went from him. He laughed aloud and beat his hand on his thigh.

'Shabash! Shabash! Oh, well done, little one! What will the healer of turquoises say to this? Now, slowly, let us hear what befell afterwards—step by step, omitting nothing.'

Step by step then, Kim told his adventures between coughs as the full-flavoured tobacco caught his lungs.

'I said,' growled Mahbub Ali to himself, 'I said it was the pony breaking out to play polo. The fruit is ripe already—except that he must learn his distances and his pacings, and his rods and his compasses. Listen now. I have turned aside the Colonel's whip from thy skin, and that is no small service.'

'True.' Kim puffed serenely. 'That is all true.'

'But it is not to be thought that this running out and in is any way good.'

'It was my holiday, Hajji. I was a slave for many weeks. Why should I not run away when the school was shut? Look, too, how I, living upon my friends or working for my bread, as I did with the Sikh, have saved the Colonel Sahib a great expense.'

Mahbub's lips twitched under his well-pruned Mohammedan moustache.

'What are a few rupees'—the Pathan threw out his open hand carelessly—'to the Colonel Sahib? He spends them for a purpose, not in any way for love of thee.'

'That,' said Kim slowly, 'I knew a very long time ago.'

'Who told?'

'The Colonel Sahib himself. Not in those many words, but plainly enough for one who is not altogether a mud-head. Yea, he told me in the te-rain when we went down to Lucknow.'

'Be it so. Then I will tell thee more, Friend of all the World, though in the telling I lend thee my head.'

'It was forfeit to me,' said Kim, with deep relish, 'in Umballa, when thou didst pick me up on the horse after the drummer-boy beat me.'

'Speak a little plainer. All the world may tell lies save thou and I. For equally is thy life forfeit to me if I chose to raise my finger here.'

'And this is known to me also,' said Kim, readjusting the live charcoal-ball on the weed. 'It is a very sure tie between us. Indeed thy hold is surer even than mine; for who would miss a boy beaten to death, or, it may be, thrown into a well by the roadside? Many people here and in Simla and

across the passes behind the Hills would, on the other hand, say: " What has come to Mahbub Ali," if he were found dead among his horses. Surely too the Colonel Sahib would make inquiries. But again,'—Kim's face puckered with cunning,—' he would not make overlong inquiry, lest people should ask: " What has this Colonel Sahib to do with that horse-dealer? " But I—if I lived— '

' As thou wouldst surely die— '

' It may be; but I say, if I lived, I, and I alone, would know that one had come by night, as a common thief perhaps, to Mahbub Ali's bulkhead in the serai, and there had slain him, either before or after that thief had made a full search into his saddle-bags and between the soles of his slippers. Is that news to tell to the Colonel, or would he say to me—(I have not forgotten when he sent me back for a cigar-case that he had not left behind him)—" What is Mahbub Ali to me? " '

Up went a gout of heavy smoke. There was a long pause; then Mahbub Ali spoke in admiration: ' And with these things on thy mind, dost thou lie down and rise again among all the Sahibs' little sons at the madrissah and meekly take instruction from thy teachers? '

' It is an order,' said Kim blandly. ' Who am I to dispute an order? '

' A most finished son of Eblis,' said Mahbub Ali. ' But what is this tale of the thief and the search? '

' That which I saw,' said Kim, ' the night that my lama and I lay next thy place in the Kashmir Serai. The door was left unlocked, which I think is not thy custom, Mahbub. He came in as one assured that thou wouldst not soon return. My eye was against a knot-hole in the plank. He searched as it were for something—not a rug, not stirrups, nor a bridle, nor brass pots—something little and most carefully hid. Else why did he prick with an iron between the soles of thy slippers? '

' Ha! ' Mahbub Ali smiled gently. ' And seeing these things, what tale didst thou fashion to thyself, Well of the Truth? '

' None. I put my hand upon my amulet, which lies always next to my skin, and, remembering the pedigree of a white stallion that I had bitten out of a piece of Mussalmani bread, I went away to Umballa perceiving that a heavy trust was laid upon me. At that hour, had I chosen, thy head was forfeit. It needed only to say to that man, " I have here a paper concerning a horse which I cannot read." And then? ' Kim peered at Mahbub under his eyebrows.

' Then thou wouldst have drunk water twice—perhaps thrice, afterwards. I do not think more than thrice,' said Mahbub simply.

' It is true. I thought of that a little, but most I thought that I loved thee, Mahbub. Therefore I went to Umballa, as thou knowest, but (and this thou dost not know) I lay hid in the garden-grass to see what Colonel Creighton Sahib might do upon reading the white stallion's pedigree.'

' And what did he? ' for Kim had bitten off the conversation.

' Dost thou give news for love, or dost thou sell it? ' Kim asked.

'I sell and—I buy.' Mahbub took a four-anna piece out of his belt and held it up.

'Eight!' said Kim, mechanically following the huckster instinct of the East.

Mahbub laughed, and put away the coin. 'It is too easy to deal in that market, Friend of all the World. Tell me for love. Our lives lie in each other's hand.'

'Very good. I saw the Jang-i-Lat Sahib (the Commander-in-Chief) come to a big dinner. I saw him in Creighton Sahib's office. I saw the two read the white stallion's pedigree. I heard the very orders given for the opening of a great war.'

'Hah!' Mahbub nodded with deepest eyes afire. 'The game is well played. That war is done now, and the evil, we hope, nipped before the flower—thanks to me—and thee. What didst thou later?'

'I made the news as it were a hook to catch me victual and honour among the villagers in a village whose priest drugged my lama. But I bore away the old man's purse, and the Brahmin found nothing. So next morning he was angry. Ho! Ho! And I also used the news when I fell into the hands of that white regiment with their Bull!'

'That was foolishness.' Mahbub scowled. 'News is not meant to be thrown about like dung-cakes, but used sparingly—like bhang.'

'So I think now, and, moreover, it did me no sort of good. But that was very long ago,'—he made as to brush it all away with a thin brown hand,—'and since then, and especially in the nights under the punkah at the madrissah, I have thought very greatly.'

'Is it permitted to ask whither the Heaven-born's thought might have led?' said Mahbub, with an elaborate sarcasm, smoothing his scarlet beard.

'It is permitted,' said Kim, and threw back the very tone. 'They say at Nucklao that no Sahib must tell a black man that he has made a fault.'

Mahbub's hand shot into his bosom, for to call a Pathan a 'black man' (kala admi) is a blood-insult. Then he remembered and laughed. 'Speak, Sahib: thy black man hears.'

'But,' said Kim, 'I am not a Sahib, and I say I made a fault when I cursed thee, Mahbub Ali, on the day at Umballa I thought I was betrayed by a Pathan. I was senseless; for I was but newly caught, and I wished to kill that low-caste drummer-boy. I say now, Hajji, that it was well done; and I see my road all clear before me to a good service. I will stay in the madrissah till I am ripe.'

'Well said. Especially are distances and numbers and the manner of using compasses to be learned in that game. One waits in the Hills above to show thee.'

'I will learn their teaching upon a condition—that my time is given to me without question when the madrissah is shut. Ask that for me of the Colonel.'

'But why not ask the Colonel in the Sahib's tongue?'

' The Colonel is the servant of the Government. He is sent hither and
yon at a word, and must consider his own advancement. (See how much I
have already learned at Nucklao!) Moreover, the Colonel I know since three
months only. I have known one Mahbub Ali for six years. So! To the
madrissah I will go. At the madrissah I will learn. In the madrissah I will be
a Sahib. But when the madrissah is shut, then must I be free and go among
my people. Otherwise I die! '

' And who are thy People, Friend of all the World? '

' This great and beautiful land,' said Kim, waving his paw round the
little clay-walled room where the oil-lamp in its niche burned heavily through
the tobacco-smoke. ' And, further, I would see my lama again. And further,
I need money.'

' That is the need of every one,' said Mahbub ruefully. ' I will give thee
eight annas, for much money is not picked out of horses' hooves, and it must
suffice for many days. As to all the rest, I am well pleased, and no further
talk is needed. Make haste to learn, and in three years, or it may be less,
thou wilt be an aid—even to me.'

' Have I been such a hindrance till now? ' said Kim, with a boy's giggle.

' Do not give answers,' Mahbub grunted. ' Thou art my new horse-boy.
Go and bed among my men. They are near the north end of the station,
with the horses.'

' They will beat me to the south end of the station if I come without
authority.'

Mahbub felt in his belt, wetted his thumb on a cake of Chinese ink,
and dabbed the impression on a piece of soft native paper. From Balkh to
Bombay men know that rough-ridged print with the old scar running
diagonally across it.

' That is enough to show my headman. I come in the morning.'

' By which road? ' said Kim.

' By the road from the City. There is but one, and then we return to
Creighton Sahib. I have saved thee a beating.'

' Allah! What is a beating when the very head is loose on the shoul-
ders? '

Kim slid out quietly into the night, walked half round the house,
keeping close to the walls, and headed away from the station for a mile or
so. Then, fetching a wide compass, he worked back at leisure, for he needed
time to invent a story if any of Mahbub's retainers asked questions.

They were camped on a piece of waste ground beside the railway, and,
being natives, had not, of course, unloaded the two trucks in which Mah-
bub's animals stood among a consignment of country-breds bought by the
Bombay tram-company. The headman, a broken-down, consumptive-looking
Mohammedan, promptly challenged Kim, but was pacified at sight of Mah-
bub's sign-manual.

' The Hajji has of his favour given me service,' said Kim testily. ' If
this be doubted, wait till he comes in the morning. Meantime, a place by

the fire.'

Followed the usual aimless babble that every low-caste native must raise on every occasion. It died down, and Kim lay out behind the little knot of Mahbub's followers, almost under the wheels of a horse-truck, a borrowed blanket for covering. Now a bed among brickbats and ballast-refuse on a damp night, between overcrowded horses and unwashed Baltis, would not appeal to many white boys; but Kim was utterly happy. Change of scene, service, and surroundings were the breath of his little nostrils, and thinking of the neat white cots of St. Xavier's all arow under the punkah gave him joy as keen as the repetition of the multiplication-table in English.

' I am very old,' he thought sleepily. ' Every month I become a year more old. I was very young, and a fool to boot, when I took Mahbub's message to Umballa. Even when I was with that white regiment I was very young and small and had no wisdom. But now I learn every day, and in three years the Colonel will take me out of the madrissah and let me go upon the Road with Mahbub hunting for horses' pedigrees, or maybe I shall go by myself; or maybe I shall find the lama and go with him. Yes; that is best. To walk again as a chela with my lama when he comes back to Benares.' The thoughts came more slowly and disconnectedly. He was plunging into a beautiful dreamland when his ears caught a whisper, thin and sharp, above the monotonous babble round the fire. It came from behind the iron-skinned horse-truck.

' He is not here then? '

' Where should he be but roystering in the City. Who looks for a rat in a frog-pond? Come away. He is not our man.'

' He must not go back beyond the Passes a second time. It is the order.'

' Hire some woman to drug him. It is a few rupees only, and there is no evidence.'

' Except the woman. It must be more certain; and remember the price upon his head.'

' Ay, but the police have a long arm, and we are far from the Border. If it were in Peshawur now! '

' Yes—in Peshawur,' the second voice sneered. ' Peshawur, full of his blood-kin—full of bolt-holes and women behind whose clothes he will hide. Yes, Peshawur or Jehannum would suit us equally well.'

' Then what is the plan? '

' O fool, have I not told it a hundred times. Wait till he comes to lie down, and then one sure shot. The trucks are between us and pursuit. We have but to run back over the lines and go our way. They will not see whence the shot came. Wait here at least till the dawn. What manner of faquir art thou to shiver at a little watching? '

' Oho! ' thought Kim, behind close-shut eyes. ' Once again it is Mahbub. Indeed a white stallion's pedigree is not a good thing to peddle to Sahibs! Or maybe Mahbub has been selling other news. Now what is to do, Kim? I know not where Mahbub houses, and if he comes here before the dawn

they will shoot him. That would be no profit for thee, Kim. And this is not a matter for the police. That would be no profit for Mahbub; and,' he giggled almost aloud, ' I do not remember any lesson at Nucklao which will help me. Allah! Here is Kim and yonder are they. First then, Kim must wake and go away, so that they shall not suspect. A bad dream wakes a man—thus—'

He threw the blanket off his face, and raised himself suddenly with the terrible, bubbling, meaningless yell of the Asiatic roused by nightmare.

' Urr-urr-urr-urr! Ya-la-la-la-la! Narain! The churel! The churel! '

A churel is the peculiarly malignant ghost of a woman who has died in child-bed. She haunts lonely roads, her feet are turned backwards on the ankles, and she leads men to torment.

Louder rose Kim's quavering howl, till at last he leaped to his feet and staggered off sleepily, while the camp cursed him for waking them. Some twenty yards farther up the line he lay down again, taking care that the whisperers should hear his grunts and groans as he recomposed himself. After a few minutes he rolled towards the road and stole away into the thick darkness.

He padded along swiftly till he came to a culvert, and dropped behind it, his chin on a level with the coping-stone. Here he could command all the night-traffic, himself unseen.

Two or three carts passed, jingling out to the suburbs; a coughing policeman and a hurrying foot-passenger or two who sang to keep off evil spirits. Then rapped the shod feet of a horse.

' Ah! This is more like Mahbub,' thought Kim, as the beast shied at the little head above the culvert.

' Ohe, Mahbub Ali,' he whispered, ' have a care! '

The horse was reined back almost on its haunches, and forced towards the culvert.

' Never again,' said Mahbub, ' will I take a shod horse for night-work. They pick up all the the bones and nails in the city.' He stooped to lift its forefoot, and that brought his head within a foot of Kim's. ' Down—keep down,' he muttered. ' The night is full of eyes.'

' Two men wait thy coming behind the horse-trucks. They will shoot thee at thy lying down, because there is a price on thy head. I heard, sleeping near the horses.'

' Didst thou see them? . . . Hold still, Sire of Devils! ' This furiously to the horse.

' No.'

' Was one dressed belike as a faquir? '

' One said to the other, " What manner of a faquir art thou, to shiver at a little watching? " '

' Good. Go back to the camp and lie down. I do not die tonight.'

Mahbub wheeled his horse and vanished. Kim tore back down the ditch till he reached a point opposite his second resting-place, slipped across the road like a weasel, and recoiled himself in the blanket.

'At least Mahbub knows,' he thought contentedly. 'And certainly he spoke as one expecting it. I do not think those two men will profit by to-night's watch.'

An hour passed, and, with the best will in the world to keep awake all night, he slept deeply. Now and again a night train roared along the metals within twenty feet of him; but he had all the Oriental's indifference to mere noise, and it did not even weave a dream through his slumber.

Mahbub was anything but asleep. It annoyed him vehemently that people outside his tribe and unaffected by his casual amours should pursue him for the life. His first and natural impulse was to cross the line lower down, work up again, and, catching his well-wishers from behind, summarily slay them. Here, he reflected with sorrow, another branch of the Government, totally unconnected with Colonel Creighton, might demand explanations which would be hard to supply; and he knew that south the Border a perfectly ridiculous fuss is made about a corpse or so. He had not been troubled in this way since he sent Kim to Umballa with the message, and hoped that suspicion had been finally diverted.

Then a most brilliant notion struck him.

'The English do eternally tell the truth,' he said, 'therefore we of this country are eternally made foolish. By Allah, I will tell the truth to an Englishman! Of what use is the Government police if a poor Kabuli be robbed of his horses in their very trucks. This is as bad as Peshawur! I should lay a complaint at the station. Better still, some young Sahib on the Railway! They are zealous, and if they catch thieves it is remembered to their honour.'

He tied up his horse outside the station, and strode on to the platform.

'Hullo, Mahbub Ali!' said a young Assistant District Traffic Superintendent who was waiting to go down the line—a tall, tow-haired, horsey youth in dingy white linen. 'What are you doing here? Selling weeds—eh?'

'No; I am not troubled for my horses. I come to look for Lutuf Ullah. I have a truck-load up the line. Could any one take them out without the Railway's knowledge?'

''Shouldn't think so, Mahbub. You can claim against us if they do.'

'I have seen two men crouching under the wheels of one of the trucks nearly all the night. Faquirs do not steal horses, so I gave them no more thought. I would find Lutuf Ullah, my partner.'

'The deuce you did? And you didn't bother your head about it? 'Pon my word, it's just almost as well that I met you. What were they like, eh?'

'They were only faquirs. They will no more than take a little grain perhaps from one of the trucks. There are many up the line. The State will never miss the dole. I came here seeking for my partner, Lutuf Ullah—'

'Never mind your partner. Where are your horse-trucks?'

'A little to this side of the farthest place where they make lamps for the trains.'

'The signal-box. Yes.'

'And upon the rail nearest to the road upon the right-hand side—look-

ing up the line thus. But as regards Lutuf Ullah—a tall man with a broken nose, and a Persian greyhound— Aie! '

The boy had hurried off to wake up a young and enthusiastic policeman; for, as he said, the Railway had suffered much from depredations in the goods-yard. Mahbub Ali chuckled in his dyed beard.

' They will walk in their boots, making a noise, and then they will wonder why there are no faquirs. They are very clever boys—Barton Sahib and Young Sahib.'

He waited idly for a few minutes, expecting to see them hurry up the line girt for action. A light engine slid through the station, and he caught a glimpse of young Barton in the cab.

' I did that child an injustice. He is not altogether a fool,' said Mahbub Ali. ' To take a fire-carriage for a thief is a new game! '

When Mahbub Ali came to his camp in the dawn, no one thought it worth while to tell him any news of the night. No one, at least, but one small horse-boy, newly advanced to the great man's service, whom Mahbub called to his tiny tent to assist in some packing.

' It is all known to me,' whispered Kim, bending above saddle-bags. ' Two Sahibs came up on a te-rain. I was running to and fro in the dark on this side of the trucks as the te-rain moved up and down slowly. They fell upon two men sitting under this truck— Hajji, what shall I do with this lump of tobacco? Wrap it in paper and put it under the salt-bag? Yes—and struck them down. But one man struck at a Sahib with a faquir's buck's horn ' (Kim meant the conjoined black-buck horns, which are a faquir's sole temporal weapon)—' the blood came. So the other Sahib, first smiting his own man senseless, smote the stabber with a short gun which had rolled from the first man's hand. They all raged as though mad together.'

Mahbub smiled with heavenly resignation. ' No! That is not so much dewanee (madness, or a case for the civil court—the word can be punned upon both ways) as nizamut (a criminal case). A gun sayest thou? Ten good years in jail.'

' Then they both lay still, but I think they were nearly dead when they were put on the te-rain. Their heads moved thus. And there is much blood on the line. Come and see? '

' I have seen blood before. Jail is the sure place—and assuredly they will give false names, and assuredly no man will find them for a long time. They were unfriends of mine. Thy Fate and mine seem on one string. What a tale for the healer of pearls! Now swiftly with the saddle-bags and the cooking-platter. We will take out the horses and away to Simla.'

Swiftly,—as Orientals understand speed,—with long explanations, with abuse and windy talk, carelessly, amid a hundred checks for little things forgotten, the untidy camp broke up and led the half-dozen stiff and fretful horses along the Kalka road in the fresh of the rain-swept dawn. Kim, regarded as Mahbub Ali's favourite by all who wished to stand well with the Pathan, was not called upon to work. They strolled on by the easiest of

stages, halting every few hours at a wayside shelter. Very many Sahibs travel along the Kalka road; and, as Mahbub Ali says, every young Sahib must needs esteem himself a judge of a horse, and, though he be over head in debt to the money-lender, must make as if to buy. That was the reason that Sahib after Sahib, rolling along in a stage-carriage, would stop and open talk. Some would even descend from their vehicles and feel the horses' legs; asking inane questions, or, through sheer ignorance of the vernacular, grossly insulting the imperturbable trader.

'When first I dealt with Sahibs, and that was when Colonel Soady Sahib was Governor of Fort Abazai and flooded the Commissioner's camping-ground for spite,' Mahbub confided to Kim as the boy filled his pipe under a tree, 'I did not know how greatly they were fools, and this made me wroth. As thus— ' and he told Kim a tale of an expression, misused in all innocence, that doubled Kim up with mirth. 'Now I see, however,'— he exhaled smoke slowly,—' that it is with them as with all men—in certain matters they are wise, and in others most foolish. Very foolish it is to use the wrong word to a stranger; for though the heart may be clean of offence, how is the stranger to know that? He is more like to search truth with a dagger.'

'True. True talk,' said Kim solemnly. 'Fools speak of a cat when a woman is brought to bed, for instance. I have heard them.'

'Therefore, in one situate as thou art, it particularly behoves thee to remember this with both kinds of faces. Among Sahibs, never forgetting thou art a Sahib; among the folk of Hind, always remembering thou art— ' he paused, with a puzzled smile.

'What am I? Mussalman, Hindu, Jain, or Buddhist? That is a hard nut.'

'Thou art beyond question an unbeliever, and therefore thou wilt be damned. So says my Law—or I think it does. But thou art also my Little Friend of all the World, and I love thee. So says my heart. This matter of creeds is like horseflesh. The wise man knows horses are good—that there is a profit to be made from all; and for myself—but that I am a good Sunni and hate the men of Tirah—I could believe the same of all the Faiths. Now manifestly a Kattiawar mare taken from the sands of her birthplace and removed to the west of Bengal founders—nor is even a Balkh stallion (and there are no better horses than those of Balkh, were they not so heavy in the shoulder) of any account in the great Northern deserts beside the snow-camels I have seen. Therefore I say in my heart the Faiths are like the horses. Each has merit in its own country.'

'But my lama said altogether a different thing.'

'Oh, he is an old dreamer of dreams from Bhotiyal. My heart is a little angry, Friend of all the World, that thou shouldst see such worth in a man so little known.'

'It is true, Hajji; but that worth do I see; and to him my heart is drawn.'

'And his to thine, I hear. Hearts are like horses. They come and they go against bit or spur. Shout Gul Sher Khan yonder to drive in that bay stallion's pickets more firmly. We do not want a horse-fight at every resting-stage, and the dun and the black will be locked in a little. . . . Now hear me. Is it necessary to the comfort of thy heart to see that lama?'

'It is one part of my bond,' said Kim. 'If I do not see him, and if he is taken from me, I will go out of that madrissah in Nucklao and, and—once gone, who is to find me again?'

'It is true. Never was colt held on a lighter heel-rope than thou.' Mahbub nodded his head.

'Do not be afraid.' Kim spoke as though he could have evanished on the moment. 'My lama has said that he will come to see me at the madrissah—'

'A beggar and his bowl in the presence of those young Sa—'

'Not all!' Kim cut in with a snort. 'Their eyes are blued and their nails are blackened with low-caste blood, many of them. Sons of methe-eranees—brothers-in-law to the bhungi' (sweeper).

We need not follow the rest of the pedigree; but Kim made his little point clearly and without heat, chewing a piece of sugar-cane the while.

'Friend of all the World,' said Mahbub, pushing over the pipe for the boy to clean, 'I have met many men, women, and boys, and not a few Sahibs. I have never in all my days met such an imp as thou art.'

'And why? When I always tell thee the truth.'

'Perhaps the very reason, for this is a world of danger to honest men.' Mahbub Ali hauled himself off the ground, girt in his belt, and went over to the horses.

'Or sell it?'

There was that in the tone that made Mahbub halt and turn. 'What new devilry?'

'Eight annas, and I will tell,' said Kim, grinning. 'It touches thy peace.'

'O Shaitan!' Mahbub gave the money.

'Rememberest thou the little business of the thieves in the dark, down yonder at Umballa?'

'Seeing they sought my life, I have not altogether forgotten. Why?'

'Rememberest thou the Kashmir Serai?'

'I will twist thy ears in a moment—Sahib.'

'No need—Pathan. Only, the second faquir, whom the Sahibs beat senseless, was the man who came to search thy bulkhead at Lahore. I saw his face as they helped him on the engine. The very same man.'

'Why didst thou not tell before?'

'Oh, he will go to jail, and be safe for some years. There is no need to tell more than is necessary at any one time. Besides, I did not then need money for sweetmeats.'

'Allah Karim!' said Mahbub Ali. 'Wilt thou some day sell my head for a few sweetmeats if the fit takes thee?'

.

Kim will remember till he dies that long, lazy journey from Umballa, through Kalka and the Pinjore Gardens near by, up to Simla. A sudden spate in the Gugger River swept down one horse (the most valuable, be sure), and nearly drowned Kim among the dancing boulders. Farther up the road the horses were stampeded by a Government elephant, and being in high condition of grass food, it cost a day and a half to get them together again. Then they met Sikandar Khan coming down with a few unsaleable screws,—remnants of his string,—and Mahbub, who has more of horse-coping in his little finger nail than Sikandar Khan in all his tents, must needs buy two of the worst, and that meant eight hours' laborious diplomacy and untold tobacco. But it was all pure delight—the wandering road, climbing, dipping, and sweeping about the growing spurs; the flush of the morning laid along the distant snows; the branched cacti, tier upon tier on the stony hillsides; the voices of a thousand water-channels; the chatter of the monkeys; the solemn deodars, climbing one after another with down-drooped branches; the vista of the Plains rolled out far beneath them; the incessant twanging of the tonga-horns and the wild rush of the led horses when a tonga swung round a curve; the halts for prayers (Mahbub was very religious in dry-washings and bellowings when time did not press); the evening conferences by the halting-places, when camels and bullocks chewed solemnly together and the stolid drivers told the news of the Road—all these things lifted Kim's heart to song within him.

'But, when the singing and dancing is done,' said Mahbub Ali, 'comes the Colonel Sahib's, and that is not so sweet.'

'A fair land—a most beautiful land is this of Hind—and the land of the Five Rivers is fairer than all,' Kim half chanted. 'Into it I will go again if Mahbub or the Colonel lift hand or foot against me. Once gone, who shall find me? Look, Hajji, is yonder the city of Simla? Allah, what a city!'

'My father's brother, and he was an old man when Mackerson Sahib's well was new at Peshawur, could recall when there were but two houses in it.'

He led the horses below the main road into the lower Simla bazar—the crowded rabbit-warren that climbs up from the valley to the town-hall at an angle of forty-five. A man who knows his way there can defy all the police of India's summer capital; so cunningly does veranda communicate with veranda, alley-way with alley-way, and bolt-hole with bolt-hole. Here live those who minister to the wants of the glad city—jhampanis who pull the pretty ladies' rickshaws by night and gamble till the dawn; grocers, oil-sellers, curio-vendors, firewood dealers, priests, pickpockets, and native employees of the Government; here are discussed by courtesans the things which are supposed to be profoundest secrets of the India Council; and here gather all the sub-sub-agents of half the native States. Here, too, Mahbub Ali rented

a room, much more securely locked than his bulkhead at Lahore, in the house of a Mohammedan cattle-dealer. It was a place of miracles, too, for there went in at twilight a Mohammedan horse-boy, and there came out an hour later a Eurasian lad—the Lucknow girl's dye was of the best—in badly fitting shop-clothes.

'I have spoken with Creighton Sahib,' quoth Mahbub Ali, 'and a second time has the Hand of Friendship averted the Whip of Calamity. He says that thou hast altogether wasted sixty days upon the Road, and it is too late, therefore, to send thee to any hill-school.'

'I have said that my holidays are my own. I do not go to school twice over. That is one part of my bond.'

'The Colonel Sahib is not yet aware of the contract. Thou art to lodge in Lurgan Sahib's house till it is time to go again to Nucklao.'

'I had sooner lodge with thee, Mahbub.'

'Thou dost not know the honour. Lurgan Sahib himself asked for thee. Thou wilt go up the hill and along the road atop, and there thou must forget for a while that thou hast ever seen or spoken to me, Mahbub Ali, who sells horses to Creighton Sahib, whom thou dost not know. Remember this order.'

Kim nodded. 'Good,' said he, 'and who is Lurgan Sahib? Nay '—he caught Mahbub's sword-keen glance—' indeed I have never heard his name. Is he by chance '—he lowered his voice—' one of us? '

'What talk is this of us, Sahib? ' Mahbub Ali returned, in the tone he used towards Europeans. 'I am a Pathan; thou art a Sahib and the son of a Sahib. Lurgan Sahib has a shop among the European shops. All Simla knows it. Ask there . . . and, Friend of all the World, he is one to be obeyed to the last wink of his eyelashes. Men say he does magic, but that should not touch thee. Go up the hill and ask. Here begins the Great Game.'

CHAPTER IX

S'doaks was son of Yelth the wise—
Chief of the Raven clan.
Itswoot the Bear had him in care
To make him a medicine-man.

He was quick and quicker to learn—
Bold and bolder to dare:
He danced the dread Kloo-Kwallie Dance
To tickle Itswoot the Bear!

OREGON LEGEND

Kim flung himself whole-heartedly upon the next turn of the wheel. He would be a Sahib again for a while. In that idea, so soon as he had reached the broad road under Simla town-hall, he cast about for one to impress. A

Hindu child, some ten years old, squatted under a lamp-post.

'Where is Mr. Lurgan's house?' demanded Kim.

'I do not understand English,' was the answer, and Kim shifted his speech accordingly.

'I will show.'

Together they set off through the mysterious dusk, full of the noises of a city below the hillside, and the breath of a cool wind in deodar-crowned Jakko, shouldering the stars. The house-lights, scattered on every level, made, as it were, a double firmament. Some were fixed, others belonged to the rickshaws of the careless, open-spoken English folk, going out to dinner.

'It is here,' said Kim's guide, and halted in a veranda flush with the main road. No door stayed them, but a curtain of beaded reeds that split up the lamp-light beyond.

'He is come,' said the boy, in a voice little louder than a sigh, and vanished. Kim felt sure that the boy had been posted to guide him from the first, but putting a bold face on it, parted the curtain. A black-bearded man, with a green shade over his eyes, sat at a table, and, one by one, with short, white hands, picked up globules of light from a tray before him, threaded them on a glancing silken string, and hummed to himself the while. Kim was conscious that beyond the circle of light the room was full of things that smelt like all the temples of all the East. A whiff of musk, a puff of sandal-wood, and a breath of sickly jessamine-oil caught his opened nostrils.

'I am here,' said Kim at last, speaking in the vernacular: the smells made him forget that he was to be a Sahib.

'Seventy-nine, eighty, eighty-one,' the man counted to himself, stringing pearl after pearl so quickly that Kim could scarcely follow his fingers. He slid off the green shade and looked fixedly at Kim for a full half-minute. The pupils of the eye dilated and closed to pin-pricks, as if at will. There was a faquir by the Taksali Gate who had just this gift and made money by it, especially when cursing silly women. Kim stared with interest. His disreputable friend could further twitch his ears, almost like a goat, and Kim was disappointed that this new man could not imitate him.

'Do not be afraid,' said Mr. Lurgan suddenly.

'Why should I fear?'

'Thou wilt sleep here to-night, and stay with me till it is time to go again to Nucklao. It is an order.'

'It is an order,' Kim repeated. 'But where shall I sleep?'

'Here, in this room.' Lurgan Sahib waved his hand towards the darkness behind him.

'So be it,' said Kim composedly. 'Now?'

He nodded and held the lamp above his head. As the light swept them, there leaped out from the walls a collection of Tibetan devil-dance masks, hanging above the fiend-embroidered draperies of those ghastly functions— horned masks, scowling masks, and masks of idiotic terror. In a corner, a Japanese warrior, mailed and plumed, menaced him with a halberd, and a

score of lances and khandas and kuttars gave back the unsteady gleam. But what interested Kim more than all these things—he had seen devil-dance masks at the Lahore Museum—was a glimpse of the soft-eyed Hindu child who had left him in the doorway, sitting cross-legged under the table of pearls with a little smile on his scarlet lips.

'I think that Lurgan Sahib wishes to make me afraid. And I am sure that the devil's brat below the table wishes to see me afraid. This place,' he said aloud, 'is like a Wonder House. Where is my bed?'

Lurgan Sahib pointed to a native quilt in a corner by the loathsome masks, picked up the lamp, and left the room black.

'Was that Lurgan Sahib?' Kim asked as he cuddled down. No answer. He could hear the Hindu boy breathing, however, and, guided by the sound, crawled across the floor, and cuffed into the darkness, crying: 'Give answer, devil! Is this the way to lie to a Sahib?'

From the darkness he fancied he could hear the echo of a chuckle. It could not be his soft-fleshed companion, because he was weeping. So Kim lifted up his voice and called aloud: 'Lurgan Sahib! O Lurgan Sahib! Is it an order that thy servant does not speak to me?'

'It is an order.' The voice came from behind him and he started.

'Very good. But remember,' he muttered, as he resought the quilt, 'I will beat thee in the morning. I do not love Hindus.'

That was no cheerful night; the room being overfull of voices and music. Kim was waked twice by some one calling his name. The second time he set out in search, and ended by bruising his nose against a box that certainly spoke with a human tongue, but in no sort of human accent. It seemed to end in a tin trumpet and to be joined by wires to a smaller box on the floor— so far, at least, as he could judge by touch. And the voice, very hard and whirring, came out of the trumpet. Kim rubbed his nose and grew furious, thinking, as usual, in Hindi.

'This with a beggar from the bazar might be good but—I am a Sahib and the son of a Sahib and, which is twice as much more beside, a student of Nucklao. Yess' (here he turned to English), 'a boy of St. Xavier's. Damn Mr. Lurgan's eyes!—It is some sort of machinery like a sewing-machine. Oh, it is a great cheek of him—we are not frightened that way at Lucknow— No!' Then in Hindi: 'But what does he gain? He is only a trader—I am in his shop. But Creighton Sahib is a Colonel—and I think Creighton Sahib gave orders that it should be done. How I will beat that Hindu in the morning! What is this?'

The trumpet-box was pouring out a string of the most elaborate abuse that even Kim had ever heard, in a high uninterested voice, that for a moment lifted the short hairs of his neck. When the vile thing drew breath, Kim was reassured by the soft, sewing-machine-like whirr.

'Chup!' (be still) he cried, and again he heard a chuckle that decided him. 'Chup—or I break your head.'

The box took no heed. Kim wrenched at the tin trumpet and something

lifted with a click. He had evidently raised a lid. If there were a devil inside, now was its time for—hc sniffed—thus did the sewing-machines of the bazar smell. He would clean that shaitan. He slipped off his jacket, and plunged it into the box's mouth. Something long and round bent under the pressure, there was a whirr and the voice stopped—as voices must if you ram a thrice-doubled coat on to the wax cylinder and into the works of an expensive phonograph. Kim finished his slumbers with a serene mind.

In the morning he was aware of Lurgan Sahib looking down on him.

' Oah! ' said Kim, firmly resolved to cling to his Sahibdom. ' There was a box in the night that gave me bad talk. So I stopped it. Was it your box? '

The man held out his hand.

' Shake hands, O'Hara,' he said. ' Yes, it was my box. I keep such things because my friends the Rajahs like them. That one is broken, but it was cheap at the price. Yes, my friends the Kings are very fond of toys—and so am I sometimes.'

Kim looked him over out of the corners of his eyes. He was a Sahib in that he wore Sahib's clothes; the accent of his Urdu, the intonation of his English, showed that he was anything but a Sahib. He seemed to understand what moved in Kim's mind ere the boy opened his mouth, and he took no pains to explain himself as did Father Victor or the Lucknow masters. Sweet-est of all—he treated Kim as an equal on the Asiatic side.

' I am sorry you cannot beat my boy this morning. He says he will kill you with a knife or poison. He is jealous, so I have put him in the corner and I shall not speak of him to-day. He has just tried to kill me. You must help me with the breakfast. He is almost too jealous to trust, just now.'

Now a genuine imported Sahib from England would have made a great to do over this tale. Lurgan Sahib stated it as simply as Mahbub Ali was used to record his little affairs in the North.

The back veranda of the shop was built out over the sheer hillside, and they looked down into their neighbors' chimney-pots, as is the custom of Simla. But even more than the purely Persian meal cooked by Lurgan Sahib with his own hands, the shop fascinated Kim. The Lahore Museum was larger, but here were more wonders—ghost-daggers and prayer-wheels from Tibet; turquoise and raw amber necklaces; green jade bangles; curiously packed incense-sticks in jars crusted over with raw garnets; the devil-masks of over-night and a wall of peacock-blue draperies; gilt figures of Buddha, and little portable lacquer altars; Russian samovars with turquoises on the lid; egg-shell china sets in quaint octagonal cane boxes; yellow ivory crucifixes —from Japan of all places in the world, so Lurgan Sahib said; carpets in dusty bales, smelling atrociously, pushed back behind torn and rotten screens of geometrical work; Persian water-jugs for the hands after meals; dull cop-per incense-burners neither Chinese nor Persian, with friezes of fantastic devils running round them; tarnished silver belts that knotted like raw hide; hairpins of jade, ivory, and plasma; arms of all sorts and kinds, and a thou-sand other oddments were cased, or piled, or merely thrown into the room,

leaving a clear space only round the rickety deal table, where Lurgan Sahib worked.

'Those things are nothing,' said his host, following Kim's glance. 'I buy them because they are pretty, and sometimes I sell—if I like the buyer's look. My work is on the table—some of it.'

It blazed in the morning light—all red and blue and green flashes, picked out with the vicious blue-white spurt of a diamond here and there. Kim opened his eyes.

'Oh, they are quite well, those stones. It will not hurt them to take the sun. Besides, they are cheap. But with sick stones it is very different.' He piled Kim's plate anew. 'There is no one but me can doctor a sick pearl and re-blue turquoises. I grant you opals—any fool can cure an opal—but for a sick pearl there is only me. Suppose I were to die! Then there would be no one. . . . Oh no! You cannot do anything with jewels. It will be quite enough if you understand a little about the turquoise—some day.'

He moved to the end of the veranda to refill the heavy, porous clay water-jug from the filter.

'Do you want drink?'

Kim nodded. Lurgan Sahib, fifteen feet off, laid one hand on the jar. Next instant, it stood at Kim's elbow, full to within half an inch of the brim—the white cloth only showing, by a small wrinkle, where it had slid into place.

'Wah!' said Kim in most utter amazement. 'That is magic.' Lurgan Sahib's smile showed that the compliment had gone home.

'Throw it back.'

'It will break.'

'I say, throw it back.'

Kim pitched it at random. It fell short and crashed into fifty pieces, while the water dripped through the rough veranda boarding.

'I said it would break.'

'All one. Look at it. Look at the largest piece.'

That lay with a sparkle of water in its curve, as it were a star on the floor. Kim looked intently; Lurgan Sahib laid one hand gently on the nape of the neck, stroked it twice or thrice, and whispered: 'Look! It shall come to life again, piece by piece. First the big piece shall join itself to two others on the right and left—on the right and the left. Look!'

To save his life, Kim could not have turned his head. The light touch held him as in a vise, and his blood tingled pleasantly through him. There was one large piece of the jar where there had been three, and above them the shadowy outline of the entire vessel. He could see the veranda through it, but it was thickening and darkening with each beat of his pulse. Yet the jar—how slowly the thoughts came!—the jar had been smashed before his eyes. Another wave of prickling fire raced down his neck, as Lurgan Sahib moved his hand.

'Look! It is coming into shape,' said Lurgan Sahib.

So far Kim had been thinking in Hindi, but a tremor came on him, and with an effort like that of a swimmer before sharks, who hurls himself half out of the water, his mind leaped up from a darkness that was swallowing it and took refuge in—the multiplication-table in English!

'Look! It is coming into shape,' whispered Lurgan Sahib.

The jar had been smashed—yess, smashed—not the native word, he would not think of that—but smashed—into fifty pieces, and twice three was six, and thrice three was nine, and four times three was twelve. He clung desperately to the repetition. The shadow-outline of the jar cleared like a mist after rubbing eyes. There were the broken shards; there was the spilt water drying in the sun, and through the cracks of the veranda showed, all ribbed, the white house-wall below—and thrice twelve was thirty-six!

'Look! Is it coming into shape?' asked Lurgan Sahib.

'But it is smashed—smashed,' he gasped—Lurgan Sahib had been muttering softly for the last half-minute. Kim wrenched his head aside. 'Look! Dekho! It is there as it was there.'

'It is there as it was there,' said Lurgan, watching Kim closely while the boy rubbed his neck. 'But you are the first of a many who have ever seen it so.' He wiped his broad forehead.

'Was that more magic?' Kim asked suspiciously. The tingle had gone from his veins; he felt unusually wide awake.

'No, that was not magic. It was only to see if there was—a flaw in a jewel. Sometimes very fine jewels will fly all to pieces if a man holds them in his hand, and knows the proper way. That is why one must be careful before one sets them. Tell me, did you see the shape of the pot?'

'For a little time. It began to grow like a flower from the ground.'

'And then what did you do? I mean, how did you think?'

'Oah! I knew it was broken, and so, I think, that was what I thought —and it was broken.'

'Hm! Has any one ever done that same sort of magic to you before?'

'If it was,' said Kim, 'do you think I should let it again? I should run away.'

'And now you are not afraid—eh?'

'Not now.'

Lurgan Sahib looked at him more closely than ever. 'I shall ask Mahbub Ali—not now, but some day later,' he muttered. 'I am pleased with you— yes; and I am pleased with you—no. You are the first that ever saved himself. I wish I knew what it was that . . . But you are right. You should not tell that—not even to me.'

He turned into the dusky gloom of the shop, and sat down at the table, rubbing his hands softly. A small, husky sob came from behind a pile of carpets. It was the Hindu child obediently facing towards the walls: his thin shoulders worked with grief.

'Ah! He is jealous, so jealous. I wonder if he will try to poison me again in my breakfast, and make me cook it twice.'

'Kubbee—kubbee nahin,' came the broken answer.

'And whether he will kill this other boy?'

'Kubbee—kubbee nahin' (never—never. No!).

'What do you think he will do?' He turned suddenly on Kim.

'Oah! I do not know. Let him go, perhaps. Why did he want to poison you?'

'Because he is so fond of me. Suppose you were fond of some one, and you saw some one come, and the man you were fond of was more pleased with him than he was with you, what would you do?'

Kim thought. Lurgan repeated the sentence slowly in the vernacular.

'I should not poison that man,' said Kim reflectively, 'but I should beat that boy—if that boy was fond of my man. But first I would ask that boy if it were true.'

'Ah! He thinks every one must be fond of me.'

'Then I think he is a fool.'

'Hearest thou?' said Lurgan Sahib to the shaking shoulders. 'The Sahib's son thinks thou art a little fool. Come out, and next time thy heart is troubled, do not try white arsenic quite so openly. Surely the Devil Dasim was lord of our table-cloth that day! It might have made me ill, child, and then a stranger would have guarded the jewels. Come!'

The child, heavy-eyed with much weeping, crept out from behind the bale and flung himself passionately at Lurgan Sahib's feet, with an extravagance of remorse that impressed even Kim.

'I will look into the ink-pools—I will faithfully guard the jewels! Oh, my father and my mother, send him away!' He indicated Kim with a backward jerk of his bare heel.

'Not yet—not yet. In a little while he will go away again. But now he is at school—at a new madrissah—and thou shalt be his teacher. Play the Play of the Jewels against him. I will keep tally.'

The child dried his tears at once, and dashed to the back of the shop, whence he returned with a copper tray.

'Give me!' he said to Lurgan Sahib. 'Let them come from thy hand, for he may say that I knew them before.'

'Gently—gently,' the man replied, and from a drawer under the table dealt a half handful of clattering trifles into the tray.

'Now,' said the child, waving an old newspaper. 'Look on them as long as thou wilt, stranger. Count and, if need be, handle. One look is enough for me.' He turned his back proudly.

'But what is the game?'

'When thou hast counted and handled and art sure that thou canst remember them all, I cover them with this paper, and thou must tell over the tally to Lurgan Sahib. I will write mine.'

'Oah!' The instinct of competition waked in his breast. He bent over the tray. There were but fifteen stones on it. 'That is easy,' he said after a minute. The child slipped the paper over the winking jewels and scribbled

in a native account-book.

'There are under that paper five blue stones—one big, one smaller, and three small,' said Kim, all in haste. 'There are four green stones, and one with a hole in it; there is one yellow stone that I can see through, and one like a pipe-stem. There are two red stones, and—and—I made the count fifteen, but two I have forgotten. No! Give me time. One was of ivory, little and brownish; and—and—give me time . . .'

'One—two'—Lurgan Sahib counted him out up to ten. Kim shook his head.

'Hear my count!' the child burst in, trilling with laughter. 'First, are two flawed sapphires—one of two ruttees and one of four as I should judge. The four-ruttee sapphire is chipped at the edge. There is one Turkestan turquoise, plain with black veins, and there are two inscribed—one with a Name of God in gilt, and the other being cracked across, for it came out of an old ring, I cannot read. We have now all five blue stones. Four flawed emeralds there are, but one is drilled in two places, and one is a little carven—'

'Their weights?' said Lurgan Sahib impassively.

'Three—five—five—and four ruttees as I judge it. There is one piece of old greenish pipe amber, and a cut topaz from Europe. There is one ruby of Burma, of two ruttees, without a flaw, and there is a balas-ruby, flawed, of two ruttees. There is a carved ivory from China representing a rat sucking an egg; and there is last—ah ha!—a ball of crystal as big as a bean set in a gold leaf.'

He clapped his hands at the close.

'He is thy master,' said Lurgan Sahib, smiling.

'Huh! He knew the names of the stones,' said Kim, flushing. 'Try again! With common things such as he and I both know.'

They heaped the tray again with odds and ends gathered from the shop, and even the kitchen, and every time the child won, till Kim marvelled.

'Bind my eyes—let me feel once with my fingers, and even then I will leave thee open-eyed behind,' he challenged.

Kim stamped with vexation when the lad made his boast good.

'If it were men—or horses,' he said, 'I could do better. This playing with tweezers and knives and scissors is too little.'

'Learn first—teach later,' said Lurgan Sahib. 'Is he thy master?'

'Truly. But how is it done?'

'By doing it many times over till it is done perfectly—for it is worth doing.'

The Hindu boy, in highest feather, actually patted Kim on the back.

'Do not despair,' he said. 'I myself will teach thee.'

'And I will see that thou art well taught,' said Lurgan Sahib, still speaking in the vernacular, 'for except my boy here—it was foolish of him to buy so much white arsenic when, if he had asked, I could have given it—except my boy here I have not in a long time met with one better worth teaching. And there are ten days more ere thou canst return to Lucknow where they

teach nothing—at the long price. We shall, I think, be friends.'

They were a most mad ten days, but Kim enjoyed himself too much to reflect on their craziness. In the morning they played the Jewel Game— sometimes with veritable stones, sometimes with piles of swords and daggers, sometimes with photographs of natives. Through the afternoons he and the Hindu boy would mount guard in the shop, sitting dumb behind a carpet-bale or a screen and watching Mr. Lurgan's many and very curious visitors. There were small Rajahs, escorts coughing in the veranda, who came to buy curiosities—such as phonographs and mechanical toys. There were ladies in search of necklaces, and men, it seemed to Kim—but his mind may have been vitiated by early training—in search of the ladies; natives from independent and feudatory courts whose ostensible business was the repair of broken necklaces—rivers of light poured out upon the table—but whose true end seemed to be to raise money for angry Maharanees or young Rajahs. There were Babus to whom Lurgan Sahib talked with austerity and authority, but at the end of each interview he gave them money in coined silver and currency notes. There were occasional gatherings of long-coated theatrical natives who discussed metaphysics in English and Bengali, to Mr. Lurgan's great edification. He was always interested in religions. At the end of the day, Kim and the Hindu boy—whose name varied at Lurgan's pleasure—were expected to give a detailed account of all that they had seen and heard— their view of each man's character, as shown in his face, talk, and manner, and their notions of his real errand. After dinner, Lurgan Sahib's fancy turned more to what might be called dressing-up, in which game he took a most informing interest. He could paint faces to a marvel; with a brush-dab here and a line there changing them past recognition. The shop was full of all manner of dresses and turbans, and Kim was apparelled variously as a young Mohammedan of good family, an oilman, and once—which was a joyous evening—as the son of an Oudh landholder in the fullest of full dress. Lurgan Sahib had a hawk's eye to detect the least flaw in the make-up; and lying on a worn teak-wood couch, would explain by the half-hour together how such and such a caste talked, or walked, or coughed, or spat, or sneezed, and, since ' hows ' matter little in this world, the ' why ' of everything. The Hindu child played this game clumsily. That little mind, keen as an icicle where tally of jewels was concerned, could not temper itself to enter another's soul; but a demon in Kim woke up and sang with joy as he put on the changing dresses, and changed speech and gesture therewith.

Carried away by enthusiasm, he volunteered to show Lurgan Sahib one evening how the disciples of a certain caste of faquir, old Lahore acquaintances, begged doles by the roadside; and what sort of language he would use to an Englishman, to a Punjabi farmer going to a fair, and to a woman without a veil. Lurgan Sahib laughed immensely, and begged Kim to stay as he was, immobile for half an hour—cross-legged, ash-smeared, and wild-eyed, in the back room. At the end of that time entered a hulking, obese Babu whose stockinged legs shook with fat, and Kim opened on him with

a shower of wayside chaff. Lurgan Sahib—this annoyed Kim—watched the Babu and not the play.

'I think,' said the Babu heavily, lighting a cigarette, 'I am of opeenion that it is most extraordinary and effeecient performance. Except that you had told me I should have opined that—that—that you were pulling my legs. How soon can he become approximately effeecient chain-man? Because then I shall indent for him.'

'That is what he must learn at Lucknow.'

'Then order him to be jolly dam-quick. Good-night, Lurgan.' The Babu swung out with the gait of a bogged cow.

When they were telling over the day's list of visitors, Lurgan Sahib asked Kim who he thought the man might be.

'God knows!' said Kim cheerily. The tone might almost have deceived Mahbub Ali, but it failed entirely with the healer of sick pearls.

'That is true. God, He knows; but I wish to know what you think.'

Kim glanced sideways at his companion, whose eye had a way of compelling truth.

'I—I think he will want me when I come from the school, but '—confidentially, as Lurgan Sahib nodded approval—'I do not understand how he can wear many dresses and talk many tongues.'

'Thou wilt understand many things later. He is a writer of tales for a certain Colonel. His honour is great only in Simla, and it is noticeable that he has no name, but only a number and a letter—that is a custom among us.'

'And is there a price upon his head too—as upon Mah—all the others?'

'Not yet; but if a boy rose up who is now sitting here and went—look, the door is open!—as far as a certain house with a red-painted veranda, behind that which was the old theatre in the Lower Bazar, and whispered through the shutters: "Hurree Chunder Mookerjee bore the bad news of last month," that boy might take away a belt full of rupees.'

'How many?' said Kim promptly.

'Five hundred—a thousand—as many as he might ask for.'

'Good. And how long might such a boy live after the news was told?' He smiled merrily at Lurgan Sahib's very beard.

'Ah! That is to be well thought of. Perhaps if he were very clever, he might live out the day—but not the night. By no means the night.'

'Then what is the Babu's pay if so much is put upon his head?'

'Eighty—perhaps a hundred—perhaps a hundred and fifty rupees; but the pay is the least part of the work. From time to time, God causes men to be born—and thou art one of them—who have a lust to go abroad at the risk of their lives and discover news—to-day it may be of far-off things, to-morrow of some hidden mountain, and the next day of some near-by men who have done a foolishness against the State. These souls are very few; and of these few, not more than ten are of the best. Among these ten I count the Babu, and that is curious. How great therefore and desirable must be a business that brazens the heart of a Bengali!'

'True. But the days go slowly for me. I am yet a boy, and it is only within two months I learned to write Angrezi. Even now I cannot read it well. And there are yet years and years and long years before I can be even a chain-man.'

'Have patience, Friend of all the World'—Kim started at the title. 'Would I had a few of the years that so irk thee. I have proved thee in several small ways. This will not be forgotten when I make my report to the Colonel Sahib.' Then, changing suddenly into English with a deep laugh:—

'By Jove! O'Hara, I think there is a great deal in you; but you must not become proud and you must not talk. You must go back to Lucknow and be a good little boy and mind your book, as the English say, and perhaps, next holidays if you care, you can come back to me!' Kim's face fell. 'Oh, I mean if you like. I know where you want to go.'

Four days later a seat was booked for Kim and his small trunk at the rear of a Kalka tonga. His companion was the whale-like Babu, who, with a fringed shawl wrapped round his head, and his fat openwork-stockinged left leg tucked under him, shivered and grunted in the morning chill.

'How comes it that this man is one of us?' thought Kim, considering the jelly-back as they jolted down the road; and the reflection threw him into most pleasant day-dreams. Lurgan Sahib had given him five rupees—a splendid sum—as well as the assurance of his protection if he worked. Unlike Mahbub, Lurgan Sahib had spoken most explicitly of the reward that would follow obedience, and Kim was content. If only, like the Babu, he could enjoy the dignity of a letter and a number—and a price upon his head! Some day he would be all that and more. Some day he might be almost as great as Mahbub Ali! The housetops of his search should be half India; he would follow Kings and ministers, as in the old days he had followed vakils and lawyers' touts across Lahore city for Mahbub Ali's sake. Meantime, there was the present, and not at all unpleasant, fact of St. Xavier's immediately before him. There would be new boys to condescend to, and there would be tales of holiday adventures to hear. Young Martin, son of the tea-planter at Manipur, had boasted that he would go to war, with a rifle, against the head-hunters. That might be, but it was certain young Martin had not been blown half across the forecourt of a Patiala palace by an explosion of fireworks; nor had he. . . . Kim fell to telling himself the story of his own adventures through the last three months. He could paralyse St. Xavier's—even the biggest boys who shaved—with the recital, were that permitted. But it was, of course, out of the question. There would be a price upon his head in good time, as Lurgan Sahib had assured him; and if he talked foolishly now, not only would that price never be set, but Colonel Creighton would cast him off—and he would be left to the wrath of Lurgan Sahib and Mahbub Ali—for the short space of life that would remain to him.

'So I should lose Delhi for the sake of a fish,' was his proverbial philosophy. It behoved him to forget his holidays (there would always remain the

fun of inventing imaginary adventures) and, as Lurgan Sahib had said, to
work.

Of all the boys hurrying back to St. Xavier's, from Sukkur in the sands
to Galle beneath the palms, none was so filled with virtue as Kimball
O'Hara, jiggeting down to Umballa behind Hurree Chunder Mookerjee,
whose name on the books of one section of the Ethnological Survey was R.17.

And if additional spur were needed, the Babu supplied it. After a huge
meal at Kalka, he spoke uninterruptedly. Was Kim going to school? Then
he, an M. A. of Calcutta University, would explain the advantages of edu-
cation. There were marks to be gained by due attention to Latin and Words-
worth's ' Excursion ' (all this was Greek to Kim). French, too, was vital, and
the best was to be picked up in Chandernagore, a few miles from Calcutta.
Also a man might go far, as he himself had done, by strict attention to plays
called ' Lear ' and ' Julius Cæsar,' both much in demand by examiners.
' Lear ' was not so full of historical allusions as ' Julius Cæsar '; the book
cost four annas, but could be bought second-hand in Bow Bazar for two.
Still more important than Wordsworth, or the eminent authors, Burke and
Hare, was the art and science of mensuration. A boy who had passed his
examination in these branches—for which, by the way, there were no cram-
books—could, by merely marching over a country with a compass and a level
and a straight eye, carry away a picture of that country which might be sold
for large sums in coined silver. But as it was occasionally inexpedient to carry
about measuring-chains, a boy would do well to know the precise length of
his own foot-pace, so that when he was deprived of what Hurree Chunder
called ' adventitious aids ' he might still tread his distances. To keep count
of thousands of paces, Hurree Chunder's experience had shown him nothing
more valuable than a rosary of eighty-one or a hundred and eight beads, for
' it was divisible and sub-divisible into many multiples and sub-multiples.'
Through the volleying drifts of English, Kim caught the general trend of the
talk, and it interested him very much. Here was a new craft that a man
could tuck away in his head; and by the look of the large wide world unfold-
ing itself before him, it seemed that the more a man knew the better for
him.

Said the Babu when he had talked for an hour and a half, ' I hope some
day to enjoy your offeecial acquaintance. Ad interim, if I may be pardoned
that expression, I shall give you this betel-box which is highly valuable article
and cost me two rupees only four years ago.' It was a cheap, heart-shaped
brass thing with three compartments for carrying the eternal betel-nut, lime
and pan-leaf; but it was filled with little tabloid-bottles. ' That is reward of
merit for your performance in character of that holy man. You see, you are
so young you think you will last for ever and not take care of your body.
It is great nuisance to go sick in the middle of business. I am fond of drugs
myself, and they are handy to cure poor people too. These are good depart-
mental drugs—quinine and so on. I give it you for souvenir. Now good-bye.
I have urgent private business here by the roadside.'

He slipped out noiselessly as a cat, on the Umballa road, hailed a passing ekka and jingled away, while Kim, tongue-tied, twiddled the brass betel-box in his hands.

.

The record of a boy's education interests few save his parents, and, as you know, Kim was an orphan. It is written in the books of St. Xavier in Partibus that a report of Kim's progress was forwarded at the end of each term to Colonel Creighton and to Father Victor, from whose hands duly came the money for his schooling. It is further recorded in the same books that he showed a great aptitude for mathematical studies as well as map-making, and carried away a prize ('The Life of Lord Lawrence,' tree-calf, two vols., nine rupees, eight annas) for proficiency therein; and the same term played in St. Xavier's eleven against the Allyghur Mohammedan College, his age being fourteen years and ten months. He was also re-vaccinated (from which we may assume that there had been another epidemic of small-pox at Lucknow) about the same time. Pencil notes on the edge of an old muster-roll record that he was punished several times for 'conversing with improper persons,' and it seems that he was once sentenced to heavy pains for 'absenting himself for a day in the company of a street beggar.' That was when he got over the gate and pleaded with the lama through a whole day down the banks of the Goomtee to accompany him on the Road next holidays—for one month—for a little week; and the lama set his face as a flint against it, averring that the time had not yet come. Kim's business, said the old man as they ate cakes together, was to get all the wisdom of the Sahibs and then he would see. The hand of friendship must in some way have averted the whip of calamity, for six weeks later Kim seems to have passed an examination in elementary surveying 'with great credit,' his age being fifteen years and eight months. From this date the record is silent. His name does not appear in the year's batch of those who entered for the subordinate Survey of India, but against it stand the words 'removed on appointment.'

Several times in those three years, cast up at the Temple of the Tir-thankers in Benares the lama, a little thinner and a shade yellower, if that were possible, but gentle and untainted as ever. Sometimes it was from the South that he came—from south of Tuticorin, whence the wonderful fire-boats go to Ceylon where are priests who know Pali; sometimes it was from the wet green West and the thousand cotton-factory chimneys that ring Bombay; and once from the North, where he had doubled back eight hundred miles to talk a day with the Keeper of the Images in the Wonder House. He would stride to his cell in the cool, cut marble—the priests of the temple were good to the old man—wash off the dust of travel, make prayer, and depart for Lucknow, well accustomed now to the ways of the rail, in a third-class carriage. Returning, it was noticeable, as his friend the Seeker pointed out to the head-priest, that he ceased for a while to mourn the loss of his

River, or to draw wondrous pictures of the Wheel of Life, but preferred to talk of the beauty and wisdom of a certain mysterious chela whom no man of the temple had ever seen. Yes, he had followed the traces of the Blessed Feet throughout all India. (The curator has still in his possession a most marvellous account of his wanderings and meditations.) There remained nothing more in life but to find the River of the Arrow. Yet it was shown to him in dreams that it was a matter not to be undertaken with any hope of success unless that seeker had with him the one chela appointed to bring the event to a happy issue, and versed in great wisdom—such wisdom as white-haired Keepers of Images possess. For example (here came out the snuff-gourd, and the kindly Jain priests made haste to be silent):—

'Long and long ago, when Devadatta was King of Benares—let all listen to the "Jataka"!—an elephant was captured for a time by the king's hunters and, ere he broke free, beringed with a grievous leg-iron. This he strove to remove with hate and frenzy in his heart, and hurrying up and down the forests, besought his brother-elephants to wrench it asunder. One by one, with their strong trunks, they tried and failed. At the last they gave it as their opinion that the ring was not to be broken by any bestial power. And in a thicket, new-born, wet with the moisture of birth, lay a day-old calf of the herd whose mother had died. The fettered elephant, forgetting his own agony, said: "If I do not help this suckling it will perish under our feet." So he stood above the young thing, making his legs buttresses against the uneasily moving herd; and he begged milk of a virtuous cow, and the calf throve, and the ringed elephant was the calf's guide and defence. Now the days of an elephant—let all listen to the "Jataka"!—are thirty-five years to his full strength, and through thirty-five Rains the ringed elephant befriended the younger, and all the while the fetter ate into the flesh.

'Then one day the young elephant saw the half-buried iron, and turning to the elder said: "What is this?" "It is even my sorrow," said he who had befriended him. Then that other put out his trunk and in the twinkling of an eyelash abolished the ring, saying: "The appointed time has come." So the virtuous elephant who had waited temperately and done kind acts was relieved, at the appointed time, by the very calf whom he had turned aside to cherish—let all listen to the "Jataka"!—for the Elephant was Ananda, and the Calf that broke the ring was none other than The Lord Himself. . . .'

Then he would shake his head benignly, and over the ever-clicking rosary point out how free that elephant calf was from the sin of pride. He was as humble as a chela who, seeing his master sitting in the dust outside the Gates of Learning, overleapt the gates (though they were locked) and took his master to his heart in the presence of the proud-stomached city. Rich would be the reward of such a master and such a chela when the time came for them to seek freedom together!

So did the lama speak, coming and going across India as softly as a bat. A sharp-tongued old woman in a house among the fruit-trees behind Saharun-

pore honoured him as the woman honoured the prophet, but his chamber
was by no means upon the wall. In an apartment of the forecourt overlooked
by cooing doves he would sit, while she laid aside her useless veil and chat-
tered of spirits and friends of Kulu, of grandchildren unborn, and of the
free-tongued brat who had talked to her in the resting-place. Once, too, he
strayed alone from the Grand Trunk Road below Umballa to the very village
whose priest had tried to drug him, but the kind heaven that guards lamas
sent him at twilight through the crops, absorbed and unsuspicious, to the
ressaldar's door. Here was like to have been a grave misunderstanding, for
the old soldier asked him why the Friend of the Stars had gone that way
only six days before.

'That may not be,' said the lama. 'He has gone back to his own
people.'

'He sat in that corner telling a hundred merry tales five nights ago,'
his host insisted. 'True, he vanished somewhat suddenly in the dawn after
foolish talk with my grand-daughter. He grows apace, but he is the same
Friend of the Stars as brought me true word of the war. Have ye parted?'

'Yes—and no,' the lama replied. 'We—we have not altogether parted,
but the time is not ripe that we should take the Road together. He acquires
wisdom in another place. We must wait.'

'All one—but if it were not the boy how did he come to speak so con-
tinually of thee?'

'And what said he?' asked the lama eagerly.

'Sweet words—an hundred thousand—that thou art his father and
mother and such all. Pity that he does not take the Queen's service. He is
fearless.'

This news amazed the lama, who did not then know how religiously
Kim kept to the contract made with Mahbub Ali, and perforce ratified by
Colonel Creighton. . . .

'There is no holding the young pony from the game,' said the horse-
dealer when the Colonel pointed out that vagabonding over India in holiday
time was absurd. 'If permission be refused to go and come as he chooses,
he will make light of the refusal. Then who is to catch him? Colonel Sahib,
only once in a thousand years is a horse born so well fitted for the game
as this our colt. And we need men.'

CHAPTER X

Your tiercel's too long at hack, Sire. He's no eyass
But a passage-hawk that footed ere we caught him,
Dangerously free o' the air. Faith! were he mine
(As mine's the glove he binds to for his tirings)
I'd fly him with a make-hawk. He's in yarak
Plumed to the very point—so manned so weathered . . .
Give him the firmament God made him for,
And what shall take the air of him?

OLD PLAY

Lurgan Sahib did not use as direct speech, but his advice tallied with Mahbub's; and the upshot was good for Kim. He knew better now than to leave Lucknow city in native garb, and if Mahbub were anywhere within reach of a letter, it was to Mahbub's camp he headed, and made his change under the Pathan's wary eye. Could the little Survey paint-box that he used for map-tinting in term-time have found a tongue to tell of holiday doings, he might have been expelled. Once Mahbub and he went together as far as the beautiful city of Bombay, with three truck-loads of tram-horses, and Mahbub nearly melted when Kim proposed a sail in a dhow across the Indian Ocean to buy Gulf Arabs, which he understood from a hanger-on of the dealer Abdul Rahman, fetched better prices than mere Kabulis.

He dipped his hand into the dish with that great trader when Mahbub and a few co-religionists were invited to a big Haj dinner. They came back by way of Karachi by sea, when Kim took his first experience of sea-sickness sitting on the fore-hatch of a coasting-steamer, well persuaded he had been poisoned. The Babu's famous drug-box proved useless, though Kim had re-stocked it at Bombay. Mahbub had business at Quetta, and there Kim, as Mahbub admitted, earned his keep, and perhaps a little over, by spending four curious days as scullion in the house of a fat Commissariat sergeant, from whose office-box, in an auspicious moment, he removed a little vellum ledger which he copied out—it seemed to deal entirely with cattle and camel sales—by moonlight, lying behind an outhouse, all through one hot night. Then he returned the ledger to its place, and, at Mahbub's word, left that service unpaid, rejoining him six miles down the road, the clean copy in his bosom.

'That soldier is a small fish,' Mahbub Ali explained, 'but in time we shall catch the larger one. He only sells oxen at two prices—one for himself and one for the Government—which I do not think is a sin.'

'Why could not I take away the little book and be done with it?'

' Then he would have been frightened, and he would have told his master. Then we should miss, perhaps, a great number of new rifles which seek their way up from Quetta to the North. The Game is so large that one sees but a little at a time.'

' Oho! ' said Kim, and held his tongue. That was in the monsoon holidays, after he had taken the prize for mathematics. The Christmas holidays he spent—deducting ten days for private amusements—with Lurgan Sahib, where he sat for the most part in front of a roaring wood-fire—Jakko-road was four feet deep in snow that year—and—the small Hindu had gone away to be married—helped Lurgan to thread pearls. He made Kim learn whole chapters of the Koran by heart, till he could deliver them with the very roll and cadence of a mullah. Moreover, he told Kim the names and properties of many native drugs, as well as the runes proper to recite when you administer them. And in the evenings he wrote charms on parchment—elaborate pentagrams crowned with the names of devils—Murra, and Awan the Companion of Kings—all fantastically written in the corners. More to the point, he advised Kim as to the care of his own body, the cure of fever-fits, and simple remedies of the Road. A week before it was time to go down, Colonel Creighton Sahib—this was unfair—sent Kim a written examination-paper that concerned itself solely with rods and chains and links and angles.

Next holidays he was out with Mahbub, and here, by the way, he nearly died of thirst, plodding through the sand on a camel to the mysterious city of Bikanir, where the wells are four hundred feet deep, and lined through-out with camel-bone. It was not an amusing trip from Kim's point of view, because—in defiance of the contract—the Colonel ordered him to make a map of that wild, walled city; and since Mohammedan horse-boys and pipe-tenders are not expected to drag Survey-chains round the capital of an independent native state, Kim was forced to pace all his distances by means of a bead rosary. He used the compass for bearings as occasion served—after dark chiefly, when the camels had been fed—and by the help of his little Survey paint-box of six colour cakes and three brushes, he achieved some thing not remotely unlike the city of Jeysalmir. Mahbub laughed a great deal, and advised him to make up a written report as well; and in the back of the big account-book that lay under the flap of Mahbub's pet saddle Kim fell to work.

' It must hold everything that thou hast seen or touched or considered. Write as though the Jung-i-Lat Sahib himself had come by stealth with a vast army outsetting to war.'

' How great an army? '

' Oh, half a lakh of men.'

' Folly! Remember how few and bad were the wells in the sand. Not a thousand thirsty men could come near by here.'

' Then write that down—also all the old breaches in the walls—and whence the firewood is cut—and what is the temper and disposition of the King. I stay here till all my horses are sold. I will hire a room by the gate-

way, and thou shalt be my accountant. There is a good lock to the door.'

The report in its unmistakable St. Xavier's running script, and the brown, yellow, and lake-daubed map, was on hand a few years ago (a careless clerk filed it with the rough notes of E.23's second Seistan survey), but by now the pencil characters must be almost illegible. Kim translated it, sweating under the light of an oil-lamp, to Mahbub, the second day of their return-journey. The Pathan rose and stooped over his dappled saddle-bags.

'I knew it would be worthy a dress of honour, and so I made one ready,' he said smiling. 'Were I Amir of Afghanistan (and some day we may see him), I would fill thy mouth with gold.' He laid the garments formally at Kim's feet. There was a gold-embroidered Peshawur turban-cap, rising to a cone, and a big turban-cloth ending in a broad fringe of gold. There was a Delhi embroidered waist-coat to slip over a milky-white shirt, fastening to the right, ample and flowing; green pyjamas with twisted silk waist-string; and that nothing might be lacking, russia-leather slippers, smelling divinely, with arrogantly curled tips.

'Upon a Wednesday, and in the morning, to put on new clothes is auspicious,' said Mahbub solemnly. 'But we must not forget the wicked folk in the world. So!'

He capped all the splendour, that was taking Kim's delighted breath away, with a mother-of-pearl, nickel-plated, self-extracting .450 revolver.

'I had thought of a smaller bore, but reflected that this takes Government bullets. A man can always come by those—especially across the Border. Stand up and let me look.' He clapped Kim on the shoulder. 'May you never be tired, Pathan! Oh, the hearts to be broken! Oh, the eyes under the eyelashes, looking sideways!'

Kim turned about, pointed his toes, stretched, and felt mechanically for the moustache that was just beginning. Then he stooped towards Mahbub's feet to make proper acknowledgment with fluttering, quick-patting hands; his heart too full for words. Mahbub forestalled and embraced him.

'My son,' said he, 'what need of words between us? But is not the little gun a delight? All six cartridges come out at one twist. It is borne in the bosom next the skin, which, as it were, keeps it oiled. Never put it elsewhere, and please God, thou shalt some day kill a man with it.'

'Hai mai!' said Kim ruefully. 'If a Sahib kills a man he is hung in the jail.'

'True: but one pace beyond the Border, men are wiser. Put it away; but fill it first. Of what use is a gun unfed?'

'When I go back to the madrissah I must return it. They do not allow little guns. Thou wilt keep it for me?'

'Son, I am wearied of that madrissah, where they take the best years of a man to teach him what he can only learn upon the Road. The folly of the Sahibs has neither top nor bottom. No matter. Maybe thy written report shall save thee further bondage; and God He knows we need men more and more in the Game.'

They marched, jaw-bound against blowing sand, across the salt desert to Jodhpore, where Mahbub and his handsome nephew Habib-Ullah did much trading; and then sorrowfully, in European clothes, which he was fast outgrowing, Kim went second-class to St. Xavier's. Three weeks later, Colonel Creighton, pricing Tibetan ghost-daggers at Lurgan's shop, faced Mahbub Ali openly mutinous. Lurgan Sahib operated as support in reserve.

'The pony is made—finished—mouthed and paced, Sahib! From now on, day by day, he will lose his manners if he is kept at tricks. Drop the rein on his back and let go,' said the horse-dealer. 'We need him.'

'But he is so young, Mahbub—not more than sixteen—is he?'

'When I was fifteen, I had shot my man and begot my man, Sahib.'

'You impenitent old heathen.' Creighton turned to Lurgan. The black beard nodded assent to the wisdom of the Afghan's dyed scarlet.

'I should have used him long ago,' said Lurgan. 'The younger the better. That is why I always have my really valuable jewels watched by a child. You sent him to me to try. I tried him in every way: he is the only boy I could not make to see things.'

'In the crystal—in the ink-pool?' demanded Mahbub.

'No. Under my hand, as I told you. That has never happened before. It means that he is strong enough—but you think it skittles, Colonel Creighton—to make any one do anything he wants. And that is three years ago. I have taught him a good deal since, Colonel Creighton. I think you waste him now.'

'Hmm! Maybe you're right. But, as you know, there is no Survey work for him at present.'

'Let him out—let him go,' Mahbub interrupted. 'Who expects any colt to carry heavy weight at first? Let him run with the caravans like our white camel-colts—for luck. I would take him myself, but—'

'There is a little business where he would be most useful—in the South,' said Lurgan, with peculiar suavity, dropping his heavy nude eyelids.

'E.23 has that in hand,' said Creighton quickly. 'He must not go down there. Besides, he knows no Turki.'

'Only tell him the shape and the smell of the letters we want and he will bring them back,' Lurgan insisted.

'No. That is a man's job,' said Creighton.

It was a wry-necked matter of unauthorised and incendiary correspondence between a person who claimed to be the ultimate authority in all matters of the Mohammedan religion throughout the world, and a younger member of a royal house who had been brought to book for kidnapping women within British territory. The Moslem Archbishop had been emphatic and over-arrogant; the young prince was merely sulky at the curtailment of his privileges, but there was no need he should continue a correspondence which might some day compromise him. One letter indeed had been procured, but the finder was later found dead by the roadside in the habit of an Arab trader, as E.23, taking up the work, duly reported.

These facts, and a few others not to be published, made both Mahbub and Creighton shake their heads.

'Let him go out with his Red Lama,' said the horse-dealer with visible effort. 'He is fond of the old man. He can learn his paces by the rosary at least.'

'I have had some dealings with the old man—by letter,' said Colonel Creighton, smiling to himself. 'Whither goes he?'

'Up and down the land, as he has these three years. He seeks a River of Healing. God's curse upon all—' Mahbub checked himself. 'He beds down at the Temple of the Tirthankers or at Buddh Gaya when he is in from the Road. Then he goes to see the boy at the madrissah as we know, for the boy was punished for it twice or thrice. He is quite mad, but a peaceful man. I have met him. The Babu also has had dealings with him. We have watched him for three years. Red Lamas are not so common in Hind that one loses track.'

'Babus are very curious,' said Lurgan meditatively. 'Do you know what Hurree Babu really wants? He wants to be made a member of the Royal Society by taking ethnological notes. I tell you, I tell him about the lama everything that Mahbub and the boy have told me. Hurree Babu goes down to Benares—at his own expense, I think.'

'I don't,' said Creighton briefly. He had paid Hurree's travelling expenses, out of a most lively curiosity to learn what the lama might be.

'And he applies to the lama for information on lamaism, and devil dances, and spells and charms, several times in these few years. Holy Virgin! I could have told him all that yee-ars ago. I think Hurree Babu is getting too old for the Road. He likes better to collect manners and customs information. Yes, he wants to be an F. R. S.'

'Hurree thinks well of the boy, doesn't he?'

'Oh, very indeed—we have had some pleasant evenings at my little place—but I think it would be waste to throw him away with Hurree on the Ethnological side.'

'Not for a first experience. How does that strike you, Mahbub? Let the boy run with the lama for six months. After that we can see. He will get experience.'

'He has it already, Sahib—as a fish controls the water he swims in; but for every reason it will be well to loose him from the school.'

'Very good, then,' said Creighton, half to himself. 'He can go with the lama, and if Hurree Babu cares to keep an eye on them so much the better. He won't lead the boy into any danger as Mahbub would. Curious—his wish to be an F. R. S. Very human, too. He is best on the Ethnological side—Hurree.'

No money and no preferment would have drawn Creighton from his work on the Indian Survey, but deep in his heart also lay an ambition to write 'F. R. S.' after his name. Honours of a sort he knew could be obtained by ingenuity and the help of friends, but, to the best of his belief, nothing

save work—papers representing a life of it—took a man into the Society
which he had bombarded for years with monographs on strange Asiatic
cults and unknown customs. Nine men out of ten would flee from a Royal
Society soiree in extremity of boredom; but Creighton was the tenth, and
at times his soul yearned for the crowded rooms in easy London where silver-
haired, bald-headed gentlemen who know nothing of the Army move among
spectroscopic experiments, the lesser plants of the frozen tundras, electric
flight-measuring machines, and apparatus for slicing into fractional milli-
metres the left eye of the female mosquito. By all right and reason, it was the
Royal Geographical that should have appealed to him, but men are as
chancy as children in their choice of playthings. So Creighton smiled, and
thought the better of Hurree Babu, moved by like desires.

He dropped the ghost-dagger and looked up at Mahbub.

'How soon can we get the colt from the stable?' said the horse-dealer,
reading his eyes.

'Hmm. If I withdraw him by order now—what will he do, think you?
I have never before assisted at the teaching of such an one.'

'He will come to me,' said Mahbub promptly. 'Lurgan Sahib and I
will prepare him for the Road.'

'So be it, then. For six months he shall run at his choice: but who
will be his sponsor?'

Lurgan slightly inclined his head. 'He will not tell anything, if that
is what you are afraid of, Colonel Creighton.'

'It's only a boy, after all.'

'Ye-es; but first, he has nothing to tell; and secondly, he knows what
would happen. Also, he is very fond of Mahbub, and of me a little.'

'Will he draw pay?' demanded the practical horse-dealer.

'Food and water allowance only. Twenty rupees a month.'

One advantage of the Secret Service is that it has no worrying audit.
The service is ludicrously starved, of course, but the funds are administered
by a few men who do not call for vouchers or present itemised accounts.
Mahbub's eyes lighted with almost a Sikh's love of money. Even Lurgan's
impassive face changed. He considered the years to come when Kim would
have been entered and made to the Great Game that never ceases day
and night, throughout India. He foresaw honour and credit in the mouths
of a chosen few, coming to him from his pupil. Lurgan Sahib had made
E.23 what E.23 was, out of a bewildered, impertinent, lying, little North-
West Province man.

But the joy of these masters was pale and smoky beside the joy of Kim
when St. Xavier's Head called him aside, with word that Colonel Creighton
had sent for him.

'I understand, O'Hara, that he has found you a place as an assistant
chain-man in the Canal Department: that comes of taking up mathematics.
It is great luck for you, for you are only seventeen; but of course you under-
stand that you do not become pukka (permanent) till you have passed the

autumn examination. So you must not think you are going out into the
world to enjoy yourself, or that your fortune is made. There is a great deal
of hard work before you. Only, if you succeed in becoming pukka, you can
rise, you know, to four hundred and fifty a month.' Whereat the Principal
gave him much good advice as to his conduct, and his manners, and his
morals; and others, his elders, who had not been wafted into billets, talked,
as only Anglo-Indian lads can, of favouritism and corruption. Indeed, young
Cazalet, whose father was a pensioner at Chunar, hinted very broadly that
Colonel Creighton's interest in Kim was directly paternal; and Kim, instead
of retaliating, did not even use language. He was thinking of the immense
fun to come, of Mahbub's letter of the day before, all neatly written in
English, making appointment for that afternoon in a house the very name
of which would have crisped the Principal's hair with horror. . . .

Said Kim to Mahbub in Lucknow railway station that evening, above
the luggage-scales—' I feared lest, at the last, the roof would fall upon me
and cheat me. Is it indeed all finished, O my father? '

Mahbub snapped his fingers to show the utterness of that end, and his
eyes blazed like red coals.

' Then where is the pistol that I may wear it? '

' Softly! A half-year, to run without heel-ropes. I begged that much
from Colonel Creighton Sahib. At twenty rupees a month. Old Red Hat
knows that thou art coming.'

' I will pay thee dustoorie (commission) on my pay for three months,'
said Kim gravely. ' Yea, two rupees a month. But first we must get rid of
these.' He plucked his thin linen trousers and dragged at his collar. ' I have
brought with me all that I need on the Road. My trunk has gone up to
Lurgan Sahib's.'

' Who sends his salaams to thee—Sahib.'

' Lurgan Sahib is a very clever man. But what dost thou do? '

' I go North again, upon the Great Game. What else? Is thy mind still
set on following old Red Hat? '

' Do not forget he made me what I am—though he did not know it.
Year by year, he sent the money that taught me.'

' I would have done as much—had it struck my thick head,' Mahbub
growled. ' Come away. The lamps are lit now, and none will mark thee in
the bazar. We go to Huneefa's house.'

On the way thither, Mahbub gave him much the same sort of advice
as his mother gave to Lemuel, and curiously enough, Mahbub was exact
to point out how Huneefa and her likes destroyed kings.

' And I remember,' he quoted maliciously, ' one who said, " Trust a
snake before a harlot and a harlot before a Pathan, Mahbub Ali." Now,
excepting as to Pathans, of whom I am one, all that is true. Most true is it
in the Great Game, for it is by means of woman that all plans come to
ruin and we lie out in dawning with our throats cut. So it happened to such
a one,'—he gave the reddest particulars.

' Then why—? ' Kim paused before a filthy staircase that climbed to the warm darkness of an upper chamber in the ward that is behind Azim Ullah's tobacco-shop. Those who know it call it The Bird-cage—it is so full of whisperings and whistlings and chirrupings.

The room, with its dirty cushions and half-smoked hookahs, smelt abominably of stale tobacco. In one corner lay a huge and shapeless woman clad in greenish gauzes, and decked, brow, nose, ear, neck, wrist, arm, waist, and ankle, with heavy native jewellery. When she turned it was like the clashing of copper pots. A lean cat in the balcony outside the window mewed hungrily. Kim checked, bewildered, at the door-curtain.

' Is that the new stuff, Mahbub? ' said Huneefa lazily, scarce troubling to remove the mouthpiece from her lips. ' O Buktanoos! '—like most of her kind, she swore by the Djinns—' O Buktanoos! He is very good to look upon.'

' That is part of the selling of the horse,' Mahbub explained to Kim, who laughed.

' I have heard that talk since my Sixth Day,' he replied, squatting by the light. ' Whither does it lead? '

' To protection. To-night we change thy colour. This sleeping under roofs has blanched thee like an almond. But Huneefa has the secret of a colour that catches. No painting of a day or two. Also, we fortify thee against the chances of the Road. That is my gift to thee, my son. Take out all metals on thee and lay them here. Make ready, Huneefa.'

Kim dragged forth his compass, Survey paint-box, and the new-filled medicine-box. They had all accompanied his travels, and boy-like he valued them immensely.

The woman rose slowly and moved with her hands a little spread before her. Then Kim saw that she was blind. ' No, no,' she muttered, ' the Pathan speaks truth—my colour does not go in a week or a month, and those whom I protect are under strong guard.'

' When one is far off and alone, it would not be well to grow blotched and leprous of a sudden,' said Mahbub. ' When thou wast with me I could oversee the matter. Besides, a Pathan is a fair-skin. Strip to the waist now and look how thou art whitened.' Huneefa felt her way back from an inner room. ' It is no matter, she cannot see.' He took a pewter bowl from her ringed hand.

The dye-stuff showed blue and gummy. Kim experimented on the back of his wrist, with a dab of cotton wool; but Huneefa heard him.

' No, no,' she cried, ' the thing is not done thus, but with the proper ceremonies. The colouring is the least part. I give thee the full protection of the Road.'

' Jadoo? ' (magic), said Kim, with a half start. He did not like the white, sightless eyes. Mahbub's hand on his neck bowed him to the floor, nose within an inch of the boards.

' Be still. No harm comes to thee, my son. I am thy sacrifice! '

He could not see what the woman was about, but heard the clish-clash of her jewellery for many minutes. A match lit up the darkness; he caught the well-known purr and fizzle of grains of incense. Then the room filled with smoke—heavy, aromatic, and stupefying. Through growing drowse he heard the names of devils—of Zulbazan, Son of Eblis, who lives in bazars and paraos, making all the sudden lewd wickedness of wayside halts; of Dulhan, invisible about mosques, the dweller among the slippers of the Faithful, who hinders folk from their prayers; and Musboot, Lord of lies and panic. Huneefa, now whispering in his ear, now talking as from an immense distance, touched him with horrible soft fingers, but Mahbub's grip never shifted from his neck till, relaxing with a sigh, the boy lost his senses.

'Allah! How he fought! We should never have done it but for the drugs. That was his White blood, I take it,' said Mahbub testily. 'Go on with the dawut (invocation). Give him full Protection.'

'O Hearer! Thou that hearest with ears, be present. Listen, O Hearer!' Huneefa moaned, her dead eyes turned to the west. The dark room filled with moanings and snortings.

From the outer balcony, a ponderous figure raised a round bullet head and coughed nervously.

'Do not interrupt this ventriloquial necromanciss, my friend,' it said in English. 'I opine that it is very disturbing to you, but no enlightened observer is jolly well upset.'

'. . . I will lay a plot for their ruin! O Prophet, bear with the unbelievers. Let them alone awhile!' Huneefa's face, turned to the northward, worked horribly, and it was as though voices from the ceiling answered her.

Hurree Babu returned to his note-book, balanced on the window-sill, but his hand shook. Huneefa, in some sort of drugged ecstasy, wrenched herself to and fro as she sat cross-legged by Kim's still head, and called upon devil after devil, in the ancient order of the ritual, binding them to avoid the boy's every action.

'With Him are the keys of the Secret Things! None knoweth them beside Himself. He knoweth that which is in the dry land and in the sea!' Again broke out the unearthly whistling responses.

'I—I apprehend it is not at all malignant in its operation?' said the Babu, watching the throat-muscles quiver and jerk as Huneefa spoke with tongues. 'It—it is not likely that she has killed the boy? If so, I decline to be witness at the trial. . . . What was the last hypothetical devil mentioned?'

'Babuji,' said Mahbub in the vernacular. 'I have no regard for the devils of Hind, but the Sons of Eblis are far otherwise, and whether they be jumalee (well-affected) or jullalee (terrible) they love not Kafirs.'

'Then you think I had better go?' said Hurree Babu, half rising. 'They are, of course, dematerialised phenomena. Spencer says—'

Huneefa's crisis passed, as these things must, in a paroxysm of howling,

with a touch of froth at the lips. She lay spent and motionless beside Kim, and the crazy voices ceased.

' Wah! That work is done. May the boy be better for it; and Huneefa is surely a mistress of dawut. Help haul her aside, Babu. Do not be afraid.'

' How am I to fear the absolutely non-existent? ' said Hurree Babu, talking English to reassure himself. It is an awful thing still to dread the magic that you contemptuously investigate—to collect folk-lore for the Royal Society with a lively belief in all Powers of Darkness.

Mahbub chuckled. He had been out with Hurree on the Road ere now. ' Let us finish the colouring,' said he. ' The boy is well protected if—if the Lords of the Air have ears to hear. I am a sufi (free-thinker), but when one can get blind-sides of a woman, a stallion, or a devil, why go round to invite a kick? Set him upon the way, Babu, and see that old Red Hat does not lead him beyond our reach. I must get back to my horses.'

' All raight,' said Hurree Babu. ' He is at present a curious spectacle.'

.

About third cock-crow, Kim woke after a sleep of thousands of years. Huneefa, in her corner, snored heavily, but Mahbub was gone.

' I hope you were not frightened,' said an oily voice at his elbow. ' I superintended entire operation, which was most interesting from ethnological point of view. It was high-class dawut.'

' Huh! ' said Kim, recognising Hurree Babu, who smiled ingratiatingly.

' And also I had honour to bring down from Lurgan your present costume. I am not in the habit offeecially of carrying such gauds to subordinates, but '—he giggled—' your case is noted as exceptional on the books. I hope Mr. Lurgan will note my action.'

Kim yawned and stretched himself. It was good to turn and twist within loose clothes once again.

' What is this? ' He looked curiously at the heavy duffle-stuff loaded with the scents of the far North.

' Oho! That is inconspicuous dress of chela attached to service of lamaistic lama. Com-plete in every particular,' said Hurree Babu, rolling into the balcony to clean his teeth at a goglet. ' I am of opeenion it is not your old gentleman's precise religion, but rather sub-variant of same. I have contributed rejected notes to " Asiatic Quarterly Review " on these subjects. Now it is curious that the old gentleman himself is totally devoid of religiosity. He is not a dam particular.'

' Do you know him? '

Hurree Babu held up his hand to show he was engaged in the prescribed rites that accompany tooth-cleaning and such things among decently bred Bengalis. Then he recited in English an Arya-Somaj prayer of a theistical nature, and stuffed his mouth with pan and betel.

' Oah yes. I have met him several times at Benares, and also at Buddh Gaya, to interrogate him on religious points and devil-worship. He is pure

agnostic—same as me.'

Huneefa stirred in her sleep, and Hurree Babu jumped nervously to the copper incense-burner, all black and discoloured in the morning-light, rubbed a finger in the accumulated lampblack, and drew it diagonally across his face.

'Who has died in thy house?' asked Kim in the vernacular.

'None. But she may have the Evil Eye—that sorceress,' the Babu replied.

'What dost thou do now, then?'

'I will set thee on thy way to Benares, if thou goest thither, and tell thee what must be known by Us.'

'I go. At what hour runs the te-rain?' He rose to his feet, looked round the desolate chamber and at the yellow-wax face of Huneefa as the low sun stole across the floor. 'Is there money to be paid that witch?'

'No. She has charmed thee against all devils and all dangers—in the name of her devils. It was Mahbub's desire.' In English: 'He is highly obsolete, I think, to indulge in such supersteetion. Why, it is all ventriloquy. Belly-speak—eh?'

Kim snapped his fingers mechanically to avert whatever evil—Mahbub, he knew, meditated none—might have crept in through Huneefa's ministrations; and Hurree giggled once more. But as he crossed the room he was careful not to step in Huneefa's blotched, squat shadow on the boards. Witches—when their time is on them—can lay hold of the heels of a man's soul if he does that.

'Now you must well listen,' said the Babu when they were in the fresh air. 'Part of these ceremonies which we witnessed they include supply of effeecient amulet to those of our Department. If you feel in your neck you will find one small silver amulet, verree cheap. That is ours. Do you understand?'

'Oah yes, hawa-dilli' (a heart-lifter), said Kim, feeling at his neck.

'Huneefa she makes them for two rupees twelve annas with—oh, all sorts of exorcisms. They are quite common, except they are partially black enamel, and there is a paper inside each one full of names of local saints and such things. Thatt is Huneefa's look-out, you see? Huneefa makes them onlee for us, but in case she does not, when we get them we put in, before issue, one small piece of turquoise. Mr. Lurgan, he gives them. There is no other source of supply; but it was me invented all this. It is strictly unoffeecial of course, but convenient for subordinates. Colonel Creighton he does not know. He is European. The turquoise is wrapped in the paper. . . . Yes, that is road to railway station. . . . Now suppose you go with the lama, or with me, I hope, some day, or with Mahbub. Suppose we get into a dam-tight place. I am a fearful man—most fearful—but I tell you I have been in dam-tight places more than hairs on my head. You say: "I am Son of the Charm." Verree good.'

'I do not understand quite. We must not be heard talking English here.'

'That is all raight. I am only Babu showing off my English to you. All we Babus talk English to show off,' said Hurree, flinging his shoulder-cloth jauntily. 'As I was about to say, "Son of the Charm" means that you may be member of the Sat Bhai—the Seven Brothers, which is Hindi and Tantric. It is popularly supposed to be extinct society, but I have written notes to show it is still extant. You see it is all my invention. Verree good. Sat Bhai has many members, and perhaps before they jolly-well-cut-your-throat they may give you just a chance for life. That is useful, anyhow. And, moreover, these foolish natives—if they are not too excited—they always stop to think before they kill a man who says he belongs to any specific organisation. You see? You say then when you are in tight place, "I am Son of the Charm," and you get—perhaps—ah—your second wind. That is only in extreme instances, or to open negotiations with a stranger. Can you quite see? Verree good. But suppose now, I, or any one of the Department, come to you dressed quite different. You would not know me at all unless I choose, I bet you. Some day I will prove it. I come as Ladakhi trader—oh anything—and I say to you: "You want to buy precious stones?" You say: "Do I look like a man who buys precious stones?" Then I say: "Even verree poor man can buy a turquoise or tarkeean."'

'That is kichree—vegetable curry,' said Kim.

'Of course it is. You say: "Let me see the tarkeean." Then I say: "It was cooked by a woman, and perhaps it is bad for your caste." Then you say: "There is no caste when men go to—look for tarkeean." You stop a little between those words, "to—look." That is thee whole secret. The little stop before the words.'

Kim repeated the test-sentence.

'That is all right. Then I will show you my turquoise if there is time, and then you know who I am, and then we exchange views and documents and those-all things. And so it is with any other man of us. We talk sometimes about turquoises and sometimes about tarkeean, but always with that little stop in the words. It is verree easy. First, "Son of the Charm," if you are in a tight place. Perhaps that may help you—perhaps not. Then what I have told you about the tarkeean, if you want to transact offeecial business with a strange man. Of course, at present, you have no offeecial business. You are—ah ha!—supernumerary on probation. Quite unique specimen. If you were Asiatic of birth you might be employed right off; but this half-year of leave is to make you de-Englishised, you see? The lama, he expects you, because I have demi-offeecially informed him you have passed all your examinations, and will soon obtain Government appointment. Oh ho! You are on acting-allowance you see: so if you are called upon to help Sons of the Charm mind you jolly well try. Now I shall say good-bye, my dear fellow, and I hope you—ah—will come out top-side all raight.'

Hurree Babu stepped back a pace or two into the crowd at the entrance

of Lucknow station and—was gone. Kim drew a deep breath and hugged himself all over. The nickel-plated revolver he could feel in the bosom of his sad-coloured robe, the amulet was on his neck; begging-gourd, rosary, and ghost-dagger (Mr. Lurgan had forgotten nothing) were all to hand, with medicine, paint-box, and compass, and in a worn old purse-belt embroidered with porcupine quill-patterns lay a month's pay. Kings could be no richer. He bought sweetmeats in a leaf-cup from a Hindu trader, and ate them with glad rapture till a policeman ordered him off the steps.

CHAPTER XI

Give the man who is not made
 To his trade
Swords to fling and catch again,
Coins to ring and snatch again,
Men to harm and cure again,
Snakes to charm and lure again—
He'll be hurt by his own blade,
By his serpents disobeyed,
By his clumsiness bewrayed,
By the people mocked to scorn.
 So 'tis not with juggler born.
Pinch of dust or withered flower,
 Chance-flung fruit or borrowed staff,
Serve his need and shore his power,
 Bind the spell, or loose the laugh!
 BUT A MAN WHO, ETC., *Op. 15*

Followed a sudden natural reaction.

'Now am I alone—all alone,' he thought. 'In all India is no one so alone as I! If I die to-day, who shall bring the news—and to whom? If I live and God is good, there will be a price upon my head, for I am a Son of the Charm—I, Kim.'

A very few white people, but many Asiatics, can throw themselves into a mazement as it were by repeating their own names over and over again to themselves, letting the mind go free upon speculation as to what is called personal identity. When one grows older, the power, usually, departs, but while it lasts it may descend upon a man at any moment.

'Who is Kim—Kim—Kim?'

He squatted in a corner of the clanging waiting-room, rapt from all other thoughts; hands folded in lap, and pupils contracted to pin-points. In a minute—in another half second—he felt he would arrive at the solution of the tremendous puzzle; but here, as always happens, his mind dropped away from those heights with the rush of a wounded bird, and passing his hand before his eyes, he shook his head.

A long-haired Hindu bairagi (holy man), who had just bought a ticket, halted before him at that moment and stared intently.

'I also have lost it,' he said sadly. 'It is one of the Gates to the Way, but for me it has been shut many years.'

'What is the talk?' said Kim, abashed.

'Thou wast wondering there in thy spirit what manner of thing thy soul might be. The seizure came of a sudden. I know. Who should know but I? Whither goest thou?'

'Toward Kashi' (Benares).

'There are no Gods there. I have proved them. I go to Prayag (Allahabad) for the fifth time—seeking the road to Enlightenment. Of what faith art thou?'

'I too am a Seeker,' said Kim, using one of the lama's pet words. 'Though'—he forgot his Northern dress for the moment—'though Allah alone knoweth what I seek.'

The old fellow slipped the bairagi's crutch under his armpit and sat down on a patch of ruddy leopard's skin as Kim rose at the call for the Benares train.

'Go in hope, little brother,' he said. 'It is a long road to the feet of the One; but thither do we all travel.'

Kim did not feel so lonely after this, and ere he had sat out twenty miles in the crowded compartment, was cheering his neighbours with a string of most wonderful yarns about his own and his master's magical gifts.

Benares struck him as a peculiarly filthy city, though it was pleasant to find how his cloth was respected. At least one-third of the population prays eternally to some group or other of the many million deities, and so revere every sort of holy man. Kim was guided to the Temple of the Tirthankers, about a mile outside the city, near Sarnath, by a chance-met Punjabi farmer —a Kamboh from Jullundur-way who had appealed in vain to every God of his homestead to cure his small son, and was trying Benares as a last resort.

'Thou art from the North?' he asked, shouldering through the press of the narrow, stinking streets much like his own pet bull at home.

'Ay, I know the Punjab. My mother was a Pahareen, but my father came from Amritzar—by Jandiala,' said Kim, oiling his ready tongue for the needs of the Road.

'Jandiala—Jullundur? Oho! Then we be neighbours in some sort, as it were.' He nodded tenderly to the wailing child in his arms. 'Whom dost thou serve?'

'A most holy man at the Temple of the Tirthankers.'

'They are all most holy and—most greedy,' said the Jat with bitterness. 'I have walked the pillars and trodden the temples till my feet are flayed, and the child is no whit better. And the mother being sick too. . . . Hush, then, little one. . . . We changed his name when the fever came. We put him into girl's clothes. There was nothing we did not do, except—I said

to his mother when she bundled me off to Benares—she should have come with me—I said Sakhi Sarwar Sultan would serve us best. We know His generosity, but these down-country Gods are strangers.'

The child turned on the cushion of the huge corded arms and looked at Kim through heavy eyelids.

'And was it all worthless?' Kim asked, with easy interest.

'All worthless—all worthless,' said the child, lips cracking with fever.

'The Gods have given him a good mind, at least,' said the father proudly. 'To think he should have listened so cleverly. Yonder is thy temple. Now I am a poor man,—many priests have dealt with me,—but my son is my son, and if a gift to thy master can cure him—I am at my very wits' end.'

Kim considered for a while, tingling with pride. Three years ago he would have made prompt profit on the situation and gone his way without a thought; but now, the very respect the Jat paid him proved that he was a man. Moreover, he had tasted fever once or twice already, and knew enough to recognise starvation when he saw it.

'Call him forth and I will give him a bond on my best yoke, so that the child is cured.'

Kim halted at the carved outer door of the temple. A white-clad Oswal banker from Ajmir, his sins of usury new wiped out, asked him what he did.

'I am chela to Teshoo Lama, an Holy One from Bhotiyal—within there. He bade me come. I wait. Tell him.'

'Do not forget the child,' cried the importunate Jat over his shoulder, and then bellowed in Punjabi: 'O Holy One—O disciple of the Holy One— O Gods above all the Worlds—behold affliction sitting at the gate!' That cry is so common in Benares that the passers never turned their heads.

The Oswal, at peace with mankind, carried the message into the darkness behind him, and the easy, uncounted Eastern minutes slid by; for the lama was asleep in his cell, and no priest would wake him. When the click of his rosary again broke the hush of the inner court where the calm images of the Arhats stand, a novice whispered, 'Thy chela is here,' and the old man strode forth, forgetting the end of that prayer.

Hardly had the tall figure shown in the doorway than the Jat ran before him, and, lifting up the child, cried: 'Look upon this, Holy One; and if the Gods will, he lives—he lives!'

He fumbled in his waist-belt and drew out a small silver coin.

'What is now?' The lama's eyes turned to Kim. It was noticeable he spoke far clearer Urdu than long ago, under Zam-Zammah; but the father would allow no private talk.

'It is no more than a fever,' said Kim. 'The child is not well fed.'

'He sickens at everything, and his mother is not here.'

'If it be permitted, I may cure, Holy One.'

'What! Have they made thee a healer? Wait here,' said the lama, and he sat down by the Jat upon the lowest step of the temple, while Kim,

looking out of the corner of his eyes, slowly opened the little betel-box. He had dreamed dreams at school of returning to the lama as a Sahib—of chaffing the old man before he revealed himself—boy's dreams all. There was more drama in this abstracted, brow-puckered search through the tabloid-bottles, with a pause here and there for thought and a muttered invocation between whiles. Quinine he had in tablets, and dark brown meat-lozenges—beef most probably, but that was not his business. The little thing would not eat, but it sucked at a lozenge greedily, and said it liked the salt taste.

'Take then these six.' Kim handed them to the man. 'Praise the Gods, and boil three in milk; other three in water. After he has drunk the milk give him this (it was the half of a quinine pill), and wrap him warm. Give him the water of the other three, and the other half of this white pill when he wakes. Meantime, here is another brown medicine that he may suck at on the way home.'

'Gods, what wisdom!' said the Kamboh, snatching.

It was as much as Kim could remember of his own treatment in a bout of autumn malaria—if you except the patter that he added to impress the lama.

'Now go! Come again in the morning.'

'But the price—the price,' said the Jat, and threw back his sturdy shoulders. 'My son is my son. Now that he will be whole again, how shall I go back to his mother and say I took help by the wayside and did not even give a bowl of curds in return?'

'They are alike, these Jats,' said Kim softly. 'The Jat stood on his dunghill and the King's elephants went by. "O driver," said he, "what will you sell those little donkeys for?"'

The Jat burst into a roar of laughter, stifled with apologies to the lama. 'It is the saying of my own country—the very talk of it. So are we Jats all. I will come to-morrow with the child; and the blessing of the Gods of the Homesteads—who are good little Gods—be on you both. . . . Now, son, we grow strong again. Do not spit it out, little Princeling! King of my Heart, do not spit it out, and we shall be strong men, wrestlers and club-wielders, by morning.'

He moved away, crooning and mumbling. The lama turned to Kim, and all the loving old soul of him looked out through his narrow eyes.

'To heal the sick is to acquire merit; but first one gets knowledge. That was wisely done, O Friend of all the World.'

'I was made wise by thee, Holy One,' said Kim, forgetting the little play just ended; forgetting St. Xavier's; forgetting his white blood; forgetting even the Great Game as he stooped, Mohammedan fashion, to touch his master's feet in the dust of the Jain temple. 'My teaching I owe to thee. I have eaten thy bread three years. My time is finished. I am loosed from the schools. I come to thee.'

'Herein is my reward. Enter! Enter! And is all well?' They passed to the inner court, where the afternoon sun sloped golden across. 'Stand that

I may see. So!' He peered critically. 'It is no longer a child, but a man, ripened in wisdom, walking as a physician. I did well—I did well when I gave thee up to the armed men on that black night. Dost thou remember our first day under Zam-Zammah?'

'Ay,' said Kim. 'Dost thou remember when I leapt off the carriage the first day I went to—'

'The Gates of Learning? Truly. And the day that we ate the cakes together at the back of the river by Nucklao. Aha! Many times hast thou begged for me, but that day I begged for thee.'

'Good reason,' quoth Kim. 'I was then a scholar in the Gates of Learning, and attired as a Sahib. Do not forget, Holy One,' he went on playfully, 'I am still a Sahib—by thy favour.'

'True. And a Sahib in most high esteem. Come to my cell, chela.'

'How is that known to thee?'

The lama smiled. 'First by means of letters from the kindly priest whom we met in the camp of armed men; but he is now gone to his own country, and I sent the money to his brother.' Colonel Creighton, who had succeeded to the trusteeship when Father Victor went to England with the Mavericks, was hardly the chaplain's brother. 'But I do not well understand Sahibs' letters. They must be interpreted to me. I chose a surer way. Many times when I returned from my Search to this temple, which has always been a nest to me, there came one seeking Enlightenment—a man from Leh—that had been, he said, a Hindu, but wearied of all those Gods.' The lama pointed to the Arhats.

'A fat man?' said Kim, a twinkle in his eye.

'Very fat; but I perceived in a little his mind was wholly given up to useless things—such as devils and charms and the form and fashion of our tea-drinkings in the monasteries, and by what road we initiated the novices. A man abounding in questions; but he was a friend of thine, chela. He told me that thou wast on the road to much honour as a scribe. And I see thou art a physician.'

'Yes, that am I—a scribe, when I am a Sahib, but it is set aside when I come as thy disciple. I have accomplished the years appointed for a Sahib.'

'As it were a novice?' said the lama, nodding his head. 'Art thou freed from the schools? I would not have thee unripe.'

'I am all free. In due time I take service under the Government as a scribe—'

'Not as a warrior. That is well.'

'But first I come to wander—with thee. Therefore I am here. Who begs for thee, these days?' he went on quickly. The ice was thin.

'Very often I beg myself; but, as thou knowest, I am seldom here, except when I come to look again at my disciple. From one end to another of Hind have I travelled afoot and in the te-rain. A great and a wonderful land! But here, when I put in, is as though I were in my own Bhotiyal.'

He looked round the little clean cell complacently. A low cushion gave

him a seat, on which he had disposed himself in the cross-legged attitude of the Bodhisat emerging from meditation; a black teak-wood table, not twenty inches high, set with copper tea-cups, was before him. In one corner stood a tiny altar, also of heavily carved teak, bearing a copper-gilt image of the seated Buddha and fronted by a lamp, an incense-holder, and a pair of copper flower-pots.

'The Keeper of the Images in the Wonder House acquired merit by giving me these a year since,' he said, following Kim's eye. 'When one is far from one's own land such things carry remembrance; and we must reverence the Lord for that He showed the Way. See!' He pointed to a curiously-built mound of coloured rice crowned with a fantastic metal ornament. 'When I was abbot in my own place—before I came to better knowledge—I made that offering daily. It is the Sacrifice of the Universe to the Lord. Thus do we of Bhotiyal offer all the world daily to the Excellent Law. And I do it even now, though I know that the Excellent One is beyond all pinchings and pattings.' He snuffed from his gourd.

'It is well done, Holy One,' Kim murmured, sinking at ease on the cushions, very happy and rather tired.

'And also,' the old man chuckled, 'I write pictures of the Wheel of Life. Three days to a picture. I was busied on it—or it may be I shut my eyes a little—when they brought word of thee. It is good to have thee here: I will show thee my art—not for pride's sake, but because thou must learn. The Sahibs have not all this world's wisdom.'

He drew from under the table a sheet of strangely scented yellow Chinese paper, the brushes, and slab of India ink. In cleanest, severest outline he had traced the Great Wheel with its six spokes, whose centre is the conjoined Hog, Snake, and Dove (Ignorance, Anger, and Lust), and whose compartments are all the heavens and hells, and all the chances of human life. Men say that the Bodhisat Himself first drew it with grains of rice upon dust, to teach His disciples the cause of things. Many ages have crystallised it into a most wonderful convention crowded with hundreds of little figures whose every line carries a meaning. Few can translate the picture-parable; there are not twenty in all the world who can draw it surely without a copy: of those who can both draw and expound are but three.

'I have a little learned to draw,' said Kim. 'But this is a marvel beyond marvels.'

'I have written it for many years,' said the lama. 'Time was when I could write it all between one lamp-lighting and the next. I will teach thee the art—after due preparation; and I will show thee the meaning of the Wheel.'

'We take the Road, then?'

'The Road and our Search. I was but waiting for thee. It was made plain to me in a hundred dreams—notably one that came upon the night of the day that the Gates of Learning first shut—that without thee I should never find my River. Again and again, as thou knowest, I put this from me,

fearing an illusion. Therefore I would not take thee with me that day at Lucknow, when we ate the cakes. I would not take thee till the time was ripe and auspicious. From the Hills to the Sea, from the Sea to the Hills have I gone, but it was vain. Then I remembered the " Jataka." '

He told Kim the story of the elephant with the leg-iron, as he had told it so often to the Jain priests.

' Further testimony is not needed,' he ended serenely. ' Thou wast sent for an aid. That aid removed, my Search came to naught. Therefore we will go out again together, and our Search is sure.'

' Whither go we? '

' What matters, Friend of all the World? The Search, I say, is sure. If need be, the River will break from the ground before us. I acquired merit when I sent thee to the Gates of Learning, and gave thee the jewel that is Wisdom. Thou didst return, I saw even now, a follower of Sakyamuni, the Physician, whose altars are many in Bhotiyal. It is sufficient. We are together, and all things are as they were—Friend of all the World—Friend of the Stars—my chela! '

Then they talked of matters secular; but it was noticeable that the lama never demanded any details of life at St. Xavier's, nor showed the faintest curiosity as to the manners and customs of Sahibs. His mind moved all in the past, and he revived every step of their wonderful first journey together, rubbing his hands and chuckling, till it pleased him to curl himself up into the sudden sleep of old age.

Kim watched the last dusty sunshine fade out of the court, and played with his ghost-dagger and rosary. The clamour of Benares, oldest of all earth's cities awake before the Gods, day and night, beat round the walls as the sea's roar round a breakwater. Now and again, a Jain priest crossed the court, with some small offering to the images, and swept the path about him lest by chance he should take the life of a living thing. A lamp twinkled, and there followed the sound of a prayer. Kim watched the stars as they rose one after another in the still, sticky dark, till he fell asleep at the foot of the altar. That night he dreamed in Hindustanee, with never an English word. . . .

' Holy One, there is the child to whom we gave the medicine,' he said, about three o'clock in the morning, when the lama, also waking from dreams, would have fared forth on pilgrimage. ' The Jat will be here at the light.'

' I am well answered. In my haste I would have done a wrong.' He sat down on the cushions and returned to his rosary. ' Surely old folk are as children,' he said pathetically. ' They desire a matter—behold, it must be done at once, or they fret and weep! Many times when I was upon the Road I have been ready to stamp with my feet at the hindrance of an ox-cart in the way, or a mere cloud of dust. It was not so when I was a man—a long time ago. None the less it is wrongful— '

' But thou art indeed old, Holy One.'

' The thing was done. A Cause was put out into the world, and, old or

young, sick or sound, knowing or unknowing, who can rein in the effect of that Cause? Does the Wheel hang still if a child spin it—or a drunkard? Chela, this is a great and a terrible world.'

'I think it good,' Kim yawned. 'What is there to eat? I have not eaten since yesterday even.'

'I had forgotten thy need. Yonder is good Bhotiyal tea and cold rice.'

'We cannot walk far on such stuff.' Kim felt all the European's lust for flesh-meat, which is not accessible in a Jain temple. Yet, instead of going out at once with the begging-bowl, he stayed his stomach on slabs of cold rice till the full dawn. It brought the farmer, voluble, stuttering with gratitude.

'In the night the fever broke and the sweat came,' he cried. 'Feel here—his skin is fresh and new! He esteemed the salt lozenges, and took milk with greed.' He drew the cloth from the child's face, and it smiled sleepily at Kim. A little knot of Jain priests, silent but all-observant, gathered by the temple door. They knew, and Kim knew that they knew, how the old lama had met his disciple. Being courteous folk, they had not obtruded themselves overnight by presence, word, or gesture. Wherefore Kim repaid them as the sun rose.

'Thank the Gods of the Jains, brother,' he said, not knowing how those Gods were named. 'The fever is indeed broken.'

'Look! See!' The lama beamed in the background upon his hosts of three years. 'Was there ever such a chela? He follows our Lord the Healer.'

Now the Jains officially recognise all the Gods of the Hindu creed, as well as the Lingam and the Snake. They wear the Brahminical thread; they adhere to every claim of Hindu caste-law. But, because they knew and loved the lama, because he was an old man, because he sought the Way, because he was their guest, and because he collogued long of nights with the head-priest—as free-thinking a metaphysician as ever split one hair into seventy—they murmured assent.

'Remember,'—Kim bent over the child,—'this trouble may come again.'

'Not if thou hast the proper spell,' said the father.

'But in a little while we go away.'

'True,' said the lama to all the Jains. 'We go now together upon the Search whereof I have often spoken. I waited till my chela was ripe. Behold him! We go North. Never again shall I look upon this place of my rest, O people of good will.'

'But I am not a beggar.' The cultivator rose to his feet, clutching the child.

'Be still. Do not trouble the Holy One,' a priest cried.

'Go,' Kim whispered. 'Meet us again under the big railway bridge, and for the sake of all the Gods of our Punjab, bring food—curry, pulse, cakes fried in fat, and sweetmeats. Specially sweetmeats. Be swift!'

The pallor of hunger suited Kim very well as he stood, tall and slim, in

his sad-coloured, sweeping robes, one hand on his rosary and the other in the attitude of benediction, faithfully copied from the lama. An English observer might have said that he looked rather like the young saint of a stained-glass window, whereas he was but a growing lad faint with emptiness.

Long and formal were the farewells, thrice ended and thrice renewed. The Seeker—he who had invited the lama to that haven from far-away Tibet, a silver-faced, hairless ascetic—took no part in it, but meditated, as always, alone among the images. The others were very human; pressing small comforts upon the old man,—a betel-box, a fine new iron pencase, a food-bag, and such like,—warning him against the dangers of the world without, and prophesying a happy end to the Search. Meantime Kim, lonelier than ever, squatted on the steps, and swore to himself in the language of St. Xavier's.

'But it is my own fault,' he concluded. 'With Mahbub, I ate Mahbub's bread, or Lurgan Sahib's. At St. Xavier's, three meals a day. Here I must jolly well look out for myself. Besides, I am not in good training. How I could eat a plate of beef now! . . . Is it finished, Holy One?'

The lama, both hands raised, intoned a final blessing in ornate Chinese. 'I must lean on thy shoulder,' said he, as the temple-gates closed. 'We grow stiff, I think.'

The weight of a six-foot man is not light to steady through miles of crowded streets, and Kim, loaded down with bundles and packages for the way, was glad to reach the shadow of the railway bridge.

'Here we eat,' he said resolutely, as the Kamboh, blue-robed and smiling, hove in sight, a basket in one hand and the child on the other.

'Fall to, Holy Ones!' he cried from fifty yards. (They were by the shoal under the first bridge-span, out of sight of hungry priests.) 'Rice and good curry, cakes all warm and well scented with hing (asafœtida), curds and sugar. King of my fields,' this to the small son, 'let us show these holy men that we Jats of Jullundur can pay a service. . . . I had heard the Jains would eat nothing that they had not cooked, but truly'—he looked away politely over the broad river—'where there is no eye there is no caste.'

'And we,' said Kim, turning his back and heaping a leaf-platter for the lama, 'are beyond all castes.'

They gorged themselves on the good food in silence. Nor till he had licked the last of the sticky sweet-stuff from his little finger did Kim note that the Kamboh too was girt for travel.

'If our roads lie together,' he said roughly, 'I go with thee. One does not often find a worker of miracles, and the child is still weak. But I am not altogether a reed.' He picked up his lathi—a five-foot male-bamboo ringed with bands of polished iron—and flourished it in the air. 'The Jats are called quarrelsome, but that is not true. Except when we are crossed, we are like our own buffaloes.'

'So be it,' said Kim. 'A good stick is a good reason.'

The lama gazed placidly up-stream, where in long, smudged perspective

the ceaseless columns of smoke go up from the burning-ghats by the river. Now and again, despite all municipal regulations, the fragment of a half-burned body bobbed by on the full current.

'But for thee,' said the Kamboh to Kim, drawing his child into his hairy breast, 'I might to-day have gone thither—with this one. The priests tell us that Benares is holy—which none doubt—and desirable to die in. But I do not know their Gods, and they ask for money; and when one has done one worship a shaved-head vows it is of none effect except one do another. Wash here! Wash there! Pour, drink, lave, and scatter flowers—but always pay the priests. No, the Punjab for me, and the soil of the Jullundur-doab for the best soil in it.'

'I have said many times—in the temple I think—that if need be, the River will open at our feet. We will therefore go North,' said the lama, rising. 'I remember a pleasant place, set about with fruit-trees, where one can walk in meditation—and the air is cooler there. It comes from the Hills and the snow of the Hills.'

'What is the name? ' said Kim.

'How should I know? Didst thou not—no, that was after the Army rose out of the earth and took thee away. I abode there in meditation in a room against the dove-cot—except when she talked eternally.'

'Oho! the woman from Kulu. That is by Saharunpore,' Kim laughed.

'How does the spirit move thy master? Does he go afoot, for the sake of past sins? ' the Jat demanded cautiously. 'It is a far cry to Delhi.'

'No,' said Kim. 'I will beg a tikkut for the te-rain.' One does not own to the possession of money in India.

'Then in the name of the Gods, let us take the fire-carriage. My son is best in his mother's arms. The Government has brought on us many taxes, but it gives us one good thing—the te-rain that joins friends and unites the anxious. A wonderful matter is the te-rain.'

They all piled into it a couple of hours later, and slept through the heat of the day. The Kamboh plied Kim with ten thousand questions as to the lama's walk and work in life, and received some curious answers. Kim was content to be where he was, to look out upon the flat North-Western landscape, and to talk to the changing mob of fellow-passengers. Even to-day, tickets and ticket-clipping are dark oppression to Indian rustics. They do not understand why, when they have paid for a magic piece of paper, strangers should punch great pieces out of the charm. So long and furious are the debates between travellers and Eurasian ticket-collectors. Kim assisted at two or three with grave advice, meant to darken council and to show off his wisdom before the lama and the admiring Kamboh. But at Somna Road the Fates sent him a matter to think upon. There tumbled into the compartment, as the train was moving off, a mean, lean little person—a Mahratta, so far as Kim could judge by the cock of the tight turban. His face was cut, his muslin upper-garment was badly torn, and one leg was bandaged. He told them that a country-cart had upset and nearly slain him:

he was going to Delhi, where his son lived. Kim watched him closely. If, as he asserted, he had been rolled over and over on the earth, there should have been signs of gravel-rash on the skin. But all his injuries seemed clean cuts, and a mere fall from a cart could not cast a man into such extremity of terror. As, with shaking fingers, he knotted up the torn cloth about his neck he laid bare an amulet of the kind called a keeper-up of the heart. Now, amulets are common enough, but they are not generally strung on square-plaited copper wire, and still fewer amulets bear black enamel on silver. There were none except the Kamboh and the lama in the compartment, which, luckily, was of an old type with solid ends. Kim made as to scratch in his bosom, and thereby lifted his own amulet. The Mahratta's face changed altogether at the sight, and he disposed the amulet fairly on his breast.

'Yes,' he went on to the Kamboh, 'I was in haste, and the cart, driven by a bastard, bound its wheel in a water-cut, and besides the harm done to me there was lost a full dish of tarkeean. I was not a Son of the Charm (a lucky man) that day.'

'That was a great loss,' said Kamboh, withdrawing interest. His experience of Benares had made his suspicious.

'Who cooked it?' said Kim.

'A woman.' The Mahratta raised his eyes.

'But all women can cook tarkeean,' said the Kamboh. 'It is a good curry, as I know.'

'Oh, yes, it is a good curry,' said the Mahratta.

'And cheap,' said Kim. 'But what about caste?'

'Oh, there is no caste where men go to—look for tarkeean,' the Mahratta replied, in the prescribed cadence. 'Of whose service art thou?'

'Of the service of this Holy One.' Kim pointed to the happy, drowsy lama, who woke with a jerk at the well-loved word.

'Ah, he was sent from Heaven to aid me. He is called the Friend of all the World. He is also called the Friend of the Stars. He walks as a physician—his time being ripe. Great is his wisdom.'

'And a Son of the Charm,' said Kim under his breath, as the Kamboh made haste to prepare a pipe lest the Mahratta should beg.

'And who is that?' the Mahratta asked, glancing sideways nervously.

'One whose child I—we have cured, who lies under great debt to us.— Sit by the window, man from Jullundur. Here is a sick one.'

'Humph! I have no desire to mix with chance-met wastrels. My ears are not long. I am not a woman wishing to overhear secrets.' The Jat slid himself heavily into a far corner.

'Art thou anything of a healer? I am ten leagues deep in calamity,' cried the Mahratta, picking up the cue.

'The man is cut and bruised all over. I go about to cure him,' Kim retorted. 'None interfered between thy babe and me.'

'I am rebuked,' said the Kamboh meekly. 'I am thy debtor for the

life of my son. Thou art a miracle-worker—I know it.'

'Show me the cuts.' Kim bent over the Mahratta's neck, his heart nearly choking him; for this was the Great Game with a vengeance. 'Now, tell thy tale swiftly, brother, while I say a charm.'

'I come from the South, where my work lay. One of us they slew by the roadside. Hast thou heard?' Kim shook his head. He, of course, knew nothing of E.23's predecessor, slain down South in the habit of an Arab trader. 'Having found a certain letter which I was sent to seek, I came away. I escaped from the city and ran to Mhow. So sure was I that none knew, I did not change my face. At Mhow a woman brought charge against me of theft of jewellery in that city which I had left. Then I saw the cry was out against me. I ran from Mhow by night, bribing the police, who had been bribed to hand me over without question to my enemies in the South. Then I lay in old Chitor city a week, a penitent in a temple, but I could not get rid of the letter which was my charge. I buried it under the Queen's Stone, at Chitor, in the place known to us all.'

Kim did not know, but not for worlds would he have broken the thread.

'At Chitor, look you, I was all in Kings' country; for Kotah to the east is beyond the Queen's law, and east again lie Jeypur and Gwalior. Neither love spies, and there is no justice. I was hunted like a wet jackal; but I broke through at Bandakui, where I heard there was a charge against me of murder in the city I had left—of the murder of a boy. They have both the corpse and the witnesses waiting.'

'But cannot the Government protect?'

'We of the Game are beyond protection. If we die, we die. Our names are blotted from the book. That is all. At Bandakui, where lives one of us, I thought to slip the scent by changing my face, and so made me a Mahratta. Then I came to Agra, and would have turned back to Chitor to recover the letter. So sure I was I had slipped them. Therefore I did not send a tar (telegram) to any one saying where the letter lay. I wished the credit of it all.'

Kim nodded. He understood that feeling well.

'But at Agra, walking in the streets, a man cried a debt against me, and approaching with many witnesses, would hale me to the courts then and there. Oh, they are clever in the South! He recognised me as his agent for cotton. May he burn in Hell for it!'

'And wast thou?'

'O fool! I was the man they sought for the matter of the letter! I ran into the Fleshers' Ward and came out by the House of the Jew, who feared a riot and pushed me forth. I came afoot to Somna Road—I had only money for my tikkut to Delhi—and there, while I lay in a ditch with a fever, one sprang out of the bushes and beat me and cut me and searched me from head to foot. Within earshot of the te-rain it was!'

'Why did he not slay thee out of hand?'

'They are not so foolish. If I am taken in Delhi at the instance of lawyers,

upon a proven charge of murder, my body is handed over to the State that desires it. I go back guarded, and then—I die slowly for an example to the rest of us. The South is not my country. I run in circles—like a goat with one eye. I have not eaten for two days. I am marked '—he touched the filthy bandage on his leg—' so that they will know me at Delhi.'

' Thou art safe in the te-rain, at least.'

' Live a year at the Great Game and tell me that again! The wires will be out against me at Delhi, describing every tear and rag upon me. Twenty— a hundred, if need be—will have seen me slay that boy. And thou art use-less! '

Kim knew enough of native methods of attack not to doubt that the case would be deadly complete—even to the corpse. The Mahratta twitched his fingers with pain from time to time. The Kamboh in his corner glared sullenly; the lama was busy over his beads; and Kim, fumbling doctor-fashion at the man's neck, thought out his plan between invocations.

' Hast thou a charm to change my shape? Else I am dead. Five—ten minutes alone, if I had not been so pressed, and I might— '

' Is he cured yet, miracle-worker? ' said the Kamboh jealously. ' Thou hast chanted long enough.'

' Nay. There is no cure for his hurts, as I see, except he sit for three days in the habit of a bairagi.' This is a common penance, often imposed on a fat trader by his spiritual teacher.

' One priest always goes about to make another priest,' was the retort. Like most grossly superstitious folk, the Kamboh could not keep his tongue from deriding his Church.

' Will thy son be a priest, then? It is time he took more of my quinine.'

' We Jats are all buffaloes,' said the Kamboh, softening anew.

Kim rubbed a finger-tip of bitterness on the child's trusting little lips. ' I have asked for nothing,' he said sternly to the father, ' except food. Dost thou grudge me that? I go to heal another man. Have I thy leave—Prince? '

Up flew the man's huge paws in supplication. ' Nay—nay. Do not mock me thus.'

' It pleases me to cure this sick one. Thou shalt acquire merit by aiding. What colour ash is there in thy pipe-bowl? White. That is auspicious. Was there raw turmeric among thy food-stuffs? '

' I—I— '

' Open thy bundle! '

It was the usual collection of small oddments: bits of cloth, quack medicines, cheap fairings, a clothful of atta,—grayish, rough-ground native flour,—twists of down-country tobacco, tawdry pipe-stems, and a packet of curry-stuff, all wrapped in a quilt. Kim turned it over with the air of a wise warlock, muttering a Mohammedan invocation.

' This is wisdom I learned from the Sahibs,' he whispered to the lama; and here, when one thinks of his training at Lurgan's, he spoke no more than the truth. ' There is a great evil in this man's fortune, as shown by the

stars, which—which troubles him. Shall I take it away?'

'Friend of the Stars, thou hast done well in all things. Let it be at thy pleasure. Is it another healing?'

'Quick! Be quick!' gasped the Mahratta. 'The train may stop.'

'A healing against the shadow of death,' said Kim, mixing the Kamboh's flour with the mingled charcoal and tobacco ash in the red-earth bowl of the pipe. E.23, without a word, slipped off his turban and shook down his long black hair.

'That is my food—priest,' the Jat growled.

'A buffalo in the temple! Hast thou dared to look even thus far?' said Kim. 'I must do mysteries before fools; but have a care for thy eyes. Is there a film before them already? I save the babe, and for return thou—oh, shameless!' The man flinched at the direct gaze, for Kim was wholly in earnest. 'Shall I curse thee, or shall I—' He picked up the outer cloth of the bundle and threw it over the bowed head. 'Dare so much as to think a wish to see, and—and—even I cannot save thee. Sit! Be dumb!'

'I am blind—dumb. Forbear to curse! Co—come, child; we will play a game of hiding. Do not, for my sake, look from under the cloth.'

'I see hope,' said E.23. 'What is thy scheme?'

'This comes next,' said Kim, plucking the thin body-shirt. E.23 hesitated, with all a North-West man's dislike of baring his body.

'What is caste to a cut throat?' said Kim, rending it to the waist. 'We must make thee a yellow Saddhu all over. Strip—strip swiftly, and shake thy hair over thy eyes while I scatter the ash. Now, a caste-mark on thy forehead.' He drew from his bosom the little Survey paint-box and a cake of crimson lake.

'Art thou only a beginner?' said E.23, labouring literally for the dear life, as he slid out of his body-wrappings and stood clear in the loin-cloth while Kim splashed in a noble caste-mark on the ash-smeared brow.

'But two days entered to the Game, brother,' Kim replied. 'Smear more ash on the bosom.'

'Hast thou met—a physician of sick pearls?' He switched out his long, tight-rolled turban-cloth and, with swiftest hands, rolled it over and under about his loins into the intricate devices of a Saddhu's cincture.

'Hah! Dost thou know his touch, then? He was my teacher for a while. We must bar thy legs. Ash cures wounds. Smear it again.'

'I was his pride once, but thou art almost better. The Gods are kind to us! Give me that.'

It was a tin box of opium pills among the rubbish of the Jat's bundle. E.23 gulped down a half handful. 'They are good against hunger, fear, and chill. And they make the eyes red too,' he explained. 'Now I shall have heart to play the Game. We lack only a Saddhu's tongs. What of the old clothes?'

Kim rolled them small, and stuffed them into the slack folds of his tunic. With a yellow-ochre paint cake he smeared the legs and breast, great

streaks against the background of flour, ash, and turmeric.

'The blood on them is enough to hang thee, brother.'

'May be; but no need to throw them out of the window. . . . It is finished.' His voice thrilled with a boy's pure delight in the Game. 'Turn and look, O Jat!'

'The Gods protect us,' said the hooded Kamboh, emerging like a buffalo from the reeds. 'But—whither went the Mahratta? What hast thou done?'

Kim had been trained by Lurgan Sahib; and E.23, by virtue of his business, was no bad actor. In place of the tremulous, shrinking trader there lolled against the corner an all but naked, ash-smeared, ochre-barred, dusty-haired Saddhu, his swollen eyes—opium takes quick effect on an empty stomach—luminous with insolence and bestial lust, his legs crossed under him, Kim's brown rosary round his neck, and a scant yard of worn, flowered chintz on his shoulders. The child buried his face in his amazed father's arms.

'Look up, Princeling! We travel with warlocks, but they will not hurt thee. Oh, do not cry. . . . What is the sense of curing a child one day and killing him with fright the next?'

'The child will be fortunate all his life. He has seen a great healing. When I was a child I made clay men and horses.'

'I have made them too. Sir Banas, he comes in the night and makes them all alive at the back of our kitchen-midden,' piped the child.

'And so thou art not frightened at anything. Eh, Prince?'

'I was frightened because my father was frightened. I felt his arms shake.'

'Oh, chicken-man,' said Kim, and even the abashed Jat laughed. 'I have done a healing on this poor trader. He must forsake his gains and his account-books, and sit by the wayside three nights to overcome the malignity of his enemies. The Stars are against him.'

'The fewer money-lenders the better, say I; but, Saddhu or no Saddhu, he should pay for my stuff on his shoulders.'

'So? But that is thy child on thy shoulder—given over to the burning-ghat not two days ago. There remains one thing more. I did this charm in thy presence because need was great. I changed his shape and his soul. None the less, if, by any chance, O man from Jullundur, thou rememberest what thou hast seen, either among the elders sitting under the village tree, or in thy own house, or in company of thy priest when be blesses thy cattle, a murrain will come among the buffaloes, and a fire in thy thatch, and rats in the corn-bin, and the curse of our Gods upon thy fields that they may be barren before thy feet and after thy ploughshare.' This was part of an old curse picked up from a faquir by the Taksali Gate in the days of Kim's innocence. It lost nothing by repetition.

'Cease, Holy One! In mercy, cease!' cried the Jat. 'Do not curse the household. I saw nothing! I heard nothing! I am thy cow!' and he made

to grab at Kim's bare foot beating rhythmically on the carriage floor.

' But since thou hast been permitted to aid me in the matter of a pinch of flour and a little opium and such trifles as I have honoured by using in my art, so will the Gods return a blessing,' and he gave it at length, to the man's immense relief. It was one that he had learned from Lurgan Sahib.

The lama stared through his spectacles as he had not stared at the business of disguisement.

' Friend of the Stars,' he said at last, ' thou hast acquired great wisdom. Beware that it do not give birth to pride. No man having the Law before his eyes speaks hastily of any matter which he has seen or encountered.'

' No—no—no indeed,' cried the former, fearful lest the master should be minded to improve on the pupil. E.23, with relaxed mouth, gave himself up to the opium that is meat, tobacco, and medicine to the spent Asiatic.

So, in a silence of awe and great miscomprehension, they slid into Delhi about lamp-lighting time.

CHAPTER XII

' Who hath desired the Sea—the sight of salt-water unbounded?
The heave and the halt and the hurl and the crash of the comber wind-
 hounded?
The sleek-barrelled swell before storm—gray, foamless, enormous, and
 growing?
Stark calm on the lap of the Line—or the crazy-eyed hurricane blowing?
His Sea in no showing the same—his Sea and the same 'neath all showing—
 His Sea that his being fulfils?
So and no otherwise—so and no otherwise Hill-men desire their Hills! '

' I have found my heart again,' said E.23, under cover of the platform's tumult. ' Hunger and fear make men dazed, or I might have thought of this escape before. I was right. They come to hunt for me. Thou hast saved my head.'

A group of yellow-trousered Punjab policemen, headed by a hot and perspiring young Englishman, parted the crowd about the carriages. Behind them, inconspicuous as a cat, ambled a small fat person who looked like a lawyer's tout.

' See the young Sahib reading from a paper. My description is in his hand,' said E.23. ' They go carriage by carriage, like fisher-folk netting a pool.'

When the procession reached their compartment, E.23 was counting his beads with a steady jerk of the wrist; while Kim jeered at him for being so drugged as to have lost the ringed fire-tongs which are the Saddhu's distinguishing mark. The lama, deep in meditation, stared straight before him; and the farmer, glancing furtively, gathered up his belongings.

'Nothing here but a parcel of holy-bolies,' said the Englishman aloud, and passed on amid a ripple of uneasiness; for native police mean extortion to the native all India over.

'The trouble now,' whispered E.23, 'lies in sending a wire as to the place where I hid that letter I was sent to find. I cannot go to the tar-office in this guise.'

'Is it not enough I have saved thy neck?'

'Not if the work be left unfinished. Did never the healer of sick pearls tell thee so? Comes another Sahib! Ah!'

This was a tallish, sallowish District Superintendent of Police,—belt, helmet, polished spurs and all,—strutting and twirling his dark moustache.

'What fools are these Police Sahibs!' said Kim genially.

E.23 glanced up under his eyelids. 'It is well said,' he muttered in a changed voice. 'I go to drink water. Keep my place.'

He blundered out almost into the Englishman's arms, and was bad-worded in clumsy Urdu.

'Tum-mut? You drunk? You mustn't bang about as though Delhi station belonged to you, my friend.'

E.23, not moving a muscle of his countenance, answered with a stream of the filthiest abuse, at which Kim naturally rejoiced. It reminded him of the drummer-boys and the barrack-sweepers at Umballa in the terrible time of his first schooling.

'My good fool,' the Englishman drawled. 'Nicklejao! Go back to your carriage.'

Step by step, withdrawing deferentially, and dropping his voice, the yellow Saddhu clomb back to the carriage, cursing the D. S. P. to remotest posterity by—here Kim almost jumped—by the curse of the Queen's Stone, by the writing under the Queen's Stone, and by an assortment of Gods with wholly new names.

'I don't know what you're saying,'—the Englishman flushed angrily, —'but it's some piece of blasted impertinence. Come out of that!'

E.23, affecting to misunderstand, gravely produced his ticket, which the Englishman wrenched angrily from his hand.

'Oh zoolum! What oppression!' growled the Jat from his corner. 'All for the sake of a jest too.' He had been grinning at the freedom of the Saddhu's tongue. 'Thy charms do not work well to-day, Holy One!'

The Saddhu followed the policeman, fawning and supplicating. The ruck of passengers, busy with their babies and their bundles, had not noticed the affair. Kim slipped out behind him; for it flashed through his head that he had heard this angry, stupid Sahib discoursing loud personalities to an old lady near Umballa three years ago.

'It is well,' the Saddhu whispered, jammed in the calling, shouting, bewildered press—a Persian greyhound between his feet and a cadgeful of yelling hawks under charge of a Rajput falconer in the small of his back. 'He has gone now to send word of the letter which I hid. They told me

he was in Peshawur. I might have known that he is like the crocodile—always at the other ford. He has saved me from present calamity, but I owe my life to thee.'

'Is he also one of Us?' Kim ducked under a Mewar camel-driver's greasy armpit and cannoned off a covey of jabbering Sikh matrons.

'Not less than the greatest. We are both fortunate! I will make report to him of what thou hast done. I am safe under his protection.'

He bored through the edge of the crowd besieging the carriages, and squatted by the bench near the telegraph-office.

'Return, or they take thy place! Have no fear for the work, brother— or my life. Thou hast given me breathing-space, and Strickland Sahib has pulled me to land. We may work together at the Game yet. Farewell!'

Kim hurried to his carriage: elated, bewildered, but a little nettled in that he had no key to the secrets about him.

'I am only a beginner at the Game, that is sure. I could not have leaped into safety as did the Saddhu. He knew it was darkest under the lamp. I could not have thought to tell news under pretence of cursing . . . and how clever was the Sahib! No matter, I saved the life of one. . . . Where is the Kamboh gone, Holy One?' he whispered, as he took his seat in the now crowded compartment.

'A fear gripped him,' the lama replied, with a touch of tender malice. 'He saw thee change the Mahratta to a Saddhu in the twinkling of an eye, as a protection against evil. That shook him. Then he saw the Saddhu fall sheer into the hands of the polis—all the effect of thy art. Then he gathered up his son and fled; for he said that thou didst change a quiet trader into an impudent bandier of words with the Sahibs, and he feared a like fate. Where is the Saddhu?'

'With the polis,' said Kim. . . . 'Yet I saved the Kamboh's child.'

The lama snuffed blandly.

'Ah, chela, see how thou art overtaken! Thou didst cure the Kamboh's child solely to acquire merit. But thou didst put a spell on the Mahratta with prideful workings—I watched thee—and with side-long glances to bewilder an old old man and a foolish farmer: whence calamity and suspicion.'

Kim controlled himself with an effort beyond his years. Not more than any other youngster did he like to eat dirt or to be misjudged, but he saw himself in a cleft stick. The train rolled out of Delhi into the night.

'It is true,' he murmured. 'Where I have offended thee I have done wrong.'

'It is more, chela. Thou hast loosed an Act upon the world, and as a stone thrown into a pool so spread the consequences thou canst not tell how far.'

This ignorance was well both for Kim's vanity and for the lama's peace of mind, when we think that there was then being handed in at Simla a code-wire reporting the arrival of E.23 at Delhi, and, more important, the whereabouts of a letter he had been commissioned to—abstract. Incidentally,

an over-zealous policeman had arrested, on charge of murder done in a far southern State, a horribly indignant Ajmir cotton-broker, who was explaining himself to a Mr. Strickland on Delhi platform, while E.23 was paddling through by-ways into the locked heart of Delhi city. In two hours several telegrams had reached the angry minister of a southern State reporting that all trace of a somewhat bruised Mahratta had been lost; and by the time the leisurely train halted at Saharunpore the last ripple of the stone Kim had helped to heave was lapping against the steps of a mosque in far-away Roum—where it disturbed a pious man at prayers.

The lama made his in ample form near the dewy bougainvillea-trellis near the platform, cheered by the clear sunshine and the presence of his disciple. 'We will put these things behind us,' he said, indicating the brazen engine and the gleaming track. 'The jolting of the te-rain—though a wonderful thing—has turned my bones to water. We will use clean air henceforward.'

'Let us go to the Kulu woman's house,' said Kim, and stepped forth cheerily under the bundles. Early morning Saharunpore-way is clean and well scented. He thought of the other mornings at St. Xavier's, and it topped his already thrice-heaped contentment.

'Where is this new haste born from? Wise men do not run about like chickens in the sun. We have come hundreds upon hundreds of kos already, and, till now, I have scarcely been alone with thee an instant. How canst thou receive instruction all jostled of crowds? How can I, whelmed by a flux of talk, meditate upon the Way?'

'Her tongue grows no shorter with the years, then?' The disciple smiled.

'Nor her desire for charms. I remember once when I spoke of the Wheel of Life '—the lama fumbled in his bosom for his latest copy—' she was only curious about the devils that besiege children. She shall acquire merit by entertaining us—in a little while—at an after-occasion—softly, softly. Now we will wander loose-foot, waiting upon the Chain of Things. The Search is sure.'

So they travelled very easily across and among the broad bloomful fruit-gardens—by way of Aminabad, Sahaigunge, Akrola of the Ford, and little Phulesa—the line of the Sewaliks always to the north, and behind them again the snows. After long, sweet sleep under the dry stars came the lordly, leisurely passage through a waking village—begging-bowl held forth in silence, but eyes roving in defiance of the Law from sky's edge to sky's edge. Then would Kim return soft-footed through the soft dust to his master under the shadow of a mango tree or the thinner shade of a white Doon siris, to eat and drink at ease. At mid-day, after talk and a little wayfaring, they slept; meeting the world refreshed when the air was cooler. Night found them adventuring into new territory—some chosen village spied three hours before across the fat land, and much discussed upon the road.

There they told their tale,—a new one each evening so far as Kim was

concerned,—and there were they made welcome, either by priest or head-man, after the custom of the kindly East.

When the shadows shortened and the lama leaned more heavily upon Kim, there was always the Wheel of Life to draw forth, to hold flat under wiped stones, and with a long straw to expound cycle by cycle. Here sat the Gods on high—and they were dreams of dreams. Here was our Heaven and the world of the demi-Gods—horsemen fighting among the hills. Here were the agonies done upon the beasts, souls ascending or descending the ladder and therefore not to be interfered with. Here were the Hells, hot and cold, and the abodes of tormented ghosts. Let the chela study the troubles that come from over-eating—bloated stomach and burning bowels. Obediently then, with bowed head and brown finger alert to follow the pointer, did the chela study; but when they came to the Human World, busy and profitless, that is just above the Hells, his mind was distracted; for by the roadside trundled the very Wheel itself, eating, drinking, trading, marrying, and quar-relling—all warmly alive. Often the lama made the living pictures the matter of his text, bidding Kim—too ready—note how the flesh takes a thousand thousand shapes, desirable or detestable as men reckon, but in truth of no account either way; and how the stupid spirit, bond-slave to the Hog, the Dove, and the Serpent—lusting after betel-nut, a new yoke of oxen, women, or the favour of kings—is bound to follow the body through all the Heavens and all the Hells, and strictly round again. Sometimes a woman or a poor man, watching the ritual—it was nothing less—when the great yellow chart was unfolded, would throw a few flowers or a handful of cowries upon its edge. It sufficed these humble ones that they had met a Holy One who might be moved to remember them in his prayers.

' Cure them if they are sick,' said the lama, when Kim's sporting in-stincts woke. ' Cure them if they have fever, but by no means work charms. Remember what befell the Mahratta.'

' Then all Doing is evil? ' Kim replied, lying out under a big tree at the fork of the Doon road, watching the little ants run over his hand.

' To abstain from action is well—except to acquire merit.'

' At the Gates of Learning we were taught that to abstain from action was unbefitting a Sahib. And I am a Sahib.'

' Friend of all the World,'—the lama looked directly at Kim,—' I am an old man—pleased with shows as are children. To those who follow the Way there is neither black nor white, Hind nor Bhotiyal. We be all souls seeking escape. No matter what thy wisdom learned among Sahibs, when we come to my River thou wilt be freed from all illusion—at my side. Hai! my bones ache for that River, as they ached in the te-rain; but my spirit sits above my bones, waiting. The Search is sure! '

' I am answered. Is it permitted to ask a question? '

The lama inclined his stately head.

' I ate thy bread for three years—as thou knowest. Holy One, whence came—? '

'There is much wealth, as men count it, in Bhotiyal,' the lama returned with composure. 'In my own place I have the illusion of honour. I ask for that I need. I am not concerned with the account. That is for my monastery. Ai! The black high seats in the monastery, and the novices all in order!'

And he told stories, tracing with a finger in the dust, of the immense and sumptuous ritual of avalanche-guarded cathedrals; of processions and devil-dances; of the changing of monks and nuns into swine; of holy cities fifteen thousand feet in the air; of intrigue between monastery and monastery; of voices among the hills, and of that mysterious mirage that dances on dry snow. He spoke even of Lhassa and of the Dalai Lama, whom he had seen and adored.

Each long, perfect day rose behind Kim for a barrier to cut him off from his race and his mother-tongue. He slipped back to thinking and dreaming in the vernacular, and mechanically followed the lama's ceremonial observances at eating, drinking, and the like. The old man's mind turned more and more to his monastery as his eyes turned to the steadfast snows. His River troubled him nothing. Now and again, indeed, he would gaze long and long at a tuft or a swig, expecting, he said, the earth to cleave and deliver its blessing; but he was content to be with his disciple, at ease in the temperate wind that comes down from the Doon. This was not Ceylon, nor Buddh Gaya, nor Bombay, nor some grass-tangled ruins that he seemed to have stumbled upon two years ago. He spoke of those places as a scholar removed from vanity, as a Seeker walking in humility, as an old man, wise and temperate, illumining knowledge with brilliant insight. Bit by bit, disconnectedly, each tale called up by some wayside thing, he spoke of all his wanderings up and down Hind; till Kim, who had loved him without reason, now loved him for fifty good reasons. So they enjoyed themselves in high felicity, abstaining, as the Rule demands, from evil words, covetous desires; not over-eating, not lying on high beds, nor wearing rich clothes. Their stomachs told them the time, and the people brought them their food, as the saying is. They were lords of the villages of Aminabad, Sahaigunge, Akrola of the Ford, and little Phulesa, where Kim gave the soulless woman a blessing.

But news travels fast in India, and too soon shuffled across the cropland, bearing a basket of fruits with a box of Kabul grapes and gilt oranges, a white-whiskered servitor—a lean, dry Oorya—begging them to bring the honour of their presence to his mistress, distressed in her mind that the lama had neglected her so long.

'Now do I remember'—the lama spoke as though it were a wholly new proposition. 'She is virtuous, but an inordinate talker.'

Kim was sitting on the edge of a cow's manger, telling stories to a village smith's children.

'She will only ask for another son for her daughter. I have not forgotten her,' he said. 'Let her acquire merit. Send word that we will come.'

They covered eleven miles through the fields in two days, and were overwhelmed with attentions at the end; for the old lady held a fine tradi-

tion of hospitality, to which she forced her son-in-law, who was under the thumb of his women-folk and brought peace by borrowing of the money-lender. Age had not weakened her tongue or her memory, and from a discreetly barred upper window, in the hearing of not less than a dozen servants, she paid Kim compliments that would have flung European audiences into unclean dismay.

'But thou art still the shameless beggar-brat of the parao,' she shrilled. 'I have not forgotten thee. Wash ye and eat. The father of my daughter's son is gone away awhile. So we poor women are dumb and useless.'

For proof, she harangued the entire household unsparingly till food and drink were brought; and in the evening—the smoke-scented evening, copper-dun and turquoise across the fields—it pleased her to order her palanquin to be set down in the untidy forecourt by smoky torch-light; and there, behind not too closely drawn curtains, she gossiped.

'Had the Holy One come alone, I should have received him otherwise; but with this rogue, who can be too careful?'

'Maharanee,' said Kim, choosing as always the amplest title, 'is it my fault that none other than a Sahib—a polis-sahib—called the Maharanee whose face he—'

'Chitt! That was on the pilgrimage. When we travel—thou knowest the proverb.'

'Called the Maharanee a Breaker of Hearts and a Dispenser of Delights?'

'To remember that! It was true. So he did. That was in the time of the bloom of my beauty.' She chuckled like a contented parrot above the sugar lump. 'Now tell me of thy goings and comings—as much as may be without shame. How many maids, and whose wives, hang upon thy eye-lashes? Ye hail from Benares? I would have gone there again this year, but my daughter—we have only two sons. Phaii! Such is the effect of these low plains. Now in Kulu men are elephants. But I would ask thy Holy One—stand aside, rogue—a charm against most lamentable windy colics that in mango-time overtake my daughter's eldest. Two years back he gave me a powerful spell.'

'Oh, Holy One!' said Kim, bubbling with mirth at the lama's rueful face.

'It is true. I gave her one against wind.'

'Teeth—teeth—teeth,' snapped the old woman.

'Cure them when they are sick,' Kim quoted relishingly, 'but by no means work charms. Remember what befell the Mahratta.'

'That was two Rains ago; she wearied me with her continual impor-tunity.' The lama groaned as the Unjust Judge had groaned before him. 'Thus it comes—take note, my chela—that even those who would follow the Way are thrust aside by idle women. Three days through, when the child was sick, she talked to me.'

'Arre! and to whom else should I talk? The boy's mother knew nothing,

and the father—in the nights of the cold weather it was—" Pray to the Gods," said he, forsooth, and turning over, snored! '

' I gave her the charm. What is an old man to do? '

' " To abstain from action is well—except when we acquire merit." '

' Ah, chela, if thou desertest me, I am all alone.'

' He found his milk-teeth easily at any rate,' said the old lady. ' But all priests are alike.'

Kim coughed severely. Being young, he did not approve of her flippancy. ' To importune the wise out of season is to invite calamity.'

' There is a talking mynah '—the thrust came back with the well-remembered snap of the jewelled fore-finger—' over the stables which has picked up the very tone of the family-priest. Maybe I forget honour to my guests, but if ye had seen him double his fists into his belly, which was like a half-grown gourd, and cry: " Here is the pain! " ye would forgive. I am half minded to take the hakim's medicine. He sells it cheap, and certainly it makes him fat as Shiv's own bull. He does not deny remedies, but I doubted for the child because of the inauspicious colour of the bottles.'

The lama, under cover of the monologue, had faded out into the darkness towards the room prepared.

' Thou hast angered him, belike,' said Kim.

' Not he. He is wearied, and I forgot, being a grandmother. (None but a grandmother should ever oversee a child. Mothers are only fit for bearing.) To-morrow, when he sees how my daughter's son is grown, he will write the charm. Then, too, he can judge of the new hakim's drugs.'

' Who is the hakim, Maharanee? '

' A wanderer, as thou art, but a most sober Bengali from Dacca—a master of medicine. He relieved me of an oppression after meat by means of a small pill that wrought like a devil unchained. He travels about now, vending preparations of great value. He has even papers, printed in Angrezi, telling what things he has done for weak-backed men and slack women. He has been here four days; but hearing ye were coming (hakims and priests are snake and tiger the world over) he has, as I take it, gone to cover.'

While she drew breath after this volley, the ancient servant, sitting unrebuked on the edge of the torch-light, muttered: ' This house is a cattle-pound, as it were, for all charlatans and—priests. Let the boy stop eating mangoes . . . but who can argue with a grandmother? ' He raised his voice respectfully: ' Sahiba, the hakim sleeps after his meat. He is in the quarters behind the dovecot.'

Kim bristled like an expectant terrier. To outface and down-talk a Calcutta-taught Bengali, a voluble Dacca drug-vendor, would be a good game. It was not seemly that the lama, and incidentally himself, should be thrown aside for such an one. He knew those curious bastard English advertisements at the backs of native newspapers. St. Xavier's boys sometimes brought them in by stealth to snigger over among their mates; for the language of the grateful patient recounting his symptoms is most simple and

revealing. The Oorya, not unanxious to play off one parasite against the other, slunk away towards the dovecot.

'Yes,' said Kim, with measured scorn. 'Their stock-in-trade is a little coloured water and a very great shamelessness. Their prey are broken-down kings and overfed Bengalis. Their profit is in children—who are not born.'

The old lady chuckled. 'Do not be envious. Charms are better, eh? I never gainsaid it. See that thy Holy One writes me a good amulet by the morning.'

'None but the ignorant deny'—a thick, heavy voice boomed through the darkness, as a figure came to rest squatting—'None but the ignorant deny the value of charms. None but the ignorant deny the value of medicines.'

'A rat found a piece of turmeric. Said he: "I will open a grocer's shop,"' Kim retorted.

Battle was fairly joined now, and they heard the old lady stiffen to attention.

'The priest's son knows the names of his nurse and three Gods. Says he: "Hear me, or I will curse you by the three million Great Ones."' Decidedly this invisible had an arrow or two in his quiver. He went on: 'I am but a teacher of the alphabet. I have learned all the wisdom of the Sahibs.'

'The Sahibs never grow old. They dance and they play like children when they are grandfathers. A strong-backed breed,' piped the voice inside the palanquin.

'I have, too, our drugs which loosen humours of the head in hot and angry men. Sina well compounded when the moon stands in the proper House; yellow earths I have—arplan from China that makes a man to renew his youth and astonish his household; saffron from Kashmir, and the best salep of Kabul. Many people have died before—'

'That I surely believe,' said Kim.

'They knew the value of my drugs. I do not give my sick the mere ink in which a charm is written, but hot and rending drugs which descend and wrestle with the evil.'

'Very mightily they do so,' sighed the old lady.

The voice launched into an immense tale of misfortune and bankruptcy, studded with plentiful petitions to the Government. 'But for my fate, which overrules all, I had been now in Government employ. I bear a degree from the great school at Calcutta—whither, maybe, the son of this house shall go.'

'He shall indeed. If our neighbour's brat can in a few years be made an F. A.' (First Arts—she used the English word, of which she had heard so often), 'how much more shall children clever as some that I know bear away prizes at rich Calcutta.'

'Never,' said the voice, 'have I seen such a child! Born in an auspicious hour, and—but for that colic which, alas! turning into black cholers, may carry him off like a pigeon—destined to many years, he is enviable.'

'Hai mai! ' said the old lady. 'To praise children is inauspicious, or I
could listen to this talk. But the back of the house is unguarded, and even
in this soft air men think themselves to be men and women we know. . . .
The child's father is away too, and I must be chowkedar (watchman) in my
old age. Up! Up! Take up the palanquin. Let the hakim and the young
priest settle between them whether charms or medicine most avail. Ho!
worthless people, fetch tobacco for the guests, and—round the homestead
go I! '

The palanquin reeled off, followed by straggling torches and a horde
of dogs. Twenty villages knew the Sahiba—her failings, her tongue, and her
large charity. Twenty villages cheated her after immemorial custom, but no
man would have stolen or robbed within her jurisdiction for any gift under
Heaven. None the less, she made great parade of her formal inspections, the
riot of which could be heard half-way to Mussoorie.

Kim relaxed, as one augur must when he meets another. The hakim,
still squatting, slid over his hookah with a friendly foot, and Kim pulled at
the good weed. The hangers-on expected grave professional debate, and per-
haps a little free doctoring.

'To discuss medicine before the ignorant is of one piece with teaching
the peacock to sing,' said the hakim.

'True courtesy,' Kim echoed, 'is very often inattention.'

These, be it understood, were company-manners, designed to impress.

'Hi! I have an ulcer on my leg,' cried a scullion. 'Look at it! '

'Get hence! Remove! ' said the hakim. 'Is it the habit of the place to
pester honoured guests? Ye crowd in like buffaloes.'

'If the Sahiba knew— ' Kim began.

'Ai! Ai! Come away. They are meat for our mistress. When her young
Shaitan's colics are cured perhaps we poor people may be suffered to— '

'The mistress fed thy wife when thou wast in jail for breaking the
money-lender's head. Who speaks against her? ' The old servitor curled his
white moustaches savagely in the young moonlight. 'I am responsible for
the honour of this house. Go! ' and he drove the underlings before him.

Said the hakim, hardly more than shaping the words with his lips: 'How
do you do, Mr. O'Hara? I am jolly glad to see you again.'

Kim's hand clenched about the pipe-stem. Anywhere on the open road,
perhaps, he would not have been astonished; but here, in this quiet back-
water of life, he was not prepared for Hurree Babu. It annoyed him, too,
that he had been hoodwinked.

'Ah ha! I told you at Lucknow—resurgam—I shall rise again and you
shall not know me. How much did you bet—eh? '

He chewed leisurely upon a few cardamom seeds, but he breathed un-
easily.

'But why come here, Babuji? '

'Ah! Thatt is the question, as Shakespeare hath said. I come to con-
gratulate you on your extraordinary effeecient performance at Delhi. Oah!

I tell you we are all proud of you. It was verree neat and handy. Our mutual friend, he is old friend of mine. He has been in some dam-tight places. Now he will be in some more. He told me; I tell Mr. Lurgan; and he is pleased you graduate so nicely. All the Department is pleased.'

For the first time in his life, Kim thrilled to the clean pride (it can be a deadly pitfall, none the less) of Departmental praise—ensnaring praise from an equal of work appreciated by fellow-workers. Earth has nothing on the same plane to compare with it. But, cried the Oriental in him, Babus do not travel far to retail compliments.

'Tell thy tale, Babu,' he said authoritatively.

'Oah, it is nothing. Onlee I was at Simla when the wire came in about what our mutual friend said he had hidden, and old Creighton—' He looked to see how Kim would take this piece of audacity.

'The Colonel Sahib,' the boy from St. Xavier's corrected.

'Of course. He found me at a loose string, and I had to go down to Chitor to find that beastly letter. I do not like the South—too much railway travel; but I drew good travelling allowance. Ha! Ha! I meet our mutual at Delhi on the way back. He lies quiett just now, and says Saddhu-disguise suits him to the ground. Well, there I hear what you have done so well, so quickly, upon the instantaneous spur of the moment. I tell our mutual friend you take the bally bun, by Jove! It was splendid. I come to tell you so.'

'Umm!'

The frogs were busy in the ditches, and the moon slid to her setting. Some happy servant had gone out to commune with the night and to beat upon a drum. Kim's next sentence was in the vernacular.

'How didst thou follow us?'

'Oah. Thatt was nothing. I know from our mutual friend you go to Saharunpore. So I come on. Red lamas are not inconspicuous persons. I buy myself my drug-box, and I am very good doctor really. I go to Akrola by the Ford, and hear all about you, and I talk here and talk there. All the common people know what you do. I know when the hospitable old lady sent the dooli. They have great recollections of the old lama's visits here. I know old ladies cannot keep their hands from medicines. So I am a doctor, and— you hear my talk? I think it is verree good. My word, Mister O'Hara, they know about you and the lama for fifty miles—the common people. So I come. Do you mind?'

'Babuji,' said Kim, looking up at the broad, grinning face, 'I am a Sahib.'

'My dear Mister O'Hara—'

'And I hope to play the Great Game.'

'You are subordinate to me departmentally at present.'

'Then why talk like an ape up in a tree? Men do not come after one from Simla and change their dress, for the sake of a few sweet words. I am not a child. Talk Hindi and let us get to the yolk of the egg. Thou art here

—speaking not one word of truth in ten. Why art thou here? Give a straight answer.'

'That is so verree disconcerting of the European, Mister O'Hara. You should know a heap better at your time of life.'

'But I want to know,' said Kim, laughing. 'If it is the Game, I may help. How can I do anything if you bukh (babble) all round the shop.'

Hurree Babu reached for the pipe, and sucked it till it guggled again.

'Now I will speak vernacular. You sit tight, Mister O'Hara. It concerns the pedigree of a white stallion.'

'Still? That was finished long ago.'

'When every one is dead the Great Game is finished. Not before. Listen to me till the end. There were Five Kings who prepared a sudden war three years ago, when thou wast given the stallion's pedigree by Mahbub Ali. Upon them, because of that news, and ere they were ready, fell our Army.'

'Ay—eight thousand men with guns. I remember that night.'

'But the war was not pushed. That is the Government custom. The troops were recalled because the Government believed the Five Kings were cowed; and it is not cheap to feed men among the high Passes. Hilas and Bunar—Rajahs with guns—undertook for a price to guard the passes against all coming from the North. They protested both fear and friendship.' He broke off with a giggle into English: ' Of course, I tell you this unoffeecially to elucidate political situation, Mister O'Hara. Offeecially, I am debarred from criticising any action of superior. Now I go on.—This pleased the Government, anxious to avoid expense, and a bond was made for so many rupees a month that Hilas and Bunar should guard the Passes as soon as the State's troops were withdrawn. At that time—it was after we two met—I, who had been selling tea in Leh, became a clerk of accounts in the Army. When the troops were withdrawn, I was left behind to pay the coolies who made new roads in the Hills. This road-making was part of the bond between Bunar, Hilas, and the Government.'

'So; and then?'

'I tell you, it was jolly beastly cold up there too, after summer,' said Hurree Babu confidentially. ' I was afraid these Bunar men would cut my throat every night for thee pay-chest. My native sepoy-guard, they laughed at me! By Jove! I was such a fearful man! Nevar mind thatt. I go on colloquially. . . . I send word many times that these two Kings were sold to the North; and Mahbub Ali, who was yet farther north, amply confirmed it. Nothing was done. Only my feet were frozen, and a toe dropped off. I sent word that the roads for which I was paying money to the diggers were being made for the feet of strangers and enemies.'

'For?'

'For the Russians. The thing was an open jest among the coolies. Then I was called down to tell what I knew by speech of tongue. Mahbub came South too. See the end! Over the Passes this year after snow-melting '—he shivered afresh—' come two strangers under cover of shooting wild goats.

They bear guns, but they bear also chains and levels and compasses.'

' Oho! The thing gets clearer.'

' They are well received by Hilas and Bunar. They make great promises; they speak as the mouthpiece of a Kaisar, with gifts. Up the valleys, down the valleys go they, saying, " Here is a place to build a breastwork; here can ye pitch a fort. Here can ye hold the road against an army "—the very roads for which I paid out the rupees monthly. The Government knows, but does nothing. The three other Kings, who were not paid for guarding the passes, tell them by runner of the bad faith of Bunar and Hilas. When all the evil is done, look you—when these two strangers with the levels and the compasses make the Five Kings to believe that a great army will sweep the Passes to-morrow or the next day—Hill-people are all fools—comes the order to me, Hurree Babu, " Go North and see what those strangers do." I say to Creighton Sahib, " This is not a lawsuit, that we go about to collect evidence." ' Hurree returned to his English with a jerk: ' " By Jove," I said, " why the dooce do you not issue demi-offeecial orders to some brave man to poison them, for an example? It is, if you permit the observation, most reprehensible laxity on your part." And Colonel Creighton, he laughed at me! It is all your beastly English pride. You think no one dare conspire! That is all tommy-rott.'

Kim smoked slowly, revolving the business, so far as he understood it, in his quick mind.

' Then thou goest forth to follow the strangers? '

' No; to meet them. They are coming in to Simla to send down their horns and heads to be dressed at Calcutta. They are exclusively sporting gentlemen, and they are allowed special faceelities by the Government. Of course, we always do that. It is our British pride.'

' Then what is to fear from them? '

' By Jove, they arc not black people. I can do all sorts of things with black people, of course. They are Russians, and highly unscrupulous people. I—I do not want to consort with them without a witness.'

' Will they kill thee? '

' Oah, thatt is nothing. I am good enough Herbert Spencerian, I trust, to meet little thing like death, which is all in my fate, you know. But—but they may beat me.'

' Why? '

Hurree Babu snapped his fingers with irritation. ' Of course I shall affeeliate myself to their camp in supernumerary capacity as perhaps interpreter, or person mentally impotent and hungree, or some such thing. And then I must pick up what I can, I suppose. That is as easy for me as playing Mister Doctor to the old lady. Onlee—onlee—you see, Mister O'Hara, I am unfortunately Asiatic, which is serious detriment in some respects. And all-so I am Bengali—a fearful man.'

' God made the Hare and the Bengali. What shame? ' said Kim, quoting the proverb.

'It was process of Evolution, I think, from Primal Necessity, but the fact remains in all its cui bono. I am, oh, awfully fearful!—I remember once they wanted to cut off my head on the road to Lhassa. (No, I have never reached to Lhassa.) I sat down and cried, Mister O'Hara, anticipating Chinese tortures. I do not suppose these two gentlemen will torture me, but I like to provide for possible contingency with European assistance in emergency.' He coughed and spat out his cardamoms. 'It is purely unoffeecial indent, to which you can say, "No, Babu." If you have no pressing engagement with your old man—perhaps you might divert him; perhaps I can seduce his fancies—I should like you to keep in Departmental touch with me till I find those sporting coves. I have great opeenion of you since I met my friend at Delhi. And also I will embody your name in my offeecial report when matter is finally adjudicated. It will be a great feather in your cap. That is why I come really."

'Humph! The end of the tale, I think, is true; but what of the forepart?'

'About the Five Kings? Oah! there is ever so much truth in it. A lots more than you would suppose,' said Hurree earnestly. 'You come—eh? I go from here straight into the Doon. It is verree verdant and painted meads. I shall go to Mussoorie—to good old Mussoorie Pahar, as the gentlemen and ladies say. Then by Rampur into Chini. That is the only way they can come. I do not like waiting in the cold, but we must wait for them. I want to walk with them to Simla. You see, one Russian is a Frenchman, and I know my French pretty well. I have friends in Chandernagore.'

'He would certainly rejoice to see the Hills again,' said Kim meditatively. 'All his speech these ten days past has been of little else. If we go together—'

'Oah! We can be quite strangers on the road, if your lama prefers. I shall just be four or five miles ahead. There is no hurry for Hurree—that is an Europe pun, ha! ha!—and you come after. There is plenty of time; they will plot and survey and map of course. I shall go to-morrow, and you the next day, if you choose. Eh? You go think on it till morning. By Jove, it is near morning now.' He yawned ponderously, and with never a civil word lumbered off to his sleeping-place. But Kim slept little, and his thoughts ran in Hindustanee:

'Well is the Game called great! I was four days a scullion at Quetta, waiting on the wife of the man whose book I stole. And that was part of the Great Game! From the South—God knows how far—came up the Mahratta, playing the Great Game in fear of his life. Now I shall go far and far into the North playing the Great Game. Truly, it runs like a shuttle throughout all Hind. And my share and my joy'—he smiled to the darkness—'I owe to the lama here. Also to Mahbub Ali—also to Creighton Sahib, but chiefly to the Holy One. He is right—a great and a wonderful world—and I am Kim—Kim—Kim—alone—one person—in the middle of it all. But I will see these strangers with their levels and chains'

' What was the upshot of last night's babble? ' said the lama, after his orisons.

' There came a strolling seller of drugs—a hanger-on of the Sahiba's. Him I abolished by arguments and prayers, proving that our charms are worthier than his coloured waters.'

' Alas! my charms. Is the virtuous woman still bent upon a new one? '

' Very strictly.'

' Then it must be written, or she will deafen me with her clamour.' He fumbled at his pencase.

' In the Plains,' said Kim, ' are always too many people. In the Hills, as I understand, there are fewer.'

' Oh! the Hills, and the snow upon the Hills.' The lama tore off a tiny square of paper fit to go in an amulet. ' But what dost thou know of the Hills? '

' They are very close.' Kim thrust open the door and looked at the long, peaceful line of the Himalayas flushed in morning-gold. ' Except in the dress of a Sahib, I have never set foot among them.'

The lama snuffed the wind wistfully.

' If we go north,'—Kim put the question to the waking sunrise,— ' would not much mid-day heat be avoided by walking among the lower hills at least? . . . Is the charm made, Holy One? '

' I have written the names of seven silly devils—not one of whom is worth a grain of dust in the eye. Thus do foolish women drag us from the Way! '

Hurree Babu come out from behind the dovecot, washing his teeth with ostentatious ritual. Full-fleshed, heavy-haunched, bull-necked, and deep-voiced, he did not look like ' a fearful man.' Kim signed almost imperceptibly that matters were in good train, and when the morning toilet was over Hurree Babu, in flowery speech, came to do honour to the lama. They ate, of course, apart, and afterwards the old lady, more or less veiled behind a window, returned to the vital business of green-mango colics in the young. The lama's knowledge of medicine was of course sympathetic only. He believed that the dung of a black horse, mixed with sulphur, and carried in a snake-skin, was a sound remedy for cholera; but the symbolism interested him far more than the science. Hurree Babu deferred to these views with enchanting politeness, so that the lama called him a courteous physician. Hurree Babu replied that he was no more than an inexpert dabbler in the mysteries; but at least—he thanked the Gods therefor—he knew when he sat in the presence of a master. He himself had been taught by the Sahibs, who do not consider expense, in the lordly halls of Calcutta; but, as he was ever first to acknowledge, there lay a wisdom behind earthly wisdom—the high and lonely lore of meditation. Kim looked on with envy. The Hurree Babu of his knowledge—oily, effusive, and nervous—was gone; gone too was the brazen drug-vendor of overnight. There remained—polished, polite, attentive—a sober, learned son of experience and adversity,

gathering wisdom from the lama's lips. The old lady confided to Kim that these rare levels were beyond her. She liked charms with plenty of ink that one could wash off in water, swallow, and be done with. Else what was the use of the Gods? She liked men and women, and she spoke of them—of kinglets she had known in the past; of her own youth and beauty; of the depredations of leopards and the eccentricities of love Asiatic; of the incidence of taxation, rack-renting, funeral ceremonies, her son-in-law (this by allusion, easy to be followed), the care of the young, and the age's lack of decency. And Kim, as interested in the life of this world as she soon to leave it, squatted with his feet under the hem of his robe, drinking all in, while the lama demolished one after another every theory of body-curing put forward by Hurree Babu.

At noon the Babu strapped up his brass-bound drug-box, took his patent-leather shoes of ceremony in one hand, a gay blue and white umbrella in the other, and set off northwards to the Doon, where, he said, he was in demand among the lesser kings of those parts.

'We will go in the cool of the evening, chela,' said the lama. 'That doctor, learned in physic and courtesy, affirms that the people among these lower hills are devout, generous, and much in need of a teacher. In a very short time—so says the hakim—we come to cool air and the smell of pines.'

'Ye go to the Hills. And by Kulu-road? Ah, thrice happy!' shrilled the old lady. 'But that I am a little pressed with the care of the homestead I would take palanquin . . . but that would be shameless, and my reputation would be cracked. Ho! Ho! I know the road—every march of the road I know. Ye will find charity throughout—it is not denied to the well-looking. I will give orders for provision. A servant to set you forth upon your journey? No. . . . Then I will at least cook ye good food.'

'What a woman is the Sahiba!' said the white-bearded Oorya, when a tumult rose by the kitchen quarters. 'She has never forgotten a friend: she has never forgotten an enemy in all her years. And her cookery—wah!' He rubbed his slim stomach.

There were cakes, there were sweetmeats, there was cold fowl stewed to rags with rice and prunes—enough to burden Kim like a mule.

'I am old and useless,' she said. 'None now love me—and none respect —but there are few to compare with me when I call on the Gods and squat to my cooking-pots. Come again, O people of good will! Holy One and disciple, come again! The room is always prepared; the welcome is always ready. . . . See the women do not follow thy chela too openly. I know the women of Kulu. Take heed, chela, lest he run away when he smells his Hills again. . . . Hai! Do not tilt the rice-bag upside down. . . . Bless the household, Holy One, and forgive thy servant her stupidities.'

She wiped her red old eyes on a corner of her veil, and clucked throatily.

'Women talk,' said the lama at last, 'but that is a woman's infirmity. I gave her a charm. She is upon the Wheel and wholly given over to the shows of this life, but none the less, chela, she is virtuous, kindly, hospitable

—of a whole and zealous heart. Who shall say she does not acquire merit?'

'Not I, Holy One,' said Kim, reslinging the bountiful provision on his shoulders. 'In my mind—behind my eyes—I have tried to picture such an one altogether freed from the Wheel—desiring nothing, causing nothing—a nun, as it were.'

'And, O imp?' The lama almost laughed aloud.

'I cannot make the picture.'

'Nor I. But there are many, many millions of lives before her. She will get wisdom a little, it may be, in each one.'

'And will she forget how to make stews with saffron upon that road?'

'Thy mind is set on things unworthy. But she has skill. I am refreshed all over. When we reach the lower hills I shall be yet stronger. The hakim spoke truly to me this morn when he said a breath from the snows blows away twenty years from the life of a man. We will go up into the Hills—the high hills—up to the sound of snow-water and the sound of the trees—for a little while. The hakim said that at any time we may return to the Plains, for we do no more than skirt the pleasant places. The hakim is full of learning; but he is in no way proud. I spoke to him—when thou wast talking to the Sahiba—of a certain dizziness that lays hold upon the back of my neck in the night, and he said it rose from excessive heat—to be cured by cool air. Upon consideration, I marvelled that I had not thought of such a simple remedy.'

'Didst thou tell him of thy Search?' said Kim, a little jealously. He preferred to sway the lama by his own speech—not through the wiles of Hurree Babu.

'Assuredly. I told him of my dream, and of the manner by which I had acquired merit by causing thee to be taught wisdom.'

'Thou didst not say I was a Sahib?'

'What need? I have told thee many times we be but two souls seeking escape. He said—and he is just herein—that the River of Healing will break forth even as I dreamed—at my feet if need be. Having found the Way, seest thou, that shall free me from the Wheel, need I trouble to find a way about the mere fields of earth—which are illusion? That were senseless. I have my dreams, night upon night repeated; I have the "Jataka"; and I have thee, Friend of all the World. It was written in thy horoscope that a Red Bull on a green field—I have not forgotten—should bring thee to honour. Who but I saw that prophecy accomplished? Indeed, I was the instrument. Thou shalt find me my River, being in return the instrument. The Search is sure!'

He set his ivory-yellow face, serene and untroubled, towards the beckoning Hills; his shadow shouldering far before him in the dust.

CHAPTER XIII

' Who hath desired the Sea—the immense and contemptuous surges?
The shudder, the stumble, the swerve ere the star-stabbing bowsprit
 emerges—
The orderly clouds of the Trades and the ridged roaring sapphire there-
 under—
Unheralded cliff-lurking flaws and the head-sails' low-volleying thunder?
His Sea is no wonder the same—his Sea and the same in each wonder—
 His Sea that his being fulfils?
So and no otherwise—so and no otherwise Hill-men desire their Hills! '

' Who goes to the Hills goes to his mother.'

They had crossed the Sewaliks and the half-tropical Doon, left Mus-
soorie behind them, and headed north along the narrow hill-roads. Day after
day they struck deeper into the huddled mountains, and day after day Kim
watched the lama return to a man's strength. Among the terraces of the
Doon he had leaned on the boy's shoulder, ready to profit by wayside halts.
Under the great ramp to Mussoorie he drew himself together as an old hunter
faces a well-remembered bank, and where he should have sunk exhausted
swung his long draperies about him, drew a deep double-lungful of the dia-
mond air, and walked as only a hillman can. Kim, plains-bred and plains-fed,
sweated and panted astonished. 'This is my country,' said the lama. ' Be-
sides Suchzen, this is flatter than a ricefield '; and with steady, driving strokes
from the loins he strode upwards. But it was on the steep downhill marches,
three thousand feet in three hours, that he went utterly away from Kim,
whose back ached with holding back, and whose big toe was nigh cut off
by his grass sandal-string. Through the speckled shadow of the great deodar-
forests; through oak feathered and plumed with ferns; birch, ilex, rhododen-
dron, and pine, out on to the bare hillsides' slippery sunburnt grass, and back
into the woodlands' coolth again, till oak gave way to bamboo and palm
of the valley, the lama swung untiring.

Glancing back in the twilight at the huge ridges behind him and the
faint, thin line of the road whereby they had come, he would lay out, with
a hillman's generous breadth of vision, fresh marches for the morrow; or,
halting in the neck of some uplifted pass that gave on Spiti and Kulu, would
stretch out his hands yearningly towards the high snows of the horizon. In
the dawns they flared windy-red above stark blue, as Kedarnath and Badri-
nath—kings of that wilderness—took the first sunlight. All day long they
lay like molten silver under the sun, and at evening put on their jewels again.
At first they breathed temperately upon the travellers, winds good to meet

when one crawled over some gigantic hogback; but in a few days, at a height of nine or ten thousand feet, those breezes bit; and Kim kindly allowed a village of hillmen to acquire merit by giving him a rough blanket-coat. The lama was mildly surprised that any one should object to the knife-edged breezes which had cut the years off his shoulders.

'These are but the lower hills, chela. There is no cold till we come to the true Hills.'

'Air and water are good, and the people are devout enough, but the food is very bad,' Kim growled; 'and we walk as though we were mad—or English. It freezes at night, too.'

'A little, maybe; but only enough to make old bones rejoice in the sun. We must not always delight in the soft beds and rich food.'

'We might at the least keep to the road.'

Kim had all a plains-man's affection for the well-trodden track, not six feet wide, that snaked among the mountains; but the lama, being Tibetan, could not refrain from short cuts over spurs and the rims of gravel-strewn slopes. As he explained to his limping disciple, a man bred among mountains can prophesy the course of a mountain-road, and though low-lying clouds might be a hindrance to a short-cutting stranger, they made no earthly difference to a thoughtful man. Thus, after long hours of what would be reckoned very fair mountaineering in civilised countries, they would pant over a saddle-back, sidle past a few landslips, and drop through forest at an angle of forty-five on to the road again. Along their track lay the villages of the hill-folk—mud and earth huts, the timbers now and then rudely carved with an axe—clinging like swallows' nests against the steeps, huddled on tiny flats half-way down a three-thousand-foot glissade; jammed into a corner between cliffs that funnelled and focused every wandering blast; or, for the sake of summer pasture, cowering down on a neck that in winter would be ten feet deep in snow. And the people—the sallow, greasy, duffle-clad people, with short bare legs and faces almost Esquimaux—would flock out and adore. The Plains—kindly and gentle—had treated the lama as a holy man among holy men. But the Hills worshipped him as one in the confidence of all the devils. Theirs was an almost obliterated Buddhism, overlaid with a nature-worship fantastic as their own landscapes, elaborate as the terracing of their tiny fields; but they recognised the big hat, the clicking rosary, and the rare Chinese texts for great authority; and they respected the man under the hat.

'We saw thee come down over the black Breasts of Eua,' said a Betah who gave them cheese, sour milk, and stone-hard bread one evening. 'We do not use that often—except when calving cows stray in summer. There is a sudden wind among those stones that casts men down on the stillest day. But what should such folk care for the Devil of Eua!'

Then did Kim, aching in every fibre, dizzy with looking down, footsore with cramping desperate toes into inadequate crannies, take joy in the day's march—such joy as a boy of St. Xavier's who had won the quarter-mile on

the flat might take in the praises of his friends. The hills sweated the ghi
and sugar suet off his bones; the dry air, taken sobbingly at the head of
cruel passes, firmed and built out his upper ribs; and tilted levels put new
hard muscles into calf and thigh.

They meditated often on the Wheel of Life—the more so since, as the
lama said, they were freed from its visible temptations. Except the gray
eagle and an occasional far-seen bear grubbing and rooting on the hillside,
the vision of a furious painted leopard met at dawn in a still valley devouring
a goat, and now and again a bright-coloured bird, they were alone with the
winds and the grass singing under the wind. The women of the smoky huts
over whose roofs the two walked as they descended the mountains, were
unlovely and unclean, wives of many husbands, and afflicted with goitre.
The men were wood-cutters when they were not farmers—meek, and of
an incredible simplicity. But that suitable discourse might not fail, Fate
sent them, overtaking and overtaken upon the road, the courteous Dacca
physician, who paid for his food in ointments good for goitre and counsels
that restore peace between men and women. He seemed to know these
hills as well as he knew the hill dialects, and gave the lama the lie of the
land towards Ladakh and Tibet. He said they could return to the Plains at
any moment. Meantime, for such as loved mountains, yonder road might
amuse. This was not all revealed in a breath, but at evening encounters on
the stone threshing-floors, when, patients disposed of, the doctor would
smoke and the lama snuff, while Kim watched the wee cows grazing on
the house-tops, or threw his soul after his eye across the deep blue gulfs
between range and range. And there were talks apart in the dark woods,
when the doctor would seek herbs, and Kim, as budding physician, must
accompany him.

'You see, Mister O'Hara, I do not know what the deuce-an'-all I shall
do when I find our sporting friends; but if you will kindly keep within sight
of my umbrella, which is fine fixed point for cadastral survey, I feel much
better.'

Kim looked out across the jungle of peaks. 'This is not my country,
hakim. Easier, I think, to find one louse in a bearskin.'

'Oah, thatt is my strong points. There is no hurry for Hurree. They
were at Leh not so long ago. They said they had come down from the
Kara Korum with their heads and horns and all. I am onlee afraid they
will have sent back all their letters and compromising things from Leh into
Russian territoree. Of course they will walk away as far to the East as
possible—just to show that they were never among the Western States. You
do not know the Hills?' He scratched with a twig on the earth. 'Look! They
should have come in by Srinagar or Abbottabad. Thatt is their short road—
down the river by Bunji and Astor. But they have made mischief in the
West. So'—he drew a furrow from left to right—'they march and they
march away East to Leh (ah! it is cold there), and down the Indus to Han-le
(I know that road), and then down, you see, to Bushahr and Chini valley.

That is ascertained by process of elimination, and also by asking questions from people that I cure so well. Our friends have been a long time playing about and producing impressions. So they are well known from far off. You will see me catch them somewhere in Chini valley. Please keep your eye on the umbrella.'

It nodded like a wind-blown harebell down the valleys and round the mountain sides, and in due time the lama and Kim, who steered by compass, would overhaul it, vending ointments and powders at eventide. 'We came by such and such a way!' The lama would throw a careless finger backward at the ridges, and the umbrella would expend itself in compliments.

They crossed a snowy pass in cold moonlight, when the lama, mildly chaffing Kim, went through up to his knees, like a Bactrian camel—the snow-bred, shag-haired sort that come into the Kashmir Serai. They dipped across beds of light snow and snow-powdered shale, where they took refuge from a gale in a camp of Tibetans hurrying down tiny sheep, each laden with a bag of borax. They came out upon grassy shoulders still snow-speckled, and through forest, to grass anew. For all their marchings, Kedarnath and Badrinath were not impressed; and it was only after days of travel that Kim, uplifted upon some insignificant ten-thousand-foot hummock, could see that a shoulder-knot or horn of the two great lords had—ever so slightly— changed outline.

At last they entered a world within a world—a valley of leagues where the high hills were fashioned of the mere rubble and refuse from off the knees of the mountains. Here one day's march carried them no farther, it seemed, than a dreamer's clogged pace bears him in a nightmare. They skirted a shoulder painfully for hours, and, behold, it was but an outlying boss in an outlying buttress of the main pile! A rounded meadow revealed itself, when they had reached it, for a vast tableland running far into the valley. Three days later, it was a dim fold in the earth to southward.

'Surely the Gods live here,' said Kim, beaten down by the silence and the appalling sweep and dispersal of the cloud-shadows after rain. 'This is no place for men!'

'Long and long ago,' said the lama, as to himself, 'it was asked of the Lord whether the world were everlasting. To this the Excellent One returned no answer. . . . When I was in Ceylon, a wise Seeker confirmed that from the gospel which is written in Pali. Certainly, since we know the way to Freedom, the question were unprofitable, but—look, and know illusion, chela! These are the true Hills! They are like my hills by Suchzen. Never were such hills!'

Above them, still enormously above them, earth towered away towards the snow-line, where from east to west across hundreds of miles, ruled as with a ruler, the last of the bold birches stopped. Above that, in scarps and blocks upheaved, the rocks strove to fight their heads above the white smother. Above these again, changeless since the world's beginning, but changing to every mood of sun and cloud, lay out the eternal snow. They

could see blots and blurs on its face where storm and wandering wullie-wa got up to dance. Below them, as they stood, the forest slid away in a sheet of blue-green for mile upon mile; below the forest was a village in its sprinkle of terraced fields and steep grazing-grounds; below the village they knew, though a thunderstorm worried and growled there for the moment, a pitch of twelve or fifteen hundred feet gave to the moist valley where the streams gather that are the mothers of young Sutluj.

As usual, the lama had led Kim by cow-track and by-road, far from the main route along which Hurree Babu, that 'fearful man,' had bucketed three days before through a storm to which nine Englishmen out of ten would have given full right of way. Hurree was no game-shot,—the snick of a trigger made him change colour,—but, as he himself would have said, he was 'fairly effeecient stalker,' and he had raked the huge valley with a pair of cheap binoculars to some purpose. Moreover, the white of worn canvas tents against green carries far. Hurree Babu had seen all he wanted to see when he sat on the threshing-floor of Ziglaur, twenty miles away as the eagle flies, and forty by road—that is to say, two small dots which one day were just below the snow-line, and the next had moved downward perhaps six inches on the hillside. Once cleaned out and set to the work, his fat bare legs could cover a surprising amount of ground, and this was the reason why, while Kim and the lama lay in a leaky hut at Ziglaur till the storm should be overpassed, an oily, wet, but always smiling Bengali, talking the best of English with the vilest of phrases, was ingratiating himself with two sodden and rather rheumatic foreigners. He had arrived, revolving many wild schemes, on the heels of a thunderstorm which had split a pine over against their camp, and so convinced a dozen or two forcibly impressed baggage-coolies the day was inauspicious for farther travel that with one accord they had thrown down their loads and jibbed. They were subjects of a Hill-Rajah who farmed out their services, as is the custom, for his private gain; and, to add to their personal distresses, the strange Sahibs had already threatened them with rifles. The most of them knew rifles and Sahibs of old; they were trackers and shikarris of the Northern valleys, keen after bear and wild goat; but they had never been thus treated in their lives. So the forest took them to her bosom, and, for all oaths and clamour, refused to restore. There was no need to feign madness or—the Babu had thought of another means of securing a welcome. He wrung out his wet clothes, slipped on his patent-leather shoes, opened the blue and white umbrella, and with mincing gait and a heart beating against his tonsils appeared as 'agent for His Royal Highness, the Rajah of Rampur, gentlemen. What can I do for you, please?'

The gentlemen were delighted. One was visibly French, the other Russian, but they spoke English not much inferior to the Babu's. They begged his kind offices. Their native servants had gone sick at Leh. They had hurried on because they were anxious to bring the spoils of the chase to Simla ere the skins grew moth-eaten. They bore a general letter of introduction (the Babu salaamed to it orientally) to all Government officials. No,

they had not met any other shooting-parties en route. They did for themselves. They had plenty of supplies. They only wished to push on as soon as might be. At this he waylaid a cowering hillman among the trees, and after three minutes' talk and a little silver (one cannot be economical upon State service, though Hurree's heart bled at the waste) the eleven coolies and the three hangers-on reappeared. At least the Babu would be a witness to oppression.

'My royal master, he will be much annoyed, but these people are onlee common people and grossly ignorant. If your honours will kindly overlook unfortunate affair, I shall be much pleased. In a little while rain will stop and we can then proceed. You have been shooting, eh? That is fine performance!'

He skipped nimbly from one kilta to the next, making pretence to adjust each conical basket. The Englishman is not, as a rule, familiar with the Asiatic, but he would not strike across the wrist a kindly Babu who had accidentally upset a kilta with a red oilskin top. On the other hand, he would not press drink upon a Babu were he never so friendly, nor would he invite him to meat. The strangers did all these things, and asked many questions,—about women mostly,—to which Hurree returned gay and unstudied answers. They gave him a glass of whitish fluid like to gin, and then more; and in a little time his gravity departed from him. He became thickly treasonous, and spoke in terms of sweeping indecency of a Government which had forced upon him a white man's education and neglected to supply him with a white man's salary. He babbled tales of oppression and wrong till the tears ran down his cheeks for the miseries of his land. Then he staggered off, singing love-songs of Lower Bengal, and collapsed upon a wet tree-trunk. Never was so unfortunate a product of English rule in India more unhappily thrust upon aliens.

'They are all just of that pattern,' said one sportsman to the other in French. 'When we get into India proper thou wilt see. I should like to visit his Rajah. One might speak the good word there. It is possible that he has heard of us and wishes to signify his goodwill.'

'We have not time. We must get into Simla as soon as may be,' his companion replied. 'For my own part, I wish our reports had been sent back from Hilas, or even Leh.'

'The English post is better and safer. Remember we are given all facilities—and name of God!—they give them to us too! Is it unbelievable stupidity?'

'It is pride—pride that deserves and will receive punishment.'

'Yes! To fight a fellow-Continental in our game is something. There is a risk attached, but these people—bah! It is too easy.'

'Pride—all pride, my friend.'

'Now what the deuce is good of Chandernagore being so close to Calcutta and all,' said Hurree, snoring open-mouthed on the sodden moss, 'if I cannot understand their French. They talk so par-tic-ularly fast! It would

have been much better to cut their beastly throats.'

When he presented himself again he was racked with a headache—
penitent, and volubly afraid that in his drunkenness he might have been
indiscreet. He loved the British Government—it was the source of all pros-
perity and honour, and his master at Rampur held the very same opinion.
Upon this the men began to deride him and to quote past words, till step
by step, with deprecating smirks, oily grins, and leers of infinite cunning, the
poor Babu was beaten out of his defences and forced to speak—truth! When
Lurgan was told the tale later, he mourned aloud that he could not have
been in the place of the stubborn, inattentive coolies, who with grass mats
over their heads and the raindrops puddling in their foot-prints, waited on
the weather. All the Sahibs of their acquaintance—rough-clad men joyously
returning year after year to their chosen gullies—had servants and cooks and
orderlies, very often hillmen. These Sahibs travelled without any retinue.
Therefore they were poor Sahibs, and ignorant; for no Sahib in his senses
would follow a Bengali's advice. But the Bengali, appearing from somewhere,
had given them money, and would make shift with their dialect. Used to
comprehensive ill-treatment from their own colour, they suspected a trap
somewhere, and stood by to run if occasion offered.

Then through the new-washed air, steaming with delicious earth-smells,
the Babu led the way down the slopes—walking ahead of the coolies in
pride; walking behind the foreigners in humility. His thoughts were many
and various. The least of them would have interested his companions beyond
words. But he was an agreeable guide, ever keen to point out the beauties of
his royal master's domain. He peopled the hills with anything they had a
mind to slay—thar, ibex, or markhor, and bear by Elisha's allowance. He
discoursed of botany and ethnology with unimpeachable inaccuracy, and his
store of local legends—he had been a trusted agent of the State for fifteen
years, remember—was inexhaustible.

'Decidedly this fellow is an original,' said the taller of the two foreigners.
'He is like the nightmare of a Viennese courier.'

'He represents in petto India in transition—the monstrous hybridism
of East and West,' the Russian replied. 'It is we who can deal with
Orientals.'

'He has lost his own country and has not acquired any other. But he
has a most complete hatred of his conquerors. Listen. He confides to me
last night,' etc.

Under the striped umbrella Hurree Babu was straining ear and brain
to follow the quick-poured French, and keeping both eyes on a kilta full of
maps and documents—an extra large one with a double red oilskin cover. He
did not wish to steal anything. He only desired to know what to steal, and,
incidentally, how to get away when he had stolen it. He thanked all the
Gods of Hindustan, and Herbert Spencer, that there remained some valu-
ables to steal.

On the second day the road rose steeply to a grass spur above the forest;

and it was here, about sunset, that they came across an aged lama—but they called him a bonze—sitting cross-legged above a mysterious chart held down by stones, which he was explaining to a young man, evidently a neophyte, of singular, though unwashen, beauty. The striped umbrella had been sighted half a march away, and Kim had suggested a halt till it came up to them.

' Ha! ' said Hurree Babu, resourceful as Puss-in-Boots. ' That is eminent local holy man. Probably subject of my royal master.'

' What is he doing? It is very curious.'

' He is expounding holy picture—all hand-worked.'

The two men stood bare-headed in the wash of the afternoon sunlight low across the gold-coloured grass. The sullen coolies, glad of the check, halted and slid down their loads.

' Look! ' said the Frenchman. ' It is like a picture for the birth of a religion—the first teacher and the first disciple. Is he a Buddhist? '

' Of some debased kind,' the other answered. ' There are no true Buddhists among the Hills. But look at the folds of the drapery. Look at his eyes—how insolent! Why does this make one feel that we are so young a people? ' The speaker struck passionately at a tall weed. ' We have nowhere left our mark yet. Nowhere! That, do you understand, is what disquiets me.' He scowled at the placid face, and the monumental calm of the pose.

' Have patience. We shall make your mark together—we and you young people. Meantime, draw his picture.'

The Babu advanced loftily; his back out of all keeping with his deferential speech, or his wink towards Kim.

' Holy One, these be Sahibs. My medicines cured one of a flux, and I go into Simla to oversee his recovery. They wish to see thy picture— '

' To heal the sick is always good. This is the Wheel of Life,' said the lama, ' the same I showed thee in the hut at Ziglaur when the rain fell.'

' And to hear thee expound it.'

The lama's eyes lighted at the prospect of new listeners. ' To expound the Most Excellent Way is good. Have they any knowledge of Hindi, such as had the Keeper of Images? '

' A little, maybe.'

Hereat, simply as a child engrossed with a new game, the lama threw back his head and began the full-throated invocation of the Doctor of Divinity ere he opens the full doctrine. The strangers leaned on their alpenstocks and listened. Kim, squatting humbly, watched the red sunlight on their faces, and the blend and parting of their long shadows. They wore un-English leggings and curious girt-in belts that reminded him hazily of the pictures in a book at St. Xavier's library: ' The Adventures of a Young Naturalist in Mexico ' was its name. Yes, they looked very like the wonderful M. Sumichrast of that tale, and very unlike the ' highly unscrupulous folk ' of Hurree Babu's imagining. The coolies, earth-coloured and mute, crouched

reverently some twenty or thirty yards away, and the Babu, the slack of his
thin gear snapping like a marking-flag in the chill breeze, stood by with an
air of happy proprietorship.

'These are the men,' Hurree whispered, as the ritual went on and the
two whites followed the grass blade sweeping from Hell to Heaven and
back again. 'All their books are in the large kilta with the reddish top,—
books and reports and maps,—and I have seen a King's letter that either
Hilas or Bunar has written. They guard it most carefully. They have sent
nothing back from Hilas or Leh. That is sure.'

'Who is with them?'

'Only the beggar-coolies. They have no servants. They are so close they
cook their own food.'

'But what am I to do?'

'Wait and see. Only if any chance comes to me thou wilt know where
to seek for the papers.'

'This were better in Mahbub Ali's hands than a Bengali's,' said Kim
scornfully.

'There are more ways of getting to a sweetheart than butting down
a wall.'

'See here the Hell appointed for avarice and greed. Flanked upon the
one side by Desire and on the other by Weariness.' The lama warmed to
his work, and one of the strangers sketched him in the quick-fading light.

'That is enough,' the man said at last brusquely. 'I cannot understand
him, but I want that picture. He is a better artist than I. Ask him if he
will sell it.'

'He says "No, sar,"' the Babu replied. The lama, of course, would
no more have parted with his chart to a casual wayfarer than an archbishop
would pawn the holy vessels of a cathedral. All Tibet is full of cheap
reproductions of the Wheel; but the lama was an artist, as well as a wealthy
abbot in his own place.

'Perhaps in three days, or four, or ten, if I perceive that the Sahib is
a Seeker and of good understanding, I may myself draw him another. But
this was used for the initiation of a novice. Tell him so, hakim.'

'He wishes it now—for money.'

The lama shook his head slowly and began to fold up the Wheel. The
Russian, on his side, saw no more than an unclean old man haggling over
a dirty piece of paper. He drew out a handful of rupees, and snatched half-
jestingly at the chart, which tore in the lama's grip. A low murmur of
horror went up from the coolies—some of whom were Spiti men and, by
their lights, good Buddhists. The lama rose at the insult; his hand went to
the heavy iron pencase that is the priest's weapon, and the Babu danced in
agony.

'Now you see—you see why I wanted witnesses. They are highly un-
scrupulous people. Oh Sar! Sar! You must not hit holy man!'

'Chela! He has defiled the Written Word!'

It was too late. Before Kim could ward him off, the Russian struck the old man full on the face. Next instant he was rolling over and over down hill with Kim at his throat. The blow had waked every unknown Irish devil in the boy's blood, and the sudden fall of his enemy did the rest. The lama dropped to his knees, half-stunned; the coolies under their loads fled up the hill as fast as plainsmen run across the level. They had seen sacrilege unspeakable, and it behoved them to get away before the Gods and devils of the hills took vengeance. The Frenchman ran towards the lama, fumbling at his revolver with some notion of making him a hostage for his companion. A shower of cutting stones—hillmen are very straight shots—drove him away, and a coolie from Ao-chung snatched the lama into the stampede. All came about as swiftly as the sudden mountain-darkness.

'They have taken the baggage and all the guns,' yelled the Frenchman, firing blindly into the twilight.

'All right, Sar! All right! Don't shoot. I go to rescue,' and Hurree, pounding down the slope, cast himself bodily upon the delighted and astonished Kim, who was banging his breathless foe's head against a boulder.

'Go back to the coolies,' whispered the Babu in his ear. 'They have the baggage. The papers are in the kilta with the red top, but look through all. Take their papers, and specially the murasla (King's letter). Go! The other man comes!'

Kim tore up hill. A revolver-bullet rang on a rock by his side, and he cowered partridge-wise.

'If you shoot,' shouted Hurree, 'they will descend and annihilate us. I have rescued the gentleman, Sar. This is par-tic-ularly dangcrous.'

'By Jove!' Kim was thinking hard in English. 'This is dam-tight place, but I think it is self-defence.' He felt in his bosom for Mahbub's gift, and uncertainly—save for a few practice shots in the Bikaner desert, he had never used the little gun—pulled trigger.

'What did I say, Sar!' The Babu seemed to be in tears. 'Come down here and assist to reouocitate. We are all up a tree, I tell you.'

The shots ceased. There was a sound of stumbling feet, and Kim hurried upward through the gloom, swearing like a cat—or a country-bred.

'Did they wound thee, chela?' called the lama above him.

'No. And thou?' He dived into a clump of stunted firs.

'Unhurt. Come away. We go with these folk to Shamlegh-under-the-Snow.'

'But not before we have done justice,' a voice cried. 'I have got the Sahibs' guns—all four. Let us go down.'

'He struck the Holy One—we saw it! Our cattle will be barren—our wives will cease to bear! The snows will slide upon us as we go home. . . . Atop of all other oppression too!'

The little fir-clump filled with clamouring coolies—panic-stricken, and in their terror capable of anything. The man from Ao-chung clicked the breech-bolt of his gun impatiently, and made as to go down hill.

'Wait a little, Holy One; they cannot go far: wait till I return.'

'It is this person who has suffered wrong,' said the lama, his hand over his brow.

'For that very reason,' was the reply.

'If this person overlooks it, your hands are clean. Moreover, ye acquire merit by obedience.'

'Wait, and we will all go to Shamlegh together,' the man insisted.

For a moment, for just so long as it needs to stuff a cartridge into a breech-loader, the lama hesitated. Then he rose to his feet, and laid a finger on the man's shoulder.

'Hast thou heard? I say there shall be no killing—I who was Abbot of Suchzen. Is it any lust of thine to be re-born as a rat, or a snake under the eaves—a worm in the belly of the most mean beast? Is it thy wish to—'

The man from Ao-chung fell to his knees, for the voice boomed like a Tibetan devil-gong.

'Ai! ai!' cried the Spiti men. 'Do not curse us—do not curse him. It was but his zeal, Holy One! . . . Put down the rifle, fool!'

'Anger on anger! Evil on evil! There will be no killing. Let the priest-beaters go in bondage to their own acts. Just and sure is the Wheel, swerving not a hair! They will be born many times—in torment.' His head drooped, and he leaned heavily on Kim's shoulder.

'I have come near to great evil, chela,' he whispered in that dead hush under the pines. 'I was tempted to loose the bullet; and truly, in Tibet there would have been a heavy and a slow death for them. . . . He struck me across the face . . . upon the flesh . . .' He slid to the ground, breathing heavily, and Kim could hear the over-driven heart bump and check.

'Have they hurt him to the death?' said the Ao-chung man, while the others stood mute.

Kim knelt over the body in deadly fear. 'Nay,' he cried passionately, 'this is only a weakness.' Then he remembered that he was a white man, with a white man's camp-fittings at his service. 'Open the kiltas! The Sahibs may have a medicine.'

'Oho! Then I know it,' said the Ao-chung man with a laugh. 'Not for five years was I Yankling Sahib's shikarri without knowing that medicine. I too have tasted it. Behold!'

He drew from his breast a bottle of cheap whisky—such as is sold to explorers at Leh—and cleverly forced a little between the lama's teeth.

'So I did when Yankling Sahib twisted his foot beyond Astor. Aha! I have already looked into their baskets—but we will make fair division at Shamlegh. Give him a little more. It is good medicine. Feel! His heart goes better now. Lay his head down and rub a little on the chest. If he had waited quietly while I accounted for the Sahibs this would never have come. But perhaps the Sahibs may chase us here. Then it would not be wrong to shoot them with their own guns, heh?'

'One is paid, I think, already,' said Kim between his teeth. 'I kicked him in the groin as we went down hill. Would I had killed him!'

'It is well to be brave when one does not live in Rampur,' said one whose hut lay within a few miles of the Rajah's rickety palace. 'If we get a bad name among the Sahibs, none will employ us as shikarris any more.'

'Oh, but these are not Angrezi Sahibs—not merry-minded men like Fostum Sahib or Yankling Sahib. They are foreigners—they cannot speak Angrezi as do Sahibs.'

Here the lama coughed and sat up, groping for the rosary.

'There shall be no killing,' he murmured. 'Just is the Wheel! Evil on evil—'

'Nay, Holy One. We are all here.' The Ao-chung man timidly patted his feet. 'Except by thy order, no one shall be slain. Rest awhile. We will make a little camp here, and later, as the moon rises, we go to Shamlegh-under-the-Snow.'

'After a blow,' said a Spiti man sententiously, 'it is best to sleep.'

'There is, as it were, a dizziness at the back of my neck, and a pinching in it. Let me lay my head on thy lap, chela. I am an old man, but not free from passion. . . . We must think of the Cause of Things.'

'Give him a blanket. We dare not light a fire lest the Sahibs see.'

'Better get away to Shamlegh. None will follow us to Shamlegh.'

This was the nervous Rampur man.

'I have been Fostum Sahib's shikarri, and I am Yankling Sahib's shikarri. I should have been with Yankling Sahib now but for this cursed beegar (the corvee). Let two men watch below with the guns lest the Sahibs do more foolishness. I shall not leave this Holy One.'

They sat down a little apart from the lama, and, after listening awhile, passed round a water-pipe whose receiver was an old Day and Martin blacking-bottle. The glow of the red charcoal as it went from hand to hand lit up the narrow, blinking eyes, the high Chinese cheek-bones, and the bull-throats that melted away into the dark duffle folds round the shoulders. They looked like kobolds from some magic mine—gnomes of the hills in conclave. And while they talked, the voices of the snow-waters round them diminished one by one as the night-frost choked and clogged the runnels.

'How he stood up against us!' said a Spiti man admiring. 'I remember an old ibex, out Ladakh-way, that Dupont Sahib missed on a shoulder-shot, seven seasons back, standing up just like him. Dupont Sahib was a good shikarri.'

'Not as good as Yankling Sahib.' The Ao-chung man took a pull at the whisky-bottle and passed it over. 'Now hear me—unless any other man thinks he knows more.'

The challenge was not taken up.

'We go to Shamlegh when the moon rises. There we will fairly divide the baggage between us. I am content with this new little rifle and all its cartridges.'

'Are the bears only bad on thy holding?' said a mate, sucking at the pipe.

'No; but musk-pods are worth six rupees apiece now, and thy women can have the canvas of the tents and some of the cooking-gear. We will do all that at Shamlegh before dawn. Then we all go our ways, remembering that we have never seen or taken service with these Sahibs, who may, indeed, say that we have stolen their baggage.'

'That is well for thee, but what will our Rajah say?'

'Who is to tell him? Those Sahibs, who cannot speak our talk, or the Babu, who for his own ends gave us money? Will he lead an army against us? What evidence will remain? That we do not need we shall throw on Shamlegh midden, where no man has yet set foot.'

'Who is at Shamlegh this summer?' The place was only a grazing centre of three or four huts.

'The Woman of Shamlegh. She has no love for Sahibs, as we know. The others can be pleased with little presents; and here is enough for us all.' He patted the fat sides of the nearest basket.

'But—but—'

'I have said they are not true Sahibs. All their skins and heads were bought in the bazar at Leh. I know the marks. I showed them to ye last march.'

'True. They were all bought skins and heads. Some had even the moth in them.'

That was a shrewd argument, and the Ao-chung man knew his fellows.

'If the worst comes to the worst, I shall tell Yankling Sahib, who is a man of a merry mind, and he will laugh. We are not doing any wrong to any Sahibs whom we know. They are priest-beaters. They frightened us. We fled! Who knows where we dropped the baggage? Do ye think Yankling Sahib will permit down-country police to wander all over the hills, disturbing his game? It is a far cry from Simla to Chini, and farther from Shamlegh to Shamlegh midden.'

'So be it, but I carry the big kilta. The basket with the red top that the Sahibs pack themselves every morning.'

'Thus it is proved,' said the Shamlegh man adroitly, 'that they are Sahibs of no account. Who ever heard of Fostum Sahib, or Yankling Sahib, or even the little Peel Sahib that sits up of nights to shoot serow—I say, who ever heard of these Sahibs coming into the hills without a down-country cook, and a bearer, and—and all manner of well-paid, high-handed and oppressive folk in their tail? How can they make trouble? What of the kilta?'

'Nothing, but that it is full of the Written Word—books and papers in which they wrote, and strange instruments, as of worship.'

'Shamlegh midden will take them all.'

'True! But how if we insult the Sahibs' Gods thereby? I do not like to handle the Written Word in that fashion. And their brass idols are beyond my comprehension. It is no plunder for simple hill-folk.'

'The old man still sleeps. Hst! We will ask his chela.' The Ao-chung

man refreshed himself, and swelled with pride of leadership.

'We have here,' he whispered, 'a kilta whose nature we do not know.'

'But I do,' said Kim cautiously. The lama drew breath in natural, easy sleep, and Kim had been thinking of Hurree's last words. As a player of the Great Game, he was disposed just then to reverence the Babu. 'It is a kilta with a red top full of very wonderful things, not to be handled by fools.'

'I said it; I said it,' cried the bearer of that burden. 'Thinkest thou it will betray us?'

'Not if it be given to me. I will draw out its magic. Otherwise it will do great harm.'

'A priest always takes his share.' Whisky was demoralising the Ao-chung man.

'It is no matter to me,' Kim answered, with the craft of his mother-country. 'Share it among you, and see what comes!'

'Not I. I was only jesting. Give the order. There is more than enough for us all. We go our way from Shamlegh in the dawn.'

They arranged and re-arranged their artless little plans for another hour, while Kim shivered with cold and pride. The humour of the situation tickled the Irish and the Oriental in his soul. Here were the emissaries of the dread Power of the North, very possibly as great in their own land as Mahbub or Colonel Creighton, suddenly smitten helpless. One of them, he privately knew, would be lame for a time. They had made promises to Kings. To-night they lay out somewhere below him, chartless, foodless, tentless, gunless— except for Hurree Babu, guideless. And this collapse of their Great Game (Kim wondered to whom they would report it), this panicky bolt into the night, had come about through no craft of Hurree's or contrivance of Kim's, but simply, beautifully, and inevitably as the capture of Mahbub's faquir-friends by the zealous young policeman at Umballa.

'They are there—with nothing; and, by Jove, it is cold! I am here with all their things. Oh, they will be angry! I am sorry for Hurree Babu.'

Kim might have saved his pity, for though at that moment the Bengali suffered acutely in the flesh, his soul was puffed and lofty. A mile down the hill, on the edge of the pine-forest, two half-frozen men—one powerfully sick at intervals—were varying mutual recriminations with the most poignant abuse of the Babu, who seemed distraught with terror. They demanded a plan of action. He explained that they were very lucky to be alive; that their coolies, if not then stalking them, had passed beyond recall; that the Rajah, his master, was ninety miles away, and, so far from lending them money and a retinue for the Simla journey, would surely cast them into prison if he heard that they had hit a priest. He enlarged on this sin and its consequences till they bade him change the subject. Their one hope, said he, was unostentatious flight from village to village till they reached civilisation; and, for the hundredth time dissolved in tears, he demanded of the high stars why the Sahibs 'had beaten holy man.'

Ten steps would have taken Hurree into the creaking gloom utterly

beyond their reach—to the shelter and food of the nearest village, where glib-tongued doctors were scarce. But he preferred to endure cold, belly-pinch, bad words, and occasional blows in the company of his honoured employers. Crouched against a tree-trunk, he sniffed dolefully.

'And have you thought,' said the uninjured man hotly, 'what sort of spectacle we shall present wandering through these hills among these aborigines?'

Hurree Babu had thought of little else for some hours, but the remark was not to his address.

'We cannot wander! I can hardly walk,' groaned Kim's victim.

'Perhaps the holy man will be merciful in loving-kindness, Sar, otherwise—'

'I promise myself a peculiar pleasure in emptying my revolver into that young bonze when next we meet,' was the unchristian answer.

'Revolvers! Vengeance! Bonzes!' Hurree crouched lower. The war was breaking out afresh. 'Have you no consideration for our loss? The baggage! The baggage!' He could hear the speaker literally dancing on the grass. 'Everything we bore! Everything we have secured! Our gains! Eight months' work! Do you know what that means? "Decidedly it is we who can deal with Orientals!" Oh, you have done well.'

They fell to it in several tongues, and Hurree smiled. Kim was with the kiltas, and in the kiltas lay eight months of good diplomacy. There was no means of communicating with the boy, but he could be trusted. For the rest, he could so stage-manage the journey through the hills that Hilas, Bunar, and four hundred miles of hill-roads should tell the tale for a generation. Men who cannot control their own coolies are little respected in the Hills, and the hillman has a very keen sense of humour.

'If I had done it myself,' thought Hurree, 'it would not have been better; and, by Jove, now I think of it, of course I arranged it myself. How quick I have been! Just when I ran down hill I thought it! Thee outrage was accidental, but onlee me could have worked it—ah—for all it was dam well worth. Consider the moral effect upon these ignorant peoples! No treaties—no papers—no written documents at all—and me to interpret for them. How I shall laugh with the Colonel! I wish I had their papers also: but you cannot occupy two places in space simultaneously. Thatt is axiomatic.'

CHAPTER XIV

My brother kneels (so saith Kabir)
 To stone and brass in heathen-wise,
But in my brother's voice I hear
 My own unanswered agonies.
His God is as his Fates assign—
His prayer is all the world's—and mine.

KABIR

At moonrise the cautious coolies got under way. The lama, refreshed
by his sleep and the spirit, needed no more than Kim's shoulder to bear
him along—a silent, swift-striding man. They held the shale-sprinkled grass
for an hour, swept round the shoulder of an immortal cliff, and climbed
into a new country entirely blocked off from all sight of Chini valley. A
huge pasture-ground ran up fan-shaped to the living snow. At its base was
perhaps half an acre of flat land, on which stood a few soil and timber huts.
Behind them—for, hill-fashion, they were perched on the edge of all things
—the ground fell sheer two thousand feet to Shamlegh midden, where
never yet man has set foot.

The men made no motion to divide the plunder till they had seen the
lama bedded down in the best room of the place, with Kim shampooing
his feet, Mohammedan fashion.

' We will send food,' said the Ao-chung man, ' and the red-topped kilta.
By dawn there will be none to give evidence, one way or the other. If any-
thing is not needed in the kilta—see here! '

He pointed through the window—opening into space that was filled
with moonlight reflected from the snow—and threw out an empty whisky-
bottle.

' No need to listen for the fall. This is the world's end,' he said, and
swung off. The lama looked forth, a hand on either sill, with eyes that shone
like yellow opals. From the enormous pit before him white peaks lifted
themselves yearning to the moonlight. The rest was as the darkness of
interstellar space.

' These,' he said slowly, ' are indeed my Hills. Thus should a man abide,
perched above the world, separated from delights, considering vast matters.'

' Yes; if he has a chela to prepare tea for him, and to fold a blanket
for his head, and to chase out calving cows.'

A smoky lamp burned in a niche, but the full moonlight beat it down;
and by the mixed light, stooping above the food-bag and cups, Kim moved
like a tall ghost.

'Ai! But now I have let the blood cool my head still beats and drums, and there is a cord round the back of my neck.'

'No wonder. It was a strong blow. May he who dealt it—'

'But for my own passions there would have been no evil.'

'What evil? Thou hast saved the Sahibs from death they deserved a hundred times.'

'The lesson is not well learnt, chela.' The lama came to rest on a folded blanket, as Kim went forward with his evening routine. 'The blow was but a shadow upon a shadow. Evil in itself—my legs weary apace these latter days!—it met evil in me—anger, rage, and a lust to return evil. These wrought in my blood, woke tumult in my stomach, and dazzled my ears.' Here he drank scalding block-tea ceremonially, taking the hot cup from Kim's hand. 'Had I been passionless, the evil blow would have done only bodily evil—a scar, or a bruise—which is illusion. But my mind was not abstracted, for rushed in straightway a lust to let the Spiti men kill. In fighting that lust, my soul was torn and wrenched beyond a thousand blows. Not till I had repeated the Blessings (he meant the Buddhist Beatitudes) did I achieve calm. But the evil planted in me by that moment's carelessness works out to its end. Just is the Wheel, swerving not a hair! Learn the lesson, chela.'

'It is too high for me,' Kim muttered. 'I am still all shaken. I am glad I hurt the man.'

'I felt that sleeping upon thy knees, in the wood below. It disquieted me in my dreams—the evil in thy soul working through to mine. Yet on the other hand'—he loosed his rosary—'I have acquired merit by saving two lives—the lives of those that wronged me. Now I must see into the Cause of Things. The boat of my soul staggers.'

'Sleep, and be strong. That is wisest.'

'I meditate: there is a need greater than thou knowest.'

Till the dawn, hour after hour, as the moonlight paled on the high peaks, and that which had been belted blackness on the sides of the far hills showed as tender green forest, the lama stared fixedly at the wall. From time to time he groaned. Outside the barred door, where discomfited kine came to ask for their old stable, Shamlegh and the coolies gave itself up to plunder and riotous living. The Ao-chung man was their leader, and once they had opened the Sahibs' tinned foods and found that they were very good they dared not turn back. Shamlegh kitchen-midden took the dunnage.

When Kim, after a night of bad dreams, stole forth to brush his teeth in the morning chill, a fair-coloured woman with turquoise-studded headgear drew him aside.

'The others have gone. They left thee this kilta as the promise was. I do not love Sahibs, but thou wilt make us a charm in return for it. We do not wish little Shamlegh to get a bad name on account of the—accident. I am the Woman of Shamlegh.' She looked him over with bold, bright eyes, unlike the usual furtive glance of hillwomen.

'Assuredly. But it must be done in secret.'

She raised the heavy kilta like a toy and slung it into her own hut.

'Out and bar the door! Let none come near till it is finished.'

'But afterwards—we may talk?'

Kim tilted the kilta on the floor—a cascade of Survey-instruments, books, diaries, letters, maps, and queerly scented native correspondence. At the very bottom was an embroidered bag covering a sealed, gilded, and illuminated document such as one King sends to another. Kim caught his breath with delight, and reviewed the situation from a Sahib's point of view.

'The books I do not want. Besides, they are logarithms—Survey, I suppose.' He laid them aside. 'The letters I do not understand, but Colonel Creighton will. They must all be kept. The maps—they draw better maps than me—of course. All the native letters—oho!—and particularly the murasla.' He sniffed the embroidered bag. 'That must be from Hilas or Bunar, and Hurree Babu spoke truth. By Jove! It is a fine haul. I wish Hurree could know. . . . The rest must go out of the window.' He fingered a superb prismatic compass and the shiny top of a theodolite. But after all, a Sahib cannot very well steal, and the things might be inconvenient evidence later. He sorted out every scrap of manuscript, every map, and the native letters. They made one softish slab. The three locked ferril-backed books, with five worn pocketbooks, he put aside.

'The letters and the murasla I must carry inside my coat and under my belt, and the hand-written books I must put into the food-bag. It will be very heavy. No. I do not think there is anything more. If there is, the coolies have thrown it down the khud, so thatt is all right. Now you go too.' He repacked the kilta with all he meant to lose, and hove it up on to the window-sill. A thousand feet below lay a long, lazy, round-shouldered bank of mist, as yet untouched by the morning sun. A thousand feet below that was an hundred-year-old pine-forest. He could see the green tops looking like a bed of moss when a wind-eddy thinned the cloud.

'No! I don't think any one will go after you!'

The wheeling basket vomited its contents as it dropped. The theodolite hit a jutting cliff-ledge and exploded like a shell; the books, inkstand, paint-boxes, compasses, and rulers showed for a few seconds like a swarm of bees. Then they vanished; and, though Kim, hanging half out of window, strained his young ears, never a sound came up from the gulf.

'Five hundred—a thousand rupees could not buy them,' he thought sorrowfully. 'It was verree wasteful, but I have all their other stuff—everything they did—I hope. Now how the deuce am I to tell Hurree Babu, and whatt the deuce am I to do? And my old man is sick. I must tie up the letters in oilcloth. That is something to do first—else they will get all sweated. . . . And I am all alone!' He bound them into a neat packet, swedging down the stiff, sticky oilcloth at the corners, for his roving life had made him as methodical as an old hunter in matters of the road. Then with double care he packed away the books at the bottom of the food-bag.

The woman rapped at the door.

'But thou hast made no charm,' she said, looking about.

'There is no need.' Kim had completely overlooked the necessity for a little patter-talk. The woman laughed at his confusion irreverently.

'None—for thee. Thou canst cast a spell by the mere winking of an eye. But think of us poor people when thou art gone! They were all too drunk last night to hear a woman. Thou art not drunk?'

'I am a priest.' Kim had recovered himself, and, the woman being aught but unlovely, thought best to stand on his office.

'I warned them that the Sahibs will be angry and will make an inquisition and a report to the Rajah. There is also the Babu with them. Clerks have long tongues.'

'Is that all thy trouble?' The plan rose fully formed in Kim's mind, and he smiled ravishingly.

'Not all,' quoth the woman, putting out a hard brown hand all covered with turquoises set in silver.

'I can finish that in a breath,' he went on quickly. 'The Babu is the very hakim (thou hast heard of him?) who was wandering among the hills by Ziglaur. I know him.'

'He will tell for the sake of a reward. Sahibs cannot distinguish one hillman from another, but Babus have eyes for men—and women.'

'Carry a word to him from me.'

'There is nothing I would not do for thee.'

He accepted the compliment calmly, as men must in lands where women make the love, tore a leaf from a note-book, and with a patent indelible pencil wrote in gross Shikast—the script that bad little boys use when they write dirt on walls: 'I have everything that they have written: their pictures of the country, and many letters. Especially the murasla. Tell me what to do. I am at Shamlegh-under-the Snow. The old man is sick.'

'Take this to him. It will altogether shut his mouth. He cannot have gone far.'

'Indeed no. They are still in the forest across the spur. Our children went to watch them when the light came, and have cried the news as they moved.'

Kim looked his astonishment; but from the edge of the sheep-pasture floated a shrill, kite-like trill. A child tending cattle had picked it up from a brother or sister on the far side of the slope that commanded Chini valley.

'My husbands are also out there gathering wood.' She drew a handful of walnuts from her bosom, split one neatly, and began to eat. Kim affected blank ignorance.

'Dost thou not know the meaning of the walnut—priest?' she said coyly, and handed him the half-shells.

'Well thought of.' He slipped the piece of paper between them quickly. 'Hast thou a little wax to close them on this letter?'

The woman sighed aloud, and Kim relented.

'There is no payment till service has been rendered. Carry this to the Babu, and say it was sent by the Son of the Charm.'

'Ai! Truly! Truly! By a magician—who is like a Sahib.'

'Nay, Son of the Charm: and ask if there be any answer.'

'But if he offer a rudeness? I—I am afraid.'

Kim laughed. 'He is, I have no doubt, very tired and very hungry. The Hills make cold bedfellows. Hai, my'—it was on the tip of his tongue to say Mother, but he turned it to Sister—'thou art a wise and witty woman. By this time all the villages know what has befallen the Sahibs—eh?'

'True. News was at Ziglaur by midnight, and by to-morrow should be at Kotgarh. The villages are both afraid and angry.'

'No need. Tell the villages to feed the Sahibs and pass them on, in peace. We must get them quietly away from our valleys. To steal is one thing—to kill another. The Babu will understand, and there will be no after-complaints. Be swift. I must tend my master when he wakes.'

'So be it. After service—thou hast said?—comes the reward. I am the Woman of Shamlegh, and I hold from the Rajah. I am no common bearer of babes. Shamlegh is thine: hoof and horn and hide, milk and butter. Take or leave.'

She turned resolutely uphill, her silver necklaces clicking on her broad breast, to meet the morning sun fifteen hundred feet above them. This time Kim thought in the vernacular as he waxed down the oilskin edges of the packets.

'How can a man follow the Way or the Great Game when he is eternally pestered by women? There was that girl at Akrola by the Ford; and there was the scullion's wife behind the dovecot—not counting the others—and now comes this one! When I was a child it was well enough, but now I am a man and they will not regard me as a man. Walnuts indeed! Ho! ho! It is almonds in the Plains!'

He went out to levy on the village—not with a begging-bowl, which might do for down-country, but in the manner of a prince. Shamlegh's summer population is only three families—four women and eight or nine men. They were all full of tinned meats and mixed drinks, from ammoniated quinine to white vodka, for they had taken their full share in the overnight loot. The neat Continental tents had been cut up and shared long ago, and there were patent aluminum saucepans abroad.

But they considered the lama's presence a perfect safeguard against all consequences, and impenitently brought Kim of their best—even to a drink of chang—the barley-beer that comes from Ladakh-way. Then they thawed out in the sun, and sat with their legs hanging over infinite abysses, chattering, laughing, and smoking. They judged India and its Government solely from their experience of wandering Sahibs who had employed them or their friends as shikarris. Kim heard tales of shots missed upon ibex, serow, or markhor, by Sahibs twenty years in their graves—every detail lighted from behind like twigs on tree-tops seen against lightning. They

told him of their little diseases, and, more important, the diseases of their
tiny, sure-footed cattle; of trips as far as Kotgarh, where the strange mission-
aries live, and beyond even to marvellous Simla, where the streets are paved
with silver, and any one, look you, can get service with the Sahibs, who ride
about in two-wheeled carts and spend money with a spade. Presently, grave
and aloof, walking very heavily, the lama joined himself to the chatter under
the eaves, and they gave him great room. The thin air refreshed him, and
he sat on the edge of precipices with the best of them, and, when talk
languished, flung pebbles into the void. Thirty miles away, as the eagle
flies, lay the next range, seamed and channelled and pitted with little patches
of brush—forests, each a day's dark march. Behind the village, Shamlegh
hill itself cut off all view to southward. It was like sitting in a swallow's nest
under the eaves of the roof of the world.

From time to time the lama stretched out his hand, and with a little,
low-voiced prompting would point out the road to Spiti and north across
the Parungla.

' Beyond, where the hills lie thickest, lies De-ch'en ' (he meant Han-le),
' the great Monastery. s'Tag-stan-ras-ch'en built it, and of him there runs
this tale.' Whereupon he told it: a fantastic piled narrative of bewitchment
and miracles that set Shamlegh agasping. Turning west a little, he speered
for the green hills of Kulu, and sought Kailung under the glaciers. ' For
thither came I in the old, old days. From Leh I came, over the Baralachi.'

' Yes, yes; we know it,' said the far-faring people of Shamlegh.

' And I slept two nights with the priests of Kailung. These are the hills
of my delight! Shadows blessed above all other shadows! There my eyes
opened on this world; there my eyes were opened to this world; there I
found Enlightenment; and there I girt my loins for my Search. Out of the
Hills I came—the high Hills and the strong winds. Oh, just is the Wheel! '
He blessed them in detail—the great glaciers, the naked rocks, the piled
moraines and tumbled shale; dry up-land, hidden salt-lake, age-old timber
and fruitful water-shot valley one after the other, as a dying man blesses his
folk, and Kim marvelled at his passion.

' Yes—yes. There is no place like our Hills,' said the people of
Shamlegh. And they fell to wondering how a man could live in the hot ter-
rible Plains where the cattle run as big as elephants, unfit to plough on a
hillside; where village touches village, they had heard, for a hundred miles;
where folk went about stealing in gangs, and what the robbers spared the
Police carried utterly away.

So the still forenoon wore through, and at the end of it Kim's messenger
dropped from the steep pasture as unbreathed as when she had set out.

' I sent a word to the hakim,' Kim explained, while she made reverence.

' He joined himself to the idolaters? Nay, I remember he did a healing
upon one of them. He has acquired merit, though the healed employed his
strength for evil. Just is the Wheel! What of the hakim? '

' I feared that thou hadst been bruised and—and I knew he was wise.'

Kim took the waxed walnut-shell and read in English on the back of his note: 'Your favour received. Cannot get away from present company at present, but shall take them into Simla. After which, hope to rejoin you. Inexpedient to follow angry gentlemen. Return by same road you came, and will overtake. Highly gratified about correspondence due to my fore-thought.' 'He says, Holy One, that he will escape from the idolaters, and will return to us. Shall we wait awhile at Shamlegh, then?'

The lama looked long and lovingly upon the hills and shook his head.

'That may not be, chela. From my bones outward I do desire it, but it is forbidden. I have seen the Cause of Things.'

'Why? When the Hills give thee back thy strength day by day? Remember we were weak and fainting down below there in the Doon.'

'I became strong to do evil and to forget. A brawler and a swashbuckler upon the hillsides was I.' Kim bit back a smile. 'Just and perfect is the Wheel, swerving not a hair. When I was a man—a long time ago—I did pilgrimage to Guru Ch'wan among the poplars' (he pointed Bhotanwards), 'where they keep the Sacred Horse.'

'Quiet, be quiet!' said Shamlegh, all arow. 'He speaks of Jamlin-nin-k'or, The Horse That Can Go Round The World In a Day.'

'I speak to my chela only,' said the lama, in gentle reproof, and they scattered like frost on south eaves of a morning. 'I did not seek truth in those days, but the talk of doctrine. All illusion! I drank the beer and ate the bread of Guru Ch'wan. Next day one said: "We go out to fight Sangor Gutok down the valley to discover (mark again how Lust is tied to Anger!) which abbot shall bear rule in the valley, and take the profit of the prayers they print at Sangor Gutok." I went, and we fought a day.'

'But how, Holy One?'

'With our long pencases as I could have shown. . . . I say, we fought under the poplars, both abbots and all the monks, and one laid open my forehead to the bone. See!' He tilted back his cap and showed a puckered silvery scar. 'Just and perfect is the Wheel! Yesterday the scar itched, and after fifty years I recalled how it was dealt and the face of him who dealt it; dwelling a little in illusion. Followed that which thou didst see—strife and stupidity. Just is the Wheel! The idolater's blow fell upon the scar. Then I was shaken in my soul: my soul was darkened, and the boat of my soul rocked upon the waters of illusion. Not till I came to Shamlegh could I meditate upon the Cause of Things, or trace the running grass-roots of Evil. I strove all the long night.'

'But, Holy One, thou art innocent of all evil. May I be thy sacrifice!'

Kim was genuinely distressed at the old man's sorrow, and Mahbub Ali's phrase slipped out unawares.

'In the dawn,' he went on more gravely, ready rosary clicking between the slow sentences, 'came enlightenment. It is here. . . . I am an old man . . . hill-bred, hill-fed, never to sit down among my Hills. Three years I travelled through Hind, but—can earth be stronger than Mother Earth? My stupid

body yearned to the Hills and the snow of the Hills, from below there. I said, and it is true, my Search is sure. So, at the Kulu woman's house I turned hillward, over-persuaded by myself. There is no blame to the hakim. He—following Desire—foretold that the Hills would make me strong. They strengthened me to do evil, to forget my Search. I delighted in life and the lust of life. I desired strong slopes to climb. I cast about to find them. I measured the strength of my body, which is evil, against the high hills. I made a mock of thee when thy breath came short under Jamnotri. I jested when thou wouldst not face the snow of the pass.'

'But what harm? I was afraid. It was just. I am not a hillman; and I loved thee for thy new strength.'

'More than once I remember,' he rested his cheek dolefully on his hand, 'I sought thy praise and the hakim's for the mere strength of my legs. Thus evil followed evil till the cup was full. Just is the Wheel! All Hind for three years did me all honour. From the Fountain of Wisdom in the Wonder House to '—he smiled—' a little child playing by a big gun— the world prepared my road. And why? '

'Because we loved thee. It is only the fever of the blow. I myself am still sick and shaken.'

'No! It was because I was upon the Way—tuned as are sinen (cymbals) to the purpose of the Law. I departed from that ordinance. The tune was broken: followed the punishment. In my own Hills, on the edge of my own country, in the very place of my evil desire, comes the buffet—here! ' (He touched his brow.) 'As a novice is beaten when he misplaces the cups, so am I beaten, who was Abbot of Suchzen. No word, look you, but a blow, chela.'

'But the Sahibs did not know thee, Holy One? '

'We were well matched. Ignorance and Lust met Ignorance and Lust upon the road, and they begat Anger. The blow was a sign to me, who am no better than a strayed yak, that my place is not here. Who can read the Cause of an act is half-way to Freedom! " Back to the path," says the Blow. " The Hills are not for thee. Thou canst not choose Freedom and go in bondage to the delight of life." '

'If we had never met that thrice-cursed Russian! '

'Our Lord Himself cannot make the Wheel swing backward. And for my merit that I had acquired I gain yet another sign.' He put his hand in his bosom, and drew forth the Wheel of Life. 'Look! I considered this after I had meditated. There remains untorn by the idolater no more than the breadth of my finger-nail.'

'I see.'

'So much, then, is the span of my life in this body. I have served the Wheel all my days. Now the Wheel serves me. But for the merit I have acquired in guiding thee upon the Way, there would have been added to me yet another life ere I had found my River. Is it plain, chela? '

Kim stared at the brutally disfigured chart. From left to right diagonally

the rent ran—from the Eleventh House where Desire gives birth to the Child (as it is drawn by Tibetans)—across the human and animal worlds, to the Fifth House—the empty House of the Senses. The logic was unanswerable.

'Before our Lord won enlightenment,' the lama folded all away with reverence, 'He was tempted. I too have been tempted, but it is finished. The Arrow fell in the Plains—not in the Hills. Therefore, what make we here?'

'Shall we at least wait for the hakim?'

'I know how long I live in this body. What can a hakim do?'

'But thou art all sick and shaken. Thou canst not walk.'

'How can I be sick if I see Freedom?' He rose unsteadily to his feet.

'Then I must get food from the village. Oh, the weary Road!' Kim felt that he too needed rest.

'That is lawful. Let us eat and go. The Arrow fell in Plains . . . but I yielded to Desire. Made ready, chela.'

Kim turned to the woman with the turquoise head-gear who had been idly pitching pebbles over the cliff. She smiled very kindly.

'I found him like a strayed buffalo in a corn-field—the Babu; snorting and sneezing with cold. He was so hungry that he forgot his dignity and gave me sweet words. The Sahibs have nothing.' She flung out an empty palm. 'One is very sick about the stomach. Thy work?'

Kim nodded, with a bright eye.

'I spoke to the Bengali first—and to the people of a nearby village after. The Sahibs will be given food as they need it—nor will the people ask money. The plunder is already distributed. That makes lying speeches to the Sahibs. Why does he not leave them?'

'Out of the greatness of his heart.'

''Was never a Bengali yet had one bigger than a dried walnut. But it is no matter. . . . Now as to walnuts. After service comes reward. I have said the village is thine.'

'It is my loss,' Kim began. 'Even now I had planned desirable things in my heart which'—there is no need to go through the compliments proper to these occasions. He sighed deeply . . . 'But my master, led by a vision—'

'Huh! What can old eyes see except a full begging-bowl?'

'—turns from this village to the Plains again.'

'Bid him stay.'

Kim shook his head. 'I know my Holy One, and his rage if he be crossed,' he replied impressively. 'His curses shake the Hills.'

'Pity they did not save him from a broken head! I heard that thou wast the tiger-hearted one who smote the Sahib. Let him dream a little longer. Stay!'

'Hillwoman,' said Kim, with austerity that could not harden the outlines of his young oval face, 'these matters are too high for thee.'

'The Gods be good to us! Since when have men and women been other than men and women?'

'A priest is a priest. He says he will go upon this hour. I am his chela, and I go with him. We need food for the Road. He is an honoured guest in all the villages, but'—he broke into a pure boyish grin—'the food here is good. Give me some.'

'What if I do not give it thee? I am the woman of this village.'

'Then I curse thee—a little—not greatly, but enough to remember.' He could not help smiling.

'Thou hast cursed me already by the down-dropped eyelash and the uplifted chin. Curses? What should I care for mere words?' She clenched her hands upon her bosom. . . . 'But I would not have thee to go in anger, thinking hardly of me—a gatherer of cow-dung and grass at Shamlegh, but still a woman of substance.'

'I think nothing,' said Kim, 'but that I am grieved to go, for I am very tired, and that we need food. Here is the bag.'

The woman snatched it angrily. 'I was foolish,' said she. 'Who is thy woman in the Plains? Fair or black? I was fair once. Laughest thou? Once, long ago, if thou canst believe, a Sahib looked on me with favour. Once, long ago, I wore European clothes at the Mission-house yonder.' She pointed towards Kotgarh. 'Once, long ago, I was Ker-lis-ti-an and spoke English—as the Sahibs speak it. Yes. My Sahib said he would return and wed me—yes, wed me. He went away—I had nursed him when he was sick—but he never returned. Then I saw that the Gods of the Kerlistians lied, and I went back to my own people. . . . I have never set eyes on a Sahib since. (Do not laugh at me. The fit is past, little priestling.) Thy face and thy walk and thy fashion of speech put me in mind of my Sahib, though thou art only a wandering mendicant to whom I give a dole. Curse me? Thou canst neither curse nor bless!' She set her hands on her hips and laughed bitterly. 'Thy Gods are lies; thy works are lies; thy words are lies. There are no Gods under all the heavens. I know it. . . . But for a while I thought it was my Sahib come back, and he was my God. Yes, once I made music on a pianno in the Mission-house at Kotgarh. Now I give alms to priests who are hea-tthen.' She wound up with the English word, and tied the mouth of the brimming bag.

'I wait for thee, chela,' said the lama, leaning against the door-post.

The woman swept the tall figure with her eyes. 'He walk? He cannot cover half a mile. Whither would old bones go?'

At this Kim, already perplexed by the lama's collapse, and foreseeing the weight of the bag, fairly lost his temper.

'What is it to thee, woman of ill-omen, where he goes?'

'Nothing—but something to thee, priest with a Sahib's face. Wilt thou carry him on thy shoulders?'

'I go to the Plains. None must hinder my return. I have wrestled with my soul till I am strengthless. The stupid body is spent, and we are far from the Plains.'

' Behold! ' she said simply, and drew aside to let Kim see his own utter helplessness. ' Curse me. May be it will give him strength. Make a charm! Call on thy great God. Thou art a priest.' She turned away.

The lama had squatted limply, still holding by the door-post. One cannot strike down an old man that he recovers again like a boy in a night. Weakness bowed him to the earth, but his eyes that hung on Kim were alive and imploring.

' It is all well,' said Kim. ' It is the thin air that weakens thee. In a little while we go! It is the mountain-sickness. I too am a little sick at stomach,' . . . and he knelt and comforted with such poor words as came first to his lips. Then the woman returned, more erect than ever.

' Thy Gods useless, heh? Try mine. I am the Woman of Shamlegh.' She hailed hoarsely, and there came out of a cow-pen her two husbands and three others with a dooli, the rude native litter of the Hills, that they use for carrying the sick and for visits of state. ' These cattle,' she did not condescend to look at them, ' are thine for so long as thou shalt need.'

' But we will not go Simla-way. We will not go near the Sahibs,' cried the first husband.

' They will not run away as the others did, nor will they steal baggage. Two I know for weaklings. Stand to the rear-pole, Sonoo and Taree.' They obeyed swiftly. ' Lower now, and lift in that holy man. I will see to the village and your virtuous wives till ye return.'

' When will that be? '

' Ask the priests. Do not pester me. Lay the food-bag at the foot, it balances better so.'

' Oh, Holy One, thy Hills are kinder than our Plains! ' cried Kim, relieved, as the lama tottered to the litter. ' It is a very king's bed—a place of honour and ease. And we owe it to— '

' A woman of ill-omen. I need thy blessings as much as I do thy curses. It is my order and none of thine. Lift and away! Here! Hast thou money for the road? '

She beckoned Kim to her hut, and stooped above a battered English cash-box under her cot.

' I do not need anything,' said Kim, angered where he should have been grateful. ' I am already rudely loaded with favours.'

She looked up with a curious smile and laid a hand on his shoulder. ' At least, thank me. I am foul-faced and a hillwoman, but, as thy talk goes, I have acquired merit. Shall I show thee how the Sahibs render thanks? ' and her hard eyes softened.

' I am but a wandering priest,' said Kim, his eyes lighting in answer. ' Thou needest neither my blessings nor my curses.'

' Nay. But for one little moment—thou canst overtake the dooli in ten strides—if thou wast a Sahib, shall I show thee what thou wouldst do? '

' How if I guess, though? ' said Kim, and putting his arm round her waist, he kissed her on the cheek, adding in English: ' Thank you verree much, my dear.'

Kissing is practically unknown among Asiatics, which may have been the reason that she leaned back with wide open eyes and a face of panic.

'Next time,' Kim went on, 'you must not be so sure of your heathen priests. Now I say good-bye.' He held out his hand English-fashion. She took it mechanically. 'Good-bye, my dear.'

'Good-bye, and—and'—she was remembering her English words one by one—'you will come back again? Good-bye, and—thee God bless you.'

Half an hour later, as the creaking litter jolted up the hill path that leads south-easterly from Shamlegh, Kim saw a tiny figure at the hut door waving a white rag.

'She has acquired merit beyond all others,' said the lama. 'For to set a man upon the way to Freedom is half as great as though she had herself found it.'

'Umm,' said Kim thoughtfully, considering the past. 'It may be that I have acquired merit also. . . . At least she did not treat me like a child.' He hitched the front of his robe, where lay the slab of documents and maps, restowed the precious food-bag at the lama's feet, laid his hand on the litter edge, and buckled down to the slow pace of the grunting husbands.

'These also acquire merit,' said the lama, after three miles.

'More than that, they shall be paid in silver,' quoth Kim. The Woman of Shamlegh had given it to him; and it was only fair, he argued, that her men should earn it back again.

CHAPTER XV

I'd not give room for an Emperor—
I'd hold my road for a King.
To the Triple Crown I'd not bow down—
But this is a different thing!
I'll not fight with the Powers of Air—
Sentries pass him through!
Drawbridge let fall—He's the Lord of us all—
The Dreamer whose dream came true!
THE SIEGE OF THE FAIRIES

Two hundred miles north of Chini, on the blue shale of Ladakh, lies Yankling Sahib, the merry-minded man, spy-glassing wrathfully across the ridges for some sign of his pet tracker—a man from Ao-chung. But that renegade, with a new Mannlicher rifle and two hundred cartridges, is elsewhere, shooting musk-deer for the market, and Yankling Sahib will learn next season how very ill he has been.

Up the valleys of Bushahr—the far-beholding eagles of the Himalayas swerve at his new blue-and-white gored umbrella—hurries a Bengali, once fat and well-looking, now lean and weather-worn. He has received the thanks of two foreigners of distinction, piloted not unskilfully to Mashobra tunnel which leads to the great and gay capital of India. It was not his fault that, blanketed by wet mists, he conveyed them past the telegraph-station and European colony of Kotgarh. It was not his fault, but that of the Gods, of whom he discoursed so engagingly, that he led them into the borders of Nahan, where the Rajah of that state mistook them for deserting British soldiery. Hurree Babu explained the greatness and glory, in their own country, of his companions, till the drowsy kinglet smiled. He explained it to every one who asked—many times—aloud—variously. He begged food, arranged accommodation, proved a skilful leech for an injury of the groin—such a blow as one may receive rolling down a rock-covered hillside in the dark—and in all things indispensable. The reason of his friendliness did him credit. With millions of fellow-serfs, he had learned to look upon Russia as the great deliverer from the North. He was a fearful man. He had been afraid that he could not save his illustrious employers from the anger of an excited peasantry. He himself would just as lief hit a holy man as not, but. . . . He was deeply grateful and sincerely rejoiced that he had done his ' little possible ' towards bringing their venture to—barring the lost baggage—a successful issue. He had forgotten the blows; denied that any blows had been dealt that unseemly first night under the pines. He asked

neither pension nor retaining fee, but, if they deemed him worthy, would they write him a testimonial? It might be useful to him later, if others, their friends, came over the Passes. He begged them to remember him in their future greatnesses, for he 'opined subtly' that he, even he, Mohendro Lal Dutt, M. A. of Calcutta, had 'done the state some service.'

They gave him a certificate praising his courtesy, helpfulness, and un-erring skill as a guide. He put it in his waist-belt and sobbed with emotion; they had endured so many dangers together. He led them at high noon along crowded Simla Mall to the Alliance Bank of Simla, where they wished to establish their identity. Thence he vanished like a dawn-cloud on Jakko.

Behold him, too fine drawn to sweat, too pressed to vaunt the drugs in his little brass-bound box, ascending Shamlegh slope, a just man made perfect. Watch him, all Babudom laid aside, smoking at noon on a cot, while a woman with turquoise-studded head-gear points south-easterly across the bare grass. Litters, she says, do not travel as fast as single men, but his birds should now be in the Plains. The holy man would not stay though Lispeth pressed him. The Babu groans heavily, girds up his huge loins, and is off again. He does not care to travel after dusk; but his days' marches—there is none to enter them in a book—would astonish folk who mock at his race. Kindly villagers, remembering the Dacca drug-vendor of two months ago, give him shelter against evil spirits of the wood. He dreams of Bengali Gods, University text-books of education, and the Royal Society, London, England. Next dawn the bobbing blue-and-white umbrella goes forward.

On the edge of the Doon, Mussoorie well behind them and the Plains spread out in golden dust before, rests a worn litter in which—all the Hills know it—lies a sick lama who seeks a River for his healing. Villages have almost come to blows over the honour of bearing it, for not only has the lama given them blessings, but his disciple good money—full one-third Sahibs' prices. Twelve miles a day has the dooli travelled, as the greasy, rubbed pole-ends show, and by roads that few Sahibs use. Over the Nilang Pass in storm when the driven snow-dust filled every fold of the impassive lama's drapery; between the black horns of Raieng where they heard the whistle of the wild goats through the clouds; pitching and strained on the shale below; hard-held between shoulder and clenched jaw when they rounded the hideous curves of the Cut Road under Bhagirati; swinging and creaking to the steady jog-trot of the descent into the Valley of the Waters; pressed along the steamy levels of that locked valley; up, up and out again, to meet the roaring gusts off Kedarnath; set down of mid-days in the dun gloom of kindly oak-forests; passed from village to village in dawn-chill, when even devotees may be forgiven for swearing at impatient holy men; or by torchlight, when the least fearful think of ghosts—the dooli has reached her last stage. The little hill-folk sweat in the modified heat of the lower Sewaliks, and gather round the priests for their blessing and their wage.

'Ye have acquired merit,' says the lama. 'Merit greater than your knowing. And ye will return to the Hills,' he sighs.

' Surely. The high hills as soon as may be.' The bearer rubs his shoulder, drinks water, spits it out again, and readjusts his grass sandal. Kim—his face is drawn and tired—pays very small silver from his belt, heaves out the food-bag, crams an oilskin packet—they are holy writings—into his bosom, and helps the lama to his feet. The peace has come again into the old man's eyes, and he does not look for the hills to fall down and crush him as he did that terrible night when they were delayed by the flooded river.

The men pick up the dooli and swing out of sight between the scrub clumps.

The lama raises a hand toward the rampart of the Himalayas. ' Not with you, O blessed among all hills, fell the Arrow of Our Lord! And never shall I breathe your air again! '

' But thou art ten times the stronger man in this good air,' says Kim, for to his wearied soul appeal the well-cropped, kindly plains. ' Here, or hereabouts, fell the Arrow, yes. We will go very softly, perhaps a kos a day, for the Search is sure. But the bag weighs heavy.'

' Ay, our Search is sure. I have come out of great temptation.'

.

It was never more than a couple of miles a day now, and Kim's shoulders bore all the weight of it—the burden of an old man, the burden of the heavy food-bag with the locked books, the load of the writings on his heart, and the details of the daily routine. He begged in the dawn, set blankets for the lama's meditation, held the weary head on his lap through the noon-day heats, fanning away the flies till his wrist ached, begged again in the evenings, and rubbed the lama's feet, who rewarded him with promise of Freedom— to-day, to-morrow, or, at furthest, the next day.

' Never was such a chela. I doubt at times whether Ananda more faithfully nursed Our Lord. And thou art a Sahib? When I was a man— a long time ago—I forgot that. Now I look upon thee often, and every time I remember that thou art a Sahib. It is strange.'

' Thou hast said there is neither black nor white. Why plague me with this talk, Holy One? Let me rub the other foot. It vexes me. I am not a Sahib. I am thy chela, and my head is heavy on my shoulders.'

' Patience a little! We reach Freedom together. Then thou and I, upon the far bank of the River, will look back upon our lives as in the Hills we saw our days' marches laid out behind us. Perhaps I was once a Sahib.'

' 'Was never a Sahib like thee, I swear it.'

' I am certain the Keeper of the Images in the Wonder House was in past life a very wise abbot. But even his spectacles do not make my eyes see. There fall shadows when I would look steadily. No matter—we know the tricks of the poor stupid carcass—shadow changing to another shadow. I am bound by the illusion of Time and Space. How far came we to-day in the flesh? '

' Perhaps half a kos.' Three-quarters of a mile, and it was a weary march.

'Half a kos. Ha! I went ten thousand thousand in the spirit. How we are all lapped and swathed and swaddled in these senseless things.' He looked at his thin blue veined hand that found the beads so heavy. ' Chela, hast thou never a wish to leave me? '

Kim thought of the oilskin packet and the books in the food-bag. If some one duly authorised would only take delivery of them the Great Game might play itself for aught he then cared. He was tired and hot in his head, and a cough that came from the stomach worried him.

' No,' he said almost sternly. ' I am not a dog or a snake to bite when I have learned to love.'

' Thou art too tender for me.'

' Not that either. I have moved in one matter without consulting thee. I have sent a message to the Kulu woman by that woman who gave us the goat's milk this morn, saying that thou wast a little feeble and would need a litter. I beat myself in my mind that I did not do it when we entered the Doon. We stay in this place till the litter returns.'

' I am content. She is a woman with a heart of gold, as thou sayest, but a talker—something of a talker.'

' She will not weary thee. I have looked to that also. Holy One, my heart is very heavy for my many carelessnesses towards thee.' An hysterical catch rose in his throat. ' I have walked thee too far; I have not picked good food always for thee; I have not considered the heat; I have talked to people on the road and left thee alone. . . . I have—I have . . . Hai mai! But I love thee . . . and it is all too late. . . . I was a child. . . . Oh why was I not a man! . . .' Overborne by strain, fatigue, and the weight beyond his years, Kim broke down and sobbed at the lama's feet.

' What a to-do is here,' said the old man gently. ' Thou hast never stepped a hair's breadth from the Way of Obedience. Neglect me? Child, I have lived on thy strength as an old tree lives on the lime of a new wall. Day by day since Shamlegh down, I have stolen strength from thee. Therefore, not through any sin of thine art thou weakened. It is the Body—the silly, stupid Body—that speaks now. Not the assured Soul. Be comforted! Know at least the devils that thou fightest. They are earth-born—children of illusion. We will go to the woman from Kulu. She shall acquire merit in housing us, and specially in tending me. Thou shalt run free till strength returns. I had forgotten the stupid Body. If there be any blame, I bear it. But we are too close to the Gates of Deliverance to weigh blame. I could praise thee, but what need? In a little—in a very little—we shall sit beyond all needs.'

And so he petted and comforted Kim with wise saws and grave texts on that little-understood beast, our Body, who, being but a delusion, insists on posing as the Soul, to the darkening of the Way, and the immense multiplication of unnecessary devils.

' Hai! hai! Let us talk of the woman from Kulu. Think you she will ask another charm for her grandsons? When I was a young man, a very long time ago, I was plagued with these vapours—and some others—and I

went to an abbot—a very holy man and a seeker after truth, though then I knew it not. Sit up and listen, child of my soul! My tale was told. Said he to me, " Chela, know this. There are many lies in the world, and not a few liars, but there are no liars like our bodies, except it be the sensations of our bodies." Considering this I was comforted, and of his great favour he suffered me to drink tea in his presence. Suffer me now to drink tea, for I am thirsty.'

With a laugh above his tears, Kim kissed the lama's feet, and went about tea-making.

' Thou leanest on me in the body, Holy One, but I lean on thee for some other things. Dost know it? '

' I have guessed maybe,' and the lama's eyes twinkled. ' We must change that.'

So, when with scufflings and scrapings and a hot air of importance, padded up nothing less than the Sahiba's pet palanquin sent twenty miles, with that same grizzled old Oorya servant in charge, and when they reached the disorderly order of the long white rambling house behind Saharunpore, the lama took his own measures.

Said the Sahiba cheerily from an upper window, after compliments: ' What is the good of an old woman's advice to an old man? I told thee— I told thee, Holy One, to keep an eye upon the chela. How didst thou do it? Never answer me! I know. He has been running among the women. Look at his eyes—hollow and sunk—and the Betraying Line from the nose down! He has been sifted out! Fie! Fie! And a priest, too! '

Kim looked up over-weary to smile, shaking his head in denial.

' Do not jest,' said the lama. ' That time is done. We are here upon great matters. A sickness of soul took me in the Hills, and him a sickness of the body. Since then I have lived upon his strength—eating him.'

' Children together—young and old,' she sniffed, but forbore to make any new jokes. ' May this present hospitality restore ye. Hold awhile and I will come to gossip of the high good hills.'

At evening time—her son-in-law was returned, so she did not need to go on inspection round the farm—she won to the meat of the matter, explained low-voicedly by the lama. The two old heads nodded wisely together. Kim had reeled to a room with a cot in it, and was dozing soddenly. The lama had forbidden him to set blankets or get food.

' I know—I know. Who but I? ' she cackled. ' We who go down to the burning-ghats clutch at the hands of those coming up from the River of Life with full water-jars—yes, brimming water-jars. I did the boy wrong. He lent thee his strength? It is true that the old eat the young daily. 'Stands now we must restore him.'

' Thou hast many times acquired merit— '

' My merit. What is it? Old bag of bones making curries for men who do not ask " Who cooked this? " Now if it were stored up for my grand-son— '

'He that had the belly-pain?'

'To think the Holy One remembers that! I must tell his mother. It is most singular honour! "He that had the belly-pain"—straightway the Holy One remembered. She will be proud.'

'My chela is to me as a son to the unenlightened.'

'Say grandson, rather. Mothers have not the wisdom of our years. If a child cries they say the heavens are falling. Now a grandmother is far enough separated from the pain of bearing and the pleasure of giving the breast to consider whether a cry is wickedness pure or the wind. And since thou speakest once again of wind, when last the Holy One was here, maybe I offended in pressing for charms.'

'Sister,' said the lama, using that form of address a Buddhist monk may sometimes employ towards a nun, 'if charms comfort thee—'

'They are better than ten thousand doctors.'

'I say, if they comfort thee, I who was Abbot of Suchzen will make as many as thou mayest desire. I have never seen thy face—'

'That even the monkeys who steal our loquats count for a gain. Hee! hee!'

'But as he who sleeps there said,' he nodded at the shut door of the guest-chamber across the forecourt, 'thou hast a heart of gold. . . . And he is in the spirit my very "grandson" to me.'

'Good! I am the Holy One's cow.' This was pure Hinduism, but the lama never heeded. 'I am old. I have borne sons in the body. Oh, once I could please men! Now I can cure them.' He heard her armlets tinkle as though she bared arms for action. 'I will take over the boy and dose him, and stuff him, and make him all whole. Hai! hai! We old people know something yet.'

Wherefore when Kim, aching in every bone, opened his eyes, and would go to the cook-house to get his master's food, he found strong coercion about him, and a veiled old figure at the door, flanked by the grizzled manservant, who told him precisely the very things that he was on no account to do.

'Thou must have? Thou shalt have nothing. What? A locked box in which to keep holy books? Oh, that is another matter. Heavens forbid I should come between a priest and his prayers! It shall be brought, and thou shalt keep the key.'

They pushed the coffer under his cot, and Kim shut away Mahbub's pistol, the oilskin packet of letters, and the locked books and diaries, with a groan of relief. For some absurd reason their weight on his shoulders was nothing to their weight on his poor mind. His neck ached under it of nights.

'Thine is a sickness uncommon in youth these days: since young folk have given up tending their betters. The remedy is sleep, and certain drugs,' said the Sahiba; and he was glad to give himself up to the blankness that half menaced and half soothed him.

She brewed drinks, in some mysterious Asiatic equivalent to the still-

room—drenches that smelt pestilently and tasted worse. She stood over Kim till they went down, and inquired exhaustively after they had come up. She laid a taboo upon the forecourt, and enforced it by means of an armed man. It is true he was seventy odd, that his scabbarded sword ceased at the hilt; but he represented the authority of the Sahiba, and loaded wains, chattering servants, calves, dogs, hens, and the like, fetched a wide compass by those parts. Best of all, when the body was cleared, she cut out from the mass of poor relations that crowded the back of the buildings—household dogs, we name them—a cousin's widow, skilled in what Europeans, who know nothing about it, call massage. And the two of them, laying him east and west, that the mysterious earth-currents which thrill the clay of our bodies might help and not hinder, took him to pieces all one long afternoon—bone by bone, muscle by muscle, ligament by ligament, and lastly, nerve by nerve. Kneaded to irresponsible pulp, half hypnotised by the perpetual flick and readjustment of the uneasy chudders that veiled their eyes, Kim slid ten thousand miles into slumber—thirty-six hours of it—sleep that soaked like rain after drought.

Then she fed him, and the house spun to her clamour. She caused fowls to be slain; she sent for vegetables, and the sober, slow-thinking gardener, nigh as old as she, sweated for it; she took spices, and milk, and onion, with little fish from the brooks—anon limes for sherbets, fat quails of the pit, then chicken-livers upon a skewer, with sliced ginger between.

'I have seen something of this world,' she said over the crowded trays, 'and there are but two sorts of women in it—those who take the strength out of a man and those who put it back. Once I was that one, and now I am this. Nay—do not play the priestling with me. Mine was but a jest. If it does not hold good now, it will when thou takest the road again. Cousin '— this to the poor relation, never wearied of extolling her patroness's charity— 'he is getting a bloom on the skin of a new-curried horse. Our work is like polishing jewels to be thrown to a dance-girl—eh?'

Kim sat up and smiled. The terrible weakness had dropped from him like an old shoe. His tongue itched for free speech again, and but a week back the lightest word clogged it like ashes. The pain in his neck (he must have caught it from the lama) had gone with the heavy dengue-aches and the evil taste in the mouth. The two old women, a little, but not much, more careful about their veils now, clucked as merrily as the hens that had entered pecking through the open door.

'Where is my Holy One?' he demanded.

'Hear him! Thy Holy One is well,' she snapped viciously. 'Though that is none of his merit. Knew I a charm to make him wise, I'd sell my jewels and buy it. To refuse good food that I cooked myself—and go roving into the fields for two nights on an empty belly—and to tumble into a brook at the end of it—call you that holiness? Then, when he has nearly broken what thou hast left of my heart with anxiety, he tells me that he has acquired merit. Oh, how like are all men! No, that was not it—he tells me that he

is freed from all sin. I could have told him that before he wetted himself
all over. He is well now—this happened a week ago—but burn me such
holiness! A babe of three would do better. Do not fret thyself for the Holy
One. He keeps both eyes on thee when he is not wading our brooks.'

'I do not remember to have seen him. I remember that the days and
nights passed like bars of white and black, opening and shutting. I was not
sick: I was only tired.'

'A lethargy that comes by right some few score years later. But it is
all done now.'

'Maharanee,' Kim began, but led by the look in her eye, changed it to
the title of plain love—'Mother, I owe my life to thee. How shall I make
thanks? Ten thousand blessings upon thy house and—'

'The house be unblessed.' (It is impossible to give exactly the old lady's
word.) 'Thank the Gods as a priest if thou wilt, but thank me if thou carest
as a son. Heavens above! Have I shifted thee and lifted thee and slapped
and twisted thy ten toes to find texts flung at my head? Somewhere a
mother must have borne thee to break her heart. What used thou to her—
son?'

'I had no mother, my mother,' said Kim. 'She died, they tell me, when
I was young.'

'Hai mai! Then none can say I have robbed her of any right if—when
thou takest the road again and this house is but one of a thousand used for
shelter and forgotten, after an easy-flung blessing. No matter. I need no
blessings, but—but—' She stamped her foot at the poor relation: 'Take
up the trays to the house. What is the good of stale food in the room, oh
woman of ill-omen?'

'I ha—have borne a son in my time too, but he died,' whimpered the
bowed sister-figure behind the chudder. 'Thou knowest he died! I only
waited for the order to take away the tray.'

'It is I that am the woman of ill-omen,' cried the old lady penitently.
'We that go down to the chattris (the big umbrellas above the burning-
ghats where the priests take their last dues) clutch hard at the bearers of
the chattis (water-jars—young folk full of the pride of life, she meant; but
the pun is clumsy). When one cannot dance in the festival one must e'en
look out of the window, and grandmothering takes all a woman's time. Thy
master gives me all the charms I now desire for my daughter's eldest, by
reason—is it?—that he is wholly free from sin. The hakim is brought very
low these days. He goes about poisoning my servants for lack of their
betters.'

'What hakim, mother?'

'That very Dacca man who gave me the pill which rent me in three
pieces. He cast up like a strayed camel a week ago, vowing that he and thou
had been blood-brothers together up Kulu-way, and feigning great anxiety
for thy health. He was very thin and hungry, so I gave orders to have him
stuffed too—him and his anxiety!'

' I would see him if he is here.'

' He eats five times a day, and lances boils for my hinds to save himself
from an apoplexy. He is so full of anxiety for thy health that he sticks to
the cook-house door and stays himself with scraps. He will keep. We shall
never get rid of him.'

' Send him here, mother '—the twinkle returned to Kim's eye for a
flash—' and I will try.'

' I'll send him, but to chase him off is an ill turn. At least he had the
sense to fish the Holy One out of the brook; thus, as the Holy One did not
say, acquiring merit.'

' He is a very wise hakim. Send him, mother.'

' Priest praising priest? A miracle! If he is any friend of thine (ye squab-
bled at your last meeting) I'll hale him here with horse-ropes and—and give
him a caste-dinner afterwards, my son. . . . Get up and see the world! This
lying abed is the mother of seventy devils . . . my son! my son! '

She trotted forth to raise a typhoon off the cook-house, and almost on
her shadow rolled in the Babu, robed as to the shoulders like a Roman
emperor, jowled like Titus, bareheaded, with new patent-leather shoes, in
highest condition of fat, exuding joy and salutations.

' By Jove, Mister O'Hara, but I am jolly glad to see you. I will kindly
shut the door. It is a pity you are sick. Are you very sick? '

' The papers—the papers from the kilta. The maps and the murasla! '
He held out the key impatiently; for the present need on his soul was to
get rid of the loot.

' You are quite right. That is correct departmental view to take. You
have got everything? '

' All that was handwritten in the kilta I took. The rest I threw down
the hill.' He could hear the key's grate in the lock, the sticky pull of the
slow-rending oil-cloth, and a quick shuffling of papers. He had been annoyed
out of all reason by the knowledge that they lay below him through the sick
idle days—a burden incommunicable. For that reason the blood tingled
through his body, when Hurree, skipping elephantinely, shook hands again.

' This is fine! This is finest! Mister O'Hara! You have—ha! ha!—swiped
the whole bag of tricks—locks, stocks, and barrels. They told me it was eight
months' work gone up the spouts! By Jove, how they beat me! . . . Look,
here is the letter from Hilas! ' He intoned a line or two of Court Persian,
which is the language of authorised and unauthorised diplomacy. ' Mister
Rajah Sahib has just about put his foot in the holes. He will have to explain
offeecially how the deuce-an'-all he is writing love-letters to the Czar. And
they are very clever maps . . . and there is three or four Prime Ministers
of these parts implicated by the correspondence. By Gad, Sar! The British
Government will change the succession in Hilas and Bunar, and nominate
new heirs to the throne. " Treason most base " . . . but you do not under-
stand? Eh? '

' Are they in thy hands? ' said Kim. It was all he cared for.

'Just you jolly well bet yourself they are.' He stowed the entire trove about his body, as only Orientals can. 'They are going up to the office, too. The old lady thinks I am permanent fixture here, but I shall go away with these straight off—immediately. Mr. Lurgan will be proud man. You are offeecially subordinate to me, but I shall embody your name in my verbal report. It is a pity we are not allowed written reports. We Bengalis excel in thee exact science.' He tossed back the key and showed the box empty.

'Good. That is good. I was very tired. My Holy One was sick, too. And did he fall into—'

'Oah yess. I am his good friend, I tell you. He was behaving very strange when I came down after you, and I thought perhaps he might have the papers. I followed him on his meditations, and to discuss ethnological points also. You see, I am verree small person here nowadays, in comparison with all his charms. By Jove, O'Hara, do you know, he is afflicted with infirmity of fits. Yess, I tell you. Cataleptic, too, if not also epileptic. I found him in such a state under a tree in articulo mortem, and he jumped up and walked into a brook and he was nearly drowned but for me. I pulled him out.'

'Because I was not there!' said Kim. 'He might have died.'

'Yes, he might have died, but he is dry now, and assert he has undergone transfiguration.' The Babu tapped his forehead knowingly. 'I took notes of his statements for Royal Society—in posse. You must make haste and be quite well and come back to Simla, and I will tell you all my tale at Lurgan's. It was splendid. The bottoms of their trousers were quite torn, and old Nahan Rajah, he thought they were European soldiers deserting.'

'Oh, the Russians? How long were they with thee?'

'One was a Frenchman. Oh, days and days and days! Now all the hill-people believe all Russians are all beggars. By Jove! they had not one dam-thing that I did not get them. And I told the common people—oah, such tales and anecdotes! I will tell you at old Lurgan's when you come up. We will have—ah—a night out! It is feather in both our caps! Yess, and they gave me a certificate. That is creaming joke. You should have seen them at the Alliance Bank identifying themselves! And thank Almighty God you got their papers so well! You do not laugh verree much, but you shall laugh when you are well. Now I will go straight to the railway and get out. You shall have all sorts of credits for your game. When do you come along? We are very proud of you, though you gave us great frights. And especially Mahbub.'

'Ay, Mahbub. And where is he?'

'Selling horses in this vi-cinity, of course.'

'Here! Why? Speak slowly. There is a thickness in my head still.'

The Babu looked shyly down his nose. 'Well, you see, I am fearful man, and I do not like responsibility. You were sick, you see, and I did not know where deuce-an'-all the papers were, and if so, how many. So when I

had come down here I slipped in private wire to Mahbub—he was at Meerut for races—and I tell him how case stands. He comes up with his men and he consorts with the lama, and then he calls me a fool, and is very rude—'

'But wherefore—wherefore?'

'That is what I ask. I only suggest that if any one steals the papers I should like some good strong, brave men to rob them back again. You see they are vitally important, and Mahbub Ali he did not know where you were.'

'Mahbub Ali to rob the Sahiba's house? Thou art mad, Babu,' said Kim with indignation.

'I wanted the papers. Suppose she had stole them? It was only practical suggestion, I think. You are not pleased, eh?'

A native proverb—unquotable—showed the blackness of Kim's disapproval.

'Well,'—Hurree shrugged his shoulders,—'there is no accounting for thee taste. Mahbub was angry too. He has sold horses all about here, and he says old lady is pukka (thorough) old lady and would not condescend to such ungentlemanly things. I do not care. I have got the papers, and I was very glad of moral support from Mahbub. I tell you I am fearful man, but, somehow or other, the more fearful I am the more dam-tight places I get into. So I was glad you came with me to Chini, and I am glad Mahbub was close by. The old lady she is sometimes very rude to me and my beautiful pills.'

'Allah be merciful,' said Kim on his elbow, rejoicing. 'What a beast of wonder is a Babu! And that man walked alone—if he did walk—with robbed and angry foreigners!'

'Oah, thatt was nothing, after they had done beating me; but if I lost the papers it was pretty jolly serious. Mahbub he nearly beat me too, and he went and consorted with the lama no end. I shall stick to ethnological investigations henceforwards. Now good-bye, Mister O'Hara. I can catch 4.25 p. m. to Umballa if I am quick. It will be good times when we all tell thee tale up at Mister Lurgan's. I shall report you offeecially better. Good-bye, my dear fallow, and when next you are under thee emotions please do not use the Mohammedan terms with the Tibetan dress.'

He shook hands twice—a Babu to his boot-heels—and opened the door. With the fall of the sunlight upon his still triumphant face he returned to the humble Dacca quack.

'He robbed them,' thought Kim, forgetting his own share in the game. 'He tricked them. He lied to them like a Bengali. They give him a chit (a testimonial). He makes them a mock at the risk of his life—I never would have gone down to them after the pistol-shots—and then he says he is a fearful man. . . . And he is a fearful man. I must get into the world again.'

At first his legs bent like bad pipe-stems, and the flood and rush of the sunlit air dazzled him. He squatted by the white wall, the mind rummaging

among the incidents of the long dooli journey, the lama's weaknesses, and, now that the stimulus of talk was removed, his own self-pity, of which, like the sick, he had great store. The unnerved brain edged away from all the outside, as a raw horse, once rowelled, sidles from the spur. It was enough, amply enough, that the spoil of the kilta was away—off his hands—out of his possession. He tried to think of the lama,—to wonder why he had tumbled into a brook,—but the bigness of the world, seen between the forecourt gates, swept linked thought aside. Then he looked upon the trees and the broad fields, with the thatched huts hidden among crops—looked with strange eyes unable to take up the size and proportion and use of things—stared for a still half-hour. All that while he felt, though he could not put it into words, that his soul was out of gear with its surroundings—a cog-wheel unconnected with any machinery, just like the idle cog-wheel of a cheap Beheea sugar-crusher laid by in a corner. The breezes fanned over him, the parrots shrieked at him, the noises of the populated house behind —squabbles, orders, and reproofs—hit on dead ears.

' I am Kim. I am Kim. And what is Kim? ' His soul repeated it again and again.

He did not want to cry,—had never felt less like crying in his life,—but of a sudden easy, stupid tears trickled down his nose, and with an almost audible click he felt the wheels of his being lock up anew on the world without. Things that rode meaningless on the eyeball an instant before slid into proper proportion. Roads were meant to be walked upon, houses to be lived in, cattle to be driven, fields to be tilled, and men and women to be talked to. They were all real and true—solidly planted upon the feet—perfectly comprehensible—clay of his clay, neither more nor less. He shook himself like a dog with a flea in his ear, and rambled out of the gate. Said the Sahiba, to whom watchful eyes reported this move: ' Let him go. I have done my share. Mother Earth must do the rest. When the Holy One comes back from meditation, tell him.'

There stood an empty bullock-cart on a little knoll half a mile away, with a young banian tree behind—a look-out, as it were, above some new-ploughed levels; and his eyelids, bathed in soft air, grew heavy as he neared it. The ground was good clean dust—no new herbage that, living, is half-way to death already, but the hopeful dust that holds the seed of all life. He felt it between his toes, patted it with his palms, and joint by joint, sigh-ing luxuriously, laid him down full length along in the shadow of the wooden-pinned cart. And Mother Earth was as faithful as the Sahiba. She breathed through him to restore the poise he had lost lying so long on a cot cut off from her good currents. His head lay powerless upon her breast, and his opened hands surrendered to her strength. The many-rooted tree above him, and even the dead man-handled wood beside, knew what he sought, as he himself did not know. Hour upon hour he lay deeper than sleep.

Towards evening, when the dust of returning kine made all the horizons

smoke, came the lama and Mahbub Ali, both afoot, walking cautiously, for the house had told them where he had gone.

' Allah! What a fool's trick to play in open country,' muttered the horse-dealer. ' He could be shot a hundred times—but this is not the Border.'

' And,' said the lama, repeating a many-times-told tale, ' never was such a chela. Temperate, kindly, wise, of ungrudging disposition, a merry heart upon the road, never forgetting, learned, truthful, courteous. Great is his reward! '

' I know the boy—as I have said.'

' And he was all those things? '

' Some of them—but I have not yet found a Red Hat's charm for making him overly truthful. He has certainly been well nursed.'

' The Sahiba is a heart of gold,' said the lama earnestly. ' She looks upon him as her son.'

' Hmph! Half Hind seems that-way disposed. I only wished to see that the boy had come to no harm and was a free agent. As thou knowest, he and I were old friends in the first days of your pilgrimage together.'

' That is a bond between us.' The lama sat down. ' We are at the end of the pilgrimage.'

' No thanks to thee thine was not cut off for good and all a week back. I heard what the Sahiba said to thee when we bore thee up on the cot.' Mahbub laughed, and tugged his newly-dyed beard.

' I was meditating upon other matters that tide. It was the hakim from Dacca broke my meditations.'

' Otherwise '—this was in Pashtu for decency's sake—' thou wouldst have ended thy meditations upon the sultry side of Hell—being an unbeliever and an idolater for all thy child's simplicity. But now, Red Hat, what is to be done? '

' This very night,'—the words came slowly, vibrating with triumph,— ' this very night he will be as free as I am from all taint of sin—assured as I am when he quits this body of Freedom from the Wheel of Things. I have a sign,' he laid his hand above the torn chart in his bosom, ' that my time is short; but I shall have safe-guarded him throughout the years. Remember, I have reached Knowledge, as I told thee only three nights back.'

' It must be true, as the Tirah priest said when I stole his cousin's wife, that I am a sufi (a freethinker); for here I sit,' said Mahbub to himself, ' drinking in blasphemy unthinkable. . . . I remember the tale. On that, then, he goes to Jannatu l'Adn (the Gardens of Eden). But how? Wilt thou slay him or drown him in that wonderful river from which the Babu dragged thee? '

' I was dragged from no river,' said the lama simply. ' Thou hast forgotten what befell. I found it by knowledge.'

' Oh, ay. True,' stammered Mahbub, divided between high indignation and enormous mirth. ' I had forgotten the exact run of what happened. Thou didst find it knowingly.'

'And to say that I would take life is—not a sin, but a madness simple. My chela aided me to the River. It is his right to be cleansed from sin— with me.'

'Ay, he needs cleansing. But afterwards, old man—afterwards? '

'What matter under all the heavens? He is sure of Nibban—enlight-ened—as I am.'

'Well said. I had a fear he might mount Mohammed's Horse and fly away.'

'Nay—he must go forth as a teacher.'

'Aha! Now I see! That is the right gait for the colt. Certainly he must go forth as a teacher. He is somewhat urgently needed as a scribe by the State, for instance.'

'To that end he was prepared. I acquired merit in that I gave alms for his sake. A good deed does not die. He aided me in my Search. I aided him in his. Just is the Wheel, O horse-seller from the North. Let him be a teacher; let him be a scribe—what matter? He will have attained Freedom at the end. The rest is illusion.'

'What matter? When I must have him with me beyond Balkh in six months! I come up with ten lame horses and three strong-backed men— thanks to that chicken of a Babu—to break a sick boy by force out of an old trot's house. It seems that I stand by while a young Sahib is hoisted into Allah knows what of an idolater's heaven by means of old Red Hat. And I am reckoned something of a player of the Game myself! But the madman is fond of the boy; and I must be very reasonably mad too.'

'What is the prayer? ' said the lama, as the rough Pashtu rumbled into the red beard.

'No matter at all; but now I understand that the boy, sure of Paradise, can yet enter Government service, my mind is easier. I must get to my horses. It grows dark. Do not wake him. I have no wish to hear him call thee master.'

'But he is my disciple. What else? '

'He has told me.' Mahbub choked down his touch of spleen and rose laughing. 'I am not altogether of thy faith, Red Hat—if so small a matter concern thee.'

'It is nothing,' said the lama.

'I thought not. Therefore it will not move thee sinless, new-washed and three parts drowned to boot, when I call thee a good man—a very good man. We have talked together some four or five evenings now, and for all I am a horse-coper I can still, as the saying is, see holiness beyond the legs of a horse. Yea, can see, too, how our Friend of all the World put his hand in thine at the first. Use him well, and suffer him to return to the world as a teacher, when thou hast—bathed his legs, if that be the proper medi-cine for the colt.'

'Why not follow the Way thyself, and so accompany the boy? '

Mahbub stared stupefied at the magnificent insolence of the demand,

which across the Border he would have paid with more than a blow. Then the humour of it touched his worldly soul.

'Softly—softly—one foot at a time, as the lame gelding went over the Umballa jumps. I may come to Paradise later—I have workings that way— great motions—and I owe them to thy simplicity. Thou hast never lied?'

'What need?'

'O Allah, hear him! "What need" in this Thy world! Nor ever harmed a man?'

'Once—with a pencase—before I was wise.'

'So? I think the better of thee. Thy teachings are good. Thou hast turned one man that I know from the path of strife.' He laughed immensely. 'He came here open-minded to commit a dacoity (a house-robbery with violence). Yes, to cut, rob, kill, and carry off what he desired.'

'A great foolishness!'

'Oh! black shame too. So he thought after he had seen thee—and a few others, male and female. So he abandoned it; and now he goes to beat a big fat Babu man.'

'I do not understand.'

'Allah forbid it! Some men are strong in knowledge, Red Hat. Thy strength is stronger still. Keep it—I think thou wilt. If the boy be not a good servant, pull his ears off.'

With a hitch of his broad Bokhariot belt the Pathan swaggered off into the gloaming, and the lama came down from his clouds so far as to look at the broad back.

'That person lacks courtesy, and is deceived by the shadow of appearances. But he spoke well of my chela, who now enters upon his reward. Let me make the prayer! . . . Wake, O fortunate above all born of women. Wake! It is found!'

Kim came up from those deep wells, and the lama attended his yawning pleasure; duly snapping fingers to head off evil spirits.

'I have slept a hundred years. Where—? Holy One, hast thou been here long? I went out to look for thee, but '—he laughed drowsily—' I slept by the way. I am all well now. Hast thou eaten? Let us go to the house. It is many days since I tended thee. And the Sahiba fed thee well? Who shampooed thy legs? What of the weaknesses—the belly and the neck, and the beating in the ears?'

'Gone—all gone. Dost thou not know?'

'I know nothing, but that I have not seen thee in a monkey's age. Know what?'

'Strange the knowledge did not reach out to thee, when all my thoughts were theeward.'

'I cannot see the face, but the voice is like a gong. Has the Sahiba made a young man of thee by her cookery?'

He peered at the cross-legged figure, outlined jet-black against the

lemon-coloured drift of light. So does the stone Bodhisat sit who looks down
upon the patent self-registering turnstiles of the Lahore Museum.

The lama held his peace. Except for the click of the rosary and a faint
' clop-clop ' of Mahbub's retreating feet, the soft, smoky silence of evening
in India wrapped them close.

' Hear me! I bring news.'

' But let us— '

Out shot the long yellow hand compelling silence. Kim tucked his feet
under his robe-edge obediently.

' Hear me! I bring news! The Search is finished. Comes now the Re-
ward. . . . Thus. When we were among the Hills, I lived on thy strength
till the young branch bowed and nigh broke. When we came out of the
Hills, I was troubled for thee and for other matters which I held in my
heart. The boat of my soul lacked direction; I could not see into the Cause
of Things. So I gave thee over to the virtuous woman altogether. I took no
food. I drank no water. Still I saw not the Way. They pressed food upon
me and cried at my shut door. So I removed myself to a hollow under a
tree. I took no food. I took no water. I sat in meditation two days and two
nights, abstracting my mind; inbreathing and outbreathing in the required
manner. . . . Upon the second night—so great was my reward—the wise
Soul loosed itself from the silly Body and went free. This I have never be-
fore attained, though I have stood on the threshold of it. Consider, for it
is a marvel! '

' A marvel indeed. Two days and two nights without food! Where was
the Sahiba? ' said Kim under his breath.

' Yea, my Soul went free, and, wheeling like an eagle, saw indeed that
there was no Teshoo Lama nor any other soul. As a drop draws to water, so
my soul drew near to the Great Soul which is beyond all things. At that
point, exalted in contemplation, I saw all Hind, from Ceylon in the sea to
the Hills, and my own Painted Rocks at Suchzen; I saw every camp and
village, to the least, where we have ever rested. I saw them at one time and
in one place; for they were within the Soul. By this I knew the Soul had
passed beyond the illusion of Time and Space and of Things. By this I knew
that I was free. I saw thee lying in thy cot, and I saw thee falling down hill
under the idolater—at one time, in one place, in my Soul, which, as I say,
had touched the Great Soul. Also I saw the stupid body of Teshoo Lama
lying down, and the hakim from Dacca kneeled beside, shouting in its ear.
Then my Soul was all alone, and I saw nothing, for I was all things, having
reached the Great Soul. And I meditated a thousand thousand years, passion-
less, well aware of the Causes of all Things. Then a voice cried: " What
shall come to the boy if thou art dead? " and I was shaken back and forth
in myself with pity for thee; and I said: " I will return to my chela, lest he
miss the Way." Upon this my Soul, which is the soul of Teshoo Lama, with-
drew itself from the Great Soul with strivings and yearnings and retchings
and agonies not to be told. As the egg from the fish, as the fish from the

water, as the water from the cloud, as the cloud from the thick air; so put forth, so leaped out, so drew away, so fumed up the soul of Teshoo Lama from the Great Soul. Then a voice cried: " The River! Take heed to the River! " and I looked down upon all the world, which was as I had seen it before—one in time, one in place—and I saw plainly the River of the Arrow at my feet. At that hour my Soul was hampered by some evil or other whereof I was not wholly cleansed, and it lay upon my arms and coiled round my waist; but I put it aside, and I cast forth as an eagle in my flight for the very place of the River. I pushed aside world upon world for thy sake. I saw the River below me—the River of the Arrow—and, descending, the waters of it closed over me; and behold I was again in the body of Teshoo Lama, but free from sin, and the hakim from Dacca bore up my head in the waters of the River. It is here! It is behind the mangotope here—even here! '

' Allah Karim! Oh, well that the Babu was by! Wast thou very wet? '

' Why should I regard? I remember the hakim was concerned for the body of Teshoo Lama. He haled it out of the holy water in his hands, and there came afterwards thy horse-seller from the North with a cot and men, and they put the body on the cot and bore it up to the Sahiba's house.'

' What said the Sahiba? '

' I was meditating in that body, and did not hear. So thus the Search is ended. For the merit that I have acquired, the River of the Arrow is here. It broke forth at our feet, as I have said. I have found it. Son of my Soul, I have wrenched my Soul back from the Threshold of Freedom to free thee from all sin—as I am free, and sinless. Just is the Wheel! Certain is our deliverance. Come! '

He crossed his hands on his lap and smiled, as a man may who has won Salvation for himself and his beloved.

THE
JUNGLE
BOOK

THE JUNGLE BOOK

MOWGLI'S BROTHERS

Now Chil the Kite brings home the night
 That Mang the Bat sets free—
The herds are shut in byre and hut
 For loosed till dawn are we.
This is the hour of pride and power,
 Talon and tush and claw.
Oh hear the call!—Good hunting all
 That keep the Jungle Law!

 Night-Song in the Jungle

ஜ IT WAS seven o'clock of a very warm evening in the Seeonee hills when Father Wolf woke up from his day's rest, scratched himself, yawned, and spread out his paws one after the other to get rid of the sleepy feeling in their tips. Mother Wolf lay with her big gray nose dropped across her four tumbling, squealing cubs, and the moon shone into the mouth of the cave where they all lived. ' Augrh! ' said Father Wolf, ' it is time to hunt again '; and he was going to spring down hill when a little shadow with a bushy tail crossed the threshold and whined: ' Good luck go with you, O Chief of the Wolves; and good luck and strong white teeth go with the noble children, that they may never forget the hungry in this world.'

It was the jackal—Tabaqui, the Dish-licker—and the wolves of India despise Tabaqui because he runs about making mischief, and telling tales, and eating rags and pieces of leather from the village rubbish-heaps. But they are afraid of him too, because Tabaqui, more than any one else in the jungle, is apt to go mad, and then he forgets that he was ever afraid of any one, and runs through the forest biting everything in his way. Even the tiger runs and hides when little Tabaqui goes mad, for madness is the most disgraceful thing that can overtake a wild creature. We call it hydrophobia, but they call it *dewanee*—the madness—and run.

' Enter, then, and look,' said Father Wolf, stiffly; ' but there is no food here.'

' For a wolf, no,' said Tabaqui; ' but for so mean a person as myself a dry bone is a good feast. Who are we, the Gidur-log [the jackal people],

to pick and choose?' He scuttled to the back of the cave, where he found the bone of a buck with some meat on it, and sat cracking the end merrily.

'All thanks for this good meal,' he said, licking his lips. 'How beautiful are the noble children! How large are their eyes! And so young too! Indeed, indeed, I might have remembered that the children of kings are men from the beginning.'

Now, Tabaqui knew as well as any one else that there is nothing so unlucky as to compliment children to their faces; and it pleased him to see Mother and Father Wolf look uncomfortable.

Tabaqui sat still, rejoicing in the mischief that he had made, and then he said spitefully:—

'Shere Khan, the Big One, has shifted his hunting grounds. He will hunt among these hills for the next moon, so he has told me.'

Shere Khan was the tiger who lived near the Waingunga River, twenty miles away.

'He has no right!' Father Wolf began angrily— 'By the Law of the Jungle he has no right to change his quarters without due warning. He will frighten every head of game within ten miles, and I—I have to kill for two, these days.'

'His mother did not call him Lungri [the Lame One] for nothing,' said Mother Wolf, quietly. 'He has been lame in one foot from his birth. That is why he has only killed cattle. Now the villagers of the Waingunga are angry with him, and he has come here to make *our* villagers angry. They will scour the jungle for him when he is far away, and we and our children must run when the grass is set alight. Indeed, we are very grateful to Shere Khan!'

'Shall I tell him of your gratitude?' said Tabaqui.

'Out!' snapped Father Wolf. 'Out and hunt with thy master. Thou hast done harm enough for one night.'

'I go,' said Tabaqui, quietly. 'Ye can hear Shere Khan below in the thickets. I might have saved myself the message.'

Father Wolf listened, and below in the valley that ran down to a little river, he heard the dry, angry, snarly, singsong whine of a tiger who has caught nothing and does not care if all the jungle knows it.

'The fool!' said Father Wolf. 'To begin a night's work with that noise! Does he think that our buck are like his fat Waingunga bullocks?'

'H'sh. It is neither bullock nor buck he hunts to-night,' said Mother Wolf. 'It is Man.' The whine had changed to a sort of humming purr that seemed to come from every quarter of the compass. It was the noise that bewilders woodcutters and gipsies sleeping in the open, and makes them run sometimes into the very mouth of the tiger.

'Man!' said Father Wolf, showing all his white teeth. 'Faugh! Are there not enough beetles and frogs in the tanks that he must eat Man, and on our ground too!'

The Law of the Jungle, which never orders anything without a reason,

forbids every beast to eat Man except when he is killing to show his children how to kill, and then he must hunt outside the hunting-grounds of his pack or tribe. The real reason for this is that man-killing means, sooner or later, the arrival of white men on elephants, with guns, and hundreds of brown men with gongs and rockets and torches. Then everybody in the jungle suffers. The reason the beasts give among themselves is that Man is the weakest and most defenceless of all living things, and it is unsportsmanlike to touch him. They say too—and it is true—that man-eaters become mangy, and lose their teeth.

The purr grew louder, and ended in the full-throated ' Aaarh! ' of the tiger's charge.

Then there was a howl—an untigerish howl—from Shere Khan. ' He has missed,' said Mother Wolf. ' What is it? '

Father Wolf ran out a few paces and heard Shere Khan muttering and mumbling savagely, as he tumbled about in the scrub.

' The fool has had no more sense than to jump at a woodcutters' camp-fire, and has burned his feet,' said Father Wolf, with a grunt. ' Tabaqui is with him.'

' Something is coming up hill,' said Mother Wolf, twitching one ear. ' Get ready.'

The bushes rustled a little in the thicket, and Father Wolf dropped with his haunches under him, ready for his leap. Then, if you had been watching, you would have seen the most wonderful thing in the world— the wolf checked in mid-spring. He made his bound before he saw what it was he was jumping at, and then he tried to stop himself. The result was that he shot up straight into the air for four or five feet, landing almost where he left the ground.

' Man! ' he snapped. ' A man's cub. Look! '

Directly in front of him, holding on by a low branch, stood a naked brown baby who could just walk—as soft and as dimpled a little atom as ever came to a wolf's cave at night. He looked up into Father Wolf's face, and laughed.

' Is that a man's cub? ' said Mother Wolf. ' I have never seen one. Bring it here.'

A wolf accustomed to moving his own cubs can, if necessary, mouth an egg without breaking it, and though Father Wolf's jaws closed right on the child's back not a tooth even scratched the skin, as he laid it down among the cubs.

' How little! How naked, and—how bold! ' said Mother Wolf, softly. The baby was pushing his way between the cubs to get close to the warm hide. ' Ahai! He is taking his meal with the others. And so this is a man's cub. Now, was there ever a wolf that could boast of a man's cub among her children? '

' I have heard now and again of such a thing, but never in our Pack or in my time,' said Father Wolf. ' He is altogether without hair, and I

could kill him with a touch of my foot. But see, he looks up and is not afraid.'

The moonlight was blocked out of the mouth of the cave, for Shere Khan's great square head and shoulders were thrust into the entrance. Tabaqui, behind him, was squeaking: 'My lord, my lord, it went in here!'

'Shere Khan does us great honour,' said Father Wolf, but his eyes were very angry. 'What does Shere Khan need?'

'My quarry. A man's cub went this way,' said Shere Khan. 'Its parents have run off. Give it to me.'

Shere Khan had jumped at a woodcutters' camp-fire, as Father Wolf had said, and was furious from the pain of his burned feet. But Father Wolf knew that the mouth of the cave was too narrow for a tiger to come in by. Even where he was, Shere Khan's shoulders and fore paws were cramped for want of room, as a man's would be if he tried to fight in a barrel.

'The Wolves are a free people,' said Father Wolf. 'They take orders from the Head of the Pack, and not from any striped cattle-killer. The man's cub is ours—to kill if we choose.'

'Ye choose and ye do not choose! What talk is this of choosing? By the bull that I killed, am I to stand nosing into your dog's den for my fair dues? It is I, Shere Khan, who speak!'

The tiger's roar filled the cave with thunder. Mother Wolf shook herself clear of the cubs and sprang forward, her eyes, like two green moons in the darkness, facing the blazing eyes of Shere Khan.

'And it is I, Raksha [The Demon], who answer. The man's cub is mine, Lungri—mine to me! He shall not be killed. He shall live to run with the Pack and to hunt with the Pack; and in the end, look you, hunter of little naked cubs—frog-eater—fish-killer—he shall hunt *thee*! Now get hence, or by the Sambhur that I killed (*I* eat no starved cattle), back thou goest to thy mother, burned beast of the jungle, lamer than ever thou camest into the world! Go!'

Father Wolf looked on amazed. He had almost forgotten the days when he won Mother Wolf in fair fight from five other wolves, when she ran in the Pack and was not called The Demon for compliment's sake. Shere Khan might have faced Father Wolf, but he could not stand up against Mother Wolf, for he knew that where he was she had all the advantage of the ground, and would fight to the death. So he backed out of the cave-mouth growling, and when he was clear he shouted:—

'Each dog barks in his own yard! We will see what the Pack will say to this fostering of man-cubs. The cub is mine, and to my teeth he will come in the end, O bush-tailed thieves!'

Mother Wolf threw herself down panting among the cubs, and Father Wolf said to her gravely:—

'Shere Khan speaks this much truth. The cub must be shown to the Pack. Wilt thou still keep him, Mother?'

'Keep him!' she gasped. 'He came naked, by night, alone and very

hungry; yet he was not afraid! Look, he has pushed one of my babes to one side already. And that lame butcher would have killed him and would have run off to the Waingunga while the villagers here hunted through all our lairs in revenge! Keep him? Assuredly I will keep him. Lie still, little frog. O thou Mowgli—for Mowgli the Frog I will call thee—the time will come when thou wilt hunt Shere Khan as he has hunted thee.'

' But what will our Pack say? ' said Father Wolf.

The Law of the Jungle lays down very clearly that any wolf may, when he marries, withdraw from the Pack he belongs to; but as soon as his cubs are old enough to stand on their feet he must bring them to the Pack Council, which is generally held once a month at full moon, in order that the other wolves may identify them. After that inspection the cubs are free to run where they please, and until they have killed their first buck no excuse is accepted if a grown wolf of the Pack kills one of them. The punishment is death where the murderer can be found; and if you think for a minute you will see that this must be so.

Father Wolf waited till his cubs could run a little, and then on the night of the Pack Meeting took them and Mowgli and Mother Wolf to the Council Rock—a hilltop covered with stones and boulders where a hundred wolves could hide. Akela, the great gray Lone Wolf, who led all the Pack by strength and cunning, lay out at full length on his rock, and below him sat forty or more wolves of every size and colour, from badger-coloured veterans who could handle a buck alone, to young black three-year-olds who thought they could. The Lone Wolf had led them for a year now. He had fallen twice into a wolf-trap in his youth, and once he had been beaten and left for dead; so he knew the manners and customs of men. There was very little talking at the rock. The cubs tumbled over each other in the centre of the circle where their mothers and fathers sat, and now and again a senior wolf would go quietly up to a cub, look at him carefully, and return to his place on noiseless feet. Sometimes a mother would push her cub far out into the moonlight, to be sure that he had not been overlooked. Akela from his rock would cry: ' Ye know the Law—ye know the Law. Look well, O Wolves! ' and the anxious mothers would take up the call: ' Look—look well, O Wolves! '

At last—and Mother Wolf's neck-bristles lifted as the time came—Father Wolf pushed ' Mowgli the Frog,' as they called him, into the centre, where he sat laughing and playing with some pebbles that glistened in the moonlight.

Akela never raised his head from his paws, but went on with the monotonous cry: ' Look well! ' A muffled roar came up from behind the rocks—the voice of Shere Khan crying: ' The cub is mine. Give him to me. What have the Free People to do with a man's cub? ' Akela never even twitched his ears: all he said was: ' Look well, O Wolves! What have the Free People to do with the orders of any save the Free People? Look well! '

There was a chorus of deep growls, and a young wolf in his fourth year

flung back Shere Khan's question to Akela: 'What have the Free People to do with a man's cub?' Now the Law of the Jungle lays down that if there is any dispute as to the right of a cub to be accepted by the Pack, he must be spoken for by at least two members of the Pack who are not his father and mother.

'Who speaks for this cub?' said Akela. 'Among the Free People who speaks?' There was no answer, and Mother Wolf got ready for what she knew would be her last fight, if things came to fighting.

Then the only other creature who is allowed at the Pack Council— Baloo, the sleepy brown bear who teaches the wolf cubs the Law of the Jungle: old Baloo, who can come and go where he pleases because he eats only nuts and roots and honey—rose up on his hind quarters and grunted.

'The man's cub—the man's cub?' he said. 'I speak for the man's cub. There is no harm in a man's cub. I have no gift of words, but I speak the truth. Let him run with the Pack, and be entered with the others. I myself will teach him.'

'We need yet another,' said Akela. 'Baloo has spoken, and he is our teacher for the young cubs. Who speaks beside Baloo?'

A black shadow dropped down into the circle. It was Bagheera the Black Panther, inky black all over, but with the panther markings showing up in certain lights like the pattern of watered silk. Everybody knew Bagheera, and nobody cared to cross his path; for he was as cunning as Tabaqui, as bold as the wild buffalo, and as reckless as the wounded elephant. But he had a voice as soft as wild honey dripping from a tree, and a skin softer than down.

'O Akela, and ye the Free People,' he purred, 'I have no right in your assembly; but the Law of the Jungle says that if there is a doubt which is not a killing matter in regard to a new cub, the life of that cub may be bought at a price. And the Law does not say who may or may not pay that price. Am I right?'

'Good! good!' said the young wolves, who are always hungry. 'Listen to Bagheera. The cub can be bought for a price. It is the Law.'

'Knowing that I have no right to speak here, I ask your leave.'

'Speak then,' cried twenty voices.

'To kill a naked cub is shame. Besides, he may make better sport for you when he is grown. Baloo has spoken in his behalf. Now to Baloo's word I will add one bull, and a fat one, newly killed, not half a mile from here, if ye will accept the man's cub according to the Law. Is it difficult?'

There was a clamour of scores of voices, saying: 'What matter? He will die in the winter rains. He will scorch in the sun. What harm can a naked frog do us? Let him run with the Pack. Where is the bull, Bagheera? Let him be accepted.' And then came Akela's deep bay, crying: 'Look well— look well, O Wolves!'

Mowgli was still deeply interested in the pebbles, and he did not notice when the wolves came and looked at him one by one. At last they all went

down the hill for the dead bull, and only Akela, Bagheera, Baloo, and Mowgli's own wolves were left. Shere Khan roared still in the night, for he was very angry that Mowgli had not been handed over to him.

'Ay, roar well,' said Bagheera, under his whiskers; 'for the time comes when this naked thing will make thee roar to another tune, or I know nothing of man.'

'It was well done,' said Akela. 'Men and their cubs are very wise. He may be a help in time.'

'Truly, a help in time of need; for none can hope to lead the Pack for ever,' said Bagheera.

Akela said nothing. He was thinking of the time that comes to every leader of every pack when his strength goes from him and he gets feebler and feebler, till at last he is killed by the wolves and a new leader comes up—to be killed in his turn.

'Take him away,' he said to Father Wolf, 'and train him as befits one of the Free People.'

And that is how Mowgli was entered into the Seeonee wolf-pack for the price of a bull and on Baloo's good word.

.

Now you must be content to skip ten or eleven whole years, and only guess at all the wonderful life that Mowgli led among the wolves, because if it were written out it would fill ever so many books. He grew up with the cubs, though they, of course, were grown wolves almost before he was a child, and Father Wolf taught him his business, and the meaning of things in the jungle, till every rustle in the grass, every breath of the warm night air, every note of the owls above his head, every scratch of a bat's claws as it roosted for a while in a tree, and every splash of every little fish jumping in a pool, meant just as much to him as the work of his office means to a business man. When he was not learning he sat out in the sun and slept, and ate and went to sleep again; when he felt dirty or hot he swam in the forest pools; and when he wanted honey (Baloo told him that honey and nuts were just as pleasant to eat as raw meat) he climbed up for it, and that Bagheera showed him how to do. Bagheera would lie out on a branch and call, 'Come along, Little Brother,' and at first Mowgli would cling like the sloth, but afterward he would fling himself through the branches almost as boldly as the gray ape. He took his place at the Council Rock, too, when the Pack met, and there he discovered that if he stared hard at any wolf, the wolf would be forced to drop his eyes, and so he used to stare for fun. At other times he would pick the long thorns out of the pads of his friends, for wolves suffer terribly from thorns and burs in their coats. He would go down the hillside into the cultivated lands by night, and look very curiously at the villagers in their huts, but he had a mistrust of men because Bagheera showed him a square box with a drop-gate so cunningly hidden in the jungle that he nearly walked into it, and told him that it was a trap. He

loved better than anything else to go with Bagheera into the dark warm heart of the forest, to sleep all through the drowsy day, and at night see how Bagheera did his killing. Bagheera killed right and left as he felt hungry, and so did Mowgli—with one exception. As soon as he was old enough to understand things, Bagheera told him that he must never touch cattle because he had been bought into the Pack at the price of a bull's life. ' All the jungle is thine,' said Bagheera, ' and thou canst kill everything that thou art strong enough to kill; but for the sake of the bull that bought thee thou must never kill or eat any cattle young or old. That is the Law of the Jungle.' Mowgli obeyed faithfully.

And he grew and grew strong as a boy must grow who does not know that he is learning any lessons, and who has nothing in the world to think of except things to eat.

Mother Wolf told him once or twice that Shere Khan was not a creature to be trusted, and that some day he must kill Shere Khan; but though a young wolf would have remembered that advice every hour, Mowgli forgot it because he was only a boy—though he would have called himself a wolf if he had been able to speak in any human tongue.

Shere Khan was always crossing his path in the jungle, for as Akela grew older and feebler the lame tiger had come to be great friends with the younger wolves of the Pack, who followed him for scraps, a thing Akela would never have allowed if he had dared to push his authority to the proper bounds. Then Shere Khan would flatter them and wonder that such fine young hunters were content to be led by a dying wolf and a man's cub. ' They tell me,' Shere Khan would say, ' that at Council ye dare not look him between the eyes'; and the young wolves would growl and bristle.

Bagheera, who had eyes and ears everywhere, knew something of this, and once or twice he told Mowgli in so many words that Shere Khan would kill him some day; and Mowgli would laugh and answer: ' I have the Pack and I have thee; and Baloo, though he is so lazy, might strike a blow or two for my sake. Why should I be afraid? '

It was one very warm day that a new notion came to Bagheera—born of something that he had heard. Perhaps Sahi the Porcupine had told him; but he said to Mowgli when they were deep in the jungle, as the boy lay with his head on Bagheera's beautiful black skin: ' Little Brother, how often have I told thee that Shere Khan is thy enemy? '

' As many times as there are nuts on that palm,' said Mowgli, who, naturally, could not count. ' What of it? I am sleepy, Bagheera, and Shere Khan is all long tail and loud talk—like Mor the Peacock.'

' But this is no time for sleeping. Baloo knows it; I know it; the Pack know it; and even the foolish, foolish deer know. Tabaqui has told thee, too.'

' Ho! ho! ' said Mowgli. ' Tabaqui came to me not long ago with some rude talk that I was a naked man's cub and not fit to dig pig-nuts; but I caught Tabaqui by the tail and swung him twice against a palm-tree to teach him better manners.'

'That was foolishness; for though Tabaqui is a mischief-maker, he would have told thee of something that concerned thee closely. Open those eyes, Little Brother. Shere Khan dare not kill thee in the jungle; but remember, Akela is very old, and soon the day comes when he cannot kill his buck, and then he will be leader no more. Many of the wolves that looked thee over when thou wast brought to the Council first are old too, and the young wolves believe, as Shere Khan has taught them, that a man-cub has no place with the Pack. In a little time thou wilt be a man.'

'And what is a man that he should not run with his brothers?' said Mowgli. 'I was born in the jungle. I have obeyed the Law of the Jungle, and there is no wolf of ours from whose paws I have not pulled a thorn. Surely they are my brothers!'

Bagheera stretched himself at full length and half shut his eyes. 'Little Brother,' said he, 'feel under my jaw.'

Mowgli put up his strong brown hand, and just under Bagheera's silky chin, where the giant rolling muscles were all hid by the glossy hair, he came upon a little bald spot.

'There is no one in the jungle that knows that I, Bagheera, carry that mark—the mark of the collar; and yet, Little Brother, I was born among men, and it was among men that my mother died—in the cages of the King's Palace at Oodeypore. It was because of this that I paid the price for thee at the Council when thou wast a little naked cub. Yes, I too was born among men. I had never seen the jungle. They fed me behind bars from an iron pan till one night I felt that I was Bagheera—the Panther— and no man's plaything, and I broke the silly lock with one blow of my paw and came away; and because I had learned the ways of men, I became more terrible in the jungle than Shere Khan. Is it not so?'

'Yes,' said Mowgli; 'all the jungle fear Bagheera—all except Mowgli.'

'Oh, *thou* art a man's cub,' said the Black Panther, very tenderly; 'and even as I returned to my jungle, so thou must go back to men at last,—to the men who are thy brothers,—if thou art not killed in the Council.'

'But why—but why should any wish to kill me?' said Mowgli.

'Look at me,' said Bagheera; and Mowgli looked at him steadily between the eyes. The big panther turned his head away in half a minute.

'*That* is why,' he said, shifting his paw on the leaves. 'Not even I can look thee between the eyes, and I was born among men, and I love thee, Little Brother. The others they hate thee because their eyes cannot meet thine; because thou art wise; because thou hast pulled out thorns from their feet—because thou art a man.'

'I did not know these things,' said Mowgli, sullenly; and he frowned under his heavy black eyebrows.

'What is the Law of the Jungle? Strike first and then give tongue. By thy very carelessness they know that thou art a man. But be wise. It is in my heart that when Akela misses his next kill,—and at each hunt it costs

him more to pin the buck,—the Pack will turn against him and against thee. They will hold a jungle Council at the Rock, and then—and then—I have it! ' said Bagheera, leaping up. ' Go thou down quickly to the men's huts in the valley, and take some of the Red Flower which they grow there, so that when the time comes thou mayest have even a stronger friend than I or Baloo or those of the Pack that love thee. Get the Red Flower.'

By Red Flower Bagheera meant fire, only no creature in the jungle will call fire by its proper name. Every beast lives in deadly fear of it, and invents a hundred ways of describing it.

' The Red Flower? ' said Mowgli. ' That grows outside their huts in the twilight. I will get some.'

' There speaks the man's cub,' said Bagheera, proudly. ' Remember that it grows in little pots. Get one swiftly, and keep it by thee for time of need.'

' Good! ' said Mowgli. ' I go. But art thou sure, O my Bagheera '—he slipped his arm round the splendid neck, and looked deep into the big eyes —' art thou sure that all this is Shere Khan's doing? '

' By the Broken Lock that freed me, I am sure, Little Brother.'

' Then, by the Bull that bought me, I will pay Shere Khan full tale for this, and it may be a little over,' said Mowgli; and he bounded away.

' That is a man. That is all a man,' said Bagheera to himself, lying down again. ' Oh, Shere Khan, never was a blacker hunting than that frog-hunt of thine ten years ago! '

Mowgli was far and far through the forest, running hard, and his heart was hot in him. He came to the cave as the evening mist rose, and drew breath, and looked down the valley. The cubs were out, but Mother Wolf, at the back of the cave, knew by his breathing that something was troubling her frog.

' What is it, Son? ' she said.

' Some bat's chatter of Shere Khan,' he called back. ' I hunt among the ploughed fields to-night '; and he plunged downward through the bushes, to the stream at the bottom of the valley. There he checked, for he heard the yell of the Pack hunting, heard the bellow of a hunted Sambhur, and the snort as the buck turned at bay. Then there were wicked, bitter howls from the young wolves: ' Akela! Akela! Let the Lone Wolf show his strength. Room for the leader of the Pack! Spring, Akela! '

The Lone Wolf must have sprung and missed his hold, for Mowgli heard the snap of his teeth and then a yelp as the Sambhur knocked him over with his fore foot.

He did not wait for anything more, but dashed on; and the yells grew fainter behind him as he ran into the crop-lands where the villagers lived.

' Bagheera spoke truth,' he panted, as he nestled down in some cattle-fodder by the window of a hut. ' To-morrow is one day both for Akela and for me.'

Then he pressed his face close to the window and watched the fire

on the hearth. He saw the husband-man's wife get up and feed it in the night with black lumps; and when the morning came and the mists were all white and cold, he saw the man's child pick up a wicker pot plastered inside with earth, fill it with lumps of red-hot charcoal, put it under his blanket, and go out to tend the cows in the byre.

'Is that all?' said Mowgli. 'If a cub can do it, there is nothing to fear'; so he strode round the corner and met the boy, took the pot from his hand, and disappeared into the mist while the boy howled with fear.

'They are very like me,' said Mowgli, blowing into the pot, as he had seen the woman do. 'This thing will die if I do not give it things to eat'; and he dropped twigs and dried bark on the red stuff. Half-way up the hill he met Bagheera with the morning dew shining like moonstones on his coat.

'Akela has missed,' said the Panther. 'They would have killed him last night, but they needed thee also. They were looking for thee on the hill.'

'I was among the ploughed lands. I am ready. See!' Mowgli held up the fire-pot.

'Good! Now, I have seen men thrust a dry branch into that stuff, and presently the Red Flower blossomed at the end of it. Art thou not afraid?'

'No. Why should I fear? I remember now—if it is not a dream—how, before I was a Wolf, I lay beside the Red Flower, and it was warm and pleasant.'

All that day Mowgli sat in the cave tending his fire-pot and dipping dry branches into it to see how they looked. He found a branch that satisfied him, and in the evening when Tabaqui came to the cave and told him rudely enough that he was wanted at the Council Rock, he laughed till Tabaqui ran away. Then Mowgli went to the Council, still laughing.

Akela the Lone Wolf lay by the side of his rock as a sign that the leadership of the Pack was open, and Shere Khan with his following of scrap-fed wolves walked to and fro openly being flattered. Bagheera lay close to Mowgli, and the fire-pot was between Mowgli's knees. When they were all gathered together, Shere Khan began to speak—a thing he would never have dared to do when Akela was in his prime.

'He has no right,' whispered Bagheera. 'Say so. He is a dog's son. He will be frightened.'

Mowgli sprang to his feet. 'Free People,' he cried, 'does Shere Khan lead the Pack? What has a tiger to do with our leadership?'

'Seeing that the leadership is yet open, and being asked to speak—' Shere Khan began.

'By whom?' said Mowgli. 'Are we *all* jackals, to fawn on this cattle-butcher? The leadership of the Pack is with the Pack alone.'

There were yells of 'Silence, thou man's cub!' 'Let him speak. He has kept our Law'; and at last the seniors of the Pack thundered: 'Let the Dead Wolf speak.' When a leader of the Pack has missed his kill, he is called the Dead Wolf as long as he lives, which is not long.

Akela raised his old head wearily:—

'Free People, and ye too, jackals of Shere Khan, for twelve seasons I have led ye to and from the kill, and in all that time not one has been trapped or maimed. Now I have missed my kill. Ye know how that plot was made. Ye know how ye brought me up to an untried buck to make my weakness known. It was cleverly done. Your right is to kill me here on the Council Rock, now. Therefore, I ask, who comes to make an end of the Lone Wolf? For it is my right, by the Law of the Jungle, that ye come one by one.'

There was a long hush, for no single wolf cared to fight Akela to the death. Then Shere Khan roared: 'Bah! what have we to do with this tooth-less fool? He is doomed to die! It is the man-cub who has lived too long. Free People, he was my meat from the first. Give him to me. I am weary of this man-wolf folly. He has troubled the jungle for ten seasons. Give me the man-cub, or I will hunt here always, and not give you one bone. He is a man, a man's child, and from the marrow of my bones I hate him!'

Then more than half the Pack yelled: 'A man! a man! What has a man to do with us? Let him go to his own place.'

'And turn all the people of the villages against us?' clamoured Shere Khan. 'No; give him to me. He is a man, and none of us can look him between the eyes.'

Akela lifted his head again, and said: 'He has eaten our food. He has slept with us. He has driven game for us. He has broken no word of the Law of the Jungle.'

'Also, I paid for him with a bull when he was accepted. The worth of a bull is little, but Bagheera's honour is something that he will perhaps fight for,' said Bagheera, in his gentlest voice.

'A bull paid ten years ago!' the Pack snarled. 'What do we care for bones ten years old?'

'Or for a pledge?' said Bagheera, his white teeth bared under his lip. 'Well are ye called the Free People!'

'No man's cub can run with the people of the jungle,' howled Shere Khan. 'Give him to me!'

'He is our brother in all but blood,' Akela went on; 'and ye would kill him here! In truth, I have lived too long. Some of ye are eaters of cattle, and of others I have heard that, under Shere Khan's teaching, ye go by dark night and snatch children from the villager's door-step. Therefore I know ye to be cowards, and it is to cowards I speak. It is certain that I must die, and my life is of no worth, or I would offer that in the man-cub's place. But for the sake of the Honour of the Pack,—a little matter that by being without a leader ye have forgotten,—I promise that if ye let the man-cub go to his own place, I will not, when my time comes to die, bare one tooth against ye. I will die without fighting. That will at least save the Pack three lives. More I cannot do; but if ye will, I can save ye the shame that comes of killing a brother against whom there is no fault,—a brother spoken for

and bought into the Pack according to the Law of the Jungle.'

'He is a man—a man—a man!' snarled the Pack; and most of the wolves began to gather round Shere Khan, whose tail was beginning to switch.

'Now the business is in thy hands,' said Bagheera to Mowgli. 'We can do no more except fight.'

Mowgli stood upright—the fire-pot in his hands. Then he stretched out his arms, and yawned in the face of the Council; but he was furious with rage and sorrow, for, wolf-like, the wolves had never told him how they hated him. 'Listen you!' he cried. 'There is no need for this dog's jabber. Ye have told me so often to-night that I am a man (and indeed I would have been a wolf with you to my life's end), that I feel your words are true. So I do not call ye my brothers any more, but *sag* [dogs], as a man should. What ye will do, and what ye will not do, is not yours to say. That matter is with *me*; and that we may see the matter more plainly, I, the man, have brought here a little of the Red Flower which ye, dogs, fear.'

He flung the fire-pot on the ground, and some of the red coals lit a tuft of dried moss that flared up, as all the Council drew back in terror before the leaping flames.

Mowgli thrust his dead branch into the fire till the twigs lit and crackled, and whirled it above his head among the cowering wolves.

'Thou art the master,' said Bagheera, in an undertone. 'Save Akela from the death. He was ever thy friend.'

Akela, the grim old wolf who had never asked for mercy in his life, gave one piteous look at Mowgli as the boy stood all naked, his long black hair tossing over his shoulders in the light of the blazing branch that made the shadows jump and quiver.

'Good!' said Mowgli, staring round slowly. 'I see that ye are dogs. I go from you to my own people—if they be my own people. The Jungle is shut to me, and I must forget your talk and your companionship; but I will be more merciful than ye are. Because I was all but your brother in blood, I promise that when I am a man among men I will not betray ye to men as ye have betrayed me.' He kicked the fire with his foot, and the sparks flew up. 'There shall be no war between any of us in the Pack. But here is a debt to pay before I go.' He strode forward to where Shere Khan sat blinking stupidly at the flames, and caught him by the tuft on his chin. Bagheera followed in case of accidents. 'Up, dog!' Mowgli cried. 'Up, when a man speaks, or I will set that coat ablaze!'

Shere Khan's ears lay flat back on his head, and he shut his eyes, for the blazing branch was very near.

'This cattle-killer said he would kill me in the Council because he had not killed me when I was a cub. Thus and thus, then, do we beat dogs when we are men. Stir a whisker, Lungri, and I ram the Red Flower down thy gullet!' He beat Shere Khan over the head with the branch, and the tiger whimpered and whined in an agony of fear.

'Pah! Singed jungle-cat—go now! But remember when next I come

to the Council Rock, as a man should come, it will be with Shere Khan's hide on my head. For the rest, Akela goes free to live as he pleases. Ye will *not* kill him, because that is not my will. Nor do I think that ye will sit here any longer, lolling out your tongues as though ye were somebodies, instead of dogs whom I drive out—thus! Go! ' The fire was burning furiously at the end of the branch, and Mowgli struck right and left round the circle, and the wolves ran howling with the sparks burning their fur. At last there were only Akela, Bagheera, and perhaps ten wolves that had taken Mowgli's part. Then something began to hurt Mowgli inside him, as he had never been hurt in his life before, and he caught his breath and sobbed, and the tears ran down his face.

' What is it? What is it? ' he said. ' I do not wish to leave the jungle, and I do not know what this is. Am I dying, Bagheera? '

' No, Little Brother. That is only tears such as men use,' said Bagheera. ' Now I know thou art a man, and a man's cub no longer. The Jungle is shut indeed to thee henceforward. Let them fall, Mowgli. They are only tears.' So Mowgli sat and cried as though his heart would break; and he had never cried in all his life before.

' Now,' he said, ' I will go to men. But first I must say farewell to my mother '; and he went to the cave where she lived with Father Wolf, and he cried on her coat, while the four cubs howled miserably.

' Ye will not forget me? ' said Mowgli.

' Never while we can follow a trail,' said the cubs. ' Come to the foot of the hill when thou art a man, and we will talk to thee; and we will come into the crop-lands to play with thee by night.'

' Come soon! ' said Father Wolf. ' Oh, wise little frog, come again soon; for we be old, thy mother and I.'

' Come soon,' said Mother Wolf, ' little naked son of mine; for, listen, child of man, I loved thee more than ever I loved my cubs.'

' I will surely come,' said Mowgli; ' and when I come it will be to lay out Shere Khan's hide upon the Council Rock. Do not forget me! Tell them in the jungle never to forget me! '

The dawn was beginning to break when Mowgli went down the hillside alone, to meet those mysterious things that are called men.

HUNTING-SONG OF THE SEEONEE PACK

As the dawn was breaking the Sambhur belled
　　Once, twice and again!
And a doe leaped up and a doe leaped up
From the pond in the wood where the wild deer sup.
This I, scouting alone, beheld,
　　Once, twice and again!

As the dawn was breaking the Sambhur belled
 Once, twice and again!
And a wolf stole back and a wolf stole back
To carry the word to the waiting pack,
And we sought and we found and we bayed on his track
 Once, twice and again!

As the dawn was breaking the Wolf Pack yelled
 Once, twice and again!
Feet in the jungle that leave no mark!
Eyes that can see in the dark—the dark!
Tongue—give tongue to it! Hark! O hark!
 Once, twice and again!

KAA'S HUNTING

His spots are the joy of the Leopard: his horns are the Buffalo's pride.
Be clean, for the strength of the hunter is known by the gloss of his hide.
If ye find that the bullock can toss you, or the heavy-browed Sambhur can
 gore;
Ye need not stop work to inform us: we knew it ten seasons before.
Oppress not the cubs of the stranger, but hail them as Sister and Brother,
For though they are little and fubsy, it may be the Bear is their mother.
'There is none like to me!' says the Cub in the pride of his earliest kill;
But the jungle is large and the Cub he is small. Let him think and be still.
Maxims of Baloo

∾§ ALL that is told here happened some time before Mowgli was turned
out of the Seeonee wolf-pack, or revenged himself on Shere Khan the tiger.
It was in the days when Baloo was teaching him the Law of the Jungle.
The big, serious, old brown bear was delighted to have so quick a pupil,
for the young wolves will only learn as much of the Law of the Jungle as
applies to their own pack and tribe, and run away as soon as they can
repeat the Hunting Verse:—'Feet that make no noise; eyes that can see
in the dark; ears that can hear the winds in their lairs, and sharp white teeth,
all these things are the marks of our brothers except Tabaqui the Jackal and
the Hyæna whom we hate.' But Mowgli, as a man-cub, had to learn a great
deal more than this. Sometimes Baghcera, the Black Panther, would come
lounging through the jungle to see how his pet was getting on, and would
purr with his head against a tree while Mowgli recited the day's lesson to
Baloo. The boy could climb almost as well as he could swim, and swim
almost as well as he could run; so Baloo, the Teacher of the Law, taught
him the Wood and Water Laws: how to tell a rotten branch from a sound
one; how to speak politely to the wild bees when he came upon a hive of
them fifty feet above ground; what to say to Mang the Bat when he dis-
turbed him in the branches at mid-day; and how to warn the water-snakes
in the pools before he splashed down among them. None of the Jungle-
People like being disturbed, and all are very ready to fly at an intruder.
Then, too, Mowgli was taught the Strangers' Hunting Call, which must
be repeated aloud till it is answered, whenever one of the Jungle-People
hunts outside his own grounds. It means, translated: 'Give me leave to
hunt here because I am hungry'; and the answer is: 'Hunt then for food,
but not for pleasure.'

 All this will show you how much Mowgli had to learn by heart, and
he grew very tired of saying the same thing over a hundred times; but, as

Baloo said to Bagheera, one day when Mowgli had been cuffed and run off in a temper: ' A man's cub is a man's cub, and he must learn *all* the Law of the Jungle.'

' But think how small he is,' said the Black Panther, who would have spoiled Mowgli if he had had his own way. ' How can his little head carry all thy long talk? '

' Is there anything in the jungle too little to be killed? No. That is why I teach him these things, and that is why I hit him, very softly, when he forgets.'

' Softly! What dost thou know of softness, old Iron-feet? ' Bagheera grunted. ' His face is all bruised to-day by thy—softness. Ugh.'

' Better he should be bruised from head to foot by me who love him than that he should come to harm through ignorance,' Baloo answered very earnestly. ' I am now teaching him the Master Words of the Jungle that shall protect him with the birds and the Snake-People, and all that hunt on four feet, except his own pack. He can now claim protection, if he will only remember the words, from all in the jungle. Is not that worth a little beating? '

' Well, look to it then that thou dost not kill the man-cub. He is no tree-trunk to sharpen thy blunt claws upon. But what are those Master Words? I am more likely to give help than to ask it '—Bagheera stretched out one paw and admired the steel-blue, ripping-chisel talons at the end of it—' still I should like to know.'

' I will call Mowgli and he shall say them—if he will. Come, Little Brother! '

' My head is ringing like a bee-tree,' said a sullen little voice over their heads, and Mowgli slid down a tree-trunk very angry and indignant, adding as he reached the ground: ' I come for Bagheera and not for *thee*, fat old Baloo! '

' That is all one to me,' said Baloo, though he was hurt and grieved. ' Tell Bagheera, then, the Master Words of the Jungle that I have taught thee this day.'

' Master Words for which people? ' said Mowgli, delighted to show off. ' The jungle has many tongues. *I* know them all.'

' A little thou knowest, but not much. See, O Bagheera, they never thank their teacher. Not one small wolfling has ever come back to thank old Baloo for his teachings. Say the word for the Hunting-Peoples then— great scholar.'

' We be of one blood, ye and I,' said Mowgli, giving the words the Bear accent which all the hunting-people use.

' Good. Now for the birds.'

Mowgli repeated, with the Kite's whistle at the end of the sentence.

' Now for the Snake-People,' said Bagheera.

The answer was a perfectly indescribable hiss, and Mowgli kicked up his feet behind, clapped his hands together to applaud himself, and

jumped on to Bagheera's back, where he sat sideways, drumming with his heels on the glossy skin and making the worst faces he could think of at Baloo.

'There—there! That was worth a little bruise,' said the brown bear tenderly. 'Some day thou wilt remember me.' Then he turned aside to tell Bagheera how he had begged the Master Words from Hathi the Wild Elephant, who knows all about these things, and how Hathi had taken Mowgli down to a pool to get the Snake Word from a water-snake, because Baloo could not pronounce it, and how Mowgli was now reasonably safe against all accidents in the jungle, because neither snake, bird, nor beast would hurt him.

'No one then is to be feared,' Baloo wound up, patting his big furry stomach with pride.

'Except his own tribe,' said Bagheera, under his breath; and then aloud to Mowgli: 'Have a care for my ribs, Little Brother! What is all this dancing up and down?'

Mowgli had been trying to make himself heard by pulling at Bagheera's shoulder fur and kicking hard. When the two listened to him he was shouting at the top of his voice: 'And so I shall have a tribe of my own, and lead them through the branches all day long.'

'What is this new folly, little dreamer of dreams?' said Bagheera.

'Yes, and throw branches and dirt at old Baloo,' Mowgli went on. 'They have promised me this. Ah!'

'*Whoof!*' Baloo's big paw scooped Mowgli off Bagheera's back, and as the boy lay between the big fore paws he could see the Bear was angry.

'Mowgli,' said Baloo, 'thou hast been talking with the *Bandar-log*—the Monkey-People.'

Mowgli looked at Bagheera to see if the Panther was angry too, and Bagheera's eyes were as hard as jade-stones.

'Thou hast been with the Monkey-People—the gray apes—the people without a Law—the eaters of everything. That is great shame.'

'When Baloo hurt my head,' said Mowgli (he was still on his back), 'I went away, and the gray apes came down from the trees and had pity on me. No one else cared.' He snuffled a little.

'The pity of the Monkey-People!' Baloo snorted. 'The stillness of the mountain stream! The cool of the summer sun! And then, man-cub?'

'And then, and then, they gave me nuts and pleasant things to eat, and they—they carried me in their arms up to the top of the trees and said I was their blood-brother except that I had no tail, and should be their leader some day.'

'They have *no* leader,' said Bagheera. 'They lie. They have always lied.'

'They were very kind and bade me come again. Why have I never been taken among the Monkey-People? They stand on their feet as I do. They do not hit me with hard paws. They play all day. Let me get up! Bad

Baloo, let me up! I will play with them again.'

'Listen, man-cub,' said the Bear, and his voice rumbled like thunder on a hot night. 'I have taught thee all the Law of the Jungle for all the peoples of the jungle—except the Monkey-Folk who live in the trees. They have no law. They are outcaste. They have no speech of their own, but use the stolen words which they overhear when they listen, and peep, and wait up above in the branches. Their way is not our way. They are without leaders. They have no remembrance. They boast and chatter and pretend that they are a great people about to do great affairs in the jungle, but the falling of a nut turns their minds to laughter and all is forgotten. We of the jungle have no dealings with them. We do not drink where the monkeys drink; we do not go where the monkeys go; we do not hunt where they hunt; we do not die where they die. Hast thou ever heard me speak of the *Bandar-log* till to-day?'

'No,' said Mowgli in a whisper, for the forest was very still now Baloo had finished.

'The Jungle-People put them out of their mouths and out of their mind. They are very many, evil, dirty, shameless, and they desire, if they have any fixed desire, to be noticed by the Jungle-People. But we do *not* notice them even when they throw nuts and filth on our heads.'

He had hardly spoken when a shower of nuts and twigs spattered down through the branches; and they could hear coughings and howlings and angry jumpings high up in the air among the thin branches.

'The Monkey-People are forbidden,' said Baloo, 'forbidden to the Jungle-People. Remember.'

'Forbidden,' said Bagheera; 'but I still think Baloo should have warned thee against them.'

'I—I? How was I to guess he would play with such dirt? The Monkey-People! Faugh!'

A fresh shower came down on their heads and the two trotted away taking Mowgli with them. What Baloo had said about the monkeys was perfectly true. They belonged to the tree-tops, and as beasts very seldom look up, there was no occasion for the monkeys and the Jungle-People to cross each other's path. But whenever they found a sick wolf, or a wounded tiger, or bear, the monkeys would torment him, and would throw sticks and nuts at any beast for fun and in the hope of being noticed. Then they would howl and shriek senseless songs, and invite the Jungle-People to climb up their trees and fight them, or would start furious battles over nothing among themselves, and leave the dead monkeys where the Jungle-People could see them. They were always just going to have a leader, and laws and customs of their own, but they never did, because their memories would not hold over from day to day, and so they compromised things by making up a saying: 'What the *Bandar-log* think now the jungle will think later,' and that comforted them a great deal. None of the beasts could reach them, but on the other hand none of the beasts would notice them, and that was

why they were so pleased when Mowgli came to play with them, and they heard how angry Baloo was.

They never meant to do any more—the *Bandar-log* never mean anything at all; but one of them invented what seemed to him a brilliant idea, and he told all the others that Mowgli would be a useful person to keep in the tribe, because he could weave sticks together for protection from the wind; so, if they caught him, they could make him teach them. Of course Mowgli, as a woodcutter's child, inherited all sorts of instincts, and used to make little huts of fallen branches without thinking how he came to do it, and the Monkey-People, watching in the trees, considered his play most wonderful. This time, they said, they were really going to have a leader and become the wisest people in the jungle—so wise that every one else would notice and envy them. Therefore they followed Baloo and Bagheera and Mowgli through the jungle very quietly till it was time for the mid-day nap, and Mowgli, who was very much ashamed of himself, slept between the Panther and the Bear, resolving to have no more to do with the Monkey-People.

The next thing he remembered was feeling hands on his legs and arms —hard, strong, little hands—and then a swash of branches in his face, and then he was staring down through the swaying boughs as Baloo woke the jungle with his deep cries and Bagheera bounded up the trunk with every tooth bared. The *Bandar-log* howled with triumph and scuffled away to the upper branches where Bagheera dared not follow, shouting: 'He has noticed us! Bagheera has noticed us. All the Jungle-People admire us for our skill and our cunning.' Then they began their flight; and the flight of the Monkey-People through tree-land is one of the things nobody can describe. They have their regular roads and cross-roads, up hills and down hills, all laid out from fifty to seventy or a hundred feet above ground, and by these they can travel even at night if necessary. Two of the strongest monkeys caught Mowgli under the arms and swung off with him through the tree-tops, twenty feet at a bound. Had they been alone they could have gone twice as fast, but the boy's weight held them back. Sick and giddy as Mowgli was he could not help enjoying the wild rush, though the glimpses

of earth far down below frightened him, and the terrible check and jerk at the end of the swing over nothing but empty air brought his heart between his teeth. His escort would rush him up a tree till he felt the thinnest topmost branches crackle and bend under them, and then with a cough and a whoop would fling themselves into the air outwards and downwards, and bring up, hanging by their hands or their feet to the lower limbs of the next tree. Sometimes he could see for miles and miles across the still green jungle, as a man on the top of a mast can see for miles across the sea, and then the branches and leaves would lash him across the face, and he and his two guards would be almost down to earth again. So, bounding and crashing and whooping and yelling, the whole tribe of *Bandar-log* swept along the tree-roads with Mowgli their prisoner.

For a time he was afraid of being dropped: then he grew angry but knew better than to struggle, and then he began to think. The first thing was to send back word to Baloo and Bagheera, for, at the pace the monkeys were going, he knew his friends would be left far behind. It was useless to look down, for he could only see the top-sides of the branches, so he stared upwards and saw, far away in the blue, Chil the Kite balancing and wheeling as he kept watch over the jungle waiting for things to die. Chil saw that the monkeys were carrying something, and dropped a few hundred yards to find out whether their load was good to eat. He whistled with surprise when he saw Mowgli being dragged up to a tree-top and heard him give the Kite call for—'We be of one blood, thou and I.' The waves of the branches closed over the boy, but Chil balanced away to the next tree in time to see the little brown face come up again. 'Mark my trail,' Mowgli shouted. 'Tell Baloo of the Seeonee Pack and Bagheera of the Council Rock.'

'In whose name, Brother?' Chil had never seen Mowgli before, though of course he had heard of him.

'Mowgli, the Frog. Man-cub they call me! Mark my tra-il!'

The last words were shrieked as he was being swung through the air, but Chil nodded and rose up till he looked no bigger than a speck of dust, and there he hung, watching with his telescope eyes the swaying of the tree-tops as Mowgli's escort whirled along.

'They never go far,' he said with a chuckle. 'They never do what they set out to do. Always pecking at new things are the *Bandar-log*. This time, if I have any eyesight, they have pecked down trouble for themselves, for Baloo is no fledgling and Bagheera can, as I know, kill more than goats.'

So he rocked on his wings, his feet gathered up under him, and waited.

Meantime, Baloo and Bagheera were furious with rage and grief. Bagheera climbed as he had never climbed before, but the thin branches broke beneath his weight, and he slipped down, his claws full of bark.

'Why didst thou not warn the man-cub?' he roared to poor Baloo, who had set off at a clumsy trot in the hope of overtaking the monkeys. 'What was the use of half slaying him with blows if thou didst not warn him?'

'Haste! O haste! We—we may catch them yet!' Baloo panted.

'At that speed! It would not tire a wounded cow. Teacher of the Law —cub-beater—a mile of that rolling to and fro would burst thee open. Sit still and think! Make a plan. This is no time for chasing. They may drop him if we follow too close.'

'Arrula! Whoo! They may have dropped him already, being tired of carrying him. Who can trust the Bandar-log? Put dead bats on my head! Give me black bones to eat! Roll me into the hives of the wild bees that I may be stung to death, and bury me with the Hyæna, for I am the most miserable of bears! Arulala! Wahooa! O Mowgli, Mowgli! why did I not warn thee against the Monkey-Folk instead of breaking thy head? Now perhaps I may have knocked the day's lesson out of his mind, and he will be alone in the jungle without the Master Words.'

Baloo clasped his paws over his ears and rolled to and fro moaning.

'At least he gave me all the Words correctly a little time ago,' said Bagheera, impatiently. ' Baloo, thou hast neither memory nor respect. What would the jungle think if I, the Black Panther, curled myself up like Sahi the Porcupine, and howled? '

'What do I care what the jungle thinks? He may be dead by now.'

' Unless and until they drop him from the branches in sport, or kill him out of idleness, I have no fear for the man-cub. He is wise and well-taught, and above all he has the eyes that make the Jungle-People afraid. But (and it is a great evil) he is in the power of the Bandar-log, and they, because they live in trees, have no fear of any of our people.' Bagheera licked one fore-paw thoughtfully.

' Fool that I am! Oh fat, brown, root-digging fool that I am,' said Baloo, uncoiling himself with a jerk, ' it is true what Hathi the Wild Elephant says: " To each his own fear "; and they, the Bandar-log, fear Kaa the Rock Snake. He can climb as well as they can. He steals the young monkeys in the night. The whisper of his name makes their wicked tails cold. Let us go to Kaa.'

' What will he do for us? He is not of our tribe, being footless—and with most evil eyes,' said Bagheera.

' He is very old and very cunning. Above all, he is always hungry,' said Baloo hopefully. ' Promise him many goats.'

' He sleeps for a full month after he has once eaten. He may be asleep now, and even were he awake what if he would rather kill his own goats? ' Bagheera, who did not know much about Kaa, was naturally suspicious.

' Then in that case, thou and I together, old hunter, might make him see reason.' Here Baloo rubbed his faded brown shoulder against the Panther, and they went off to look for Kaa the Rock-python.

They found him stretched out on a warm ledge in the afternoon sun, admiring his beautiful new coat, for he had been in retirement for the last ten days changing his skin, and now he was very splendid—darting his big blunt-nosed head along the ground, and twisting the thirty feet of his body

into fantastic knots and curves, and licking his lips as he thought of his dinner to come.

'He has not eaten,' said Baloo, with a grunt of relief, as soon as he saw the beautifully mottled brown and yellow jacket. 'Be careful, Bagheera! He is always a little blind after he has changed his skin, and very quick to strike.'

Kaa was not a poison-snake—in fact he rather despised the poison-snakes as cowards—but his strength lay in his hug, and when he had once lapped his huge coils round anybody there was no more to be said. 'Good hunting!' cried Baloo, sitting up on his haunches. Like all snakes of his breed Kaa was rather deaf, and did not hear the call at first. Then he curled up ready for any accident, his head lowered.

'Good hunting for us all,' he answered. 'Oho, Baloo, what dost thou do here? Good hunting, Bagheera. One of us at least needs food. Is there any news of game afoot? A doe now, or even a young buck? I am as empty as a dried well.'

'We are hunting,' said Baloo carelessly. He knew that you must not hurry Kaa. He is too big.

'Give me permission to come with you,' said Kaa. 'A blow more or less is nothing to thee, Bagheera or Baloo, but I—I have to wait and wait for days in a wood-path and climb half a night on the mere chance of a young ape. Psshaw! The branches are not what they were when I was young. Rotten twigs and dry boughs are they all.'

'Maybe thy great weight has something to do with the matter,' said Baloo.

'I am a fair length—a fair length,' said Kaa, with a little pride. 'But for all that, it is the fault of this new-grown timber. I came very near to falling on my last hunt—very near indeed—and the noise of my slipping, for my tail was not tight wrapped round the tree, waked the *Bandar-log*, and they called me most evil names.'

'Footless, yellow earth-worm,' said Bagheera under his whiskers, as though he were trying to remember something.

'Sssss! Have they ever called me *that*?' said Kaa.

'Something of that kind it was that they shouted to us last moon, but we never noticed them. They will say anything—even that thou hast lost all thy teeth, and wilt not face anything bigger than a kid, because (they are indeed shameless, these *Bandar-log*)—because thou art afraid of the he-goats' horns,' Bagheera went on sweetly.

Now a snake, especially a wary old python like Kaa, very seldom shows that he is angry, but Baloo and Bagheera could see the big swallowing-muscles on either side of Kaa's throat ripple and bulge.

'The *Bandar-log* have shifted their grounds,' he said quietly. 'When I came up into the sun to-day I heard them whooping among the tree-tops.'

'It—it is the *Bandar-log* that we follow now,' said Baloo, but the words stuck in his throat, for that was the first time in his memory that one of the

Jungle-People had owned to being interested in the doings of the monkeys.

'Beyond doubt then it is no small thing that takes two such hunters—leaders in their own jungle I am certain—on the trail of the *Bandar-log*,' Kaa replied, courteously, as he swelled with curiosity.

'Indeed,' Baloo began, 'I am no more than the old and sometimes very foolish Teacher of the Law to the Seeonee wolf-cubs, and Bagheera here——'

'Is Bagheera,' said the Black Panther, and his jaws shut with a snap, for he did not believe in being humble. 'The trouble is this, Kaa. Those nut-stealers and pickers of palm leaves have stolen away our man-cub of whom thou hast perhaps heard.'

'I heard some news from Sahi (his quills make him presumptuous) of a man-thing that was entered into a wolf-pack, but I did not believe. Sahi is full of stories half heard and very badly told.'

'But it is true. He is such a man-cub as never was,' said Baloo. 'The best and wisest and boldest of man-cubs—my own pupil, who shall make the name of Baloo famous through all the jungles; and besides, I—we—love him, Kaa.'

'Ts! Ts!' said Kaa, weaving his head to and fro. 'I also have known what love is. There are tales I could tell that——'

'That need a clear night when we are all well fed to praise properly,' said Bagheera, quickly. 'Our man-cub is in the hands of the *Bandar-log* now, and we know that of all the Jungle-People they fear Kaa alone.'

'They fear me alone. They have good reason,' said Kaa. 'Chattering, foolish, vain—vain, foolish, and chattering, are the monkeys. But a man-thing in their hands is in no good luck. They grow tired of the nuts they pick, and throw them down. They carry a branch half a day, meaning to do great things with it, and then they snap it in two. That man-thing is not to be envied. They called me also—yellow fish was it not?'

'Worm—worm—earth-worm,' said Bagheera, 'as well as other things which I cannot now say for shame.'

'We must remind them to speak well of their master. Aaa-ssp! We must help their wandering memories. Now, whither went they with the cub?'

'The jungle alone knows. Towards the sunset, I believe,' said Baloo. 'We had thought that thou wouldst know, Kaa.'

'I? How? I take them when they come in my way, but I do not hunt the *Bandar-log*, or frogs—or green scum on a water-hole for that matter. Hsss!'

'Up, Up! Up, Up! Hillo! Illo! Illo, look up, Baloo of the Seeonee Wolf Pack!'

Baloo looked up to see where the voice came from, and there was Chil the Kite, sweeping down with the sun shining on the upturned flanges of his wings. It was near Chil's bed-time, but he had ranged all over the jungle looking for the Bear and missed him in the thick foliage.

' What is it? ' said Baloo.

' I have seen Mowgli among the *Bandar-log*. He bade me tell you. I watched. The *Bandar-log* have taken him beyond the river to the monkey city—to the Cold Lairs. They may stay there for a night, or ten nights, or an hour. I have told the bats to watch through the dark time. That is my message. Good hunting, all you below! '

' Full gorge and a deep sleep to you, Chil,' cried Bagheera. ' I will remember thee in my next kill, and put aside the head for thee alone—oh best of kites! '

' It is nothing. It is nothing. The boy held the Master Word. I could have done no less,' and Chil circled up again to his roost.

' He has not forgotten to use his tongue,' said Baloo, with a chuckle of pride. ' To think of one so young remembering the Master Word for the birds too while he was being pulled across-trees! '

' It was most firmly driven into him,' said Bagheera. ' But I am proud of him, and now we must go to the Cold Lairs.'

They all knew where that place was, but few of the Jungle-People ever went there, because what they called the Cold Lairs was an old deserted city, lost and buried in the jungle, and beasts seldom use a place that men have once used. The wild boar will, but the hunting-tribes do not. Besides, the monkeys lived there as much as they could be said to live anywhere, and no self-respecting animal would come within eye-shot of it except in times of drouth, when the half-ruined tanks and reservoirs held a little water.

' It is half a night's journey—at full speed,' said Bagheera, and Baloo looked very serious. ' I will go as fast as I can,' he said, anxiously.

' We dare not wait for thee. Follow, Baloo. We must go on the quick-foot—Kaa and I.'

' Feet or no feet, I can keep abreast of all thy four,' said Kaa, shortly. Baloo made one effort to hurry, but had to sit down panting, and so they left him to come on later, while Bagheera hurried forward, at the quick panther-canter. Kaa said nothing, but, strive as Bagheera might, the huge Rock-python held level with him. When they came to a hill-stream, Bagheera gained, because he bounded across while Kaa swam, his head and two feet of his neck clearing the water, but on level ground Kaa made up the distance.

' By the Broken Lock that freed me,' said Bagheera, when twilight had fallen, ' thou art no slow goer! '

' I am hungry,' said Kaa. ' Besides, they called me speckled frog.'

' Worm—earth-worm, and yellow to boot.'

' All one. Let us go on,' and Kaa seemed to pour himself along the ground, finding the shortest road with his steady eyes, and keeping to it.

In the Cold Lairs the Monkey-People were not thinking of Mowgli's friends at all. They had brought the boy to the Lost City, and were very pleased with themselves for the time. Mowgli had never seen an Indian city before, and though this was almost a heap of ruins it seemed very wonderful

and splendid. Some king had built it long ago on a little hill. You could still trace the stone causeways that led up to the ruined gates where the last splinters of wood hung to the worn, rusted hinges. Trees had grown into and out of the walls; the battlements were tumbled down and decayed, and wild creepers hung out of the windows of the towers on the walls in bushy hanging clumps.

A great roofless palace crowned the hill, and the marble of the court-yards and the fountains was split, and stained with red and green, and the very cobblestones in the courtyard where the king's elephants used to live had been thrust up and apart by grasses and young trees. From the palace you could see the rows and rows of roofless houses that made up the city looking like empty honeycombs filled with blackness; the shapeless block of stone that had been an idol, in the square where four roads met; the pits and dimples at street-corners where the public wells once stood, and the shattered domes of temples with wild figs sprouting on their sides. The monkeys called the place their city, and pretended to despise the Jungle-People because they lived in the forest. And yet they never knew what the buildings were made for nor how to use them. They would sit in circles on the hall of the king's council chamber, and scratch for fleas and pretend to be men; or they would run in and out of the roofless houses and collect pieces of plaster and old tricks in a corner, and forget where they had hidden them, and fight and cry in scuffling crowds, and then break off to play up and down the terraces of the king's garden, where they would shake the rose trees and the oranges in sport to see the fruit and flowers fall. They explored all the passages and dark tunnels in the palace and the hundreds of little dark rooms, but they never remembered what they had seen and what they had not; and so drifted about in ones and twos or crowds telling each other that they were doing as men did. They drank at the tanks and made the water all muddy, and then they fought over it, and then they would all rush together in mobs and shout: 'There is no one in the jungle so wise and good and clever and strong and gentle as the *Bandar-log*.' Then all would begin again till they grew tired of the city and went back to the tree-tops, hoping the Jungle-People would notice them.

Mowgli, who had been trained under the Law of the Jungle, did not like or understand this kind of life. The monkeys dragged him into the Cold Lairs late in the afternoon, and instead of going to sleep, as Mowgli would have done after a long journey, they joined hands and danced about and sang their foolish songs. One of the monkeys made a speech and told his companions that Mowgli's capture marked a new thing in the history of the *Bandar-log*, for Mowgli was going to show them how to weave sticks and canes together as a protection against rain and cold. Mowgli picked up some creepers and began to work them in and out, and the monkeys tried to imitate; but in a very few minutes they lost interest and began to pull their friends' tails or jump up and down on all fours, coughing.

' I wish to eat,' said Mowgli. ' I am a stranger in this part of the jungle. Bring me food, or give me leave to hunt here.'

Twenty or thirty monkeys bounded away to bring him nuts and wild pawpaws; but they fell to fighting on the road, and it was too much trouble to go back with what was left of the fruit. Mowgli was sore and angry as well as hungry, and he roamed through the empty city giving the Strangers' Hunting Call from time to time, but no one answered him, and Mowgli felt that he had reached a very bad place indeed. 'All that Baloo has said about the *Bandar-log* is true,' he thought to himself. 'They have no Law, no Hunting Call, and no leaders—nothing but foolish words and little picking thievish hands. So if I am starved or killed here, it will be all my own fault. But I must try to return to my own jungle. Baloo will surely beat me, but that is better than chasing silly rose leaves with the *Bandar-log.*'

No sooner had he walked to the city wall than the monkeys pulled him back, telling him that he did not know how happy he was, and pinching him to make him grateful. He set his teeth and said nothing, but went with the shouting monkeys to a terrace above the red sandstone reservoirs that were half-full of rain water. There was a ruined summer-house of white marble in the centre of the terrace, built for queens dead a hundred years ago. The domed roof had half fallen in and blocked up the underground passage from the palace by which the queens used to enter; but the walls were made of screens of marble tracery—beautiful milk-white fret-work, set with agates and cornelians and jasper and lapis lazuli, and as the moon came up behind the hill it shone through the open work, casting shadows on the ground like black velvet embroidery. Sore, sleepy, and hungry as he was, Mowgli could not help laughing when the *Bandar-log* began, twenty at a time, to tell him how great and wise and strong and gentle they were, and how foolish he was to wish to leave them. 'We are great. We are free. We are wonderful. We are the most wonderful people in all the jungle! We all say so, and so it must be true,' they shouted. 'Now as you are a new listener and can carry our words back to the Jungle-People so that they may notice us in future, we will tell you all about our most excellent selves.' Mowgli made no objection, and the monkeys gathered by hundreds and hundreds on the terrace to listen to their own speakers singing the praises of the *Bandar-log*, and whenever a speaker stopped for want of breath they would all shout together: 'This is true; we all say so.' Mowgli nodded and blinked, and said 'Yes' when they asked him a question, and his head spun with the noise. 'Tabaqui, the Jackal, must have bitten all these people,' he said to himself, 'and now they have the madness. Certainly this is *dewanee*, the madness. Do they never go to sleep? Now there is a cloud coming to cover that moon. If it were only a big enough cloud I might try to run away in the darkness. But I am tired.'

That same cloud was being watched by two good friends in the ruined ditch below the city wall, for Bagheera and Kaa, knowing well how dangerous the Monkey-People were in large numbers, did not wish to run any risks. The monkeys never fight unless they are a hundred to one, and few in the jungle care for those odds.

'I will go to the west wall,' Kaa whispered, 'and come down swiftly with the slope of the ground in my favour. They will not throw themselves upon *my* back in their hundreds, but——'

'I know it,' said Bagheera. 'Would that Baloo were here; but we must do what we can. When that cloud covers the moon I shall go to the terrace. They hold some sort of council there over the boy.'

'Good hunting,' said Kaa, grimly, and glided away to the west wall. That happened to be the least ruined of any, and the big snake was delayed awhile before he could find a way up the stones. The cloud hid the moon, and as Mowgli wondered what would come next he heard Bagheera's light feet on the terrace. The Black Panther had raced up the slope almost without a sound and was striking—he knew better than to waste time in biting—right and left among the monkeys, who were seated round Mowgli in circles fifty and sixty deep. There was a howl of fright and rage, and then as Bagheera tripped on the rolling kicking bodies beneath him, a monkey shouted: 'There is only one here! Kill him! Kill.' A scuffling mass of monkeys, biting, scratching, tearing, and pulling, closed over Bagheera, while five or six laid hold of Mowgli, dragged him up the wall of the summer-house and pushed him through the hole of the broken dome. A man-trained boy would have been badly bruised, for the fall was a good fifteen feet, but Mowgli fell as Baloo had taught him to fall, and landed on his feet.

'Stay there,' shouted the monkeys, 'till we have killed thy friends, and later we will play with thee—if the Poison-People leave thee alive.'

'We be of one blood, ye and I,' said Mowgli, quickly giving the Snake's Call. He could hear rustling and hissing in the rubbish all round him and gave the Call a second time, to make sure.

'Even ssso! Down hoods all!' said half a dozen low voices (every ruin in India becomes sooner or later a dwelling-place of snakes, and the old summer-house was alive with cobras). 'Stand still, Little Brother, for thy feet may do us harm.'

Mowgli stood as quietly as he could, peering through the open work and listening to the furious din of the fight round the Black Panther—the yells and chatterings and scufflings, and Bagheera's deep, hoarse cough as he backed and bucked and twisted and plunged under the heaps of his enemies. For the first time since he was born, Bagheera was fighting for his life.

'Baloo must be at hand; Bagheera would not have come alone,' Mowgli thought; and then he called aloud: 'To the tank, Bagheera. Roll to the water-tanks. Roll and plunge! Get to the water!'

Bagheera heard, and the cry that told him Mowgli was safe gave him new courage. He worked his way desperately, inch by inch, straight for the reservoirs, halting in silence. Then from the ruined wall nearest the jungle rose up the rumbling war-shout of Baloo. The old Bear had done his best, but he could not come before. 'Bagheera,' he shouted, 'I am here. I climb! I haste! *Ahuwora!* The stones slip under my feet! Wait my coming, oh most infamous *Bandar-log!*' He panted up the terrace only to disappear to the

head in a wave of monkeys, but he threw himself squarely on his haunches, and, spreading out his fore-paws, hugged as many as he could hold, and then began to hit with a regular *bat-bat-bat*, like the flipping strokes of a paddle-wheel. A crash and a splash told Mowgli that Bagheera had fought his way to the tank where the monkeys could not follow. The Panther lay gasping for breath, his head just out of water, while the monkeys stood three deep on the red steps, dancing up and down with rage, ready to spring upon him from all sides if he came out to help Baloo. It was then that Bagheera lifted up his dripping chin, and in despair gave the Snake's Call for protection— ' We be of one blood, ye and I '—for he believed that Kaa had turned tail at the last minute. Even Baloo, half smothered under the monkeys on the edge of the terrace, could not help chuckling as he heard the Black Panther asking for help.

Kaa had only just worked his way over the west wall, landing with a wrench that dislodged a coping-stone into the ditch. He had no intention of losing any advantage of the ground, and coiled and uncoiled himself once or twice, to be sure that every foot of his long body was in working order. All that while the fight with Baloo went on, and the monkeys yelled in the tank round Bagheera, and Mang, the Bat, flying to and fro, carried the news of the great battle over the jungle, till even Hathi the Wild Elephant trumpeted, and, far away, scattered bands of the Monkey-Folk woke and came leaping along the tree-roads to help their comrades in the Cold Lairs, and the noise of the fight roused all the day-birds for miles round. Then Kaa came straight, quickly, and anxious to kill. The fighting-strength of a python is in the driving blow of his head backed by all the strength and weight of his body. If you can imagine a lance, or a battering ram, or a hammer weighing nearly half a ton driven by a cool, quiet mind living in the handle of it, you can roughly imagine what Kaa was like when he fought. A python four or five feet long can knock a man down if he hits him fairly in the chest, and Kaa was thirty feet long, as you know. His first stroke was delivered into the heart of the crowd round Baloo—was sent home with shut mouth in silence, and there was no need of a second. The monkeys scattered with cries of—' Kaa! It is Kaa! Run! Run! '

Generations of monkeys had been scared into good behavior by the stories their elders told them of Kaa, the night-thief, who could slip along the branches as quietly as moss grows, and steal away the strongest monkey that ever lived; of old Kaa, who could make himself look so like a dead branch or a rotten stump that the wisest were deceived, till the branch caught them. Kaa was everything that the monkeys feared in the jungle, for none of them knew the limits of his power, none of them could look him in the face, and none had ever come alive out of his hug. And so they ran, stammering with terror, to the walls and the roofs of the houses, and Baloo drew a deep breath of relief. His fur was much thicker than Bagheera's, but he had suffered sorely in the fight. Then Kaa opened his mouth for the first time and spoke one long hissing word, and the far away monkeys, hurrying

to the defence of the Cold Lairs, stayed where they were, cowering, till the loaded branches bent and crackled under them. The monkeys on the walls and the empty houses stopped their cries, and in the stillness that fell upon the city Mowgli heard Bagheera shaking his wet sides as he came up from the tank. Then the clamour broke out again. The monkeys leaped higher up the walls; they clung round the necks of the big stone idols and shrieked as they skipped along the battlements, while Mowgli, dancing in the summerhouse, put his eye to the screen work and hooted owl-fashion between his front teeth, to show his derision and contempt.

'Get the man-cub out of that trap; I can do no more,' Bagheera gasped. 'Let us take the man-cub and go. They may attack again.'

'They will not move till I order them. Stay you ssssoï' Kaa hissed, and the city was silent once more. 'I could not come before, Brother, but I *think* I heard thee call '—this was to Bagheera.

'I—I may have cried out in the battle,' Bagheera answered. 'Baloo, art thou hurt?'

'I am not sure that they did not pull me into a hundred little bearlings,' said Baloo, gravely shaking one leg after the other. 'Wow! I am sore. Kaa, we owe thee, I think, our lives—Bagheera and I.'

'No matter. Where is the manling?'

'Here, in a trap. I cannot climb out,' cried Mowgli. The curve of the broken dome was above his head.

'Take him away. He dances like Mor, the Peacock. He will crush our young,' said the cobras inside.

'Hah!' said Kaa with a chuckle, 'he has friends everywhere, this manling. Stand back, manling; and hide you, O Poison-People. I break down the wall.'

Kaa looked carefully till he found a discoloured crack in the marble tracery showing a weak spot, made two or three light taps with his head to get the distance, and then lifting up six feet of his body clear of the ground, sent home half-a-dozen full-power smashing blows, nose-first. The screenwork broke and fell away in a cloud of dust and rubbish, and Mowgli leaped through the opening and flung himself between Baloo and Bagheera—an arm round each big neck.

'Art thou hurt?' said Baloo, hugging him softly.

'I am sore, hungry, and not a little bruised; but oh they have handled ye grievously, my Brothers! Ye bleed.'

'Others also,' said Bagheera, licking his lips and looking at the monkeydead on the terrace and round the tank.

'It is nothing, it is nothing if thou art safe, oh my pride of all little frogs!' whimpered Baloo.

'Of that we shall judge later,' said Bagheera, in a dry voice that Mowgli did not at all like. 'But here is Kaa to whom we owe the battle and thou owest thy life. Thank him according to our customs, Mowgli.'

Mowgli turned and saw the great Python's head swaying a foot above his own.

' So this is the manling,' said Kaa. ' Very soft is his skin, and he is not unlike the *Bandar-log*. Have a care, manling, that I do not mistake thee for a monkey some twilight when I have newly changed my coat.'

' We be one blood, thou and I,' Mowgli answered. ' I take my life from thee to-night. My kill shall be thy kill if ever thou art hungry, O Kaa.'

' All thanks, Little Brother,' said Kaa, though his eyes twinkled. ' And what may so bold a hunter kill? I ask that I may follow when next he goes abroad.'

' I kill nothing—I am too little—but I drive goats towards such as can use them. When thou art empty come to me and see if I speak the truth. I have some skill in these '—he held out his hands—' and if ever thou art in a trap, I may pay the debt which I owe to thee, to Bagheera, and to Baloo, here. Good hunting to ye all, my masters.'

' Well said,' growled Baloo, for Mowgli had returned thanks very prettily. The Python dropped his head lightly for a minute on Mowgli's shoulder. ' A brave heart and a courteous tongue,' said he. ' They shall carry thee far through the jungle, manling. But now go hence quickly with thy friends. Go and sleep for the moon sets, and what follows it is not well that thou shouldst see.'

The moon was sinking behind the hills and the lines of trembling monkeys huddled together on the walls and battlements looked like ragged shaky fringes of things. Baloo went down to the tank for a drink and Bagheera began to put his fur in order, as Kaa glided out into the centre of the terrace and brought his jaws together with a ringing snap that drew all the monkeys' eyes upon him.

' The moon sets,' he said. ' Is there yet light enough to see? '

From the walls came a moan like the wind in the tree-tops—' We see, O Kaa.'

' Good. Begins now the dance—the Dance of the Hunger of Kaa. Sit still and watch.' He turned twice or thrice in a big circle, weaving his head from right to left. Then he began making loops and figures of eight with his body, and soft, oozy triangles that melted into squares and five-sided figures, and coiled mounds, never resting, never hurrying, and never stopping his low humming song. It grew darker and darker, till at last the dragging, shifting coils disappeared, but they could hear the rustle of the scales.

Baloo and Bagheera stood still as stone, growling in their throats, their neck-hair bristling, and Mowgli watched and wondered.

' *Bandar-log*,' said the voice of Kaa at last, ' can ye stir foot or hand without my order? Speak! '

' Without thy order we cannot stir foot or hand, O Kaa! '

' Good! Come all one pace nearer to me.'

The lines of the monkeys swayed forward helplessly, and Baloo and Bagheera took one stiff step forward with them.

' Nearer! ' hissed Kaa, and they all moved again.

Mowgli laid his hands on Baloo and Bagheera to get them away, and

the two great beasts started as though they had been waked from a dream.

'Keep thy hand on my shoulder,' Bagheera whispered. 'Keep it there, or I must go back—must go back to Kaa. Aah!'

'It is only old Kaa making circles on the dust,' said Mowgli; 'let us go'; and the three slipped off through a gap in the walls to the jungle.

'*Whoof!*' said Baloo, when he stood under the still trees again. 'Never more will I make an ally of Kaa,' and he shook himself all over.

'He knows more than we,' said Bagheera, trembling. 'In a little time, had I stayed, I should have walked down his throat.'

'Many will walk by that road before the moon rises again,' said Baloo. 'He will have good hunting—after his own fashion.'

'But what was the meaning of it all?' said Mowgli, who did not know anything of a python's powers of fascination. 'I saw no more than a big snake making foolish circles till the dark came. And his nose was all sore. Ho! Ho!'

'Mowgli,' said Bagheera, angrily, 'his nose was sore on *thy* account, as my ears and sides and paws, and Baloo's neck and shoulders are bitten on *thy* account. Neither Baloo nor Bagheera will be able to hunt with pleasure for many days.'

'It is nothing,' said Baloo; 'we have the man-cub again.'

'True; but he has cost us heavily in time which might have been spent in good hunting, in wounds, in hair—I am half plucked along my back—and last of all, in honour. For, remember, Mowgli, I, who am the Black Panther, was forced to call upon Kaa for protection, and Baloo and I were both made stupid as little birds by the Hunger-Dance. All this, man-cub, came of thy playing with the *Bandar-log*.'

'True; it is true,' said Mowgli, sorrowfully. 'I am an evil man-cub, and my stomach is sad in me.'

'Mf! What says the Law of the Jungle, Baloo?'

Baloo did not wish to bring Mowgli into any more trouble, but he could not tamper with the Law, so he mumbled: 'Sorrow never stays punishment. But remember, Bagheera, he is very little.'

'I will remember; but he has done mischief, and blows must be dealt now. Mowgli, hast thou anything to say?'

'Nothing. I did wrong. Baloo and thou art wounded. It is just.'

Bagheera gave him half a dozen love-taps from a panther's point of view (they would hardly have waked one of his own cubs), but for a seven-year-old boy they amounted to as severe a beating as you could wish to avoid. When it was all over Mowgli sneezed, and picked himself up without a word.

'Now,' said Bagheera, 'jump on my back, Little Brother, and we will go home.'

One of the beauties of Jungle Law is that punishment settles all scores. There is no nagging afterwards.

Mowgli laid his head down on Bagheera's back and slept so deeply that he never waked when he was put down in the home-cave.

ROAD-SONG OF THE BANDAR-LOG

Here we go in a flung festoon,
Half way up to the jealous moon!
Don't you envy our pranceful bands?
Don't you wish you had extra hands?
Wouldn't you like if your tails were—*so*—
Curved in the shape of a Cupid's Bow?
 Now you're angry, but—never mind,
 Brother, thy tail hangs down behind!

Here we sit in a branchy row,
Thinking of beautiful things we know.
Dreaming of deeds that we mean to do,
All complete, in a minute or two—
Somefhing noble and wise and good,
Done by merely wishing we could.
 We've forgotten, but—never mind,
 Brother, thy tail hangs down behind!

All the talk we ever have heard
Uttered by bat or beast or bird—
Hide or fin or scale or feather—
Jabber it quickly and all together!
Excellent! Wonderful! Once again!
Now we are talking just like men!
 Let's pretend we are—never mind,
 Brother, thy tail hangs down behind!
 This is the way of the monkey-kind.

Then join our leaping lines that scumfish through the pines,
That rocket by where, light and high, the wild grape swings.
By the rubbish in our wake, and the noble noise we make,
Be sure, be sure, we're going to do some splendid things!

HOW FEAR CAME

The stream is shrunk—the pool is dry,
And we be comrades, thou and I;
With fevered jowl and dusty flank
Each jostling each along the bank;
And by one drouthy fear made still
Foregoing thought of quest or kill.
Now 'neath his dam the fawn may see,
The lean Packwolf as cowed as he,
And the tall buck, unflinching, note
The fangs that tore his father's throat.
The pools are shrunk—the streams are dry,
And we be playmates, thou and I,
Till yonder cloud—Good Hunting!—loose
The rain that breaks our Water Truce.

~§ THE Law of the Jungle—which is by far the oldest law in the world—
has arranged for almost every kind of accident that may befall the Jungle
People, till now its code is as perfect as time and custom can make it. If
you have read the other stories about Mowgli, you will remember that he
spent a great part of his life in the Seeonee Wolf-Pack, learning the Law
from Baloo the brown bear; and it was Baloo who told him, when the boy
grew impatient at the constant orders, that the Law was like the Giant
Creeper, because it dropped across every one's back and no one could
escape. 'When thou hast lived as long as I have, Little Brother, thou wilt
see how all the Jungle obeys at least one Law. And that will be no pleasant
sight,' said Baloo.

This talk went in at one ear and out at the other, for a boy who
spends his life eating and sleeping does not worry about anything till it
actually stares him in the face. But one year Baloo's words came true, and
Mowgli saw all the Jungle working under one Law.

It began when the winter Rains failed almost entirely, and Sahi, the
Porcupine, meeting Mowgli in a bamboo thicket, told him that the wild
yams were drying up. Now everybody knows that Sahi is ridiculously
fastidious in his choice of food, and will eat nothing but the very best
and ripest. So Mowgli laughed and said, 'What is that to me?'

'Not much *now*,' said Sahi, rattling his quills in a stiff, uncomfortable
way, 'but later we shall see. Is there any more diving into the deep rock-
pool below the Bee-Rocks, Little Brother?'

'No. The foolish water is going all away, and I do not wish to break

my head,' said Mowgli, who was quite sure he knew as much as any five of the Jungle People put together.

'That is thy loss. A small crack might let in some wisdom.' Sahi ducked quickly to prevent Mowgli from pulling his nose-bristles, and Mowgli told Baloo what Sahi had said. Baloo looked very grave, and mumbled half to himself: 'If I were alone I would change my hunting-grounds now, before the others began to think. And yet—hunting among strangers ends in fighting—and they might hurt my Man-cub. We must wait and see how the *mohwa* blooms.'

That spring the *mohwa* tree, that Baloo was so fond of, never flowered. The greeny, cream-coloured, wax blossoms were heat-killed before they were born, and only a few bad-smelling petals came down when he stood on his hind legs and shook the tree. Then, inch by inch, the untempered heat crept into the heart of the Jungle, turning it yellow, brown, and at last black. The green growths in the sides of the ravines burned up to broken wires and curled films of dead stuff; the hidden pools sank down and caked over, keeping the last least footmark on their edges as if it had been cast in iron; the juicy-stemmed creepers fell away from the trees they clung to and died at their feet; the bamboos withered, clanking when the hot winds blew, and the moss peeled off the rocks deep in the Jungle, till they were as bare and as hot as the quivering blue boulders in the bed of the stream.

The birds and the monkey-people went north early in the year, for they knew what was coming; and the deer and the wild pig broke far away into the perished fields of the villages, dying sometimes before the eyes of men too weak to kill them. Chil, the Kite, stayed and grew fat, for there was a great deal of carrion, and evening after evening he brought the news to the beasts, too weak to force their way to fresh hunting-grounds, that the sun was killing the Jungle for three days' flight in every direction.

Mowgli, who had never known what real hunger meant, fell back on stale honey, three years old, scraped out of deserted rock-hives—honey black as a sloe, and dusty with dried sugar. He hunted, too, for deep-boring grubs under the bark of the trees, and robbed the wasps of their new broods. All the game in the Jungle was no more than skin and bone, and Bagheera could kill thrice in a night and hardly get a full meal. But the want of water was the worst, for though the Jungle People drink seldom they must drink deep.

And the heat went on and on, and sucked up all the moisture, till at last the main channel of the Waingunga was the only stream that carried a trickle of water between its dead banks; and when Hathi, the wild elephant, who lives for a hundred years and more, saw a long, lean blue ridge of rock show dry in the very centre of the stream, he knew that he was looking at the Peace Rock, and then and there he lifted up his trunk and proclaimed the Water Truce, as his father before him had proclaimed it fifty years ago. The deer, wild pig, and buffalo took up the cry hoarsely;

and Chil, the Kite, flew in great circles far and wide, whistling and shriek-
ing the warning.

By the Law of the Jungle it is death to kill at the drinking-places
when once the Water Truce has been declared. The reason for this is that
drinking comes before eating. Every one in the Jungle can scramble along
somehow when only game is scarce; but water is water, and when there
is but one source of supply, all hunting stops while the Jungle People
go there for their needs. In good seasons, when water was plentiful, those
who came down to drink at the Waingunga—or anywhere else, for that
matter—did so at the risk of their lives, and that risk made no small part
of the fascination of the night's doings. To move down so cunningly that
never a leaf stirred; to wade knee-deep in the roaring shallows that drown
all noise from behind; to drink, looking backward over one shoulder, every
muscle ready for the first desperate bound of keen terror; to roll on the
sandy margin, and return, wet-muzzled and well plumped out, to the ad-
miring herd, was a thing that all glossy-horned young bucks took a delight
in, precisely because they knew that at any moment Bagheera or Shere
Khan might leap upon them and bear them down. But now that life-and-
death fun was ended, and the Jungle People came up, starved and weary,
to the shrunken river,—tiger, bear, deer, buffalo, and pig together,—drank
the fouled waters, and hung above them, too exhausted to move off.

The deer and pig had tramped all day in search of something better
than dried bark and withered leaves. The buffaloes had found no wallows to
be cool in, and no green crops to steal. The snakes had left the Jungle
and come down to the river in the hope of catching a stray frog. They
curled round wet stones, and never offered to strike when the snout of a
rooting pig dislodged them. The river-turtles had long ago been killed by
Bagheera, cleverest of hunters, and the fish had buried themselves deep in
the cracked mud. Only the Peace Rock lay across the shallows like a long
snake, and the little tired ripples hissed as they dried on its hot side.

It was here that Mowgli came nightly for the cool and the com-
panionship. The most hungry of his enemies would hardly have cared for
the boy then. His naked skin made him look more lean and wretched
than any of his fellows. His hair was bleached to tow-colour by the sun;
his ribs stood out like the ribs of a basket, and the lumps on his knees
and elbows, where he was used to track on all fours, gave his shrunken
limbs the look of knotted grass-stems. But his eye, under his matted fore-
lock, was cool and quiet, for Bagheera, his adviser in this time of trouble,
told him to move quietly, hunt slowly, and never, on any account, to lose
his temper.

' It is an evil time,' said the Black Panther, one furnace-hot evening,
' but it will go if we can live till the end. Is thy stomach full, Man-cub? '

' There is stuff in my stomach, but I get no good of it. Think you,
Bagheera, the Rains have forgotten us and will never come again? '

' Not I. We shall see the *mohwa* in blossom yet, and the little fawns

all fat with new grass. Come down to the Peace Rock and hear the news. On my back, Little Brother.'

'This is no time to carry weight. I can still stand alone, but—indeed we be no fatted bullocks, we two.'

Bagheera looked along his ragged, dusty flank and whispered: 'Last night I killed a bullock under the yoke. So low was I brought that I think I should not have dared to spring if he had been loose. *Wou!*'

Mowgli laughed. 'Yes, we are great hunters now,' said he. 'I am very bold—to eat grubs,' and the two came down together through the crackling undergrowth to the river bank and the lace-work of shoals that ran out from it in every direction.

'The water cannot live long,' said Baloo, joining them. 'Look across! Yonder are trails like the roads of Man.'

On the level plain of the farther bank the stiff jungle-grass had died standing, and, dying, had mummied. The beaten tracks of the deer and the pig, all heading towards the river, had striped that colourless plain with dusty gullies driven through the ten-foot grass, and, early as it was, each long avenue was full of first-comers hastening to the water. You could hear the does and fawns coughing in the snuff-like dust.

Up-stream, at the bend of the sluggish pool round the Peace Rock and Warden of the Water Truce, stood Hathi, the wild elephant, with his sons, gaunt and gray in the moonlight, rocking to and fro—always rocking. Below him a little were the vanguard of the deer; below these, again, the pig and the wild buffalo; and on the opposite bank, where the tall trees came down to the water's edge, was the place set apart for the Eaters of Flesh—the tiger, the wolves, the panther, the bear, and the others.

'We be under one Law, indeed,' said Bagheera, wading into the water and looking across at the lines of clicking horns and starting eyes where the deer and the pig pushed each other to and fro. 'Good hunting, all of you of my blood,' he added, lying down at full length, one flank thrust out of the shallows; and then, between his teeth, 'But for that which is the Law it would be *very* good hunting.'

The quick-spread ears of the deer caught the last sentence, and a frightened whisper ran along the ranks. 'The Truce! Remember the Truce!'

'Peace there, peace!' gurgled Hathi, the wild elephant. 'The Truce holds, Bagheera. This is no time to talk of hunting.'

'Who should know better than I?' Bagheera answered, rolling his yellow eyes up-stream. 'I am an eater of turtle—a fisher of frogs. *Ngaayah!* Would I could get good from chewing branches!'

'*We* wish so, very greatly,' bleated a young fawn, who had only been born that spring, and did not at all like it. Wretched as the Jungle People were, even Hathi could not help chuckling; while Mowgli, lying on his elbows in the warm water, laughed aloud, and beat up the foam with his feet.

'Well spoken, little bud-horn,' Bagheera purred. 'When the Truce ends that shall be remembered in thy favour,' and he looked keenly through

the darkness to make sure of recognising the fawn again.

Gradually the talk spread up and down the drinking-places. You could hear the scuffling, snorting pig asking for more room; the buffaloes grunting among themselves as they lurched out across the sandbars, and the deer telling pitiful stories of their long footsore searches in quest of food. Now and again they asked some question of the Eaters of Flesh across the river, but all the news was bad, and the roaring hot wind of the Jungle came and went, between the rocks and the rattling branches, and scattered twigs and dust on the water.

' The men-folk too, they die beside their ploughs,' said a young *sambhur*. ' I passed three between sunset and night. They lay still, and their bullocks with them. We also shall lie still in a little.'

' The river has fallen since last night,' said Baloo. ' O Hathi, hast thou ever seen the like of this drought? '

' It will pass, it will pass,' said Hathi, squirting water along his back and sides.

' We have one here that cannot endure long,' said Baloo; and he looked towards the boy he loved.

' I? ' said Mowgli indignantly, sitting up in the water. ' I have no long fur to cover my bones, but—but if thy hide were pulled off, Baloo—— '

Hathi shook all over at the idea, and Baloo said severely:

' Man-cub, that is not seemly to tell a Teacher of the Law. *Never* have I been seen without my hide.'

' Nay, I meant no harm, Baloo; but only that thou art, as it were, like the cocoanut in the husk, and I am the same cocoanut all naked. Now that brown husk of thine—— ' Mowgli was sitting cross-legged, and explaining things with his forefinger in his usual way, when Bagheera put out a paddy paw and pulled him over backwards into the water.

' Worse and worse,' said the Black Panther, as the boy rose spluttering. ' First, Baloo is to be skinned and now he is a cocoanut. Be careful that he does not do what the ripe cocoanuts do.'

' And what is that? ' said Mowgli, off his guard for the minute, though that is one of the oldest catches in the Jungle.

' Break thy head,' said Bagheera quietly, pulling him under again.

' It is not good to make a jest of thy teacher,' said the Bear, when Mowgli had been ducked for the third time.

' Not good! What would ye have? That naked thing running to and fro makes a monkey-jest of those who have once been good hunters, and pulls the best of us by the whiskers for sport.' This was Shere Khan, the Lame Tiger, limping down to the water. He waited a little to enjoy the sensation he made among the deer on the opposite bank; then he dropped his square, frilled head and began to lap, growling: ' The Jungle has become a whelping-ground for naked cubs now. Look at me, Man-cub! '

Mowgli looked—stared, rather—as insolently as he knew how, and in a minute Shere Khan turned away uneasily. ' Man-cub this, and Man-

cub that,' he rumbled, going on with his drink. 'The cub is neither man nor cub, or he would have been afraid. Next season I shall have to beg his leave for a drink. *Aurgh!* '

'That may come, too,' said Bagheera, looking him steadily between the eyes. 'That may come, too . . . Faugh, Shere Khan! What new shame hast thou brought here? '

The Lame Tiger had dipped his chin and jowl in the water, and dark oily streaks were floating from it down-stream.

'Man! ' said Shere Khan coolly, 'I killed an hour since.' He went on purring and growling to himself.

The line of beasts shook and wavered to and fro, and a whisper went up that grew to a cry: 'Man! Man! He has killed Man! ' Then all looked towards Hathi, the wild elephant, but he seemed not to hear. Hathi never does anything till the time comes, and that is one of the reasons why he lives so long.

'At such a season as this to kill Man! Was there no other game afoot? ' said Bagheera scornfully, drawing himself out of the tainted water, and shaking each paw, cat-fashion, as he did so.

'I killed for choice—not for food.' The horrified whisper began again, and Hathi's watchful little white eye cocked itself in Shere Khan's direction. 'For choice,' Shere Khan drawled. 'Now come I to drink and make me clean again. Is there any to forbid? '

Bagheera's back began to curve like a bamboo in a high wind, but Hathi lifted up his trunk and spoke quietly.

'Thy kill was from choice? ' he asked; and when Hathi asks a question it is best to answer.

'Even so. It was my right and my Night. Thou knowest, O Hathi.' Shere Khan spoke almost courteously.

'Yea, I know,' Hathi answered; and, after a little silence, 'Hast thou drunk thy fill? '

'For to-night, yes.'

'Go, then. The river is to drink, and not to defile. None but the Lame Tiger would have boasted of his right at this season when—when we suffer together—Man and Jungle People alike. Clean or unclean, get to thy lair, Shere Khan! '

The last words rang out like silver trumpets, and Hathi's three sons rolled forward half a pace, though there was no need. Shere Khan slunk away, not daring to growl, for he knew—what every one else knows—that when the last comes to the last Hathi is the Master of the Jungle.

'What is this right Shere Khan speaks of? ' Mowgli whispered in Bagheera's ear. 'To kill Man is *always* shameful. The Law says so. And yet Hathi says—— '

'Ask him. I do not know, Little Brother. Right or no right, if Hathi had not spoken I would have taught that lame butcher his lesson. To come to the Peace Rock fresh from a kill of Man—and to boast of it, is a

jackal's trick. Besides, he tainted the good water.'

Mowgli waited for a minute to pick up his courage, because no one cared to address Hathi directly, and then he cried: ' What is Shere Khan's right, O Hathi? ' Both banks echoed his words, for all the People of the Jungle are intensely curious, and they had just seen something that no one, except Baloo, who looked very thoughtful, seemed to understand.

' It is an old tale,' said Hathi; ' a tale older than the Jungle. Keep silence along the banks, and I will tell that tale.'

There was a minute or two of pushing and shouldering among the pigs and the buffalo, and then the leaders of the herds grunted, one after another, ' We wait,' and Hathi strode forward till he was almost knee-deep in the pool by the Peace Rock. Lean and wrinkled and yellow-tusked though he was, he looked what the Jungle held him to be—their master.

' Ye know, children,' he began, ' that of all things ye most fear Man.' There was a mutter of agreement.

' This tale touches thee, Little Brother,' said Bagheera to Mowgli.

' I? I am of the Pack—a hunter of the Free People,' Mowgli answered. ' What have I to do with Man? '

' And ye do not know why ye fear Man? ' Hathi went on. ' This is the reason. In the beginning of the Jungle, and none know when that was, we of the Jungle walked together, having no fear of one another. In those days there was no drought, and leaves and flowers and fruit grew on the same tree, and we ate nothing at all except leaves and flowers and grass and fruit and bark.'

' I am glad I was not born in those days,' said Bagheera. ' Bark is only good to sharpen claws.'

' And the Lord of the Jungle was Tha, the First of the Elephants. He drew the Jungle out of deep waters with his trunk, and where he made furrows in the ground with his tusks, there the rivers ran, and where he struck with his foot, there rose ponds of good water, and when he blew through his trunk—thus—the trees fell. That was the manner in which the Jungle was made by Tha; and so the tale was told to me.'

' It has not lost fat in the telling,' Bagheera whispered, and Mowgli laughed behind his hand.

' In those days there was no corn or melons or pepper or sugar-cane, nor were there any little huts such as ye have all seen; and the Jungle People knew nothing of Man, but lived in the Jungle together, making one people. But presently they began to dispute over their food, though there was grazing enough for all. They were lazy. Each wished to eat where he lay, as sometimes we may do now when the Spring rains are good. Tha, the First of the Elephants, was busy making new jungles and leading the rivers in their beds. He could not walk everywhere, so he made the First of the Tigers the master and the judge of the Jungle, to whom the Jungle People should bring their disputes. In those days the First of the Tigers ate fruit and grass with the others. He was as large as I am, and

he was very beautiful, in colour all over like the blossom of the yellow
creeper. There was never stripe nor bar upon his hide in those good days
when the Jungle was new. All the Jungle People came before him without
fear, and his word was the Law of all the Jungle. We were then, remember
ye, one people. Yet, upon a night, there was a dispute between two bucks
—a grazing-quarrel such as ye now try out with the head and the forefeet
—and it is said that as the two spoke together before the First of the
Tigers lying among the flowers, a buck pushed him with his horns, and the
First of the Tigers forgot that he was the master and judge of the Jungle,
and, leaping upon that buck, broke his neck.

'Till that night never one of us had died, and the First of the Tigers,
seeing what he had done, and being made foolish by the scent of the blood,
ran away into the marshes of the North, and we of the Jungle, left without
a judge, fell to fighting among ourselves. Tha heard the noise of it and
came back; and some of us said this and some of us said that, but he saw
the dead buck among the flowers, and asked who had killed, and we of the
Jungle would not tell because the smell of the blood made us foolish, even
as that same smell makes us foolish to-day. We ran to and fro in circles,
capering and crying out and shaking our heads. So therefore Tha gave an
order to the trees that hang low, and to the trailing creepers of the Jungle,
that they should mark the killer of the buck that he should know him
again; and Tha said, "Who will now be Master of the Jungle People?"
Then up leaped the Gray Ape who lives in the branches, and said, "I will
now be Master of the Jungle." At this Tha laughed, and said, "So be it,"
and went away very angry.

'Children, ye know the Gray Ape. He was then as he is now. At the
first he made a wise face for himself, but in a little while he began to
scratch and to leap up and down, and when Tha returned he found the
Gray Ape hanging, head down, from a bough, mocking those who stood
below; and they mocked him again. And so there was no Law in the
Jungle—only foolish talk and senseless words.

'Then Tha called us all together and said: "The first of your masters
has brought Death into the Jungle, and the second Shame. Now it is time
there was a Law, and a Law that ye may not break. Now ye shall know
Fear, and when ye have found him ye shall know that he is your master,
and the rest shall follow." Then we of the Jungle said, "What is Fear?"
And Tha said, "Seek till ye find." So we went up and down the Jungle
seeking for Fear, and presently the buffaloes——'

'Ugh!' said Mysa, the leader of the buffaloes, from their sandbank.

'Yes, Mysa, it was the buffaloes. They came back with the news that
in a cave in the Jungle sat Fear, and that he had no hair, and went upon
his hind legs. Then we of the Jungle followed the herd till we came to
that cave, and Fear stood at the mouth of it, and he was, as the buffaloes
had said, hairless, and he walked upon his hinder legs. When he saw us
he cried out, and his voice filled us with the fear that we have now, and

we ran away, tramping upon and tearing each other because we were afraid. That night, it was told to me, we of the Jungle did not lie down together as used to be our custom, but each tribe drew off by itself—the pig with the pig, the deer with the deer; horn to horn, hoof to hoof—like keeping to like, and so lay shaking in the Jungle.

' Only the First of the Tigers was not with us, for he was still hidden in the marshes of the North, and when word was brought to him of the Thing we had seen in the cave, he said: " I will go to this Thing and break his neck." So he ran all the night till he came to the cave, but the trees and the creepers on his path, remembering the order Tha had given, let down their branches and marked him as he ran, drawing their fingers across his back, his flank, his forehead and his jowl. Wherever they touched him there was a mark and a stripe upon his yellow hide. *And those stripes do his children wear to this day!* When he came to the cave, Fear, the Hairless One, put out his hand and called him ' The Striped One that comes by night,' and the First of the Tigers was afraid of the Hairless One, and ran back to the swamps howling.'

Mowgli chuckled quietly here, his chin in the water.

' So loud did he howl that Tha heard him and said, " What is the sorrow? " And the First of the Tigers, lifting up his muzzle to the new-made sky, which is now so old, said: " Give me back my power, O Tha. I am made ashamed before all the Jungle, and I have run away from an Hairless One, and he has called me a shameful name." " And why? " said Tha. " Because I am smeared with the mud of the marshes," said the First of the Tigers. " Swim, then, and roll on the wet grass, and if it be mud it will surely wash away," said Tha; and the First of the Tigers swam, and rolled, and rolled, till the Jungle ran round and round before his eyes, but not one little bar upon his hide was changed, and Tha, watching him, laughed. Then the First of the Tigers said, " What have I done that this comes to me? " Tha said, " Thou hast killed the buck, and thou hast let Death loose in the Jungle, and with Death has come Fear, so that the People of the Jungle are afraid one of the other as thou art afraid of the Hairless One." The First of the Tigers said, " They will never fear me, for I knew them since the beginning." Tha said, " Go and see." And the First of the Tigers ran to and fro, calling aloud to the deer and the pig and the *sambhur* and the porcupine and all the Jungle Peoples; but they all ran away from him who had been their Judge, because they were afraid.

' Then the First of the Tigers came back, his pride was broken in him, and, beating his head upon the ground, he tore up the earth with all his feet and said: " Remember that I was once the Master of the Jungle! Do not forget me, O Tha. Let my children remember that I was once without shame or fear! " And Tha said: " This much will I do, because thou and I together saw the Jungle made. For one night of each year it shall be as it was before the buck was killed—for thee and for thy children. In that one night, if ye meet the Hairless One—and his name is Man—

ye shall not be afraid of him, but he shall be afraid of you as though ye were judges of the Jungle and masters of all things. Show him mercy in that night of his fear; for thou hast known what Fear is."

'Then the First of the Tigers answered, "I am content"; but when next he drank he saw the black stripes upon his flank and his side, and he remembered the name that the Hairless One had given him, and he was angry. For a year he lived in the marshes, waiting till Tha should keep his promise. And upon a night when the Jackal of the Moon (the Evening Star) stood clear of the Jungle, he felt that his Night was upon him, and he went to that cave to meet the Hairless One. Then it happened as Tha promised, for the Hairless One fell down before him and lay along the ground, and the First of the Tigers struck him and broke his back, for he thought that there was but one such a Thing in the Jungle, and that he had killed Fear. Then, nosing above the kill, he heard Tha coming down from the woods of the north, and presently the voice of the First of the Elephants, which is the voice that we hear now—— '

The thunder was rolling up and down the dry, scarred hills, but it brought no rain—only heat-lightning that flickered behind the ridges—and Hathi went on: ' *That* was the voice he heard, and it said: " Is this thy mercy? " The First of the Tigers licked his lips and said: " What matter? I have killed Fear." And Tha said: " O blind and foolish! Thou hast untied the feet of Death, and he will follow thy trail till thou diest. Thou hast taught Man to kill! "

'The First of the Tigers, standing stiffly to his kill, said: " He is as the buck was. There is no Fear. Now I will judge the Jungle Peoples once more.'

'And Tha said: " Never again shall the Jungle Peoples come to thee. They shall never cross thy trail, nor sleep near thee, nor follow after thee, nor browse by thy lair. Only Fear shall follow thee, and with a blow that thou canst not see shall bid thee wait his pleasure. He shall make the ground to open under thy feet, and the creeper to twist about thy neck, and the tree-trunks to grow together about thee higher than thou canst leap, and at the last he shall take thy hide to wrap his cubs when they are cold. Thou hast shown him no mercy, and none will he show thee."

'The First of the Tigers was very bold, for his Night was still on him, and he said: " The Promise of Tha is the Promise of Tha. He will not take away my Night? " And Tha said: " Thy one Night is thine, as I have said, but there is a price to pay. Thou hast taught Man to kill, and he is no slow learner."

'The First of the Tigers said: " He is here under my foot, where his back is broken. Let the Jungle know that I have killed Fear."

'Then Tha laughed and said: " Thou hast killed one of many, but thou thyself shalt tell the Jungle—for thy Night is ended! "

'So the day came; and from the mouth of the cave went out another Hairless One, and he saw the kill in the path, and the First of the Tigers above it, and he took a pointed stick—— '

' They throw a thing that cuts now,' said Sahi, rustling down the bank; for Sahi was considered uncommonly good eating by the Gonds—they called him Ho-Igoo—and he knew something of the wicked little Gondee ax that whirls across a clearing like a dragon-fly.

' It was a pointed stick, such as they set in the foot of a pit-trap,' said Hathi; ' and throwing it, he struck the First of the Tigers deep in the flank. Thus it happened as Tha said, for the First of the Tigers ran howling up and down the Jungle till he tore out the stick, and all the Jungle knew that the Hairless One could strike from far off, and they feared more than before. So it came about that the First of the Tigers taught the Hairless One to kill—and ye know what harm that has since done to all our peoples—through the noose, and the pitfall, and the hidden trap, and the flying stick, and the stinging fly that comes out of white smoke [Hathi meant the rifle], and the Red Flower that drives us into the open. Yet for one night in the year the Hairless One fears the Tiger, as Tha promised, and never has the Tiger given him cause to be less afraid. Where he finds him, there he kills him, remembering how the First of the Tigers was made ashamed. For the rest, Fear walks up and down the Jungle by day and by night.'

' Ahi! Aoo! ' said the deer, thinking of what it all meant to them.

' And only when there is one great Fear over all, as there is now, can we of the Jungle lay aside our little fears, and meet together in one place as we do now.'

' For one night only does Man fear the Tiger? ' said Mowgli.

' For one night only,' said Hathi.

' But I—but we—but all the Jungle knows that Shere Khan kills Man twice and thrice in a moon.'

' Even so. *Then* he springs from behind and turns his head aside as he strikes, for he is full of fear. If Man looked at him he would run. But on his Night he goes openly down to the village. He walks between the houses and thrusts his head into the doorway, and the men fall on their faces, and there he does his kill. One kill in that night.'

' Oh! ' said Mowgli to himself, rolling over in the water. ' *Now* I see why Shere Khan bade me look at him. He got no good of it, for he could not hold his eyes steady, and—and I certainly did not fall down at his feet. But then I am not a man; being of the Free People.'

' Umm! ' said Bagheera deep in his furry throat. ' Does the Tiger know his Night? '

' Never till the Jackal of the Moon stands clear of the evening mist. Sometimes it falls in the dry summer and sometimes in the wet Rains—this one Night of the Tiger. But for the First of the Tigers this would never have been, nor would any of us have known fear.'

The deer grunted sorrowfully, and Bagheera's lips curled in a wicked smile. ' Do men know this—tale? ' said he.

' None know it except the tigers, and we, the elephants—the Children of

Tha. Now ye by the pools have heard it, and I have spoken.'

Hathi dipped his trunk into the water as a sign that he did not wish to talk.

'But—but—but,' said Mowgli, turning to Baloo, 'why did not the First of the Tigers continue to eat grass and leaves and trees? He did but break the buck's neck. He did not *eat*. What led him to the hot meat?'

'The trees and the creepers marked him, Little Brother, and made him the striped thing that we see. Never again would he eat their fruit; but from that day he revenged himself upon the deer, and the others, the Eaters of Grass,' said Baloo.

'Then *thou* knowest the tale. Heh? Why have I never heard?'

'Because the Jungle is full of such tales. If I made a beginning there would never be an end to them. Let go my ear, Little Brother.'

THE LAW OF THE JUNGLE

 JUST to give you an idea of the immense variety of the Jungle Law, I have translated into verse (Baloo always recited them in a sort of singsong) a few of the laws that apply to the Wolves. There are, of course, hundreds and hundreds more, but these will serve as specimens of the simpler rulings.

Now this is the Law of the Jungle—as old and as true as the sky;
And the Wolf that shall keep it may prosper, but the Wolf that shall break
* it must die.*
As the creeper that girdles the tree-trunk the Law runneth forward and
* back—*
For the strength of the Pack is the Wolf, and the strength of the Wolf is
* the Pack.*

Wash daily from nose-tip to tail-tip; drink deeply, but never too deep;
And remember the night is for hunting, and forget not the day is for sleep.

The Jackal may follow the Tiger, but, Cub, when thy whiskers are grown,
Remember the Wolf is a Hunter—go forth and get food of thine own.

Keep peace with the Lords of the Jungle—the Tiger, the Panther, and Bear.
And trouble not Hathi the Silent, and mock not the Boar in his lair.

When Pack meets with Pack in the Jungle, and neither will go from the trail,
Lie down till the leaders have spoken—it may be fair words shall prevail.

When ye fight with a Wolf of the Pack, ye must fight him alone and afar,
Lest others take part in the quarrel, and the Pack be diminished by war.

The Lair of the Wolf is his refuge, and where he has made him his home,
Not even the Head Wolf may enter, not even the Council may come.

The Lair of the Wolf is his refuge, but where he has digged it too plain,
The Council shall send him a message, and so he shall change it again.

If ye kill before midnight, be silent, and wake not the woods with your bay,
Lest ye frighten the deer from the crop, and your brothers go empty away.

Ye may kill for yourselves, and your mates, and your cubs as they need, and
 ye can;
But kill not for pleasure of killing, and *seven times never kill Man!*

If ye plunder his Kill from a weaker, devour not all in thy pride;
Pack-Right is the right of the meanest; so leave him the head and the hide.

The Kill of the Pack is the meat of the Pack. Ye must eat where it lies;
And no one may carry away of that meat to his lair, *or he dies.*

The Kill of the Wolf is the meat of the Wolf. He may do what he will;
But, till he has given permission, the Pack may not eat of that Kill.

Cub-Right is the right of the Yearling. From all of his Pack he may claim
Full-gorge when the killer has eaten; and none may refuse him the same.

Lair-Right is the right of the Mother. From all of her year she may claim
One haunch of each kill for her litter, and none may deny her the same.

Cave-Right is the right of the Father—to hunt by himself for his own:
He is freed of all calls to the Pack; he is judged by the Council alone.

Because of his age and his cunning, because of his gripe and his paw,
In all that the Law leaveth open, the word of your Head Wolf is Law.

Now these are the Laws of the Jungle, and many and mighty are they;
But the head and the hoof of the Law and the haunch and the hump is—
 Obey!

'TIGER! TIGER!'

What of the hunting, hunter bold?
Brother, the watch was long and cold.
What of the quarry ye went to kill?
Brother, he crops in the jungle still.
Where is the power that made your pride?
Brother, it ebbs from my flank and side.
Where is the haste that ye hurry by?
Brother, I go to my lair—to die.

WHEN Mowgli left the wolf's cave after the fight with the Pack at the Council Rock, he went down to the ploughed lands where the villagers lived, but he would not stop there because it was too near to the jungle, and he knew that he had made at least one bad enemy at the Council. So he hurried on, keeping to the rough road that ran down the valley, and followed it at a steady jog-trot for nearly twenty miles, till he came to a country that he did not know. The valley opened out into a great plain dotted over with rocks and cut up with ravines. At one end stood a little village, and at the other the thick jungle came down in a sweep to the grazing-grounds, and stopped there as though it had been cut off with a hoe. All over the plain, cattle and buffaloes were grazing, and when the little boys in charge of the herds saw Mowgli they shouted and ran away, and the yellow pariah dogs that hang about every Indian village barked. Mowgli walked on, for he was feeling hungry, and when he came to the village gate he saw the big thorn-bush that was drawn up before the gate at twilight, pushed to one side.

'Umph!' he said, for he had come across more than one such barricade in his night rambles after things to eat. 'So men are afraid of the People of the Jungle here also.' He sat down by the gate, and when a man came out he stood up, opened his mouth, and pointed down it to show that he wanted food. The man stared, and ran back up the one street of the village shouting for the priest, who was a big, fat man dressed in white, with a red and yellow mark on his forehead. The priest came to the gate, and with him at least a hundred people, who stared and talked and shouted and pointed at Mowgli.

'They have no manners, these Men Folk,' said Mowgli to himself. 'Only the gray ape would behave as they do.' So he threw back his long hair and frowned at the crowd.

'What is there to be afraid of?' said the priest. 'Look at the marks on his arms and legs. They are the bites of wolves. He is but a wolf-child run away from the jungle.'

Of course, in playing together, the cubs had often nipped Mowgli harder than they intended, and there were white scars all over his arms and legs. But he would have been the last person in the world to call these bites, for he knew what real biting meant.

'Arré! arré!' said two or three women together. 'To be bitten by wolves, poor child! He is a handsome boy. He has eyes like red fire. By my honour, Messua, he is not unlike thy boy that was taken by the tiger.'

'Let me look,' said a woman with heavy copper rings on her wrists and ankles, and she peered at Mowgli under the palm of her hand. 'Indeed he is not. He is thinner, but he has the very look of my boy.'

The priest was a clever man, and he knew that Messua was wife to the richest villager in the place. So he looked up at the sky for a minute, and said solemnly: 'What the jungle has taken the jungle has restored. Take the boy into thy house, my sister, and forget not to honour the priest who sees so far into the lives of men.'

'By the Bull that bought me,' said Mowgli to himself, 'but all this talking is like another looking over by the Pack! Well, if I am a man, a man I must be.'

The crowd parted as the woman beckoned Mowgli to her hut, where there was a red lacquered bedstead, a great earthen grain-chest with funny raised patterns on it, half a dozen copper cooking-pots, an image of a Hindu god in a little alcove, and on the wall a real looking-glass, such as they sell at the country fairs for eight cents.

She gave him a long drink of milk and some bread, and then she laid her hand on his head and looked into his eyes; for she thought perhaps that he might be her real son come back from the jungle where the tiger had taken him. So she said: 'Nathoo, O Nathoo!' Mowgli did not show that he knew the name. 'Dost thou not remember the day when I gave thee thy new shoes?' She touched his foot, and it was almost as hard as horn. 'No,' she said, sorrowfully; 'those feet have never worn shoes, but thou art very like my Nathoo, and thou shalt be my son.'

Mowgli was uneasy, because he had never been under a roof before; but as he looked at the thatch, he saw that he could tear it out any time if he wanted to get away, and that the window had no fastenings. 'What is the good of a man,' he said to himself at last, 'if he does not understand man's talk? Now I am as silly and dumb as a man would be with us in the jungle. I must speak their talk.'

He had not learned while he was with the wolves to imitate the challenge of bucks in the jungle and the grunt of the little wild pig for fun. So, as soon as Messua pronounced a word Mowgli would imitate it almost perfectly, and before dark he had learned the name of many things in the hut.

There was a difficulty at bedtime, because Mowgli would not sleep under anything that looked so like a panther-trap as that hut, and when they shut the door he went through the window. 'Give him his will,' said Messua's husband. 'Remember he can never till now have slept on a bed. If he is

indeed sent in the place of our son he will not run away.'

So Mowgli stretched himself in some long clean grass at the edge of the field, but before he had closed his eyes a soft gray nose poked him under the chin.

'Phew!' said Gray Brother (he was the eldest of Mother Wolf's cubs). 'This is a poor reward for following thee twenty miles. Thou smellest of wood-smoke and cattle—altogether like a man already. Wake, Little Brother; I bring news.'

'Are all well in the jungle?' said Mowgli, hugging him.

'All except the wolves that were burned with the Red Flower. Now, listen. Shere Khan has gone away to hunt far off till his coat grows again, for he is badly singed. When he returns he swears that he will lay thy bones in the Waingunga.'

'There are two words to that. I also have made a little promise. But news is always good. I am tired to-night,—very tired with new things, Gray Brother,—but bring me the news always.'

'Thou wilt not forget that thou art a wolf? Men will not make thee forget?' said Gray Brother, anxiously.

'Never. I will always remember that I love thee and all in our cave; but also I will always remember that I have been cast out of the Pack.'

'And that thou may'st be cast out of another pack. Men are only men, Little Brother, and their talk is like the talk of frogs in a pond. When I come down here again, I will wait for thee in the bamboos at the edge of the grazing-ground.'

For three months after that night Mowgli hardly ever left the village gate, he was so busy learning the ways and customs of men. First he had to wear a cloth round him, which annoyed him horribly; and then he had to learn about money, which he did not in the least understand, and about ploughing, of which he did not see the use. Then the little children in the village made him very angry. Luckily, the Law of the Jungle had taught him to keep his temper, for in the jungle, life and food depend on keeping your temper; but when they made fun of him because he would not play games or fly kites, or because he mispronounced some word, only the knowledge that it was unsportsmanlike to kill little naked cubs kept him from picking them up and breaking them in two. He did not know his own strength in the least. In the jungle he knew he was weak compared with the beasts, but in the village, people said that he was as strong as a bull. He certainly had no notion of what fear was, for when the village priest told him that the god in the temple would be angry with him if he ate the priest's mangoes, he picked up the image, brought it over to the priest's house, and asked the priest to make the god angry and he would be happy to fight him. It was a horrible scandal, but the priest hushed it up, and Messua's husband paid much good silver to comfort the god. And Mowgli had not the faintest idea of the difference that caste makes between man and man. When the potter's donkey slipped in the clay-pit, Mowgli hauled it out by the tail, and helped

to stack the pots for their journey to the market at Khanhiwara. That was very shocking, too, for the potter is a low-caste man, and his donkey is worse. When the priest scolded him, Mowgli threatened to put him on the donkey, too, and the priest told Messua's husband that Mowgli had better be set to work as soon as possible; and the village head-man told Mowgli that he would have to go out with the buffaloes next day, and herd them while they grazed. No one was more pleased than Mowgli; and that night, because he had been appointed a servant of the village, as it were, he went off to a circle that met every evening on a masonry platform under a great fig-tree. It was the village club, and the head-man and the watchman and the barber, who knew all the gossip of the village, and old Buldeo, the village hunter, who had a Tower musket, met and smoked. The monkeys sat and talked in the upper branches, and there was a hole under the platform where a cobra lived, and he had his little platter of milk every night because he was sacred; and the old men sat around the tree and talked, and pulled at the big *huqas* (the water-pipes) till far into the night. They told wonderful tales of gods and men and ghosts; and Buldeo told even more wonderful ones of the ways of beasts in the jungle, till the eyes of the children sitting outside the circle bulged out of their heads. Most of the tales were about animals, for the jungle was always at their door. The deer and the wild pig grubbed up their crops, and now and again the tiger carried off a man at twilight, within sight of the village gates.

Mowgli, who naturally knew something about what they were talking of, had to cover his face not to show that he was laughing, while Buldeo, the Tower musket across his knees, climbed on from one wonderful story to another, and Mowgli's shoulders shook.

Buldeo was explaining how the tiger that had carried away Messua's son was a ghost-tiger, and his body was inhabited by the ghost of a wicked old money-lender, who had died some years ago. 'And I know that this is true,' he said, 'because Purun Dass always limped from the blow that he got in a riot when his account-books were burned, and the tiger that I speak of *he* limps, too, for the tracks of his pads are unequal.'

'True, true, that must be the truth,' said the graybeards nodding together.

'Are all these tales such cobwebs and moon-talk?' said Mowgli. 'That tiger limps because he was born lame, as every one knows. To talk of the soul of a money-lender in a beast that never had the courage of a jackal is child's talk.'

Buldeo was speechless with surprise for a moment, and the head-man stared.

'Oho! It is the jungle brat, is it?' said Buldeo. 'If thou art so wise, better bring his hide to Khanhiwara, for the Government has set a hundred rupees on his life. Better still, talk not when thy elders speak.'

Mowgli rose to go. 'All the evening I have lain here listening,' he called back, over his shoulder, 'and, except once or twice, Buldeo has not said one

word of truth concerning the jungle, which is at his very doors. How then shall I believe the tales of ghosts, and gods, and goblins which he says he has seen? '

' It is full time that boy went to herding,' said the head-man, while Buldeo puffed and snorted at Mowgli's impertinence.

The custom of most Indian villages is for a few boys to take the cattle and buffaloes out to graze in the early morning, and bring them back at night; and the very cattle that would trample a white man to death allow themselves to be banged and bullied and shouted at by children that hardly come up to their noses. So long as the boys keep with the herds they are safe, for not even the tiger will charge a mob of cattle. But if they straggle to pick flowers or hunt lizards, they are sometimes carried off. Mowgli went through the village street in the dawn, sitting on the back of Rama, the great herd bull; and the slaty-blue buffaloes, with their long, backward-sweeping horns and savage eyes, rose out their byres, one by one, and followed him, and Mowgli made it very clear to the children with him that he was the master. He beat the buffaloes with a long, polished bamboo, and told Kamya, one of the boys, to graze the cattle by themselves, while he went on with the buffaloes, and to be very careful not to stray away from the herd.

An Indian grazing-ground is all rocks, and scrubs, and tussocks, and little ravines, among which the herds scatter and disappear. The buffaloes generally keep to the pools and muddy places, where they lie wallowing or basking in the warm mud for hours. Mowgli drove them on to the edge of the plain where the Waingunga came out of the jungle; then he dropped from Rama's neck, trotted off to a bamboo clump and found Gray Brother. ' Ah,' said Gray Brother, ' I have waited here very many days. What is the meaning of this cattle-herding work? '

' It is an order,' said Mowgli; ' I am a village herd for a while. What news of Shere Khan? '

' He has come back to this country, and has waited here a long time for thee. Now he has gone off again, for the game is scarce. But he means to kill thee.'

' Very good,' said Mowgli. ' So long as he is away do thou or one of the four brothers sit on that rock, so that I can see thee as I come out of the village. When he comes back wait for me in the ravine by the *dhâk*-tree in the centre of the plain. We need not walk into Shere Khan's mouth.'

Then Mowgli picked out a shady place, and lay down and slept while the buffaloes grazed round him. Herding in India is one of the laziest things in the world. The cattle move and crunch, and lie down, and move on again, and they do not even low. They only grunt, and the buffaloes very seldom say anything, but get down into the muddy pools one after another, and work their way into the mud till only their noses and staring china-blue eyes show above the surface, and then they lie like logs. The sun makes the rocks dance in the heat, and the herd-children hear one kite (never any more) whistling almost out of sight, overhead, and they know that if they died,

or a cow died, that kite would sweep down, and the next kite miles away would see him drop and follow, and the next, and the next, and almost before they were dead there would be a score of hungry kites come out of nowhere. Then they sleep and wake and sleep again, and weave little baskets of dried grass and put grasshoppers in them, or catch two praying mantises and make them fight; or string a necklace of red and black jungle-nuts, or watch a lizard basking on a rock, or a snake hunting a frog near the

wallows. Then they sing long, long songs with odd native quavers at the end of them, and the day seems longer than most people's whole lives, and perhaps they make a mud castle with mud figures of men and horses and buffaloes, and put reeds into the men's hands, and pretend that they are kings and the figures are their armies, or that they are gods to be worshipped. Then evening comes and the children call, and the buffaloes lumber up out of the sticky mud with noises like gunshots going off one after the other, and they all string across the gray plain back to the twinkling village lights.

Day after day Mowgli would lead the buffaloes out to their wallows, and day after day he would see Gray Brother's back a mile and a half away across the plain (so he knew that Shere Khan had not come back), and day after day he would lie on the grass listening to the noises round him, and dreaming of old days in the jungle. If Shere Khan had made a false

step with his lame paw up in the jungles by the Waingunga, Mowgli would have heard him in those long still mornings.

At last a day came when he did not see Gray Brother at the signal place, and he laughed and headed the buffaloes for the ravine by the *dhâk*-tree, which was all covered with golden-red flowers. There sat Gray Brother, every bristle on his back lifted.

'He has hidden for a month to throw thee off thy guard. He crossed the ranges last night with Tabaqui, hot-foot on thy trail,' said the Wolf, panting.

Mowgli frowned. 'I am not afraid of Shere Khan, but Tabaqui is very cunning.'

'Have no fear,' said Gray Brother, licking his lips a little. 'I met Tabaqui in the dawn. Now he is telling all his wisdom to the kites, but he told *me* everything before I broke his back. Shere Khan's plan is to wait for thee at the village gate this evening—for thee and for no one else. He is lying up now, in the big dry ravine of the Waingunga.'

'Has he eaten to-day, or does he hunt empty?' said Mowgli, for the answer meant life and death to him.

'He killed at dawn—a pig—and he has drunk too. Remember, Shere Khan could never fast, even for the sake of revenge.'

'Oh! fool, fool! What a cub's cub it is! Eaten and drunk too, and he thinks that I shall wait till he has slept! Now, where does he lie up? If there were but ten of us we might pull him down as he lies. These buffaloes will not charge unless they wind him, and I cannot speak their language. Can we get behind his track so that they may smell it?'

'He swam far down the Waingunga to cut that off,' said Gray Brother.

'Tabaqui told him that, I know. He would never have thought of it alone.' Mowgli stood with his finger in his mouth, thinking. 'The big ravine of the Waingunga. That opens out on the plain not half a mile from here. I can take the herd round through the jungle to the head of the ravine and then sweep down—but he would slink out at the foot. We must block that end. Gray Brother, canst thou cut the herd in two for me?'

'Not I, perhaps—but I have brought a wise helper.' Gray Brother trotted off and dropped into a hole. Then there lifted up a huge gray head that Mowgli knew well, and the hot air was filled with the most desolate cry of all the jungle—the hunting-howl of a wolf at mid-day.

'Akela! Akela!' said Mowgli, clapping his hands. 'I might have known that thou wouldst not forget me. We have a big work in hand. Cut the herd in two, Akela. Keep the cows and calves together, and the bulls and the plough-buffaloes by themselves.'

The two wolves ran, ladies'-chain fashion, in and out of the herd, which snorted and threw up its head, and separated into two clumps. In one, the cow-buffaloes stood with their calves in the centre, and glared and pawed, ready, if a wolf would only stay still, to charge down and trample the life out of him. In the other, the bulls and the young bulls snorted and stamped,

but though they looked more imposing they were much less dangerous, for they had no calves to protect. No six men could have divided the herd so neatly.

'What orders!' panted Akela. 'They are trying to join again.'

Mowgli slipped on to Rama's back. 'Drive the bulls away to the left, Akela. Gray Brother, when we are gone, hold the cows together, and drive them into the foot of the ravine.'

'How far?' said Gray Brother, panting and snapping.

'Till the sides are higher than Shere Khan can jump,' shouted Mowgli. 'Keep them there till we come down.' The bulls swept off as Akela bayed, and Gray Brother stopped in front of the cows. They charged down on him, and he ran just before them to the foot of the ravine, as Akela drove the bulls far to the left.

'Well done! Another charge and they are fairly started. Careful, now—careful, Akela. A snap too much, and the bulls will charge. *Hujah!* This is wilder work than driving black-buck. Didst thou think these creatures could move so swiftly?' Mowgli called.

'I have—have hunted these too in my time,' gasped Akela in the dust. 'Shall I turn them into the jungle?'

'Ay! Turn. Swiftly turn them! Rama is mad with rage. Oh, if I could only tell him what I need of him to-day.'

The bulls were turned, to the right this time, and crashed into the standing thicket. The other herd-children, watching with the cattle half a mile away, hurried to the village as fast as their legs could carry them, crying that the buffaloes had gone mad and run away. But Mowgli's plan was simple enough. All he wanted to do was to make a big circle uphill and get at the head of the ravine, and then take the bulls down it and catch Shere Khan between the bulls and the cows; for he knew that after a meal and a full drink Shere Khan would not be in any condition to fight or to clamber up the sides of the ravine. He was soothing the buffaloes now by voice, and Akela had dropped far to the rear, only whimpering once or twice to hurry the rear-guard. It was a long, long circle, for they did not wish to get too near the ravine and give Shere Khan warning. At last Mowgli rounded up the bewildered herd at the head of the ravine on a grassy patch that sloped steeply down to the ravine itself. From that height you could see across the tops of the trees down to the plain below; but what Mowgli looked at was the sides of the ravine, and he saw with a great deal of satisfaction that they ran nearly straight up and down, while the vines and creepers that hung over them would give no foothold to a tiger who wanted to get out.

'Let them breathe, Akela,' he said, holding up his hand. 'They have not winded him yet. Let them breathe. I must tell Shere Khan who comes. We have him in the trap.'

He put his hands to his mouth and shouted down the ravine,—it was almost like shouting down a tunnel,—and the echoes jumped from rock to rock.

After a long time there came back the drawling, sleepy snarl of a full-fed tiger just wakened.

'Who calls?' said Shere Khan, and a splendid peacock fluttered up out of the ravine screeching.

'I, Mowgli. Cattle thief, it is time to come to the Council Rock! Down—hurry them down, Akela! Down, Rama, down!'

The herd paused for an instant at the edge of the slope, but Akela gave tongue in the full hunting yell, and they pitched over one after the other just as steamers shoot rapids, the sand and stones spurting up round them. Once started, there was no chance of stopping, and before they were fairly in the bed of the ravine Rama winded Shere Khan and bellowed.

'Ha! Ha!' said Mowgli, on his back. 'Now thou knowest!' and the torrent of black horns, foaming muzzles, and staring eyes whirled down the ravine just as boulders go down in flood-time; the weaker buffaloes being shouldered out to the sides of the ravine where they tore through the creepers. They knew what the business was before them—the terrible charge of the buffalo herd against which no tiger can hope to stand. Shere Khan heard the thunder of their hoofs, picked himself up, and lumbered down the ravine, looking from side to side for some way of escape, but the walls of the ravine were straight and he had to hold on, heavy with his dinner and his drink, willing to do anything rather than fight. The herd splashed through the pool he had just left, bellowing till the narrow cut rang. Mowgli heard an answering bellow from the foot of the ravine, saw Shere Khan turn (the tiger knew if the worst came to the worst it was better to meet the bulls than the cows with their calves), and then Rama tripped, stumbled, and went on again over something soft, and, with the bulls at his heels, crashed full into the other herd, while the weaker buffaloes were lifted clean off their feet by the shock of the meeting. That charge carried both herds out into the plain, goring and stamping and snorting. Mowgli watched his time, and slipped off Rama's neck, laying about him right and left with his stick.

'Quick, Akela! Break them up. Scatter them, or they will be fighting one another. Drive them away, Akela. *Hai*, Rama! *Hai! hai! hai!* my children. Softly now, softly! It is all over.'

Akela and Gray Brother ran to and fro nipping the buffaloes' legs, and though the herd wheeled once to charge up the ravine again, Mowgli managed to turn Rama, and the others followed him to the wallows.

Shere Khan needed no more trampling. He was dead, and the kites were coming for him already.

'Brothers, that was a dog's death,' said Mowgli, feeling for the knife he always carried in a sheath round his neck now that he lived with men. 'But he would never have shown fight. *Wallah!* his hide will look well on the Council Rock. We must get to work swiftly.'

A boy trained among men would never have dreamed of skinning a ten-foot tiger alone, but Mowgli knew better than any one else how an

animal's skin is fitted on, and how it can be taken off. But it was hard work, and Mowgli slashed and tore and grunted for an hour, while the wolves lolled out their tongues, or came forward and tugged as he ordered them. Presently a hand fell on his shoulder, and looking up he saw Buldeo with the Tower musket. The children had told the village about the buffalo stampede, and Buldeo went out angrily, only too anxious to correct Mowgli for not taking better care of the herd. The wolves dropped out of sight as soon as they saw the man coming.

'What is this folly?' said Buldeo, angrily. 'To think that thou canst skin a tiger! Where did the buffaloes kill him? It is the Lame Tiger, too, and there is a hundred rupees on his head. Well, well, we will overlook thy letting the herd run off, and perhaps I will give thee one of the rupees of the reward when I have taken the skin to Khanhiwara.' He fumbled in his waist-cloth for flint and steel, and stooped down to singe Shere Khan's whiskers. Most native hunters always singe a tiger's whiskers to prevent his ghost from haunting them.

'Hum!' said Mowgli, half to himself as he ripped back the skin of a forepaw. 'So thou wilt take the hide to Khanhiwara for the reward, and perhaps give me one rupee? Now it is in my mind that I need the skin for my own use. Heh! old man, take away that fire!'

'What talk is this to the chief hunter of the village? Thy luck and the stuidity of thy buffaloes have helped thee to this kill. The tiger has just fed, or he would have gone twenty miles by this time. Thou canst not even skin him properly, little beggar brat, and forsooth I, Buldeo, must be told not to singe his whiskers. Mowgli, I will not give thee one anna of the reward, but only a very big beating. Leave the carcass!'

'By the Bull that bought me,' said Mowgli, who was trying to get at the shoulder, 'must I stay babbling to an old ape all noon? Here, Akela, this man plagues me.'

Buldeo, who was still stooping over Shere Khan's head, found himself sprawling on the grass, with a gray wolf standing over him, while Mowgli went on skinning as though he were alone in all India.

'Ye-es,' he said, between his teeth. 'Thou art altogether right, Buldeo. Thou wilt never give me one anna of the reward. There is an old war between this lame tiger and myself—a very old war, and—I have won.'

To do Buldeo justice, if he had been ten years younger he would have taken his chance with Akela had he met the wolf in the woods, but a wolf who obeyed the orders of this boy who had private wars with man-eating tigers was not a common animal. It was sorcery, magic of the worst kind, thought Buldeo, and he wondered whether the amulet round his neck would protect him. He lay as still as still, expecting every minute to see Mowgli turn into a tiger, too.

'Maharaj! Great King,' he said at last, in a husky whisper.

'Yes,' said Mowgli, without turning his head, chuckling a little.

'I am an old man. I did not know that thou wast anything more than

a herdsboy. May I rise up and go away, or will thy servant tear me to pieces?'

'Go, and peace go with thee. Only, another time do not meddle with my game. Let him go, Akela.'

Buldeo hobbled away to the village as fast as he could, looking back over his shoulder in case Mowgli should change into something terrible. When he got to the village he told a tale of magic and enchantment and sorcery that made the priest look very grave.

Mowgli went on with his work, but it was nearly twilight before he and the wolves had drawn the great gay skin clear of the body.

'Now we must hide this and take the buffaloes home! Help me to herd them, Akela.'

The herd rounded up in the misty twilight, and when they got near the village Mowgli saw lights, and heard the conches and bells in the temple blowing and banging. Half the village seemed to be waiting for him by the gate. 'That is because I have killed Shere Khan,' he said to himself; but a shower of stones whistled about his ears, and the villagers shouted: 'Sorcerer! Wolf's brat! Jungle-demon! Go away! Get hence quickly, or the priest will turn thee into a wolf again. Shoot, Buldeo, shoot!'

The old Tower musket went off with a bang, and a young buffalo bellowed in pain.

'More sorcery!' shouted the villagers. 'He can turn bullets. Buldeo, that was *thy* buffalo.'

'Now what is this?' said Mowgli, bewildered, as the stones flew thicker.

'They are not unlike the Pack, these brothers of thine,' said Akela, sitting down composedly. 'It is in my head that, if bullets mean anything, they would cast thee out.'

'Wolf! Wolf's cub! Go away!' shouted the priest, waving a sprig of the sacred *tulsi* plant.

'Again? Last time it was because I was a man. This time it is because I am a wolf. Let us go, Akela.'

A woman—it was Messua—ran across to the herd, and cried: 'Oh, my son, my son! They say thou art a sorcerer who can turn himself into a beast at will. I do not believe, but go away or they will kill thee. Buldeo says thou art a wizard, but I know thou hast avenged Nathoo's death.'

'Come back, Messua!' shouted the crowd. 'Come back, or we will stone thee.'

Mowgli laughed a little short ugly laugh, for a stone had hit him in the mouth. 'Run back, Messua. This is one of the foolish tales they tell under the big tree at dusk. I have at least paid for thy son's life. Farewell; and run quickly, for I shall send the herd in more swiftly than their brickbats. I am no wizard, Messua. Farewell!'

'Now, once more, Akela,' he cried. 'Bring the herd in.'

The buffaloes were anxious enough to get to the village. They hardly needed Akela's yell, but charged through the gate like a whirlwind, scattering the crowd right and left.

'Keep count!' shouted Mowgli, scornfully. 'It may be that I have stolen one of them. Keep count, for I will do your herding no more. Fare you well, children of men, and thank Messua that I do not come in with my wolves and hunt you up and down your street.'

He turned on his heel and walked away with the Lone Wolf; and as he looked up at the stars he felt happy. 'No more sleeping in traps for me, Akela. Let us get Shere Khan's skin and go away. No; we will not hurt the village, for Messua was kind to me.'

When the moon rose over the plain, making it look all milky, the horrified villagers saw Mowgli, with two wolves at his heels and a bundle on his head, trotting across at the steady wolf's trot that eats up the long miles like fire. Then they banged the temple bells and blew the conches louder than ever; and Messua cried, and Buldeo embroidered the story of his adventures in the jungle, till he ended by saying that Akela stood up on his hind legs and talked like a man.

The moon was just going down when Mowgli and the two wolves came to the hill of the Council Rock, and they stopped at Mother Wolf's cave.

'They have cast me out from the man Pack, Mother,' shouted Mowgli, 'but I come with the hide of Shere Khan to keep my word.' Mother Wolf walked stiffly from the cave with the cubs behind her, and her eyes glowed as she saw the skin.

'I told him on that day, when he crammed his head and shoulders into this cave, hunting for thy life, little frog—I told him that the hunter would be the hunted. It is well done.'

'Little Brother, it is well done,' said a deep voice in the thicket. 'We were lonely in the jungle without thee,' and Bagheera came running to Mowgli's bare feet. They clambered up the Council Rock together, and Mowgli spread the skin out on the flat stone where Akela used to sit, and pegged it down with four slivers of bamboo, and Akela lay down upon it, and called the old call to the Council, 'Look, look well, O Wolves,' exactly as he had called when Mowgli was first brought there.

Ever since Akela had been deposed, the Pack had been without a leader, hunting and fighting at their own pleasure. But they answered the call from habit; and some of them were lame from the traps they had fallen into, and some limped from shot-wounds, and some were mangy from eating bad food, and many were missing; but they came to the Council Rock, all that were left of them, and saw Shere Khan's striped hide on the rock, and the huge claws dangling at the end of the empty dangling feet.

'Look well, O Wolves. Have I kept my word?' said Mowgli; and the wolves bayed Yes, and one tattered wolf howled:—

'Lead us again, O Akela. Lead us again, O man-cub, for we be sick of this lawlessness, and we would be the Free People once more.'

'Nay,' purred Bagheera, 'that may not be. When ye are full-fed, the madness may come upon you again. Not for nothing are ye called the Free People. Ye fought for freedom, and it is yours. Eat it, O Wolves.'

'Man Pack and wolf Pack have cast me out,' said Mowgli. 'Now I will hunt alone in the jungle.'

'And we will hunt with thee,' said the four cubs.

So Mowgli went away and hunted with the four cubs in the jungle from that day on. But he was not always alone, because years afterward, he became a man and married.

But that is a story for grown-ups.

MOWGLI'S SONG

'THAT HE SANG AT THE COUNCIL ROCK WHEN HE DANCED ON SHERE KHAN'S HIDE.'

The Song of Mowgli—I, Mowgli, am singing. Let the Jungle listen to the things I have done.

Shere Khan said he would kill—would kill! At the gates in the twilight he would kill Mowgli, the Frog!

He ate and he drank. Drink deep, Shere Khan, for when wilt thou drink again? Sleep and dream of the kill.

I am alone on the grazing-grounds. Gray Brother come to me! Come to me, Lone Wolf, for there is big game afoot!

Bring up the great bull-buffaloes, the blue-skinned herd-bulls with the angry eyes. Drive them to and fro as I order. Sleepest thou still, Shere Khan? Wake, O wake! Here come I, and the bulls are behind.

Rama the king of the buffaloes stamped with his foot. Waters of the Waingunga whither went Shere Khan?

He is not Sahi to dig holes, nor Mor, the Peacock, that he should fly. He is not Mang, the Bat, to hang in the branches. Little bamboos that creak together tell me where he ran?

Ow! he is there. Ahoo! he is there. Under the feet of Rama lies the Lame One! Up, Shere Khan! Up and kill! Here is meat; break the necks of the bulls!

Hsh! he is asleep. We will not wake him, for his strength is very great. The kites have come down to see it. The black ants have come up to know it. There is a great assembly in his honour.

Alala! I have no cloth to wrap me. The kites will see that I am naked. I am ashamed to meet all these people.

Lend me thy coat, Shere Khan. Lend me thy gay striped coat that I may go to the Council Rock.

By the Bull that bought me I made a promise—a little promise. Only thy coat is lacking before I keep my word.

With the knife, with the knife that men use, with the knife of the hunter, I will stoop down for my gift.

Waters of the Waingunga, Shere Khan gives me his coat for the love that he bears me. Pull, Gray Brother! Pull, Akela! Heavy is the hide of Shere Khan.

The Man Pack are angry. They throw stones and talk child's talk. My mouth is bleeding. Let me run away.

Through the night, through the hot night, run swiftly with me, my brothers. We will leave the lights of the village and go to the low moon.

Waters of the Waingunga the Man Pack have cast me out. I did them no harm, but they were afraid of me. Why?

Wolf Pack, ye have cast me out too. The Jungle is shut to me and the village gates are shut. Why?

As Mang flies between the beasts and birds so fly I between the village and the Jungle. Why?

I dance on the hide of Shere Khan, but my heart is very heavy. My mouth is cut and wounded with the stones from the village, but my heart is very light, because I have come back to the Jungle. Why?

These two things fight together in me as the snakes fight in the spring. The water comes out of my eyes; yet I laugh while it falls. Why?

I am two Mowglis, but the hide of Shere Khan is under my feet.

All the Jungle knows that I have killed Shere Khan. Look, look well, O Wolves!

Ahae! my heart is heavy with the things that I do not understand.

LETTING IN THE JUNGLE

Veil them, cover them, wall them round,
 Blossom and creeper and weed;
Let us forget the sight and the sound,
 And the smell and the touch of the breed!

Fat black ash by the altarstone
 Here is the white-foot rain!
And the does bring forth in the fields unsown,
 And none may affright them again;
And the blind-walls crumble, unknown, o'erthrown,
 And none may inhabit again!

&§ YOU will remember, if you have read the tales in the first Jungle Book, that after Mowgli had pinned Shere Khan's hide to the Council Rock, he told as many as were left of the Seeonee Pack that henceforward he would hunt in the Jungle alone; and the four children of Mother and Father Wolf said that they would hunt with him. But it is not easy to change all one's life at once—particularly in the Jungle. The first thing Mowgli did, when the disorderly Pack had slunk off, was to go to the home-cave, and sleep for a day and a night. Then he told Mother Wolf and Father Wolf as much as they could understand of his adventures among men; and when he made the morning sun flicker up and down the blade of his skinning-knife —the same he had skinned Shere Khan with—they said he had learned something. Then Akela and Gray Brother had to explain their share of the great buffalo-drive in the ravine, and Baloo toiled up the hill to hear all about it, and Bagheera scratched himself all over with pure delight at the way in which Mowgli had managed his war.

It was long after sunrise, but no one dreamed of going to sleep, and from time to time, Mother Wolf would throw up her head, and sniff a deep snuff of satisfaction as the wind brought her the smell of the tiger-skin on the Council Rock.

' But for Akela and Gray Brother here,' Mowgli said, at the end, ' I could have done nothing. Oh, mother, mother! if thou hadst seen the blue herd-bulls pour down the ravine, or hurry through the gates when the Man-Pack flung stones at me! '

' I am glad I did not see that last,' said Mother Wolf, stiffly. ' It is not *my* custom to suffer my cubs to be driven to and fro like jackals! *I* would have taken a price from the Man-Pack; but I would have spared the woman who gave thee the milk. Yes, I would have spared her alone.'

'Peace, peace, Raksha!' said Father Wolf, lazily. 'Our Frog has come back again—so wise that his own father must lick his feet; and what is a cut, more or less, on the head? Leave Man alone.' Baloo and Bagheera both echoed: 'Leave Man alone.'

Mowgli, his head on Mother Wolf's side, smiled contentedly, and said that, for his own part, he never wished to see, or hear, or smell Man again.

'But what,' said Akela, cocking one ear, 'but what if men do not leave thee alone, Little Brother?'

'We be *five*,' said Gray Brother, looking round at the company, and snapping his jaws on the last word.

'We also might attend to that hunting,' said Bagheera, with a little *switch-switch* of his tail, looking at Baloo. 'But why think of Man now, Akela?'

'For this reason,' the Lone Wolf answered. 'When that yellow thief's hide was hung up on the rock, I went back along our trail to the village, stepping in my tracks, turning aside, and lying down, to make a mixed trail in case any should follow us. But when I had fouled the trail so that I myself hardly knew it again, Mang, the Bat, came hawking between the trees, and hung up above me. Said Mang, "The village of the Man-Pack, where they cast out the Man-cub, hums like a hornet's nest."'

'It was a big stone that I threw,' chuckled Mowgli, who had often amused himself by throwing ripe paw-paws into a hornet's nest, and racing to the nearest pool before the hornets caught him.

'I asked of Mang what he had seen. He said that the Red Flower blossomed at the gate of the village, and men sat about it carrying guns. Now I know, for I have good cause,'—Akela looked here at the old dry scars on his flank and side,—'that men do not carry guns for pleasure. Presently, Little Brother, a man with a gun follows our trail—if, indeed, he be not already on it.'

'But why should he? Men have cast me out. What more do they need?' said Mowgli angrily.

'Thou art a man, Little Brother,' Akela returned. 'It is not for us, the Free Hunters, to tell thee what thy brethren do, or why.'

He had just time to snatch up his paw as the skinning-knife cut deep into the ground below. Mowgli struck quicker than an average human eye could follow, but Akela was a wolf; and even a dog, who is very far removed from the wild wolf, his ancestor, can be waked out of deep sleep by a cartwheel touching his flank, and can spring away unharmed before that wheel comes on.

'Another time,' Mowgli said, quietly, returning the knife to its sheath, 'speak of the Man-Pack and of Mowgli in *two* breaths—not one.'

'Phff! That is a sharp tooth,' said Akela, snuffing at the blade's cut in the earth, 'but living with the Man-Pack has spoiled thine eye, Little Brother. I could have killed buck while thou wast striking.'

Bagheera sprang to his feet, thrust up his head as far as he could, sniffed, and stiffened through every curve in his body. Gray Brother followed his example quickly, keeping a little to his left to get the wind that was blowing from the right, while Akela bounded fifty yards up-wind, and, half-crouching, stiffened too. Mowgli looked on enviously. He could smell things as very few human beings could, but he had never reached the hair-trigger-like sensitiveness of a Jungle nose; and his three months in the smoky village had put him back sadly. However, he dampened his finger, rubbed it on his nose, and stood erect to catch the upper scent, which, though the faintest, is the truest.

'Man!' Akela growled, dropping on his haunches.

'Buldeo!' said Mowgli, sitting down. 'He follows our trail, and yonder is the sunlight on his gun. Look!'

It was no more than a splash of sunlight, for a fraction of a second, on the brass clamps of the old Tower musket, but nothing in the Jungle winks with just that flash, except when the clouds race over the sky. Then a piece of mica, or a little pool, or even a highly-polished leaf will flash like a heliograph. But that day was cloudless and still.

'I knew men would follow,' said Akela, triumphantly. 'Not for nothing have I led the Pack!'

Mowgli's four wolves said nothing, but ran down hill on their bellies, melting into the thorn and under-brush.

'Whither go ye, and without word?' Mowgli called.

'H'sh! We roll his skull here before midday!' Gray Brother answered.

'Back! Back and wait! Man does not eat Man!' Mowgli shrieked.

'Who was a wolf but now? Who drove the knife at me for thinking he might be a man?' said Akela, as the Four turned back sullenly and dropped to heel.

'Am I to give reason for all I choose to do?' said Mowgli, furiously.

'That is Man! There speaks Man!' Bagheera muttered under his whiskers. 'Even so did men talk round the King's cages at Oodeypore. We of the Jungle know that Man is wisest of all. If we trusted our ears we should know that of all things he is most foolish.' Raising his voice, he added, 'The Man-cub is right in this. Men hunt in packs. To kill one, unless we know what the others will do, is bad hunting. Come, let us see what this Man means towards us.'

'We will not come,' Gray Brother growled. 'Hunt alone, Little Brother. We know our own minds! The skull would have been ready to bring by now.'

Mowgli had been looking from one to the other of his friends, his chest heaving and his eyes full of tears. He strode forward, and, dropping on one knee, said: 'Do I not know my mind? Look at me!'

They looked uneasily, and when their eyes wandered, he called them back again and again, till their hair stood up all over their bodies, and they trembled in every limb, while Mowgli stared and stared.

'Now,' said he, 'of us five, which is leader?'

'Thou art leader, Little Brother,' said Gray Brother, and he licked Mowgli's foot.

'Follow, then,' said Mowgli, and the four followed at his heels with their tails between their legs.

'This comes of living with the Man-Pack,' said Bagheera, slipping down after them. 'There is more in the Jungle now than Jungle Law, Baloo.'

The old bear said nothing, but he thought many things.

Mowgli cut across noiselessly through the Jungle, at right angles to Buldeo's path, till, parting the undergrowth, he saw the old man, his musket on his shoulder, running up the old trail at a dog-trot.

You will remember that Mowgli had left the village with the heavy weight of Shere Khan's raw hide on his shoulders, while Akela and Gray Brother trotted behind, so that the trail was very clearly marked. Presently Buldeo came to where Akela, as you know, had gone back and mixed it all up. Then he sat down, and coughed and grunted, and made little casts round and about into the Jungle to pick it up again, and all the time he could have thrown a stone over those who were watching him. No one can be so silent as a wolf when he does not care to be heard; and Mowgli, though the wolves thought he moved very clumsily, could come and go like a shadow. They ringed the old man as a school of porpoises ring a steamer at full speed, and as they ringed him they talked unconcernedly, for their speech began below the lowest end of the scale that untaught human beings can hear. [The other end is bounded by the high squeak of Mang, the Bat, which very many people cannot catch at all. From that note all the bird and bat and insect talk takes on.]

'This is better than any kill,' said Gray Brother, as Buldeo stooped and peered and puffed. 'He looks like a lost pig in the Jungles by the river. What does he say?' Buldeo was muttering savagely.

Mowgli translated. 'He says that packs of wolves must have danced round me. He says that he never saw such a trail in his life. He says he is tired.'

'He will be rested before he picks it up again,' said Bagheera coolly, as he slipped round a tree-trunk, in the game of blind-man's-buff that they were playing. 'Now, what does the lean thing do?'

'Eat or blow smoke out of his mouth. Men always play with their mouths,' said Mowgli; and the silent trailers saw the old man fill and light, and puff at a water-pipe, and they took good note of the smell of the tobacco, so as to be sure of Buldeo in the darkest night, if necessary.

Then a little knot of charcoal-burners came down the path, and naturally halted to speak to Buldeo, whose fame as a hunter reached for at least twenty miles round. They all sat down and smoked, and Bagheera and the others came up and watched while Buldeo began to tell the story of Mowgli, the Devil-child, from one end to another, with additions and inventions. How he himself had really killed Shere Khan; and how Mowgli had

turned himself into a wolf, and fought with him all the afternoon, and changed into a boy again and bewitched Buldeo's rifle, so that the bullet turned the corner, when he pointed it at Mowgli, and killed one of Buldeo's own buffaloes; and how the village, knowing him to be the bravest hunter in Seeonee, had sent him out to kill this Devil-child. But meantime the village had got hold of Messua and her husband, who were undoubtedly the father and mother of this Devil-child, and had barricaded them in their own hut, and presently would torture them to make them confess they were witch and wizard, and then they would be burned to death.

' When? ' said the charcoal-burners, because they would very much like to be present at the ceremony.

Buldeo said that nothing would be done till he returned, because the village wished him to kill the Jungle Boy first. After that they would dispose of Messua and her husband, and divide their land and buffaloes among the village. Messua's husband had some remarkably fine buffaloes, too. It was an excellent thing to destroy wizards, Buldeo thought; and people who entertained Wolf-children out of the Jungle were clearly the worst kind of witches.

But, said the charcoal-burners, what would happen if the English heard of it? The English, they had been told, were a perfectly mad people, who would not let honest farmers kill witches in peace.

Why, said Buldeo, the head-man of the village would report that Messua and her husband had died of snake-bite. That was all arranged, and the only thing now was to kill the Wolf-child. They did not happen to have seen anything of such a creature?

The charcoal-burners looked round cautiously, and thanked their stars they had not; but they had no doubt that so brave a man as Buldeo would find him if any one could. The sun was getting rather low, and they had an idea that they would push on to Buldeo's village and see the wicked witch. Buldeo said that, though it was his duty to kill the Devil-child he could not think of letting a party of unarmed men go through the Jungle, which might reveal the Wolf-demon at any minute, without his escort. He, therefore, would accompany them, and if the sorcerer's child appeared—well, he would show them how the best hunter in Seeonee dealt with such things. The Brahmin, he said, had given him a charm against the creature that made everything perfectly safe.

' What says he? What says he? What says he? ' the wolves repeated every few minutes; and Mowgli translated until he came to the witch part of the story, which was a little beyond him, and then he said that the man and woman who had been so kind to him were trapped.

' Do men trap men? ' said Gray Brother.

' So he says. I cannot understand the talk. They are all mad together. What have Messua and her man to do with me that they should be put in a trap; and what is all this talk about the Red Flower? I must look to this. Whatever they would do to Messua they will not do till Buldeo returns. And so—— ' Mowgli thought hard with his fingers playing around the haft of

his skinning-knife, while Buldeo and the charcoal-burners went off very valiantly in single file.

'I go hot-foot back to the Man-Pack,' Mowgli said at last.

'And those?' said Gray Brother, looking hungrily after the brown backs of the charcoal-burners.

'Sing them home,' said Mowgli with a grin; 'I do not wish them to be at the village gate till it is dark. Can ye hold them?'

Gray Brother bared his white teeth in contempt. 'We can head them round and round in circles like tethered goats—if I know Man.'

'That I do not need. Sing to them a little lest they be lonely on the road, and, Gray Brother, the song need not be of the sweetest. Go with them, Bagheera, and help make that song. When night is laid down, meet me by the village—Gray Brother knows the place.'

'It is no light hunting to track for a Man-cub. When shall I sleep?' said Bagheera, yawning, though his eyes showed he was delighted with the amusement. 'Me to sing to naked men! But let us try.'

He lowered his head so that the sound would travel, and cried a long, long, 'Good hunting'—a midnight call in the afternoon, which was quite awful enough to begin with. Mowgli heard it rumble, and rise, and fall, and die off in a creepy sort of whine behind him, and laughed to himself as he ran through the Jungle. He could see the charcoal-burners huddled in a knot; old Buldeo's gun-barrel waving, like a banana-leaf, to every point of the compass at once. Then Gray Brother gave the *Ya-la-hi! Yalaha!* call for the buck-driving, when the Pack drives the Nilghai, the big blue cow, before them, and it seemed to come from the very ends of the earth, nearer, and nearer, and nearer, till it ended in a shriek snapped off short. The other three answered, till even Mowgli could have vowed that the Full Pack was in full cry, and then they all broke into the magnificent Morning-song in the Jungle, with every turn, and flourish, and grace-note, that a deep-mouthed wolf of the Pack knows. This is a rough rendering of the song, but you must imagine what it sounds like when it breaks the afternoon hush of the Jungle.

> One moment past our bodies cast
> No shadow on the plain;
> Now clear and black they stride our track,
> And we run home again.
> In morning-hush, each rock and bush
> Stands hard, and high, and raw:
> Then give the Call: '*Good rest to all*
> *That keep the Jungle Law!*'
>
> Now horn and pelt our peoples melt
> In covert to abide;
> Now crouched and still, to cave and hill
> Our Jungle Barons glide.

Now, stark and plain, Man's oxen strain,
　　That draw the new-yoked plough;
Now stripped and dread the dawn is red
　　Above the lit *talao*.

Ho! Get to lair! The sun's aflare
　　Behind the breathing grass:
And creaking through the young bamboo
　　The warning whispers pass.
By day made strange, the woods we range
　　With blinking eyes we scan;
While down the skies the wild duck cries:
　　'*The Day—the Day to Man!*'

The dew is dried that drenched our hide,
　　Or washed about our way;
And where we drank, the puddled bank
　　Is crisping into clay.
The traitor Dark gives up each mark
　　Of stretched or hooded claw;
Then hear the Call: '*Good rest to all*
　　That keep the Jungle Law!'

But no translation can give the effect of it, or the yelping scorn the
four threw into every word of it, as they heard the trees crash when the men
hastily climbed up into the branches, and Buldeo began repeating incanta-
tions and charms. Then they laid down and slept, for like all who live by
their own exertions, they were of a methodical cast of mind; and no one
can work well without sleep.

Meantime, Mowgli was putting the miles behind him, nine to the hour,
swinging on, delighted to find himself so fit after all his cramped months
among men. The one idea in his head was to get Messua and her husband
out of the trap, whatever it was, for he had a natural mistrust of traps. Later
on, he promised himself, he would begin to pay his debts to the village at
large.

It was at twilight when he saw the well-remembered grazing-grounds,
and the *dhak*-tree where Gray Brother had waited for him on the morning
that he killed Shere Khan. Angry as he was at the whole breed and com-
munity of Man, something jumped up in his throat and made him catch
his breath when he looked at the village roofs. He noticed that every one
had come in from the fields unusually early, and that, instead of getting
to their evening cooking, they gathered in a crowd under the village tree,
and chattered, and shouted.

'Men must always be making traps for men, or they are not content,'
said Mowgli. 'Two nights ago it was Mowgli—but that night seems many
Rains old. To-night it is Messua and her man. To-morrow, and for very
many nights after, it will be Mowgli's turn again.'

He crept along outside the wall till he came to Messua's hut, and looked through the window into the room. There lay Messua, gagged, and bound hand and foot, breathing hard, and groaning; her husband was tied to the gaily painted bedstead. The door of the hut that opened into the street was shut fast, and three or four people were sitting with their backs to it.

Mowgli knew the manners and customs of the villagers very fairly. He argued that so long as they could eat, and talk, and smoke, they would not do anything else; but as soon as they had fed they would begin to be dangerous. Buldeo would be coming in before long, and if his escort had done its duty Buldeo would have a very interesting tale to tell. So he went in through the window, and, stooping over the man and the woman, cut their thongs, pulling out the gags, and looked round the hut for some milk.

Messua was half wild with pain and fear (she had been beaten and stoned all the morning), and Mowgli put his hand over her mouth just in time to stop a scream. Her husband was only bewildered and angry, and sat picking dust and things out of his torn beard.

'I knew—I knew he would come,' Messua sobbed at last. 'Now do I *know* that he is my son'; and she caught Mowgli to her heart. Up to that time Mowgli had been perfectly steady, but here he began to tremble all over, and that surprised him immensely.

'Why are these thongs? Why have they tied thee?' he asked, after a pause.

'To be put to the death for making a son of thee—what else?' said the man, sullenly. 'Look! I bleed.'

Messua said nothing, but it was at *her* wounds that Mowgli looked, and they heard him grit his teeth when he saw the blood.

'Whose work is this?' said he. 'There is a price to pay.'

'The work of all the village. I was too rich. I had too many cattle. *Therefore* she and I are witches, because we gave thee shelter.'

'I do not understand. Let Messua tell the tale.'

'I gave thee milk, Nathoo; dost thou remember?' Messua said, timidly. 'Because thou wast my son, whom the tiger took, and because I loved thee very dearly. They said that I was thy mother, the mother of a devil, and therefore worthy of death.'

'And what is a devil?' said Mowgli. 'Death I have seen.'

The man looked up gloomily under his eyebrows, but Messua laughed. 'See!' she said to her husband, 'I knew—I said that he was no sorcerer! He is my son—my son!'

'Son or sorcerer, what good will that do us?' the man answered. 'We be as dead already.'

'Yonder is the road through the Jungle'—Mowgli pointed through the window. 'Your hands and feet are free. Go now.'

'We do not know the Jungle, my son, as—as thou knowest,' Messua began. 'I do not think that I could walk far.'

'And the men and women would be upon our backs and drag us here again,' said the husband.

'H'm!' said Mowgli, and he tickled the palm of his hand with the tip of his skinning-knife; 'I have no wish to do harm to any one of this village—*yet*. But I do not think they will stay thee. In a little while they will have much to think upon. Ah!' he lifted his head and listened to shouting and trampling outside. 'So they have let Buldeo come home at last?'

'He was sent out this morning to kill thee,' Messua cried. 'Didst thou meet him?'

'Yes—we—I met him. He has a tale to tell; and while he is talking it there is time to do much. But first I will learn what they mean. Think where ye would go, and tell me when I come back.'

He bounded through the window and ran along again outside the wall of the village till he came within earshot of the crowd round the peepul tree. Buldeo was lying on the ground, coughing and groaning, and every one was asking him questions. His hair had fallen about his shoulders; his hands and legs were skinned from climbing up trees, and he could hardly speak, but he felt the importance of his position keenly. From time to time he said something about devils and singing devils, and magic enchantment, just to give the crowd a taste of what was coming. Then he called for water.

'Bah!' said Mowgli. 'Chatter—chatter! Talk, talk! Men are blood-brothers of the *Bandar-log*. Now he must wash his mouth with water; now he must blow smoke; and when all that is done he has still his story to tell. They are very wise people—men. They will leave no one to guard Messua till their ears are stuffed with Buldeo's tales. And—I grow as lazy as they!'

He shook himself and glided back to the hut. Just as he was at the window he felt a touch on his foot.

'Mother,' said he, for he knew that tongue well, 'what dost *thou* here?'

'I heard my children singing through the woods, and I followed the one I loved best. Little Frog, I have a desire to see that woman who gave thee milk,' said Mother Wolf, all wet with the dew.

'They have bound and mean to kill her. I have cut those ties, and she goes with her man through the Jungle.'

'I also will follow. I am old, but not yet toothless.' Mother Wolf reared herself up on end, and looked through the window into the dark of the hut.

In a minute she dropped noiselessly, and all she said was: 'I gave thee thy first milk; but Bagheera speaks truth: Man goes to Man at the last.'

'Maybe,' said Mowgli, with a very unpleasant look on his face; 'but to-night I am very far from that trail. Wait here, but do not let her see.'

'*Thou* wast never afraid of *me*, Little Frog,' said Mother Wolf, backing into the high grass, and blotting herself out, as she knew how.

'And now,' said Mowgli, cheerfully, as he swung into the hut again, 'they are all sitting round Buldeo, who is saying that which did not happen.

When his talk is finished, they say they will assuredly come here with the Red—with fire and burn you both. And then?'

'I have spoken to my man,' said Messua. 'Kanhiwara is thirty miles from here, but at Kanhiwara we may find the English——'

'And what Pack are they?' said Mowgli.

'I do not know. They be white, and it is said that they govern all the land, and do not suffer people to burn or beat each other without witnesses. If we can get thither to-night we live. Otherwise we die.'

'Live then. No man passes the gates to-night. But what does *he* do?' Messua's husband was on his hands and knees digging up the earth in one corner of the hut.

'It is his little money,' said Messua. 'We can take nothing else.'

'Ah, yes. The stuff that passes from hand to hand and never grows warmer. Do they need it outside this place also?' said Mowgli.

The man stared angrily. 'He is a fool, and no devil,' he muttered. 'With the money I can buy a horse. We are too bruised to walk far, and the village will follow us in an hour.'

'I say they will *not* follow till I choose, but a horse is well thought of, for Messua is tired.' Her husband stood up and knotted the last of the rupees into his waist-cloth. Mowgli helped Messua through the window, and the cool night air revived her, but the Jungle in the starlight looked very dark and terrible.

'Ye know the trail to Kanhiwara?' Mowgli whispered.

They nodded.

'Good. Remember, now, not to be afraid. And there is no need to go quickly. Only—only there may be some small singing in the Jungle behind you and before.'

'Think you we would have risked a night in the Jungle through anything less than the fear of burning? It is better to be killed by beasts than by men,' said Messua's husband; but Messua looked at Mowgli and smiled.

'I say,' Mowgli went on, just as though he were Baloo repeating an old Jungle Law for the hundredth time to an inattentive cub, 'I say that not a tooth in the Jungle is bared against you; not a foot in the Jungle is lifted against you. Neither man nor beast shall stay you till you come within eye-shot of Kanhiwara. There will be a watch about you.' He turned quickly to Messua, saying, 'He does not believe, but thou wilt believe?'

'Ay, surely, my son. Man, ghost, or wolf of the Jungle, I believe.'

'He will be afraid when he hears my people singing. Thou wilt know and understand. Go now, and slowly, for there is no need of any haste. The gates are shut.'

Messua flung herself sobbing at Mowgli's feet, but he lifted her very quickly with a shiver. Then she hung about his neck and called him every name of blessing she could think of, but her husband looked enviously across his fields, and said: 'If we reach Kanhiwara, and I get the ear of the English, I will bring such a lawsuit against the Brahmin and old Buldeo

and the others as shall eat this village to the bone. They shall pay me twice over for my crops untilled and my buffaloes unfed. I will have a great justice.'

Mowgli laughed. ' I do not know what justice is, but—come thou back next Rains and see what is left.'

They went off toward the Jungle, and Mother Wolf leaped from her place of hiding.

' Follow! ' said Mowgli; ' and look to it that all the Jungle knows these two are safe. Give tongue a little. I would call Bagheera.'

The long, low howl rose and fell, and Mowgli saw Messua's husband flinch and turn, half minded to run back to the hut.

' Go on,' Mowgli shouted, cheerfully. ' I said there might be singing. That call will follow up to Kanhiwara. It is the Favour of the Jungle.'

Messua urged her husband forward, and the darkness shut down on them and Mother Wolf as Bagheera rose up almost under Mowgli's feet, trembling with delight of the night that drives the Jungle People wild.

' I am ashamed of thy brethren,' he said, purring.

' What? Did they not sing sweetly to Buldeo? ' said Mowgli.

' Too well! Too well! They made even *me* forget my pride, and, by the Broken Lock that freed me, I went singing through the Jungle as though I were out wooing in the spring! Didst thou not hear us? '

' I had other game afoot. Ask Buldeo if he liked the song. But where are the Four? I do not wish one of the Man-Pack to leave the gates to-night.'

' What need of the Four, then? ' said Bagheera, shifting from foot to foot, his eyes ablaze, and purring louder than ever. ' I can hold them, Little Brother. Is it killing at last? The singing and the sight of the men climbing up the trees have made me very ready. Who is Man that we should care for him—the naked brown digger, the hairless and toothless, the eater of earth? I have followed him all day—at noon—in the white sunlight. I herded him as the wolves herd buck. I am Bagheera! Bagheera! Bagheera! As I dance with my shadow so I danced with those men. Look! ' The great panther leaped as a kitten leaps at a dead leaf whirling overhead, struck left and right into the empty air, that sung under the strokes, landed noiselessly, and leaped again and again, while the half purr, half growl gathered head as steam rumbles in a boiler. ' I am Bagheera—in the Jungle—in the night, and my strength is in me. Who shall stay my stroke? Man-cub, with one blow of my paw I could beat thy head flat as a dead frog in the summer! '

' Strike, then! ' said Mowgli, in the dialect of the village, *not* the talk of the Jungle; and the human words brought Bagheera to a full stop, flung back on his haunches that quivered under him, his head just at the level of Mowgli's. Once more Mowgli stared, as he had stared at the rebellious cubs, full into the beryl-green eyes, till the red glare behind their green went out like the light of a lighthouse shut off twenty miles

across the sea; till the eyes dropped, and the big head with them—dropped lower and lower, and the red rasp of a tongue grated on Mowgli's instep.

'Brother—Brother—Brother!' the boy whispered, stroking steadily and lightly from the neck along the heaving back: 'Be still, be still! It is the fault of the night, and no fault of thine.'

'It was the smells of the night,' said Bagheera, penitently. 'This air cries aloud to me. But how dost *thou* know?'

Of course the air round an Indian village is full of all kinds of smells, and to any creature who does nearly all his thinking through his nose, smells are as maddening as music and drugs are to human beings. Mowgli gentled the panther for a few minutes longer, and he lay down like a cat before a fire, his paws tucked under his breast, and his eyes half shut.

'Thou art of the Jungle and *not* of the Jungle,' he said at last. 'And I am only a black panther. But I love thee, Little Brother.'

'They are very long at their talk under the tree,' Mowgli said, without noticing the last sentence. 'Buldeo must have told many tales. They should come soon to drag the woman and her man out of the trap and put them into the Red Flower. They will find that trap sprung. Ho! Ho!'

'Nay, listen,' said Bagheera. 'The fever is out of my blood now. Let them find *me* there! Few would leave their houses after meeting me. It is not the first time I have been in a cage; and I do not think they will tie *me* with cords.'

'Be wise, then,' said Mowgli, laughing; for he was beginning to feel as reckless as the panther, who had glided into the hut.

'Pah!' Bagheera grunted. 'This place is rank with Man, but here is just such a bed as they gave me to lie upon in the King's cages at Oodeypore. Now I lie down.' Mowgli heard the strings of the cot crack under the great brute's weight. 'By the Broken Lock that freed me, they will think they have caught big game! Come and sit beside me, Little Brother; we will give them " good hunting " together!'

'No; I have another thought in my stomach. The Man-Pack shall not know what share I have in the sport. Make thine own hunt. I do not wish to see them.'

'Be it so,' said Bagheera. 'Now they come!'

The conference under the peepul-tree had been growing noisier and noisier, at the far end of the village. It broke in wild yells, and a rush up the street of men and women, waving clubs and bamboos and sickles and knives. Buldeo and the Brahmin were at the head of it, but the mob was close at their heels, and they cried, 'The witch and the wizard! Let us see if hot coins will make them confess! Burn the hut over their heads! We will teach them to shelter Wolf-devils! Nay, beat them first! Torches! More torches! Buldeo, heat the gun-barrel!'

Here was some little difficulty with the catch of the door. It had been very firmly fastened, but the crowd tore it away bodily, and the light of the torches streamed into the room where, stretched at full length on

the bed, his paws crossed and lightly hung down over one end, black as the Pit and terrible as a demon, was Bagheera. There was one half-minute of desperate silence, as the front ranks of the crowd clawed and tore their way back from the threshold, and in that minute Bagheera raised his head and yawned—elaborately, carefully, and ostentatiously—as he would yawn when he wished to insult an equal. The fringed lips drew back and up; the red tongue curled; the lower jaw dropped and dropped till you could see half-way down the hot gullet; and the gigantic dog-teeth stood clear to the pit of the gums till they rang together, upper and under, with the snick of steel-faced wards shooting home round the edges of a safe. Next minute the street was empty; Bagheera had leaped back through the window, and stood at Mowgli's side, while a yelling, screaming torrent scrambled and tumbled one over another in their panic haste to get to their huts.

' They will not stir till the day comes,' said Bagheera, quietly. ' And now? '

The silence of the afternoon sleep seemed to have overtaken the village, but, as they listened, they could hear the sound of heavy grain-boxes being dragged over earthen floors and pushed against doors. Bagheera was quite right; the village would not stir till daylight. Mowgli sat still and thought, and his face grew darker and darker.

' What have I done? ' said Bagheera, at last, fawning.

' Nothing but great good. Watch them now till the day. I sleep.' Mowgli ran off into the Jungle, and dropped across a rock, and slept and slept the day round, and the night back again.

When he waked, Bagheera was at his side, and there lay a newly-killed buck at his feet. Bagheera watched curiously while Mowgli went to work with his skinning-knife, ate and drank, and turned over with his chin in his hands.

' The man and thy woman came safe within eye-shot of Kanhiwara,' Bagheera said. ' Thy mother sent the word back by Chil. They found a horse before midnight of the night they were freed, and went very quickly. Is not that well? '

' That is well,' said Mowgli.

' And thy Man-Pack in the village did not stir till the sun was high this morning. Then they ate their food and ran back quickly to their houses.'

' Did they, by chance, see thee? '

' It may have been. I was rolling in the dust before the gate at dawn, and I may have made also some small song to myself. Now, Little Brother, there is nothing more to do. Come hunting with me and Baloo. He has new hives that he wishes to show, and we all desire thee back again as of old. Take off that look which makes even *me* afraid. The man and woman will not be put into the Red Flower, and all goes well in the Jungle. Is it not true? Let us forget the Man-Pack.'

' They shall be forgotten—in a little while. Where does Hathi feed to-night? '

'Where he chooses. Who can answer for the Silent One? But why? What is there Hathi can do which we cannot?'

'Bid him and his three sons come here to me.'

'But, indeed, and truly, Little Brother, it is not—it is not seemly to say "Come," and "Go," to Hathi. Remember, he is the Master of the Jungle, and before the Man-Pack changed the look on thy face, he taught thee a Master-word of the Jungle.'

'That is all one. I have a Master-word for him now. Bid him come to Mowgli, the Frog, and if he does not hear at first, bid him come because of the Sack of the Fields of Bhurtpore.'

'The Sack of the Fields of Bhurtpore,' Bagheera repeated two or three times to make sure. 'I go. Hathi can but be angry at the worst, and I would give a moon's hunting to hear a Master-word that compels the Silent One.'

He went away, leaving Mowgli stabbing furiously with his skinning-knife into the earth. Mowgli had never seen human blood in his life before till he had seen, and—what meant much more to him—smelled Messua's blood on the thongs that bound her. And Messua had been kind to him, and, so far as he knew anything about love, he loved Messua as completely as he hated the rest of mankind. But deeply as he loathed them, their talk, their cruelty and their cowardice, not for anything the Jungle had to offer could he bring himself to take a human life, and have that terrible scent of blood back again in his nostrils. His plan was simpler but much more thorough; and he laughed to himself when he thought that it was one of old Buldeo's tales told under the peepul-tree in the evening that had put the idea into his head.

'It *was* a Master-word,' Bagheera whispered in his ear. 'They were feeding by the river, and they obeyed as though they were bullocks. Look, where they come now!'

Hathi and his three sons had appeared in their usual way, without a sound. The mud of the river was still fresh on their flanks, and Hathi was thoughtfully chewing the green stem of a young plantain-tree that he had gouged up with his tusks. But every line in his vast body showed to Bagheera, who could see things when he came across them, that it was not the Master of the Jungle speaking to a Man-cub, but one who was afraid coming before one who was not. His three sons rolled side by side, behind their father.

Mowgli hardly lifted his head as Hathi gave him 'Good hunting.' He kept him swinging and rocking, and shifting from one foot to another, for a long time before he spoke, and when he opened his mouth it was to Bagheera, not to the elephants.

'I will tell a tale that was told to me by the hunter ye hunted to-day,' said Mowgli. 'It concerns an elephant, old and wise, who fell into a trap, and the sharpened stake in the pit scarred him from a little above his heel to the crest of his shoulder, leaving a white mark.' Mowgli threw out his hand, and as Hathi wheeled the moonlight showed a long white scar on

his slaty side, as though he had been struck with a red-hot whip. 'Men came to take him from the trap,' Mowgli continued, 'but he broke his ropes, for he was strong, and he went away till his wound was healed. Then came he, angry, by night to the fields of those hunters. And I remember now that he had three sons. These things happened many, many Rains ago, and very far away—among the fields of Bhurtpore. What came to those fields at the next reaping, Hathi?'

'They were reaped by me and by my three sons,' said Hathi.

'And to the ploughing that follows the reaping?' said Mowgli.

'There was no ploughing,' said Hathi.

'And to the men that live by the green crops on the ground?' said Mowgli.

'They went away.'

'And to the huts in which the men slept?' said Mowgli.

'We tore the roofs to pieces, and the Jungle swallowed up the walls,' said Hathi.

'And what more, besides?' said Mowgli.

'As much good ground as I can walk over in two nights from the east to the west, and from the north to the south as much as I can walk over in three nights, the Jungle took. We let in the Jungle upon five villages; and in those villages, and in their lands, the grazing-ground and the soft crop-grounds, there is not one man to-day who gets his food from the ground. That was the Sack of the Fields of Bhurtpore, which I and my three sons did; and now I ask, Man-cub, how the news of it came to thee?' said Hathi.

'A man told me; and now I see even Buldeo can speak truth. It was well done, Hathi with the white mark; but the second time it shall be done better, for the reason that there is a man to direct. Thou knowest the village of the Man-Pack that cast me out? They are idle, senseless, and cruel; they play with their mouths, and they do not kill their weaker for food, but for sport. When they are full-fed they would throw their own breed into the Red Flower. This I have seen. It is not well that they should live here any more. I hate them!'

'Kill, then,' said the youngest of Hathi's three sons, picking up a tuft of grass, dusting it against his fore-legs, and throwing it away, while his little red eyes glanced furtively from side to side.

'What good are white bones to me?' Mowgli answered furiously. 'Am I the cub of a wolf to play in the sun with a raw head? I have killed Shere Khan, and his hide rots on the Council Rock; but—but I do not know whither Shere Khan is gone, and my stomach is still empty. Now I will take that which I can see and touch. Let in the Jungle upon that village, Hathi!'

Bagheera shivered, and cowered down. He could understand, if the worst came to the worst, a quick rush down the village street, and a right and left blow into a crowd, or a crafty killing of men as they ploughed in

the twilight, but this scheme for deliberately blotting out an entire village from the eyes of man and beast frightened him. Now he saw why Mowgli had sent for Hathi. No one but the long-lived elephant could plan and carry through such a war.

'Let them run as the men ran from the fields of Bhurtpore, till we have the rain-water for the only plough, and the noise of the rain on the thick leaves for the pattering of their spindles—till Bagheera and I lair in the house of the Brahmin, and the buck drink at the tank behind the temple! Let in the Jungle, Hathi!'

'But I—but we have no quarrel with them, and it needs the red rage of great pain ere we tear down the places where men sleep,' said Hathi, rocking doubtfully.

'Are ye the only eaters of grass in the Jungle? Drive in your peoples. Let the deer and the pig and the nilghai look to it. Ye need never show a hand's-breadth of hide till the fields are naked. Let in the Jungle, Hathi!'

'There will be no killing? My tusks were red at the Sack of the Fields of Bhurtpore, and I would not wake that smell again.'

'Nor I. I do not wish even their bones to lie on our clean earth. Let them go find a fresh lair. They cannot stay here! I have seen and smelt the blood of the woman that gave me food—the woman whom they would have killed but for me. Only the smell of the new grass on their door-steps can take away that smell. It burns in my mouth. Let in the Jungle, Hathi!'

'Ah!' said Hathi. 'So did the scar of the stake burn on my hide till we watched their villages die under in the spring growth. Now I see. Thy war shall be our war. We will let in the Jungle.'

Mowgli had hardly time to catch his breath—he was shaking all over with rage and hate—before the place where the elephants had stood was empty, and Bagheera was looking at him with terror.

'By the Broken Lock that freed me!' said the Black Panther at last. 'Art *thou* the naked thing I spoke for in the Pack when all was young? Master of the Jungle, when my strength goes, speak for me—speak for Baloo—speak for us all! We are cubs before thee! Snapped twigs under foot! Fawns that have lost their doe!'

The idea of Bagheera being a stray fawn upset Mowgli altogether, and he laughed and caught his breath, and sobbed and laughed again, till he had to jump into a pool to make himself stop. Then he swam round and round, ducking in and out of the bars of the moonlight like the frog, his namesake.

By this time Hathi and his three sons had turned, each to one point of the compass, and were striding silently down the valleys a mile away. They went on and on for two days' march—that is to say, a long sixty miles—through the Jungle; while every step they took, and every wave of their trunks, was known and noted and talked over by Mang and Chil and the Monkey People and all the birds. Then they began to feed, and fed

quietly for a week or so. Hathi and his sons are like Kaa the Rock Python. They never hurry till they have to.

At the end of that time—and none knew who had started it—a rumour went through the Jungle that there was better food and water to be found in such and such a valley. The pig—who, of course, will go to the ends of the earth for a full meal—moved first by companies, scuffling over the rocks, and the deer followed, with the little wild foxes that live on the dead and dying of the herds; and the heavy-shouldered nilghai moved parallel with the deer, and the wild buffaloes of the swamps came after the nilghai. The least little thing would have turned the scattered, straggling droves that grazed and sauntered and drank and grazed again; but whenever there was an alarm some one would rise up and soothe them. At one time it would be Sahi the Porcupine, full of news of good feed just a little farther on; at another Mang would cry cheerily and flap down a glade to show it was all empty; or Baloo, his mouth full of roots, would shamble alongside a wavering line and half frighten, half romp it clumsily back to the proper road. Very many creatures broke back or ran away or lost interest, but very many were left to go forward. At the end of another ten days or so the situation was this. The deer and the pig and the nilghai were milling round and round in a circle of eight or ten miles' radius, while the Eaters of Flesh skirmished round its edge. And the centre of that circle was the village, and round the village the crops were ripening, and in the crops sat men on what they call *machans*—platforms like pigeon-perches, made of sticks at the top of four poles—to scare away birds and other stealers. Then the deer were coaxed no more. The Eaters of Flesh were close behind them, and forced them forward and inward.

It was a dark night when Hathi and his three sons slipped down from the Jungle, and broke off the poles of the *machans* with their trunks, and they fell as a snapped stalk of hemlock in bloom falls, and the men that tumbled from them heard the deep gurgling of the elephants in their ears. Then the vanguard of the bewildered armies of the deer broke down and flooded into the village grazing-grounds and the ploughed fields; and the sharp-hoofed, rooting wild pig came with them, and what the deer left the pig spoiled, and from time to time an alarm of wolves would shake the herds, and they would rush to and fro desperately, treading down the young barley, and cutting flat the banks of the irrigating channels. Before the dawn broke the pressure on the outside of the circle gave way at one point. The Eaters of Flesh had fallen back and left an open path to the south, and drove upon drove of buck fled along it. Others, who were bolder, lay up in the thickets to finish their meal next night.

But the work was practically done. When the villagers looked in the morning they saw their crops were lost. That meant death if they did not get away, for they lived year in and year out as near to starvation as the Jungle was near to them. When the buffaloes were sent to graze the hungry brutes found that the deer had cleared the grazing-grounds, and so wandered

into the Jungle and drifted off with their wild mates; and when twilight fell the three or four ponies that belonged to the village lay in their stables with their heads beaten in. Only Bagheera could have given those strokes, and only Bagheera would have thought of insolently dragging the last carcase to the open street.

The villagers had no heart to make fires in the fields that night, so Hathi and his three sons went gleaning among what was left; and where Hathi gleans there is no need to follow. The men decided to live on their stored seed-corn until the rains had fallen, and then to take work as servants till they could catch up with the lost year; but as the grain-dealer was thinking of his well-filled crates of corn, and the prices he would levy at the sale of it, Hathi's sharp tusks were picking out the corner of his mud-house, and smashing up the big wicker-chest, leeped with cow-dung, where the precious stuff lay.

When that last loss was discovered, it was the Brahmin's turn to speak. He had prayed to his own Gods without answer. It might be, he said, that, unconsciously, the village had offended some one of the Gods of the Jungle, for, beyond doubt, the Jungle was against them. So they sent for the head man of the nearest tribes of wandering Gonds—little, wise, and very black hunters, living in the deep Jungle, whose fathers came of the oldest race in India—the aboriginal owners of the land. They made the Gond welcome with what they had, and he stood on one leg, his bow in his hand, and two or three poisoned arrows stuck through his top-knot, looking half afraid and half contemptuously at the anxious villagers and their ruined fields. They wished to know whether his Gods—the Old Gods—were angry with them, and what sacrifices should be offered. The Gond said nothing, but picked up a trail of the Karela, the vine that bears the bitter wild gourd, and laced it to and fro across the temple door in the face of the staring red Hindu image. Then he pushed with his hand in the open air along the road to Kanhiwara, and went back to his Jungle, and watched the Jungle people drifting through it. He knew that when the Jungle moves only white men can hope to turn it aside.

There was no need to ask his meaning. The wild gourd would grow where they had worshipped their God, and the sooner they saved themselves the better.

But it is hard to tear a village from its moorings. They stayed on as long as any summer food was left to them, and they tried to gather nuts in the Jungle, but shadows with glaring eyes watched them, and rolled before them even at midday, and when they ran back afraid to their walls, on the tree trunks they had passed not five minutes before the bark would be striped and chiselled with the stroke of some great taloned paw. The more they kept to their village, the bolder grew the wild things that gambolled and bellowed on the grazing-grounds by the Waingunga. They had no heart to patch and plaster the rear walls of the empty byres that backed on to the Jungle; the wild pig trampled them down, and the knotty-

rooted vines hurried after and threw their elbows over the new-won ground, and the coarse grass bristled behind the vines. The unmarried men ran away first, and carried the news far and near that the village was doomed. Who could fight, they said, against the Jungle, or the Gods of the Jungle, when the very village cobra had left his hole in the platform under the peepul? So their little commerce with the outside world shrunk as the trodden paths across the open grew fewer and fainter. And the nightly trumpetings of Hathi and his three sons ceased to trouble them; they had no more to go. The crop on the ground and the seed in the ground had been taken. The outlying fields were already losing their shape, and it was time to throw themselves on the charity of the English at Kanhiwara.

Native fashion, they delayed their departure from one day to another till the first Rains caught them and the unmended roofs let in a flood, and the grazing-ground stood ankle deep, and all green things came on with a rush after the heat of the summer. Then they waded out—men, women, and children—through the blinding hot rain of the morning, but turned naturally for one farewell look at their homes.

They heard, as the last burdened family filed through the gate, a crash of falling beams and thatch behind the walls. They saw a shiny, snaky black trunk lifted for an instant, scattering sodden thatch. It disappeared, and there was another crash, followed by a squeal. Hathi had been plucking off the roofs of the huts as you pluck water-lilies, and a rebounding beam had pricked him. He needed only this to unchain his full strength, for of all things in the Jungle the wild elephant enraged is the most wantonly destructive. He kicked backward at a mud wall that crumbled at the stroke, and, crumbling, melted to yellow mud under the torrents of rain. Then he wheeled and squealed, and tore through the narrow streets, leaning against the huts right and left, shivering the crazy doors, and crumpling up the eaves; while his three sons raged behind as they had raged at the Sack of the Fields of Bhurtpore.

'The Jungle will swallow these shells,' said a quiet voice in the wreckage. 'It is the outer walls that must lie down,' and Mowgli, with the rain sluicing over his bare shoulders and arms, leaped back from a wall that was settling like a tired buffalo.

'All in good time,' panted Hathi. 'Oh, but my tusks were red at Bhurtpore! To the outer wall, children! With the head! Together! Now! '

The four pushed side by side; the outer wall bulged, split, and fell, and the villagers, dumb with horror, saw the savage, clay-streaked heads of the wreckers in the ragged gap. Then they fled, houseless and foodless, down the valley, as their village, shredded and tossed and trampled, melted behind them.

A month later the place was a dimpled mound, covered with soft, green young stuff; and by the end of the Rains there was the roaring Jungle in full blast on the spot that had been under plough not six months before.

MOWGLI'S SONG AGAINST PEOPLE

I will let loose against you the fleet-footed vines—
I will call in the Jungle to stamp out your lines!
 The roofs shall fade before it,
 The house-beams shall fall,
 And the *Karela*, the bitter *Karela*,
 Shall cover it all!

In the gates of these your councils my people shall sing,
In the doors of these your garners the Bat-folk shall cling;
 And the snake shall be your watchman,
 By a hearthstone unswept;
 For the *Karela*, the bitter *Karela*,
 Shall fruit where ye slept!

Ye shall not see my strikers; ye shall hear them and guess;
By night, before the moon-rise, I will send for my cess,
 And the wolf shall be your herdsman
 By a landmark removed,
 For the *Karela*, the bitter *Karela*,
 Shall seed where ye loved!

I will reap your fields before you at the hands of a host;
Ye shall glean behind my reapers for the bread that is lost;
 And the deer shall be your oxen
 By a headland untilled,
 For the *Karela*, the bitter *Karela*,
 Shall leaf where ye build!

I have untied against you the club-footed vines,
I have sent in the Jungle to swamp out your lines.
 The trees—the trees are on you!
 The house-beams shall fall,
 And the *Karela*, the bitter *Karela*,
 Shall cover you all!

THE KING'S ANKUS

These are the Four that are never content: that have never been filled
 since the Dews began—
Jacala's mouth, and the glut of the Kite, and the hands of the Ape and
 the Eyes of Man.

Jungle Saying

꿿 KAA, the big rock-python, had changed his skin for perhaps the two
hundredth time since his birth; and Mowgli, who never forgot that he
owed his life to Kaa for a night's work at Cold Lairs, which you may
perhaps remember, went to congratulate him. Skin-changing always makes a
snake moody and depressed till the new skin begins to shine and look beau-
tiful. Kaa never made sport of Mowgli any more, but accepted him, as the
other Jungle People did, for the Master of the Jungle, and brought him all
the news that a python of his size would naturally hear. What Kaa did not
know about the Middle Jungle, as they call it—the life that runs close
to the earth or under it, the boulder, burrow, and the tree-bole life—might
have been written upon the smallest of his scales.

That afternoon Mowgli was sitting in the circle of Kaa's great coils,
fingering the flaked and broken old skin that lay all looped and twisted
among the rocks just as Kaa had left it. Kaa had very courteously
packed himself under Mowgli's broad, bare shoulders, so that the boy was
really resting in a living arm-chair.

'Even to the scales of the eyes it is perfect,' said Mowgli, under his
breath, playing with the old skin. 'Strange to see the covering of one's
own head at one's own feet.'

'Ay, but I lack feet,' said Kaa; 'and since this is the custom of all
my people, I do not find it strange. Does thy skin never feel old and harsh?'

'Then go I and wash, Flathead; but, it is true, in the great heats I have
wished I could slough my skin without pain, and run skinless.'

'I wash, and *also* I take off my skin. How looks the new coat?'

Mowgli ran his hand down the diagonal checkerings of the immense
back. 'The Turtle is harder-backed, but not so gay,' he said judgmatically.
'The Frog, my name-bearer, is more gay, but not so hard. It is very beauti-
ful to see—like the mottling in the mouth of a lily.'

'It needs water. A new skin never comes to full colour before the first
bath. Let us go bathe.'

'I will carry thee,' said Mowgli; and he stooped down, laughing, to lift
the middle section of Kaa's great body, just where the barrel was thickest.
A man might just as well have tried to heave up a two-foot water-main;

and Kaa lay still, puffing with quiet amusement. Then their regular evening game began—the Boy in the flush of his great strength, and the Python in his sumptuous new skin, standing up one against the other for a wrestling match—a trial of eye and strength. Of course, Kaa could have crushed a dozen Mowglis had he let himself go; but he played carefully, and never loosed one-tenth of his power. Ever since Mowgli was strong enough to endure a little rough handling, Kaa had taught him this game, and it suppled his limbs as nothing else could. Sometimes Mowgli would stand lapped almost to his throat in Kaa's shifting coils, striving to get one arm free and catch him by the throat. Then Kaa would give way limply, and Mowgli, with both quick-moving feet, would try to cramp the purchase of that huge tail as it flung backward feeling for a rock or a stump. They would rock to and fro, head to head, each waiting for his chance, till the beautiful, statue-like group melted in a whirl of black-and-yellow coils and struggling legs and arms, to rise up again and again. 'Now! now! now!' said Kaa, making feints with his head that even Mowgli's quick hand could not turn aside. 'Look! I touch thee here, Little Brother! Here, and here! Are thy hands numb? Here again! '

The game always ended in one way—with a straight, driving blow of the head that knocked the boy over and over. Mowgli could never learn the guard for that lightning lunge, and, as Kaa said, there was not the least use in trying.

'Good hunting! ' Kaa grunted at last; and Mowgli, as usual, was shot away half a dozen yards, gasping and laughing. He rose with his fingers full of grass, and followed Kaa to the wise snake's pet bathing-place—a deep, pitchy-black pool surrounded with rocks, and made interesting by sunken tree-stumps. The boy slipped in, Jungle-fashion, without a sound, and dived across; rose, too, without a sound, and turned on his back, his arms behind his head, watching the moon rising above the rocks, and breaking up her reflection in the water with his toes. Kaa's diamond-shaped head cut the pool like a razor, and came out to rest on Mowgli's shoulder. They lay still, soaking luxuriously in the cool water.

'It is very good,' said Mowgli at last, sleepily. 'Now, in the Man-Pack, at this hour, as I remember, they laid them down upon hard pieces of wood in the inside of a mud-trap, and, having carefully shut out all the clean winds, drew foul cloth over their heavy heads, and made evil songs through their noses. It is better in the Jungle.'

A hurrying cobra slipped down over a rock and drank, gave them ' Good hunting! ' and went away.

'Sssh! ' said Kaa, as though he had suddenly remembered something. ' So the Jungle gives thee all that thou hast ever desired, Little Brother? '

'Not all,' said Mowgli, laughing; ' else there would be a new and strong Shere Khan to kill once a moon. Now, I could kill with my own hands, asking no help of buffaloes. And also I have wished the sun to shine in the middle of the Rains, and the Rains to cover the sun in the deep of

summer; and also I have never gone empty but I wished that I had killed a goat; and also I have never killed a goat but I wished it had been buck; nor buck but I wished it had been nilghai. But thus do we feel, all of us.'

'Thou hast no other desire?' the big snake demanded.

'What more can I wish? I have the Jungle, and the Favour of the Jungle! Is there more between sunrise and sunset?'

'Now, the Cobra said—— ' Kaa began.

'What cobra? He that went away just now said nothing. He was hunting.'

'It was another.'

'Hast thou many dealings with the Poison People? I give them their own path. They carry death in the fore-tooth, and that is not good—for they are so small. But what hood is this thou hast spoken with?'

Kaa rolled slowly in the water like a steamer in a beam sea. 'Three or four moons since,' said he, 'I hunted in Cold Lairs, which place, may be, thou hast not forgotten. And the thing I hunted fled shrieking past the tanks and to that house whose side I once broke for thy sake, and ran into the ground.'

'But the people of Cold Lairs do not live in burrows.' Mowgli knew that Kaa was talking of the Monkey People.

'This thing was not living, but seeking to live,' Kaa replied, with a quiver of his tongue. 'He ran into a burrow that led very far. I followed, and having killed, I slept. When I waked I went forward.'

'Under earth?'

'Even so. Coming at last upon a White Hood [a white cobra], who spoke of things beyond my knowledge, and showed me many things I had never before seen.'

'New game? Was it good hunting?' Mowgli turned quickly on his side.

'It was no game, and would have broken all my teeth; but the White Hood said that a man—he spoke as one that knew the breed—that a man would give the hot breath under his ribs for only the sight of those things.'

'We will look,' said Mowgli. 'I now remember that I was once a man.'

'Slowly—slowly. It was haste killed the Yellow Snake that ate the sun. We two spoke together under the earth, and I spoke of thee, naming thee as a man. Said the White Hood (and he is indeed as old as the Jungle): "It is long since I have seen a man. Let him come, and he shall see all these things, for the least of which very many men would die."'

'That *must* be new game. And yet the Poison People do not tell us when game is afoot. They are unfriendly folk.'

'It is *not* game. It is—it is—I cannot say what it is.'

'We will go there. I have never seen a White Hood, and I wish to see the other things. Did he kill them?'

'They are all dead things. He says he is the keeper of them all.'

'Ah! As a wolf stands above meat he has taken to his own lair. Let us go.'

Mowgli swam to bank, rolled in the grass to dry himself, and the two set off for Cold Lairs, the deserted city of which you may have heard. Mowgli was not in the least afraid of the Monkey People in those days, but the Monkey People had the liveliest horror of Mowgli. Their tribes, however, were raiding in the Jungle, and so Cold Lairs stood empty and silent in the moonlight. Kaa led up to the ruins of the queen's pavilion that stood on the terrace, slipped over the rubbish, and dived down the half-choked staircase that went underground from the centre of the pavilion. Mowgli gave the Snake-call—'We be of one blood, ye and I,'—and followed on his hands and knees. They crawled a long distance down a sloping passage that turned and twisted several times, and at last came to where the root of some great tree, growing thirty feet overhead, had forced out a solid stone in the wall. They crept through the gap, and found themselves in a large vault, whose domed roof had been also broken away by tree-roots so that a few streaks of light dropped down into the darkness.

'A safe lair,' said Mowgli, rising to his firm feet, 'but over-far to visit daily. And now what do we see?'

'Am I nothing?' said a voice in the middle of the vault; and Mowgli saw something white move, till, little by little, there stood up the hugest cobra he had ever set eyes on—a creature nearly eight feet long, and bleached by being in darkness to an old ivory-white. Even the spectacle marks of his spread hood had faded to a faint yellow. His eyes were as red as rubies, and altogether he was most wonderful to see.

'Good hunting!' said Mowgli, who carried his manners with his knife, and that never left him.

'What of the city?' said the White Cobra, without answering the greeting. 'What of the great, the walled city—the city of an hundred elephants and twenty thousand horses, and cattle past counting—the city of the King of Twenty Kings? I grow deaf here, and it is long since I heard the war-gongs.'

'The Jungle is above our heads,' said Mowgli. 'I know only Hathi and his sons among elephants. Bagheera has slain all the horses in one village, and—what is a King?'

'I told thee,' said Kaa softly to the Cobra,—'I told thee, four moons ago, that thy city was not.'

'The city—the great city of the forest whose gates are guarded by the King's towers—can never pass. They built it before my father's father came from the egg, and it shall endure when my sons' sons are as white as I. Salomdhi, son of Chandrabija, son of Viyeja, son of Yegasuri, built it in the days of Bappa Rawal. Whose cattle are ye?'

'It is a lost trail,' said Mowgli, turning to Kaa. 'I know not his talk.'

'Nor I. He is very old. Father of Cobras, there is only the Jungle here, as it has been since the beginning.'

'Then who is he,' said the White Cobra, 'sitting down before me, unafraid, knowing not the name of the King, talking our talk through a

man's lips? Who is he with the knife and the snake's tongue? '

'Mowgli they call me,' was the answer. 'I am of the Jungle. The Wolves are my people, and Kaa here is my brother. Father of Cobras, who art thou? '

'I am the Warden of the King's Treasure. Kurrun Raja built the stone above me, in the days when my skin was dark, that I might teach death to those who came to steal. Then they let down the treasure through the stone, and I heard the song of the Brahmins my masters.'

'Umm! ' said Mowgli to himself. 'I have dealt with one Brahmin already, in the Man-Pack, and—I know what I know. Evil comes here in a little.'

'Five times since my wardship has the stone been lifted, but always to let down more, and never to take away. There are no riches like these riches—the treasures of an hundred kings. But it is long and long since the stone was last moved, and I think that my city has forgotten.'

'There is no city. Look up. Yonder are the roots of the great trees tearing the stones apart. Trees and men do not grow together,' Kaa insisted.

'Twice and thrice have men found their way here,' the White Cobra answered savagely; 'but they never spoke till I came upon them groping in the dark, and then they cried only a little time. But ye come with lies, Man and Snake both, and would have me believe that my city is not, and that my wardship ends. Little do men change in the years. But I change never! Till the stone is lifted, and the Brahmins come down singing the songs that I know, and feed me with warm milk, and take me to the light again, I—I—I, and no other, am the Warden of the King's Treasure! The city is dead, ye say, and here are the roots of the trees? Stoop down, then, and take what ye will. Earth has no treasure like these. Man with the snake's tongue, if thou canst go alive by the way that thou hast entered at, the lesser kings will be thy servants! '

'Again the trail is lost,' said Mowgli, coolly. 'Can any jackal have burrowed so deep and bitten this great White Hood? He is surely mad. Father of Cobras, I see nothing here to take away.'

'By the Gods of the Sun and Moon, it is the madness of death upon the boy! ' hissed the cobra. 'Before thine eyes close I will allow thee this favour. Look thou, and see what man has never seen before! '

'They do not well in the Jungle who speak to Mowgli of favours,' said the boy, between his teeth; 'but the dark changes all, as I know. I will look, if that please thee.'

He stared with puckered-up eyes round the vault, and then lifted up from the floor a handful of something that glittered.

'Oho! ' said he, 'this is like the stuff they play with in the Man-Pack: only this is yellow and the other was brown.'

He let the gold pieces fall, and moved forward. The floor of the vault was buried some five or six feet deep in coined gold and silver that had burst from the sacks it had been originally stored in, and, in the long years,

the metal had packed and settled as sand packs at low tide. On it and in it, and rising through it, as wrecks lift through the sand, were jewelled elephant-howdahs of embossed silver, studded with plates of hammered gold, and adorned with carbuncles and turquoises. There were palanquins and litters for carrying queens, framed and braced with silver and enamel, with jade-handled poles and amber curtain-rings; there were golden candlesticks hung with pierced emeralds that quivered on the branches; there were studded images, five feet high, of forgotten gods, silver with jewelled eyes; there were coats of mail, gold inlaid on steel, and fringed with rotted and blackened seed-pearls; there were helmets, crested and beaded with pigeon's-blood rubies; there were shields of lacquer, of tortoise-shell and rhinoceros-hide, strapped and bossed with red gold and set with emeralds at the edge; there were sheaves of diamond-hilted swords, daggers, and hunting-knives; there were golden sacrificial bowls and ladles, and portable altars of a shape that never sees the light of day; there were jade cups and bracelets; there were incense-burners, combs, and pots for perfume, henna, and eye-powder, all in embossed gold; there were nose-rings, armlets, headbands, finger-rings, and girdles past any counting; there were belts seven fingers broad, of square-cut diamonds and rubies, and wooden boxes, trebly clamped with iron, from which the wood had fallen away in powder, showing the pile of uncut star-sapphires, opals, cat's-eyes, sapphires, rubies, diamonds, emeralds, and garnets within.

The White Cobra was right. No mere money would begin to pay the value of this treasure, the sifted pickings of centuries of war, plunder, trade, and taxation. The coins alone were priceless, leaving out of count all the precious stones; and the dead weight of the gold and silver alone might be two or three hundred tons. Every native ruler in India to-day, however poor, has a hoard to which he is always adding; and, though once in a long while, some enlightened prince may send off forty or fifty bullock-cart loads of silver to be exchanged for Government securities, the bulk of them keep their treasure and the knowledge of it very closely to themselves.

But Mowgli naturally did not understand what these things meant. The knives interested him a little, but they did not balance as well as his own, and so he dropped them. At last he found something really fascinating laid on the front of a howdah half buried in the coins. It was a two-foot ankus, or elephant-goad—something like a small boat-hook. The top was one round shining ruby, and eight inches of the handle below it were studded with rough turquoises close together, giving a most satisfactory grip. Below them was a rim of jade with a flower-pattern running round it—only the leaves were emeralds, and the blossoms were rubies sunk in the cool, green stone. The rest of the handle was a shaft of pure ivory, while the point— the spike and hook—was gold-inlaid steel with pictures of elephant-catching: and the pictures attracted Mowgli, who saw that they had something to do with his friend Hathi.

The White Cobra had been following him closely.

'Is it not worth dying to behold?' he said. 'Have I not done thee a great favour?'

'I do not understand,' said Mowgli. 'The things are hard and cold, and by no means good to eat. But this'—he lifted the ankus—'I desire to take away, that I may see it in the sun. Thou sayest they are all thine. Wilt thou give it to me, and I will bring thee frogs to eat?'

The White Cobra fairly shook with evil delight. 'Assuredly I will give it,' he said. 'All that is here I will give thee—till thou goest away.'

'But I go now. This place is dark and cold, and I wish to take the thorn-pointed thing to the Jungle.'

'Look by thy foot! What is that there?'

Mowgli picked up something white and smooth. 'It is the bone of a man's head,' he said quietly. 'And here are two more.'

'They came to take the treasure away many years ago. I spoke to them in the dark, and they lay still.'

'But what do I need of this that is called treasure? If thou wilt give me the ankus to take away, it is good hunting. If not, it is good hunting none the less. I do not fight with the Poison People, and I was also taught the Master-word of thy tribe.'

'There is but one Master-word here. It is mine!'

Kaa flung himself forward with blazing eyes. 'Who bade me bring the Man?' he hissed.

'I surely,' the old Cobra lisped. 'It is long since I have seen Man, and this Man speaks our tongue.'

'But there was no talk of killing. How can I go to the Jungle and say that I have led him to his death?' said Kaa.

'I talk not of killing till the time. And as to thy going or not going, there is a hole in the wall. Peace, now, thou fat monkey-killer! I have but to touch thy neck, and the Jungle will know thee no longer. Never Man came here that went away with the breath under his ribs. I am the Warden of the Treasure of the King's City!'

'But, thou white worm of the dark, I tell thee there is neither king nor city! The Jungle is all about us!' cried Kaa.

'There is still the Treasure. But this can be done. Wait a while, Kaa of the Rocks, and see the boy run. There is room for great sport here. Life is good. Run to and fro a while, and make sport, boy!'

Mowgli put his hand on Kaa's head quietly.

'The white thing has dealt with men of the Man-Pack until now. He does not know me,' he whispered. 'He has asked for this hunting. Let him have it.' Mowgli had been standing with the ankus held point down. He flung it from him quickly, and it dropped crossways just behind the great snake's hood, pinning him to the floor. In a flash, Kaa's weight was upon the writhing body, paralysing it from hood to tail. The red eyes burned, and the six spare inches of the head struck furiously right and left.

'Kill!' said Kaa, as Mowgli's hand went to his knife.

' No,' he said, as he drew the blade; ' I will never kill again save for food. But look you, Kaa! ' He caught the snake behind the hood, forced the mouth open with the blade of the knife, and showed the terrible poison-fangs of the upper jaw lying black and withered in the gum. The White Cobra had outlived his poison, as a snake will.

' *Thuu* ' ('It is dried up '),[1] said Mowgli; and motioning Kaa away, he picked up the ankus, setting the White Cobra free.

' The King's Treasure needs a new Warden,' he said gravely. ' Thuu, thou hast not done well. Run to and fro and make sport, Thuu! '

' I am shamed. Kill me! ' hissed the White Cobra.

' There has been too much talk of killing. We will go now. I take the thorn-pointed thing, Thuu, because I have fought and worsted thee.'

' See, then, that the thing does not kill thee at last. It is Death! Remember, it is Death! There is enough in that thing to kill the men of all my city. Not long wilt thou hold it, Jungle Man, nor he who takes it from thee. They will kill, and kill, and kill for its sake! My strength is dried up, but the ankus will do my work. It is Death! It is Death! It is Death! '

Mowgli crawled out through the hole into the passage again, and the last that he saw was the White Cobra striking furiously with his harmless fangs at the stolid golden faces of the gods that lay on the floor, and hissing, ' It is Death! '

They were glad to get to the light of day once more; and when they were back in their own Jungle and Mowgli made the ankus glitter in the morning light, he was almost as pleased as though he had found a bunch of new flowers to stick in his hair.

' This is brighter than Bagheera's eyes,' he said delightedly, as he twirled the ruby. ' I will show it to him; but what did the Thuu mean when he talked of death? '

' I cannot say. I am sorrowful to my tail's tail that he felt not thy knife. There is always evil at Cold Lairs—above ground and below. But now I am hungry. Dost thou hunt with me this dawn? ' said Kaa.

' No; Bagheera must see this thing. Good hunting! ' Mowgli danced off, flourishing the great ankus, and stopping from time to time to admire it, till he came to that part of the Jungle Bagheera chiefly used, and found him drinking after a heavy kill. Mowgli told him all his adventures from beginning to end, and Bagheera sniffed at the ankus between whiles. When Mowgli came to the White Cobra's last words, Bagheera purred approvingly.

' Then the White Hood spoke the thing which is? ' Mowgli asked quickly.

' I was born in the King's cages at Oodeypore, and it is in my stomach that I know some little of Man. Very many men would kill thrice in a night for the sake of that one red stone alone.'

[1] Literally, a rotted out tree-stump.

'But the stone makes it heavy to the hand. My little bright knife is better; and—see! the red stone is not good to eat. Then *why* would they kill? '

'Mowgli, go thou and sleep. Thou hast lived among men, and—— '

'I remember. Men kill because they are not hunting;—for idleness and pleasure. Wake again, Bagheera. For what use was this thorn-pointed thing made? '

Bagheera half opened his eyes—he was very sleepy—with a malicious twinkle.

'It was made by men to thrust into the head of the Sons of Hathi, so that the blood should pour out. I have seen the like in the streets of Oodeypore, before our cages. That thing has tasted the blood of many such as Hathi.'

'But why do they thrust into the heads of elephants? '

'To teach them Man's Law. Having neither claws nor teeth, men make these things—and worse.'

'Always more blood when I come near, even to the things the Man-Pack have made! ' said Mowgli, disgustedly. He was a little tired of the weight of the ankus. 'If I had known this, I would not have taken it. First it was Messua's blood on the thongs, and now it is Hathi's. I will use it no more. Look! '

The ankus flew sparkling, and buried itself point down fifty yards away, between the trees. 'So my hands are clean of Death,' said Mowgli, rubbing his hands on the fresh, moist earth. 'The Thuu said Death would follow me. He is old and white and mad.'

'White or black, or death or life, *I* am going to sleep, Little Brother. I cannot hunt all night and howl all day, as do some folk.'

Bagheera went off to a hunting-lair that he knew, about two miles off. Mowgli made an easy way for himself up a convenient tree, knotted three or four creepers together, and in less time than it takes to tell was swinging in a hammock fifty feet above the ground. Though he had no positive objection to strong daylight, Mowgli followed the custom of his friends, and used it as little as he could. When he waked among the very loud-voiced peoples that live in the trees, it was twilight once more, and he had been dreaming of the beautiful pebbles he had thrown away.

'At least I will look at the thing again,' he said, and slid down a creeper to the earth; but Bagheera was before him. Mowgli could hear him snuffing in the half light.

'Where is the thorn-pointed thing? ' cried Mowgli.

'A man has taken it. Here is his trail.'

'Now we shall see whether the Thuu spoke truth. If the pointed thing is Death, that man will die. Let us follow.'

'Kill first,' said Bagheera. 'An empty stomach makes a careless eye. Men go very slowly, and the Jungle is wet enough to hold the lightest mark.'

They killed as soon as they could, but it was nearly three hours before

they finished their meat and drink and buckled down to the trail. The Jungle People know that nothing makes up for being hurried over your meals.

'Think you the pointed thing will turn in the man's hand and kill him?' Mowgli asked. 'The Thuu said it was Death.'

'We shall see when we find,' said Bagheera, trotting with his head low. 'It is single-foot' (he meant that there was only one man), 'and the weight of the thing has pressed his heel far into the ground.'

'Hai! This is as clear as summer lightning,' Mowgli answered; and they fell into the quick, choppy trail-trot in and out through the checkers of the moonlight, following the marks of those two bare feet.

'Now he runs swiftly,' said Mowgli. 'The toes are spread apart.' They went on over some wet ground. 'Now why does he turn aside here?'

'Wait!' said Bagheera, and flung himself forward with one superb bound as far as ever he could. The first thing to do when a trail ceases to explain itself is to cast forward without leaving your own confusing foot-marks on the ground. Bagheera turned as he landed, and faced Mowgli, crying, 'Here comes another trail to meet him. It is a smaller foot, this second trail, and the toes turn inward.'

Then Mowgli ran up and looked. 'It is the foot of a Gond hunter,' he said. 'Look! Here he dragged his bow on the grass. That is why the first trail turned aside so quickly. Big Foot hid from Little Foot.'

'That is true,' said Bagheera. 'Now, lest by crossing each other's tracks we foul the signs, let each take one trail. I am Big Foot, Little Brother, and thou art Little Foot, the Gond.'

Bagheera leaped back to the original trail, leaving Mowgli stooping above the curious in-toed track of the wild little man of the woods.

'Now,' said Bagheera, moving step by step along the chain of footprints, 'I, Big Foot, turn aside here. Now I hide me behind a rock and stand still, not daring to shift my feet. Cry thy trail, Little Brother.'

'Now, I, Little Foot, come to the rock,' said Mowgli, running up his trail. 'Now sit I down under the rock, leaning upon my right hand, and resting my bow between my toes. I wait long, for the mark of my feet is deep here.'

'I also,' said Bagheera, hidden behind the rock. 'I wait, resting the end of the thorn-pointed thing upon a stone. It slips, for here is a scratch upon the stone. Cry thy trail, Little Brother.'

'One, two twigs and a big branch are broken here,' said Mowgli, in an undertone. 'Now, how shall I cry that? Ah! It is plain now. I, Little Foot, go away making noises and tramplings so that Big Foot may hear me.' He moved away from the rock pace by pace among the trees, his voice rising in the distance as he approached a little cascade. 'I—go—far—away—to—where—the—noise—of—falling—water—covers—my—noise; and—here—I—wait. Cry thy trail, Bagheera, Big Foot!'

The panther had been casting in every direction to see how Big Foot's trail led away from behind the rock. Then he gave tongue.

'I come from behind the rock upon my knees, dragging the thorn-pointed thing. Seeing no one, I run. I, Big Foot, run swiftly. The trail is clear. Let each follow his own. I run!'

Bagheera swept on along the clearly-marked trail, and Mowgli followed the steps of the Gond. For a time there was silence in the Jungle.

'Where art thou, Little Foot?' cried Bagheera. Mowgli's voice answered him not fifty yards to the right.

'Um!' said the Panther, with a deep cough. 'The two run side by side, drawing nearer!'

They raced on another half mile, always keeping about the same distance, till Mowgli, whose head was not so close to the ground as Bagheera's, cried: 'They have met. Good hunting—look! Here stood Little Foot, with his knee on a rock—and yonder is Big Foot.'

Not ten yards in front of them, stretched across a pile of broken rocks, lay the body of a villager of the district, a lean, small-feathered Gond arrow through his back and breast.

'Was the Thuu so old and so mad, Little Brother?' said Bagheera, gently. 'Here is one death, at least.'

'Follow on. But where is the drinker of elephant's blood—the red-eyed thorn?'

'Little Foot has it—perhaps. It is single-foot again now.'

The single trail of a light man who had been running quickly and bearing a burden on his left shoulder, held on round a long, low spur of dried grass, where each footfall seemed to the sharp eyes of the trackers marked in hot iron.

Neither spoke till the trail ran up to the ashes of a camp-fire hidden in a ravine.

'Again!' said Bagheera, checking as though he had been turned into stone.

The body of a little wizened Gond lay with its feet in the ashes, and Bagheera looked inquiringly at Mowgli.

'That was done with a bamboo,' said the boy, after one glance. 'I have used such a thing among the buffaloes when I served the Man-Pack. The Father of Cobras—I am sorrowful that I made a jest of him—knew the breed well, as I might have known. Said I not that men kill for idleness?'

'Indeed, they killed for the sake of red and blue stones,' Bagheera answered. 'Remember, I was in the King's cages at Oodeypore.'

'One, two, three, four tracks,' said Mowgli, stooping over the ashes. 'Four tracks of men with shod feet. They do not go so quickly as Gonds. Now, what evil had the little woodman done to them? See, they talked together, all five, standing up, before they killed him. Bagheera, let us go back. My stomach is heavy in me, and yet it dances up and down like an oriole's nest at the end of a branch.'

'It is no good hunting to leave game afoot. Follow!' said the panther. 'Those eight shod feet have not gone far.'

No more was said for fully an hour, as they took up the broad trail of the four men with shod feet.

It was clear, hot daylight now, and Bagheera said, ' I smell smoke.'

' Men are always more ready to eat than to run,' Mowgli answered, trotting in and out between the low scrub bushes of the new Jungle they were exploring. Bagheera, a little to his left, made an indescribable noise in his throat.

' Here is one that is done with feeding,' said he. A tumbled bundle of gay-coloured clothes lay under a bush, and round it was some spilt flour.

' That was done by the bamboo again,' said Mowgli. ' See! That white dust is what men eat. They have taken the kill from this one,—he carried their food,—and given him for a kill to Chil, the Kite.'

' It is the third,' said Bagheera.

' I will go with new, big frogs to the Father of Cobras, and feed him fat,' said Mowgli to himself. ' This drinker of elephant's blood is Death himself—but still I do not understand! '

' Follow! ' said Bagheera.

They had not gone half a mile farther when they heard Ko, the Crow, singing a death-song in the top of a tamarisk under whose shade three men were lying. A half-dead fire smoked in the centre of the circle, beneath an iron plate which held a blackened and burned cake of unleavened bread. Close to the fire, and blazing in the sunshine, lay the ruby-and-turquoise ankus.

THE SONG OF THE LITTLE HUNTER

Ere Mor the Peacock flutters, ere the Monkey-People cry,
 Ere Chil the Kite swoops down a furlong sheer,
Through the Jungle very softly flits a shadow and a sigh—
 He is Fear, O Little Hunter, he is Fear!
Very softly down the glade runs a waiting, watching shade,
 And the whisper spreads and widens far and near;
And the sweat is on thy brow, for he passes even now—
 He is Fear, O Little Hunter, he is Fear!

Ere the moon has climbed the mountain, ere the rocks are ribbed with light,
 When the downward-dipping tails are dank and drear,
Comes a breathing hard behind thee, *snuffle-snuffle* through the night—
 It is Fear, O Little Hunter, it is Fear!
On thy knees and draw the bow; bid the shrilling arrow go;
 In the empty mocking thicket plunge the spear;
But thy hands are loosed and weak, and the blood has left thy cheek—
 It is Fear, O Little Hunter, it is Fear!

When the heat-cloud sucks the tempest, when the slivered pine trees fall,
　　When the blinding, blaring rain-squalls lash and veer;
Through the trumpets of the thunder rings a voice more loud than all—
　　It is Fear, O Little Hunter, it is Fear!
Now the spates are banked and deep; now the footless boulders leap;
　　Now the lightning shows each littlest leaf-rib clear,
But thy throat is shut and dried, and thy heart against thy side
　　Hammers: Fear, O Little Hunter—this is Fear!

RED DOG

For our white and our excellent nights—for the nights of swift running,
 Fair ranging, far-seeing, good hunting, sure cunning!
For the smells of the dawning, untainted ere dew has departed!
For the rush through the mist, and the quarry blend-started!
For the cry of our mates when the *sambhur* has wheeled and is standing at
 bay,
 For the risk and the riot of night!
 For the sleep at the lair-mouth by day—
 It is met, and we go to the fight.
 Bay! O Bay!

IT WAS after the letting in of the Jungle that the pleasant part of Mowgli's life began. He had the good conscience that comes from paying a just debt; and all the Jungle was his friend, for all the Jungle was afraid of him. The things that he did and saw and heard when he was wandering from one people to another, with or without his four companions, would make many, many stories, each as long as this one. So you will never be told how he met and escaped from the Mad Elephant of Mandla, who killed two-and-twenty bullocks drawing eleven carts of coined silver to the Government Treasury, and scattered the shiny rupees in the dust; how he fought Jacala, the Crocodile, all one long night in the Marshes of the North, and broke his skinning knife on the brute's back-plates; how he found a new and longer knife round the neck of a man who had been killed by a wild boar, and how he tracked that boar and killed him as a fair price for the knife; how he was caught up in the Great Famine by the moving of the deer, and nearly crushed to death in the swaying hot herds; how he saved Hathi the Silent from being caught in a pit with a stake at the bottom, and how next day he himself fell into a very cunning leopard-trap, and how Hathi broke the thick wooden bars to pieces about him; how he milked the wild buffaloes in the swamp, and how——

But we must tell one tale at a time. Father and Mother Wolf died, and Mowgli rolled a big boulder against the mouth of the cave and cried the Death Song over them, and Baloo grew very old and stiff, and even Bagheera, whose nerves were steel and whose muscles were iron, seemed slower at the kill. Akela turned from gray to milky white with pure age; his ribs stuck out, and he walked as though he had been made of wood, and Mowgli killed for him. But the young wolves, the children of the disbanded Seeonee Pack, throve and increased, and when there were some forty of them, masterless, clean-footed five-year-olds, Akela told them that they ought to gather them-

selves together and follow the Law, and run under one head, as befitted the Free People.

This was not a matter in which Mowgli gave advice, for, as he said, he had eaten sour fruit, and he knew the tree it hung from; but when Phao, son of Phaona (his father was the Gray Tracker in the days of Akela's headship), fought his way to the leadership of the Pack according to the Jungle Law, and when the old calls and the old songs began to ring under the stars once more, Mowgli came to the Council Rock for memory's sake. If he chose to speak the Pack waited till he had finished, and he sat at Akela's side on the rock above Phao. Those were the days of good hunting and good sleeping. No stranger cared to break into the jungles that belonged to Mowgli's people, as they called the Pack, and the young wolves grew fat and strong, and there were many cubs to bring to the Looking-over. Mowgli always attended a Looking-over, for he remembered the night when a black panther brought a naked brown baby into the pack, and the long call, ' Look, look well, O Wolves,' made his heart flutter with strange feelings. Otherwise, he would be far away in the jungle; tasting, touching, seeing, and feeling new things.

One twilight when he was trotting leisurely across the ranges to give Akela the half of a buck that he had killed, while his four wolves were jogging behind him, sparring a little and tumbling one over another for joy of being alive, he heard a cry that he had not heard since the bad days of Shere Khan. It was what they call in the Jungle the *Pheeal*, a kind of shriek that the jackal gives when he is hunting behind a tiger, or when there is some big killing afoot. If you can imagine a mixture of hate, triumph, fear, and despair, with a kind of leer running through it, you will get some notion of the *Pheeal* that rose and sank and wavered and quivered far away across the Waingunga. The Four began to bristle and growl. Mowgli's hand went to his knife and he too checked as though he had been turned into stone.

' There is no Striped One would dare kill here,' he said, at last.

' That is not the cry of the Forerunner,' said Gray Brother. ' It is some great killing. Listen! '

It broke out again, half sobbing and half chuckling, just as though the jackal had soft human lips. Then Mowgli drew deep breath, and ran to the Council Rock, overtaking on his way hurrying wolves of the Pack. Phao and Akela were on the Rock together, and below them, every nerve strained, sat the others. The mothers and the cubs were cantering to their lairs; for when the *Pheeal* cries is no time for weak things to be abroad.

They could hear nothing except the Waingunga gurgling in the dark and the evening winds among the tree-tops, till suddenly across the river a wolf called. It was no wolf of the Pack, for those were all at the rock. The note changed to a long despairing bay; and ' Dhole! ' it said, ' Dhole! Dhole! Dhole! ' In a few minutes they heard tired feet on the rocks, and a gaunt, dripping wolf, streaked with red on his flanks, his right fore-paw useless, and his jaws white with foam, flung himself into the circle and lay gasping at Mowgli's feet.

'Good hunting? Under whose headship?' said Phao gravely.

'Good hunting! Won-tolla am I,' was the answer. He meant that he was a solitary wolf, fending for himself, his mate, and his cubs in some lonely lair. Won-tolla means an outlier—one who lies out from any pack. When he panted they could see his heart shake him backwards and forwards.

'What moves?' said Phao, for that is the question all the Jungle asks after the *Pheeal*.

'The dhole, the dhole of the Dekkan—Red Dog, the Killer! They came north from the south saying the Dekkan was empty and killing out by the way. When this moon was new there were four to me—my mate and three cubs. She would teach them to kill on the grass plains, hiding to drive the buck, as we do who are of the open. At midnight I heard them together full tongue on the trail. At the dawn-wind I found them stiff in the grass—four, Free People, four when this moon was new! Then sought I my Blood-Right and found the dhole.'

'How many?' said Mowgli; the Pack growled deep in their throats.

'I do not know. Three of them will kill no more, but at the last they drove me like the buck; on three legs they drove me. Look, Free People!'

He thrust out his mangled fore-foot, all dark with dried blood. There were cruel bites low down on his side, and his throat was torn and worried.

'Eat,' said Akela, rising up from the meat Mowgli had brought him; the outlier flung himself on it famishing.

'This shall be no loss,' he said humbly when he had taken off the edge of his hunger. 'Give me a little strength, Free People, and I also will kill! My lair is empty that was full when this moon was new, and the Blood Debt is not all paid.'

Phao heard his teeth crack on a haunch-bone and grunted approvingly.

'We shall need those jaws,' said he. 'Were their cubs with the dhole?'

'Nay, nay. Red hunters all: grown dogs of their pack, heavy and strong.'

That meant that the dhole, the red hunting-dog of the Dekkan, was moving to fight, and the wolves knew well that even the tiger will surrender a new kill to the dhole. They drive straight through the Jungle, and what they meet they pull down and tear to pieces. Though they are not as big nor half as cunning as the wolf, they are very strong and very numerous. The dhole, for instance, do not begin to call themselves a pack till they are a hundred strong, whereas forty wolves make a very fair pack. Mowgli's wanderings had taken him to the edge of the high grassy downs of the Dekkan, and he had often seen the fearless dholes sleeping and playing and scratching themselves among the little hollows and tussocks that they use for lairs. He despised and hated them because they did not smell like the Free People, because they did not live in caves, and above all, because they had hair between their toes while he and his friends were clean-footed. But he knew, for Hathi had told him, what a terrible thing a dhole hunting-pack was. Hathi himself moves aside from their line, and until they are all killed, or till

game is scarce, they go forward killing as they go.

Akela knew something of the dholes, too; he said to Mowgli quietly: ' It is better to die in the Full Pack than leaderless and alone. It is good hunting, and—my last. But, as men live, thou hast very many more nights and days, Little Brother. Go north and lie down, and if any wolf live after the dhole has gone by he shall bring thee word of the fight.'

' Ah,' said Mowgli, quite gravely, ' must I go to the marshes and catch little fish and sleep in a tree, or must I ask help of the *bandar-log* and eat nuts while the pack fights below? '

' It is to the death,' said Akela. ' Thou hast never met the dhole—the Red Killer. Even the Striped One— '

' Aowa! Aowa! ' said Mowgli pettingly. ' I have killed one striped ape. Listen now: There was a wolf, my father, and there was a wolf, my mother, and there was an old gray wolf (not too wise: he is white now) was my father and my mother. Therefore I— ' he raised his voice, ' I say that when the dhole come, and if the dhole come, Mowgli and the Free People are of one skin for that hunting; and I say, by the Bull that bought me, by the bull Bagheera paid for me in the old days which ye of the Pack do not remember, I say, that the Trees and the River may hear and hold fast if I forget; I say that this my knife shall be as a tooth to the Pack—and I do not think it is so blunt. This is my Word which has gone from me.'

' Thou dost not know the dhole, man with a wolf's tongue,' Won-tolla cried. ' I look only to clear my Blood Debt against them ere they have me in many pieces. They move slowly, killing out as they go, but in two days a little strength will come back to me and I turn again for my Blood Debt. But for *ye*, Free People, my counsel is that ye go north and eat but little for a while till the dhole are gone. There is no sleep in this hunting.'

' Here the Outlier! ' said Mowgli with a laugh. ' Free People, we must go north and eat lizards and rats from the bank, lest by any chance we meet the dhole. He must kill out our hunting grounds while we lie hid in the north till it please him to give us our own again. He is a dog—and the pup of a dog —red, yellow-bellied, lairless, and haired between every toe! He counts his cubs six and eight at the litter, as though he were Chikai, the little leaping rat. Surely we must run away, Free People, and beg leave of the peoples of the north for the offal of dead cattle! Ye know the saying: North are the vermin; South are the lice. *We* are the Jungle. Choose ye, O choose. It is good hunting! For the Pack—for the Full Pack—for the lair and the litter; for the in-kill and the out-kill; for the mate that drives the doe and the little, little cub within the cave, it is met—it is met—it is met! '

The Pack answered with one deep crashing bark that sounded in the night like a tree falling. ' It is met,' they cried.

' Stay with these,' said Mowgli to his Four. ' We shall need every tooth. Phao and Akela must make ready the battle. I go to count the dogs.'

' It is death! ' Won-tolla cried, half rising. ' What can such an hairless one do against the Red Dog? Even the Striped One, remember—— '

'Thou art indeed an outlier,' Mowgli called back, ' but we will speak when the dholes are dead. Good hunting all! '

He hurried off into the darkness wild with excitement, hardly looking where he set foot, and the natural consequence was that he tripped full length over Kaa's great coils where the python lay watching a deer-path near the river.

'Kssha! ' said Kaa angrily. ' Is this jungle work to stamp and ramp and undo a night's hunting—when the game are moving so well, too? '

'The fault was mine,' said Mowgli, picking himself up. ' Indeed I was seeking thee, Flathead, but each time we meet thou art longer and broader by the length of my arm. There is none like thee in the Jungle, wise, old, strong, and most beautiful Kaa.'

'Now whither does *this* trail lead? ' Kaa's voice was gentler. ' Not a moon since there was a Manling with a knife threw stones at my head and called me bad little tree-cat names because I lay asleep in the open.'

'Ay, and turned every driven deer to all the winds, and Mowgli was hunting, and this same Flathead was too deaf to hear his whistle and leave the deer-roads free,' Mowgli answered composedly, sitting down among the painted coils.

'Now this same Manling comes with soft, tickling words to this same Flathead, telling him that he is wise, and strong, and beautiful, and this same old Flathead believes and coils a place, thus, for this same stone-throwing Manling and . . . Art thou at ease now? Could Bagheera give thee so good a resting-place? '

Kaa had, as usual, made a sort of soft half-hammock of himself under Mowgli's weight. The boy reached out in the darkness and gathered in the supple cable-like neck till Kaa's head rested on his shoulder, and then he told him all that had happened in the jungle that night.

'Wise I may be,' said Kaa at the end, ' but deaf I surely am. Else I should have heard the *Pheeal*. Small wonder the eaters-of-grass are uneasy. How many be the dhole? '

'I have not seen yet. I came hot foot to thee. Thou art older than Hathi. But, oh, Kaa,'—here Mowgli wriggled with joy, ' it will be good hunting! Few of us will see another moon.'

'Dost *thou* strike in this? Remember thou art a man; and remember what pack cast thee out. Let the wolf look to the dog. *Thou* art a man.'

'Last year's nuts are this year's black earth,' said Mowgli. ' It is true that I am a man, but it is in my stomach that this night I have said that I am a wolf. I called the River and the Trees to remember. I am of the Free People, Kaa, till the dhole has gone by.'

'Free People,' Kaa grunted. ' Free thieves! And thou hast tied thyself into the Death-knot for the sake of the memory of dead wolves! This is no good hunting.'

'It is my Word which I have spoken. The Trees know, the River knows. Till the dhole have gone by my Word comes not back to me.'

'Ngssh! That changes all trails. I had thought to take thee away with me to the northern marshes, but the Word—even the Word of a little, naked, hairless Manling—is the Word. Now I, Kaa, say——'

'Think well, Flathead, lest thou tie thyself into the Death-knot also. I need no word from thee, for well I know—— '

'Be it so, then,' said Kaa. 'I will give no Word; but what is in thy stomach to do when the dhole come? '

'They must swim the Waingunga. I thought to meet them with my knife in the shallows, the Pack behind me; and so stabbing and thrusting we might turn them down stream, or cool their throats a little.'

'The dhole do not turn and their throats are hot,' said Kaa. 'There will be neither Manling nor wolf-cub when that hunting is done, but only dry bones.'

'Alala! If we die we die. It will be most good hunting. But my stomach is young, and I have not seen many Rains. I am not wise nor strong. Hast thou a better plan, Kaa? '

'I have seen a hundred and a hundred Rains. Ere Hathi cast his milk-tushes my trail was big in the dust. By the First Egg I am older than many trees, and I have seen all that the Jungle has done.'

'But *this* is new hunting,' said Mowgli. 'Never before has the dhole crossed our trail.'

'What is has been. What will be is no more than a forgotten year striking backwards. Be still while I count those my years.'

For a long hour Mowgli lay back among the coils, playing with his knife, while Kaa, his head motionless on the ground, thought of all that he had seen and known since the day he came from the egg. The light seemed to go out of his eyes and leave them like stale opals, and now and again he made little stiff passes with his head to right and left, as though he were hunting in his sleep. Mowgli dozed quietly, for he knew that there is nothing like sleep before hunting, and he was trained to take it at any hour of the day or night.

Then he felt Kaa grow bigger and broader below him as the huge python puffed himself out, hissing with the noise of a sword drawn from a steel scabbard.

'I have seen all the dead seasons,' Kaa said at last, 'and the great trees and the old elephants and the rocks that were bare and sharp-pointed ere the moss grew. Art *thou* still alive, Manling? '

'It is only a little after moonrise,' said Mowgli. 'I do not understand—— '

'Hssh! I am again Kaa. I knew it was but a little time. Now we will go to the river, and I will show thee what is to be done against the dhole.'

He turned, straight as an arrow, for the main stream of the Waingunga, plunging in a little above the pool that hid the Peace Rock, Mowgli at his side.

'Nay, do not swim. I go swiftly. My back, Little Brother.'

Mowgli tucked his left arm round Kaa's neck, dropped his right close to his body and straightened his feet. Then Kaa breasted the current as he alone could, and the ripple of the checked water stood up in a frill round Mowgli's neck and his feet were waved to and fro in the eddy under the python's lashing sides. A mile or so above the Peace Rock the Waingunga narrows between a gorge of marble rocks from eighty to a hundred feet high, and the current runs like a mill-race between and over all manner of ugly stones. But Mowgli did not trouble his head about the water: no water in the world could have given him a moment's fear. He was looking at the gorge on either side and sniffing uneasily, for there was a sweetish-sourish smell in the air, very like the smell of a big ant-hill on a hot day. Instinctively he lowered himself in the water, only raising his head to breathe, and Kaa came to anchor with a double twist of his tail round a sunken rock, holding Mowgli in the hollow of a coil, while the water raced by.

' This is the Place of Death,' said the boy. ' Why do we come here? '

' They sleep,' said Kaa. ' Hathi will not turn aside for the Striped One. Yet Hathi and the Striped One together turn aside for the dhole, and the dhole they say turns aside for nothing. And yet for whom do the Little People of the Rocks turn aside? Tell me, Master of the Jungle, who is the Master of the Jungle? '

' These,' Mowgli whispered. ' It is the Place of Death. Let us go.'

' Nay, look well, for they are asleep. It is as it was when I was not the length of thy arm.'

The split and weatherworn rocks of the gorge of the Waingunga had been used since the beginning of the Jungle by the Little People of the Rocks —the busy, furious, black, wild bees of India; and, as Mowgli knew well, all trails turned off half a mile away from their country. For centuries the Little People had hived and swarmed from cleft to cleft and swarmed again, staining the white marble with stale honey, and made their combs tall and deep and black in the dark of the inner caves, and neither man nor beast nor fire nor water had ever touched them. The length of the gorge on both sides was hung as it were with black shimmery velvet curtains, and Mowgli sank as he looked, for those were the clotted millions of the sleeping bees. There were other lumps and festoons and things like decayed tree-trunks studded on the face of the rock—the old combs of past years, or new cities built in the shadow of the windless gorge—and huge masses of spongy, rotten trash had rolled down and stuck among the trees and creepers that clung to the rock-face. As he listened he heard more than once the rustle and slide of a honey-loaded comb turning over or falling away somewhere in the dark galleries; then a booming of angry wings and the sullen drip, drip, drip, of the wasted honey, guttering along till it lipped over some ledge in the open and sluggishly trickled down on the twigs. There was a tiny little beach, not five feet broad, on one side of the river, that was piled high with the rubbish of uncounted years. There lay dead bees, drones, sweepings, stale combs, and wings of marauding moths and beetles that had strayed in after honey, all tumbled

in smooth piles of the finest black dust. The mere sharp smell of it was enough to frighten anything that had no wings, and knew what the Little People were.

Kaa moved up stream again till he came to a sandy bar at the head of the gorge.

'Here is this season's kill,' said he. 'Look!'

On the bank lay the skeletons of a couple of young deer and a buffalo. Mowgli could see that no wolf nor jackal had touched the bones, which were laid out naturally.

'They came beyond the line, they did not know,' murmured Mowgli, 'and the Little People killed them. Let us go ere they awake.'

'They do not wake till the dawn,' said Kaa. 'Now I will tell thee. A hunted buck from the south, many, many Rains ago, came hither from the south, not knowing the Jungle, a pack on his trail. Being made blind by fear he leaped from above, the pack running by sight, for they were hot and blind on the trail. The sun was high, and the Little People were many and very angry. Many, too, were those of the pack who leaped into the Waingunga, but they were dead ere they took water. Those who did not leap died also in the rocks above. But the buck lived.'

'How?'

'Because he came first, running for his life, leaping ere the Little People were aware, and was in the river when they gathered to kill. The pack, following, was altogether lost under the weight of the Little People, who had been roused by the feet of that buck.'

'The buck lived?' Mowgli repeated slowly.

'At least he did not die *then*, though none waited his coming down with a strong body to hold him safe against the water, as a certain old fat, deaf, yellow Flathead would wait for a Manling—yea, though there were all the dholes of the Dekkan on his trail. What is in thy stomach?'

Kaa's head lay on Mowgli's wet shoulder, and his tongue quivered by the boy's ear. There was a long silence before Mowgli whispered:—

'It is to pull the very whiskers of Death, but—Kaa, thou art, indeed, the wisest of all the Jungle.'

'So many have said. Look now, if the dholes follow thee——'

'As surely they will follow. Ho! ho! I have many little thorns under my tongue to prick into their hides.'

'If they follow thee hot and blind, looking only at thy shoulders, those who do not die up above will take water either here or lower down, for the Little People will rise up and cover them. Now the Waingunga is hungry water, and they will have no Kaa to hold them, but will go down, such as live, to the shallows by the Seeonee lairs, and there thy Pack may meet them by the throat.'

'Ahai! Eowawa! Better could not be till the Rains fall in the dry season. There is now only the little matter of the run and the leap. I will make me known to the dholes, so that they shall follow me very closely.'

' Hast thou seen the rocks above thee? From the landward side? '

' Indeed no. That I had forgotten.'

' Go look. It is all rotten ground, cut and full of holes. One of thy clumsy feet set down without seeing would end the hunt. See, I leave thee here, and for thy sake only I will carry word to the Pack that they may know where to look for the dhole. For myself, I am not of one skin with *any* wolf.'

When Kaa disliked an acquaintance he could be more unpleasant than any of the Jungle people, except perhaps Bagheera. He swam down stream, and opposite the Rock he came on Phao and Akela listening to the night noises.

' Hssh! dogs,' he said cheerfully. ' The dhole will come down stream. If ye be not afraid ye can kill them in the shallows.'

' When come they? ' said Phao. ' And where is my Man-cub? ' said Akela.

' They come when they come,' said Kaa. ' Wait and see. As for *thy* Man-cub, from whom thou hast taken his Word and so laid him open to Death, *thy* Man-cub is with *me*, and if he be not already dead the fault is none of thine, bleached dog! Wait here for the dhole, and be glad that the Man-cub and I strike on thy side.'

Kaa flashed up stream again and moored himself in the middle of the gorge, looking upwards at the line of the cliff. Presently he saw Mowgli's head move against the stars: then there was a whizz in the air, the keen clean *schloop* of a body falling feet first; next minute the body was at rest again in the loop of Kaa's body.

' It is no leap by night,' said Mowgli quietly. ' I have jumped twice as far for sport; but that is an evil place above—low bushes and gullies that go down deep—all full of the Little People. I have put big stones one above the other by the side of three gullies. These I shall throw down with my feet in running, and the Little People will rise up behind me angry.'

' That is man's cunning,' said Kaa. ' Thou art wise, but the Little People are always angry.'

' Nay, at twilight all wings near and far rest for awhile. I will play with the dhole at twilight, for the dhole hunts best by day. He follows now Won-tolla's blood-trail.'

' Chil does not leave a dead ox, nor the dhole a blood-trail,' said Kaa.

' Then I will make him a new blood-trail—of his own blood if I can, and give him dirt to eat. Thou wilt stay here, Kaa, till I come with my dholes? '

' Ay, but what if they kill thee in the Jungle, or the Little People kill thee before thou canst leap down to the river? '

' When to-morrow comes we will kill to-morrow,' said Mowgli, quoting a Jungle saying; and again, ' When I am dead it is time to sing the Death Song. Good hunting, Kaa.'

He loosed his arm from the python's neck and went down the gorge like a log in a freshet, paddling towards the far bank, where he found slack water, and laughing aloud from sheer happiness. There was nothing Mowgli liked better than, as he himself said, 'to pull the whiskers of Death' and make the Jungle feel that he was their overlord. He had often, with Baloo's help, robbed bees' nests in single trees, and he knew that the Little People disliked the smell of wild garlic. So he gathered a small bundle of it, tied it up with a bark string, and then followed Won-tolla's blood-trail as it ran southerly from the lairs, for some five miles, looking at the trees with his head on one side and chuckling as he looked.

'Mowgli the Frog have I been,' said he to himself, 'Mowgli the Wolf have I said that I am. Now Mowgli the Ape must I be before I am Mowgli the Buck. At the end I shall be Mowgli the Man. Ho!' and he slid his thumb along the eighteen-inch blade of his knife.

Won-tolla's trail, all rank with dark blood-spots, ran under a forest of thick trees that grew close together and stretched away north-eastward, gradually growing thinner and thinner to within two miles of the Bee Rocks. From the last tree to the low scrub of the Bee Rocks was open country, where there was hardly cover enough to hide a wolf. Mowgli trotted along under the trees, judging distances between branch and branch, occasionally climbing up a trunk and taking a trial leap from one tree to another, till he came to the open ground, which he studied very carefully for an hour. Then he turned, picked up Won-tolla's trail where he had left it, settled himself in a tree with an outrunning branch some eight feet from the ground, hung his bunch of garlic in a safe crotch, and sat still sharpening his knife on the sole of his foot.

A little before midday when the sun was very warm, he heard the patter of feet and smelt the abominable smell of the dhole pack as they trotted steadily and pitilessly along Won-tolla's trail. Seen from above the red dhole does not look half the size of a wolf, but Mowgli knew how strong his feet and jaws were. He watched the sharp bay head of the leader snuffing along the trail and gave him 'Good hunting!'

The brute looked up and his companions halted behind him, scores and scores of red dogs with low-hung tails, heavy shoulders, weak quarters, and bloody mouths. The dholes are a very silent people as a rule, and they have no manners even in their own Dekkan. Fully two hundred must have gathered below him, but he could see that the leaders sniffed hungrily on Won-tolla's trail, and tried to drag the pack forward. That would never do, or they would be at the lairs in broad daylight, and Mowgli meant to hold them under his tree till twilight.

'By whose leave do ye come here?' said Mowgli.

'All jungles are our jungle,' was the reply, and the dhole that gave it bared his white teeth. Mowgli looked down with a smile and imitated perfectly the sharp chitter-chatter of Chikai, the leaping rat of the Dekkan, meaning the dholes to understand that he considered them no better than

Chikai. The pack closed up round the tree trunk and the leader bayed savagely, calling Mowgli a tree-ape. For an answer Mowgli stretched down one naked leg and wriggled his bare toes just above the leader's head. That was enough, and more than enough to wake the pack to stupid rage. Those who have hair between their toes do not care to be reminded of it. Mowgli caught his foot away as the leader leaped and said sweetly: ' Dog, red dog! Go back to the Dekkan and eat lizards. Go to Chikai thy brother, dog, dog, red, red dog! There is hair between every toe! ' He twiddled his toes a second time.

' Come down ere we starve thee out, hairless ape,' yelled the pack, and this was exactly what Mowgli wanted. He laid himself down along the branch, his cheek to the bark, his right arm free, and for some five minutes he told the pack what he thought and knew about them, their manners, their customs, their mates, and their puppies. There is no speech in the world so rancorous and so stinging as the language the Jungle People use to show scorn and contempt. When you come to think of it you will see how this must be so. As Mowgli told Kaa, he had many little thorns under his tongue, and slowly and deliberately he drove the dholes from silence to growls, from growls to yells, and from yells to hoarse slavery ravings. They tried to answer his taunts, but a cub might as well have tried to answer Kaa in a rage, and all the while Mowgli's right hand lay crooked at his side, ready for action, his feet locked round the branch. The big bay leader had leaped many times into the air, but Mowgli dared not risk a false blow. At last, made furious beyond his natural strength, he bounded up seven or eight feet clear of the ground. Then Mowgli's hand shot out like the head of a tree-snake, and gripped him by the scruff of his neck, and the branch shook with the jar as his weight fell back, and Mowgli was almost wrenched on to the ground. But he never loosed his grip, and inch by inch he hauled the beast, hanging like a drowned jackal, up on the branch. With his left hand he reached for his knife and cut off the red, bushy tail, flinging the dhole back to earth again. That was all he needed. The dhole would not go forward on Won-tolla's trail now till they had killed Mowgli, or Mowgli had killed them. He saw them settle down in circles with a quiver of the haunches that meant revenge to the death, and so he climbed to a higher crotch, settled his back comfortably and went to sleep.

After three or four hours he waked and counted the pack. They were all there, silent, husky, and dry, with eyes of steel. The sun was beginning to sink. In half an hour the Little People of the Rocks would be ending their labours, and, as you know, the dhole does not fight well in the twilight.

' I did not need such faithful watchers,' he said, standing up on a branch, ' but I will remember this. Ye be true dholes, but to my thinking too much of one kind. For that reason I do not give the big lizard-eater his tail again. Art thou not pleased, Red Dog? '

' I myself will tear out thy stomach,' yelled the leader, biting the foot of the tree.

'Nay, but consider, wise rat of Dekkan. There will now be many litters of little tailless red dogs, yea, with raw red stumps that sting when the sand is hot. Go home, Red Dog, and cry that an ape has done this. Ye will not go? Come then with me, and I will make ye very wise.'

He moved monkey-fashion into the next tree, and so on and the next and the next, the pack following with lifted hungry heads. Now and then he would pretend to fall, and the pack would tumble one over the other in their haste to be in at the death. It was a curious sight—the boy with the knife that shone in the low sunlight as it sifted through the upper branches, and the silent pack with their red coats all aflame huddling and following below. When he came to the last tree he took the garlic and rubbed him-

self all over carefully, and the dholes yelled with scorn. 'Ape with a wolf's tongue, dost thou think to cover thy scent?' they said. 'We will follow to the death.'

'Take thy tail,' said Mowgli, flinging it back along the course he had taken. The pack naturally rushed back a little when they smelt the blood. 'And follow now—to the death!'

He had slipped down the tree trunk, and headed like the wind in bare feet for the Bee Rocks, before the dholes saw what he would do.

They gave one deep howl and settled down to the long lobbing canter that can, at the last, run down anything that lives. Mowgli knew their pack pace to be much slower than that of the wolves, or he would never

have risked a two-mile run in full sight. They were sure that the boy was theirs at last, and he was sure that he had them to play with as he pleased. All his trouble was to keep them sufficiently hot behind him to prevent them turning off too soon. He ran cleanly, evenly, and springily; the tailless leader not five yards behind him; and the pack stringing out over perhaps a quarter of a mile of ground, crazy and blind with the rage of slaughter. So he kept his distance by ear, reserving his last effort for the rush across the Bee Rocks.

The Little People had gone to sleep in the early twilight, for it was not the season of late blossoming flowers; but as Mowgli's first footfalls rang hollow on the hollow ground he heard a sound as though all the earth were humming. Then he ran as he had never run in his life before, spurned aside one—two—three of the piles of stones into the dark sweet-smelling gullies; heard a roar like the roar of the sea in a cave, saw with the tail of his eye the air grow dark behind him, saw the current of the Waingunga far below, and a flat, diamond-shaped head in the water; leaped outward with all his strength, the tailless dhole snapping at his shoulder in mid-air, and dropped feet first to the safety of the river, breathless and triumphant. There was not a sting on his body, for the smell of the garlic had checked the Little People for just the few seconds that carried him across the rocks. When he rose Kaa's coils were steadying him and things were bounding over the edge of the cliff—great lumps, it seemed, of clustered bees falling like plummets; and as each lump touched water the bees flew upward and the body of a dhole whirled down stream. Overhead they could hear furious short yells that were drowned in a roar like thunder—the roar of the wings of the Little People of the Rocks. Some of the dholes, too, had fallen into the gullies that communicated with the underground caves, and there choked, and fought, and snapped among the tumbled honeycombs, and at last, borne up dead on the heaving waves of bees beneath them, shot out of some hole in the river face, to roll over on the black rubbish heaps. There were dholes who had leaped short into the trees on the cliffs, and the bees blotted out their shapes; but the greater number of them, maddened by the stings, had flung themselves into the river; and, as Kaa said, the Waingunga was hungry water.

Kaa held Mowgli fast till the boy had recovered his breath.

'We may not stay here,' he said. 'The Little People are roused indeed. Come!'

Swimming low and diving as often as he could, Mowgli went down the river with the knife in his hand.

'Slowly, slowly!' said Kaa. 'One tooth does not kill a hundred unless it be a cobra's, and many of the dholes took water swiftly when they saw the Little People rise. *They* are unhurt.'

'The more work for my knife, then. Phai! How the Little People follow.' Mowgli sank again. The face of the water was blanketed with wild bees buzzing sullenly and stinging all they found.

'Nothing was ever yet lost by silence,' said Kaa—no sting could penetrate his scales—'and thou hast all the long night for the hunting. Hear them howl!'

Nearly half the pack had seen the trap their fellows rushed into, and, turning sharp aside, had flung themselves into the water where the gorge broke down in steep banks. Their cries of rage and their threats against the 'tree-ape' who had brought them to their shame mixed with the yells and growls of those who had been punished by the Little People. To remain ashore was death, and every dhole knew it. The pack was swept along the current, down and down to the rocks of the Peace Pool, but even there the angry Little People followed and forced them to the water again. Mowgli could hear the voice of the tailless leader bidding his people hold on and kill out every wolf in Seeonee. But he did not waste his time in listening.

'One kills in the dark behind us!' snapped a dhole. 'Here is tainted water!'

Mowgli had dived forward like an otter, twitched a struggling dhole under water before he could open his mouth, and dark, oily rings rose in the Peace Pool as the body plopped up, turning on its side. The dholes tried to turn, but the current forced them by, and the Little People darted at their heads and ears, and they could hear the challenge of the Seeonee Pack growing louder and deeper in the gathering darkness ahead. Again Mowgli dived, and again a dhole went under and rose dead, and again the clamour broke out at the rear of the pack, some howling that it was best to go ashore, others calling on their leader to lead them back to the Dekkan, and others bidding Mowgli show himself and be killed.

'They come to the fight with two stomachs and many voices,' said Kaa. 'The rest is with thy brethren below yonder. The Little People go back to sleep, and I will turn also. I do not help wolves.'

A wolf came running along the bank on three legs, leaping up and down, laying his head sideways close to the ground, hunching his back, and breaking a couple of feet into the air, as though he were playing with his cubs. It was Won-tolla, the Outlier, and he said never a word, but continued his horrible sport beside the dholes. They had been long in the water now, and were swimming laboriously, their coats drenched and heavy, and their bushy tails dragging like sponges, so tired and shaken that they, too, were silent, watching the pair of blazing eyes that moved abreast of them.

'This is no good hunting,' said one at last.

'Good hunting!' said Mowgli as he rose boldly at the brute's side and sent the long knife home behind the shoulder, pushing hard to avoid the dying snap.

'Art thou there, Man-cub?' said Won-tolla, from the bank.

'Ask of the dead, Outlier,' Mowgli replied. 'Have none come down stream? I have filled these dogs' mouths with dirt; I have tricked them in the broad daylight, and their leader lacks his tail, but here be some few for thee still. Whither shall I drive them?'

' I will wait,' said Won-tolla. ' The long night is before me, and I shall see well.'

Nearer and nearer came the bay of the Seeonee wolves. ' For the Pack, for the Full Pack it is met! ' and a bend in the river drove the dholes forward among the sands and shoals opposite the Seeonee lairs.

Then they saw their mistake. They should have landed half a mile higher up and rushed the wolves on dry ground. Now it was too late. The bank was lined with burning eyes, and except for the horrible *Pheeal* cry that had never stopped since sundown there was no sound in the jungle. It seemed as though Won-tolla was fawning on them to come ashore; and ' Turn and take hold! ' said the leader of the dholes. The entire pack flung themselves at the shore, threshing and squattering through the shoal water till the face of the Waingunga was all white and torn, and the great ripples went from side to side like bow-waves from a boat. Mowgli followed the rush, stabbing and slicing as the dholes, huddled together, rushed up the river-beach in a wave.

Then the long fight began, heaving and straining and splitting and scattering and narrowing and broadening along the red wet sands, and over and between the tangled tree-roots, and through and among the bushes, and in and out of the grass clumps, for even now the dholes were two to one. But they met wolves fighting for all that made the Pack, and not only the short, deep-chested white-tusked hunters of the Pack, but the wild-eyed lahinis—the she-wolves of the lair, as the saying is—fighting for their litters, with here and there a yearling wolf, his first coat still half woolly, tugging and grappling by their sides. A wolf, you must know, flies at the throat or snaps at the flank, while a dhole by preference bites low, so when the dholes were struggling out of the water and had to raise their heads the odds were with the wolves; on dry land the wolves suffered, but in the water or on land Mowgli's knife came and went the same. The Four had worked their way to his aid. Gray Brother, crouched between the boy's knees, protected his stomach, while the others guarded his back and either side, or stood over him when the shock of a leaping, yelling dhole who had thrown himself on the steady blade bore him down. For the rest, it was one tangled confusion—a locked and swaying mob that moved from right to left and from left to right along the bank, and also ground round and round slowly on its own centre. Here would be a heaving mound, like a water-blister in a whirlpool, which would break like a water-blister, and throw up four or five mangled dogs, each striving to get back to the centre; here would be a single wolf borne down by two or three dholes dragging him forward, and sinking the while; here a yearling cub would be held up by the pressure round him, though he had been killed early in the fight, while his mother, crazed with dumb rage, rolled over snapping and passing on; and in the middle of the thickest fight, perhaps, one wolf and one dhole, forgetting everything else, would be manœuvring for first hold till they were swept away by a rush of yelling fighters. Once Mowgli passed Akela, a

dhole on either flank, and his all but toothless jaws closed over the loins of a third; and once he saw Phao, his teeth set in the throat of a dhole, tugging the unwilling beast forward till the yearlings could finish him. But the bulk of the fight was blind flurry and smother in the dark; hit, trip, and tumble, yelp, groan and worry-worry-worry round him and behind him and above him.

As the night wore on the quick giddy-go-round motion increased. The dholes were wearied and afraid to attack the stronger wolves, though they did not yet dare to run away; but Mowgli felt that the end was coming soon, and contented himself with striking to cripple. The yearlings were growing bolder; there was time to breathe; and now the mere flicker of the knife would sometimes turn a dhole aside.

' The meat is very near the bone,' Gray Brother gasped. He was bleeding from a score of flesh-wounds.

' But the bone is yet to be cracked,' said Mowgli. ' Aowawa! *Thus* do we do in the Jungle! ' The red blade ran like a flame along the side of a dhole whose hind-quarters were hidden by the weight of a clinging wolf.

' My kill! ' snorted the wolf through his wrinkled nostrils. ' Leave him to me! '

' Is thy stomach *still* empty, Outlier? ' said Mowgli. Won-tolla was fearfully punished, but his grip had paralysed the dhole, who could not turn round and reach him.

' By the Bull that bought me,' Mowgli cried, with a bitter laugh, ' it is the tailless one! ' And indeed it was the big bay-coloured leader.

' It is not wise to kill cubs and lahinis,' Mowgli went on philosophically, wiping the blood out of his eyes, ' unless one also kills the lair-father, and it is in my stomach that this lair-father kills thee.'

A dhole leaped to his leader's aid, but before his teeth had found Won-tolla's flank, Mowgli's knife was in his chest, and Gray Brother took what was left.

' And thus do we do in the Jungle,' said Mowgli.

Won-tolla said not a word, only his jaws were closing and closing on the backbone as life ebbed. The dhole shuddered, his head dropped and he lay still, and Won-tolla dropped above him.

' Huh! The Blood Debt is paid,' said Mowgli. ' Sing the song, Won-tolla.'

' He hunts no more,' said Gray Brother, ' and Akela too is silent, this long time.'

' The bone is cracked! ' thundered Phao, son of Phaon. ' They go! Kill, kill out, O hunters of the Free People! '

Dhole after dhole was slinking away from those dark and bloody sands to the river, to the thick jungle, up stream or down stream as he saw the road clear.

' The debt! The debt! ' shouted Mowgli. ' Pay the debt! They have slain the Lone Wolf! Let not a dog go! '

He was flying to the river, knife in hand, to check any dhole who dared to take water, when, from under a mound of nine dead, rose Akela's head and fore-quarters, and Mowgli dropped on his knees beside the Lone Wolf.

'Said I not it would be my last fight?' Akela gasped. 'It is good hunting. And thou, Little Brother?'

'I live, having killed many.'

'Even so. I die, and I would—I would die by thee, Little Brother.' Mowgli took the terrible scarred head on his knees, and put his arms round the torn neck.

'It is long since the old days of Shere Khan and a Man-cub that rolled naked in the dust,' coughed Akela.

'Nay, nay, I am a wolf. I am of one skin with the Free People,' Mowgli cried. 'It is no will of mine that I am a man.'

'Thou art a man, Little Brother, wolfling of my watching. Thou art all a man, or else the Pack had fled before the dhole. My life I owe to thee, and to-day thou hast saved the Pack even as once I saved thee. Hast thou forgotten? All debts are paid now. Go to thine own people. I tell thee again, eye of my eye, this hunting is ended. Go to thine own people.'

'I will never go. I will hunt alone in the Jungle. I have said it.'

'After the summer come the rains, and after the rains come the spring. Go back before thou art driven.'

'Who will drive me?'

'Mowgli will drive Mowgli. Go back to thy people. Go to Man.'

'When Mowgli drives Mowgli I will go,' Mowgli answered.

'There is no more for thee,' said Akela. 'Now I would speak to my kind. Little Brother, canst thou raise me to my feet? I also am a leader of the Free People.'

Very carefully and gently Mowgli raised Akela to his feet, both arms round him, and the Lone Wolf drew a deep breath and began the Death Song that a leader of the Pack should sing when he dies. It gathered strength as he went on, lifting and lifting and ringing far across the river, till it came to the last 'Good hunting!' and Akela shook himself clear of Mowgli for an instant, and leaping into the air, fell backwards dead upon his last and most terrible kill.

Mowgli sat with his head on his knees, careless of anything else, while the last of the dying dholes were being overtaken and run down by the merciless lahinis. Little by little the cries died away, and the wolves came back limping as their wounds stiffened to take stock of the dead. Fifteen of the pack, as well as half a dozen lahinis, were dead by the river, and of the others not one was unmarked. Mowgli sat through it all till the cold day-break, when Phao's wet red muzzle was dropped in his hand, and Mowgli drew back to show the gaunt body of Akela.

'Good hunting!' said Phao, as though Akela were still alive, and then

over his bitten shoulder to the others: 'Howl, dogs! A wolf has died to-night!'

But of all the pack of two hundred fighting dholes, Red Dogs of the Dekkan, whose boast is that no living thing in the Jungle dare stand before them, not one returned to the Dekkan to carry that news.

CHIL'S SONG

[This is the song that Chil sang as the kites dropped down one after another to the river-bed, when the great fight was finished. Chil is good friends with everybody, but he is a cold-blooded kind of creature at heart, because he knows that almost everybody in the Jungle comes to him in the long-run.]

These were my companions going forth by night,
 (*Chil! Look you, for Chil!*)
Now come I to whistle them the ending of the fight.
 (*Chil! Vanguards of Chil!*)
Word they gave me overhead of quarry newly slain,
Word I gave them underfoot of buck upon the plain.
Here's an end of every trail—they shall not speak again!

They that gave the hunting cry—they that followed fast—
 (*Chil! Look you, for Chil!*)
They that bade the *sambhur* wheel, and pinned him as he passed—
 (*Chil! Vanguards of Chil!*)
They that lagged behind the scent—they that ran before,
They that shunned the level horn—they that overbore,
Here's an end of every trail—they shall not follow more.

These were my companions. Pity 'twas they died!
 (*Chil! Look you, for Chil!*)
Now come I to comfort them that knew them in their pride.
 (*Chil! Vanguards of Chil!*)
Tattered flank and sunken eye, open mouth and red,
Locked and lank and lone they lie, the dead upon their dead.
Here's an end of every trail—and here my hosts are fed!

THE SPRING RUNNING

Man goes to Man! Cry the challenge through the Jungle!
 He that was our Brother goes away.
Hear, now, and judge, O ye People of the Jungle,
 Answer, who shall turn him—who shall stay?

Man goes to Man! He is weeping in the Jungle:
 He that was our Brother sorrows sore!
Man goes to Man! (Oh, we loved him in the Jungle!)
 To the Man-trail where we may not follow more.

THE second year after the great fight with Red Dog and the death of Akela, Mowgli must have been nearly seventeen years old. He looked older, for hard exercise, the best of good eating, and baths whenever he felt in the least hot or dusty had given him strength and growth far beyond his age. He could swing by one hand from a top branch for half an hour at a time, when he had occasion to look along the tree-roads. He could stop a young buck in mid-gallop and throw him sideways by the head. He could even jerk over the big blue wild boars that lived in the Marshes of the North. The Jungle People, who used to fear him for his wits, feared him now for his mere strength, and when he moved quietly on his own affairs the whisper of his coming cleared the wood paths. And yet the look in his eyes was always gentle. Even when he fought his eyes never blazed as Bagheera's did. They only grew more and more interested and excited, and that was one of the things that Bagheera himself did not understand.

He asked Mowgli about it, and the boy laughed and said, ' When I miss the kill I am angry. When I must go empty for two days I am very angry. Do not my eyes talk then? '

' The mouth is hungry,' said Bagheera, ' but the eyes say nothing. Hunting, eating, or swimming, it is all one—like a stone in wet or dry weather.' Mowgli looked at him lazily from under his long eyelashes, and, as usual, the panther's head dropped. Bagheera knew his master.

They were lying out far up the side of a hill overlooking the Waingunga, and the morning mists lay below them in bands of white and green. As the sun rose they changed into bubbling seas of red and gold, churned off and let the low rays stripe the dried grass on which Mowgli and Bagheera were resting. It was the end of the cold weather, the leaves and the trees looked worn and faded, and there was a dry ticking rustle when the wind blew. A little leaf tap-tap-tapped furiously against a twig as a single leaf caught in a current will. It roused Bagheera, for he snuffed the morning air with a

deep hollow cough, threw himself on his back and struck with his fore paws at the nodding leaf above.

'The year turns,' he said. 'The Jungle goes forward. The Time of New Talk is near. That leaf knows. It is very good.'

'The grass is dry,' Mowgli answered, pulling up a tuft. 'Even Eye-of-the-Spring [that is a little trumpet-shaped waxy red flower that runs in and out among the grasses]—even Eye-of-the-Spring is shut and . . . Bagheera, is it well for the Black Panther so to lie on his back and beat with his paws in the air as though he were the tree-cat?'

'Aowh!' said Bagheera. He seemed to be thinking of other things.

'I say, is it well for the Black Panther so to mouth and cough and howl and roll. Remember, we be the Masters of the Jungle, thou and I.'

'Indeed, yes; I hear, Man-cub.' Bagheera rolled over hurriedly, and sat up, the dust on his ragged black flanks. (He was just casting his winter coat.) 'We be surely the Masters of the Jungle! Who is so strong as Mowgli? Who so wise?' There was a curious drawl in the voice that made Mowgli turn to see whether by any chance the Black Panther were making fun of him, for the Jungle is full of words that sound like one thing but mean another. 'I said we be beyond question the Masters of the Jungle,' Bagheera repeated. 'Have I done wrong? I did not know that the Man-cub no longer lay upon the ground. Does he fly, then?'

Mowgli sat with his elbows on his knees looking out across the valley at the daylight. Somewhere down in the woods below a bird was trying over in a husky, reedy voice the first few notes of his spring song. It was no more than a shadow of the full-throated tumbling call he would be crying later, but Bagheera heard it.

'I said the Time of New Talk was near,' growled the Panther, switching his tail.

'I hear,' Mowgli answered. 'Bagheera, why dost thou shake all over? The sun is warm.'

'That is Ferao, the scarlet woodpecker,' said Bagheera. 'He has not forgotten. Now I too must remember my song,' and he began purring and crooning to himself, hearking back dissatisfied again and again.

'There is no game afoot,' said Mowgli, lazily.

'Little Brother, are both thine ears stopped? That is no killing-word but my song that I make ready against the need.'

'I had forgotten. I shall know when the Time of New Talk is here, because then thou and the others run away and leave me single-foot.' Mowgli spoke rather savagely.

'But, indeed, Little Brother,' Bagheera began, 'we do not always——'

'I say ye do,' said Mowgli, shooting out his fore-finger angrily. 'Ye do run away, and I, who am the Master of the Jungle, must needs walk single-foot. How was it last season, when I would gather sugar-cane from the fields of a Man-Pack? I sent a runner—I sent thee!—to Hathi bidding him to come upon such a night and pluck the sweet grass for me with his trunk.'

' He came only two nights later,' said Bagheera, cowering a little, ' and of that long sweet grass that pleased thee so, he gathered more than any Man-cub could eat in all the nights of the Rains. His was no fault of mine.'

' He did not come upon the night when I sent him the word. No, he was trumpeting and running and roaring through valleys in the moonlight. His trail was like the trail of three elephants, for he would not hide among the trees. He danced in the moonlight before the houses of the Man-Pack. I saw him, and yet he would not come to me; and I am the Master of the Jungle! '

' It was the Time of New Talk,' said the Panther, always very humble. ' Perhaps, Little Brother, thou didst not that time call him by a master-word? Listen to Ferao! '

Mowgli's bad temper seemed to have boiled itself away. He lay back with his head on his arms, his eyes shut. ' I do not know—nor do I care,' he said sleepily. ' Let us sleep, Bagheera. My stomach is heavy in me. Make me a rest for my head.'

The Panther lay down again with a sigh, because he could hear Ferao practising and repractising his song against the spring-time of New Talk, as they say.

In an Indian Jungle the seasons slide one into the other almost without division. There seem to be only two—the wet and the dry, but if you look closely below the torrents of rain and the clouds of char and dust you will find all four going round in their regular order. Spring is the most wonderful, because she has not to cover a clean bare field with new leaves and flowers, but to drive before her and to put away the hanging-on, over-surviving raffle of half-green things which the gentle winter has suffered to live, and to make the partly dressed, stale earth feel new and young once more. And this she does so well that there is no spring in the world like the Jungle spring.

There is one day when all things are tired, and the very smells as they drift on the heavy air are old and used. One cannot explain, but it feels so. Then there is another day—to the eye nothing whatever has changed —when all the smells are new and delightful and the whiskers of the Jungle People quiver to their roots, and the winter hair comes away from their sides in long draggled locks. Then, perhaps, a little rain falls, and all the trees and the bushes and the bamboos and the mosses and the juicy-leaved plants wake with a noise of growing that you can almost hear, and under this noise runs, day and night, a deep hum. *That* is the noise of the Spring—a vibrating boom which is neither bees nor falling water nor the wind in the tree-tops, but the purring of the warm, happy world.

Up to this year Mowgli had always delighted in the turn of the seasons. It was he who generally saw the first Eye-of-the-Spring deep down among the grasses, and the first bank of spring clouds which are like nothing else in the Jungle. His voice could be heard in all sorts of wet star-lighted blossoming places, helping the big frogs through their choruses, or mocking the

little upside down owls that hoot through the white nights. Like all his people, spring was the season he chose for his flittings—moving for mere joy of rushing through the warm air, thirty, forty, or fifty miles between twilight and the morning star, and coming back panting and laughing and wreathed with strange flowers. The Four did not follow him on these wild ringings of the Jungle, but went off to sing songs with other wolves. The Jungle People are very busy in the spring, and Mowgli could hear them grunting and screaming and whistling according to their kind. Their voices then are different from their voices at other times of the year, and that is one of the reasons why spring is called the Time of New Talk.

But that spring, as he told Bagheera, his stomach was new in him. Ever since the bamboo shoots turned spotty-brown he had been looking forward to the morning when the smells should change. But when that morning came, and Mor, the Peacock, blazing in bronze and blue and gold, cried it aloud all along the misty woods, and Mowgli opened his mouth to send on the cry, the words choked between his teeth, and a feeling came over him that began at his toes, and ended in his hair—a feeling of pure unhappiness, and he looked himself over to be sure that he had not trodden on a thorn. Mor cried the new smells, the other birds took it over, and from the rocks by the Waingunga he heard Bagheera's hoarse scream—something between the scream of an eagle and the neighing of a horse. There was a yelling and scattering of *bandar-log* in the new-budding branches above, and there stood Mowgli, his chest, filled to answer Mor, sinking in little gasps as the breath was driven out of it by this unhappiness.

He stared, but he could see no more than the mocking *bandar-log* scudding through the trees, and Mor, his tail spread in full splendour, dancing on the slopes below.

'The smells have changed,' screamed Mor. 'Good hunting, Little Brother! Where is thy answer?'

'Little Brother, good hunting!' whistled Chil the Kite and his mate swooping down together. The two baffed under Mowgli's nose so close that a pinch of downy white feathers brushed out.

A light spring rain—elephant-rain they call it—drove across the Jungle in a belt half a mile wide, left the new leaves wet and nodding behind, and died out in a double rainbow and a light roll of thunder. The spring-hum broke out for a minute and was silent, but all the Jungle folk seemed to be giving tongue at once. All except Mowgli.

'I have eaten good food,' he said to himself. 'I have drunk good water. Nor does my throat burn and grow small, as it did when I bit the blue-spotted root that Oo the Turtle said was clean food. But my stomach is heavy, and I have, for no cause, given very bad talk to Bagheera and others, people of the Jungle and my people. Now, too, I am hot and now I am cold, and now I am neither hot nor cold, but angry with that which I cannot see. Huhu! It is time to make a running! To-night I will cross the ranges; yes, I will make a spring running to the Marshes of the North and

back again. I have hunted too easily too long. The Four shall come with me, for they grow as fat as white grubs.'

He called, but never one of the Four answered. They were far beyond earshot, singing over the spring songs—the Moon and Sambhur Songs—with the wolves of the Pack, for in the spring-time the Jungle People make little difference between the day and the night. He gave the sharp barking note, but his only answer was the mocking *maiou* of the little spotted tree-cat winding in and out among the branches for early birds' nests. At this he shook all over with rage and half drew his knife. Then he became very haughty, though there was no one to see him, and stalked severely down the hillside, chin up and eyebrows down. But never a single one of his people asked him a question, for they were all too busy with their own affairs.

'Yes,' said Mowgli to himself, though in his heart he knew that he had no reason. 'Let the Red Dhole come from the Dekkan or the Red Flower dance among the bamboos, and all the Jungle runs whining to Mowgli calling him great elephant names. But now, because Eye-of-the-Spring is red; and Mor, forsooth, must show his naked legs in some spring-dance, the Jungle goes mad as Tabaqui. . . . By the Bull that bought me, am I the Master of the Jungle or am I not? Be silent! What do ye hear?'

A couple of young wolves of the pack were cantering down a path looking for open ground in which to fight. (You will remember that the Law of the Jungle forbids fighting where the pack can see.) Their neck-bristles were as stiff as wire, and they bayed, furiously crouching for the first grapple. Mowgli leaped forward, caught one outstretched throat in either hand, expecting to fling the creatures backwards, as he had often done in games or Pack hunts. But he had never before interfered with a spring fight. The two leaped forward and dashed him aside to the earth, and without word to waste rolled over and over close locked.

Mowgli was on his feet almost before he fell, his knife and his white teeth were bared, and at that minute he would have killed both for no reason but that they were fighting when he wished them to be quiet, although every wolf has full right under the Law to fight. He danced round them with lowered shoulders and quivering hand ready to send in a double blow when the first flurry of the scuffle should be over, but while he waited the strength seemed to go out of his body, the knife point lowered, and he sheathed the knife and watched.

'I have eaten poison,' he said at last. 'Since I broke up the council with the Red Flower—since I killed Shere Khan none of the pack could fling me aside. And these be only tail-wolves in the pack, little hunters. My strength is gone from me, and presently I shall die. Oh, Mowgli, why dost thou not kill them both?'

The fight went on till one wolf ran away, and Mowgli sat alone on the torn and bloody ground looking now at his knife, and now at his legs and

arms, while the feeling of unhappiness he had never known before covered him as water covers a log.

He killed early that evening and eat but little, so as to be in good fettle for his spring running, and he eat alone because all the Jungle People were away singing or fighting. It was a perfect white night, as they call it. All green things seemed to have made a month's growth since the morning. The branch that was yellow-leaved the day before dripped sap when Mowgli broke it. The mosses curled deep and warm over his feet, the young grass had no cutting edges, and all the voices of the jungle boomed like one deep harp-string touched by the moon—the full moon of New Talk, who splashed her light full on rock and pool, slipped it between trunk and creeper, and sifted it through the million leaves. Unhappy as he was, Mowgli sang aloud with pure delight as he settled into his stride. It was more like flying than anything else, for he had chosen the long downward slope that leads to the Northern Marshes through the heart of the main Jungle, where the springy ground deadened the fall of his feet. A man-taught man would have picked his way with many stumbles through the cheating moonlight, but Mowgli's muscles, trained by years of experience, bore him up as though he were a feather. When a rotten log or a hidden stone turned under his foot he saved himself, never checking his pace, without effort and without thought. When he tired of ground-going he threw up his hands monkey-fashion to the nearest creeper, and seemed to float rather than to climb up into the thin branches, whence he would follow a tree-road till his mood changed, and he shot downwards in a long leafy curve to the levels again. There were still hot hollows surrounded by wet rocks where he could hardly breathe for the heavy scents of the night-flowers, and the bloom along the creeper-buds; dark avenues where the moonlight lay in belts as regular as chequered marbles in a church aisle; thickets where the wet young growth stood breast-high about him and threw its arms round his waist; and hill tops crowned with broken rock, where he leaped from stone to stone above the lairs of the frightened little foxes. He would hear, very faint and far off, the *chug-drug* of a boar sharpening his tusks on a bole; and later would come across the great brute all alone, scribing and rending the red bark of a tree, his mouth dripping with foam and his eyes blazing like fire. Or he would turn aside to the sound of clashing horns and hissing grunts and dash past a couple of furious sambhur, staggering to and fro with lowered heads, striped with blood that shows black in the moonlight. Or at some rushing ford he would hear Jacala the Crocodile bellowing like a bull: or disturb a knot of the Poison People; but before they could strike he would be away and across the glistening shingle, and deep into the Jungle again.

So he ran, sometimes shouting, sometimes singing to himself, the happiest thing in all the Jungle that night, till the smell of the flowers warned him that he was near the Marshes, and those lay far beyond his furthest hunting-grounds.

Here, again, a man-trained man would have sunk over head in three strides, but Mowgli's feet had eyes in them and they passed him from tussock to tussock and clump to quaking clump without asking help from the eyes in his head. He headed out to the middle of the swamp, disturbing the duck as he ran, and sat down on a moss-coated tree-trunk lopped in the black water. The marsh was awake all round him, for in the spring the Bird People sleep very lightly, and companies of them were coming or going the night through. But no one took any notice of Mowgli sitting among the tall reeds humming songs without words and looking at the soles of his hard brown feet in case of neglected thorns. All his unhappiness seemed to have been left behind in his own Jungle, and he was just beginning a song when it came back again—ten times worse than before. To make all worse the moon was setting.

This time Mowgli was frightened. ' It is here also! ' he said half aloud. ' It has followed me,' and he looked over his shoulder to see whether the It were not standing behind him. ' There is no one here.' The night noises in the marsh went on, but never bird or beast spoke to him, and the new feeling of misery grew.

' I have eaten poison,' he said, in an awe-stricken voice. ' It must be that carelessly I have eaten poison, and my strength is going from me. I was afraid—and yet it was not *I* that was afraid—Mowgli was afraid when the two wolves fought. Akela, or even Phao, would have silenced them; yet Mowgli was afraid. That is sure sign I have eaten poison. . . . But what do they care in the Jungle? They sing and howl and fight, and run in companies under the moon, and I—*Hai mai!*—I am dying in the marshes, of that poison which I have eaten.' He was so sorry for himself that he nearly wept. ' And after,' he went on, ' they will find me lying in the black water. Nay, I will go back to my own Jungle and I will die upon the Council Rock, and Bagheera whom I love, if he is not screaming in the valley, Bagheera, perhaps, may watch by what is left for a little, lest Chil use me as he used Akela.'

A large warm tear splashed down on his knee, and, miserable as he was, Mowgli felt happy that he was so miserable, if you can understand that upside down sort of happiness. ' As Chil the Kite used Akela,' he repeated, ' on the night I saved the Pack from Red Dog.' He was quiet for a little, thinking of the last words of the Lone Wolf, which you, of course, remember. ' Now Akela said to me many foolish things before he died, for when we die our stomachs change. He said . . . None the less, I *am* of the Jungle! '

In his excitement, as he remembered the fight on Waingunga bank, he shouted the last words aloud, and a wild buffalo-cow among the reeds sprang to her knees, snorting, ' Man! '

' Uhh! ' said Mysa, the Wild Buffalo (Mowgli could hear him turn in his wallow), ' *that* is no man. It is only the hairless wolf of the Seeonee Pack. On such nights runs he to and fro.'

' Uhh! ' said the cow, dropping her head again to graze, ' I thought it was Man.'

' I say no. Oh, Mowgli, is it danger? ' lowed Mysa.

' Oh, Mowgli, is it danger? ' the boy called back mockingly. ' That is all Mysa thinks for: Is it danger? But for Mowgli, who goes to and fro in the Jungle by night watching, what care ye? '

' How loud he cries! ' said the cow.

' Thus do they cry,' Mysa answered contemptuously, ' who having torn the grass up know not how to eat it.'

' For less than this,' Mowgli groaned to himself, ' for less than this even last Rains I had pricked Mysa out of his wallow and ridden him through the swamp on a rush halter.' He stretched his hand to break one of the feathery reeds, but drew it back with a sigh. Mysa went on steadily chewing the cud and the long grass ripped where the cow grazed. ' I will not die *here*,' he said angrily. ' Mysa, who is of one blood with Jacala and the pig, would mock me. Let us go beyond the swamp, and see what comes. Never have I run such a spring-running—hot and cold together. Up, Mowgli! '

He could not resist the temptation of stealing across the reeds to Mysa and pricking him with the point of his knife. The great dripping bull broke out of his wallow like a shell exploding, while Mowgli laughed till he sat down.

' Say now that the hairless wolf of the Seeonee Pack once herded thee, Mysa,' he called.

' Wolf! *Thou*? ' the bull snorted, stamping in the mud. ' All the Jungle knows thou wast a herder of tame cattle—such a man's brat as shouts in the dust by the crops yonder. *Thou* of the Jungle! What hunter would have crawled like a snake among the leeches, and for a muddy jest—a jackal's jest —have shamed me before my cow? Come to firm ground, and I will—I will ' . . . Mysa frothed at the mouth, for he has nearly the worst temper of any one in the Jungle.

Mowgli watched him puff and blow with eyes that never changed. When he could make himself heard through the spattering mud-shower, he said: ' What Man-Pack lair here by the marshes, Mysa? This is new Jungle to me.'

' Go north, then,' roared the angry bull, for Mowgli had pricked him rather sharply. ' It was a naked cow-herd's jest. Go and tell them at the village at the foot of the marsh.'

' The Man-Pack do not love jungle-tales, nor do I think, Mysa, that a scratch more or less on thy hide is any matter for a council. But I will go and look at this village. Yes, I will go. Softly now! It is not every night that the Master of the Jungle comes to herd thee.'

He stepped out to the shivering ground on the edge of the marsh, well knowing that Mysa would never charge over it, and laughed, as he ran, to think of the bull's anger.

'My strength is not altogether gone,' he said. 'It may be the poison is not to the bone. There is a star sitting low yonder.' He looked at it steadily between half-shut hands. 'By the Bull that bought me, it is the Red Flower—the Red Flower that I lay beside before—before I came even to the first Seeonee Pack! Now that I have seen I will finish the running.'

The marsh ended in a broad plain where a light twinkled. It was a long time since Mowgli had concerned himself with the doings of men, but this night the glimmer of the Red Flower drew him forward as if it had been new game.

'I will look,' said he, 'and I will see how far the Man-Pack has changed.'

Forgetting that he was no longer in his own Jungle where he could do what he pleased, he trod carelessly through the dew-loaded grasses till he came to the hut where the light stood. Three or four yelping dogs gave tongue, for he was on the outskirts of a village.

'Ho!' said Mowgli, sitting down noiselessly, after sending back a deep wolf-growl that silenced the curs. 'What comes will come. Mowgli, what hast thou to do any more with the lairs of the Man-Pack?' He rubbed his mouth, remembering where a stone had struck it years ago when the other Man-Pack had cast him out.

The door of the hut opened and a woman stood peering out into the darkness. A child cried, and the woman said over her shoulder, 'Sleep. It was but a jackal that waked the dogs. In a little time morning comes.'

Mowgli in the grass began to shake as though he had the fever. He knew that voice well, but to make sure he cried softly, surprised to find how man's talk came back, 'Messua! O Messua!'

'Who calls?' said the woman, a quiver in her voice.

'Hast thou forgotten?' said Mowgli: his throat was dry as he spoke.

'If it be *thou*, what name did I give thee? Say!' She had half-shut the door, and her hand was clutching at her breast.

'Nathoo! Ohé Nathoo!' said Mowgli, for, as you know, that was the name Messua gave him when he first came to the Man-Pack.

'Come, my son,' she called, and Mowgli stepped into the light, and looked full at Messua, the woman who had been good to him, and whose life he had saved from the Man-Pack so long before. She was older, and her hair was grey, but her eyes and her voice had not changed. Woman-like, she expected to find Mowgli where she had left him, and her eyes travelled upwards in a puzzled fashion from his chest to his head, that touched the top of the door.

'My son,' she stammered, and then sinking to his feet: 'but it is no longer my son. It is a Godling of the woods! Ahai!'

As he stood in the red light of the oil-lamp, strong, tall, and beautiful, his long black hair sweeping over his shoulders, the knife swinging at his neck, and his head crowned with a wreath of white jasmine, he might easily have been mistaken for some wild god of a jungle legend. The child half

asleep on a cot sprang up and shrieked aloud with terror. Messua turned to soothe him while Mowgli stood still, looking in at the water-jars and cooking-pots, the grain-bin and all the other human belongings that he found himself remembering so well.

'What wilt thou eat or drink?' Messua murmured. 'This is all thine. We owe our lives to thee. But art thou him I called Nathoo, or a Godling, indeed?'

'I am Nathoo,' said Mowgli. 'I am very far from my own place. I saw this light and came hither. I did not know thou wast here.'

'After we came to Kanhiwara,' Messua said timidly, 'the English would have helped us against those villagers that sought to burn us. Rememberest thou?'

'Indeed, I have not forgotten.'

'But when the English Law was made ready we went to the village of those evil people and it was no more to be found.'

'That also I remember,' said Mowgli, with a quiver of the nostril.

'My man, therefore, took service in the fields, and at last, for indeed he was a strong man, we held a little land here. It is not so rich as the old village, but we do not need much—we two.'

'Where is he—the man that dug in the dirt when he was afraid on that night?'

'He is dead—a year.'

'And he?' Mowgli pointed to the child.

'My son that was born two Rains ago. If thou art a Godling give him the Favour of the Jungle that he may be safe among thy—thy people as we were safe on that night.'

She lifted up the child, who, forgetting his fright, reached out to play with the knife that hung on Mowgli's chest, and Mowgli put the little fingers aside very carefully.

'And if thou art Nathoo whom the tigers carried away,' Messua went on choking, 'he is then thy younger brother. Give him an elder brother's blessing.'

'*Hai mai!* What do I know of the thing called a blessing? I am neither a Godling nor his brother, and— O mother, mother, my heart is heavy in me.' He shivered as he set down the child.

'Like enough,' said Messua, bustling among the cooking-pots. 'This comes of running about the marshes by night. Beyond question, a fever has soaked thee to the marrow.' Mowgli smiled a little at the idea of anything in the Jungle hurting him. 'I will make a fire and thou shalt drink warm milk. Put away the jasmine wreath, the smell is heavy in so small a place.'

Mowgli sat down, muttering, his face in his hands. All manner of strange feelings were running over him, exactly as though he had been poisoned, and he felt dizzy and a little sick. He drank the warm milk in long gulps, Messua patting him on the shoulder from time to time, not quite sure whether he were her son Nathoo of the long ago days or some wonderful Jungle being, but glad to feel that he was at least flesh and blood.

' Son,' she said at last; her eyes were full of pride, ' have any told thee that thou art beautiful beyond all men? '

' Ha? ' said Mowgli, for of course he had never heard anything of the kind. Messua laughed softly and happily. The look in his face was enough for her.

' I am the first, then? It is right, though it comes seldom, that a mother should tell her son these good things. Thou art very beautiful. Never have I looked upon such a man.'

Mowgli twisted his head and tried to see over his own hard shoulder, and Messua laughed again so long that Mowgli, not knowing why, was forced to laugh with her, and the child ran from one to the other laughing too.

' Nay, thou must not mock thy brother,' said Messua, catching him to her breast. ' When thou art one-half as fair we will marry thee to the youngest daughter of a king and thou shalt ride great elephants.'

Mowgli could not understand one word in three of the talk here; the warm milk was taking effect on him after his forty-mile run; so he curled up and in a minute was deep asleep, and Messua put the hair back from his eyes, threw a cloth over him and was happy. Jungle fashion, he slept out the rest of that night and all the next day, for his instincts, which never wholly slept, warned him there was nothing to fear. He waked at last with a bound that shook the hut, for the cloth over his face made him dream of traps; and there he stood, his hand on his knife, the sleep all heavy in his rolling eyes, ready for any fight.

Messua laughed and set the evening meal before him. There were only a few coarse cakes baked over the smoky fire, some rice, and a lump of sour preserved tamarinds—just enough to go on with till he could get to his evening kill. The smell of the dew in the marshes made him hungry and restless. He wanted to finish his spring running, but the child insisted on sitting in his arms, and Messua would have it that his long blue-black hair must be combed out. So she sang as she combed, foolish little baby songs, now calling Mowgli her son, and now begging him to give some of his jungle-power to the child. The hut door was closed, but Mowgli heard a sound he knew well, and saw Messua's jaw drop with horror as a great gray paw came under the bottom of the door, and Gray Brother outside whined a muffled and penitent whine of anxiety and fear.

' Out and wait. Ye would not come when I called,' said Mowgli in Jungle-talk, never turning his head; and the great gray paw disappeared.

' Do not—do not bring thy—thy servants with thee,' said Messua. ' I—we have always lived at peace with the Jungle.'

' It is peace,' said Mowgli rising. ' Think of that night on the road to Kanhiwara. There were scores of such folk before thee and behind thee. But I see that even in springtime the Jungle people do not always forget. Mother, I go.'

Messua drew aside humbly—he was indeed a wood-god she thought—but as his hand was on the door the mother in her made her throw her arms round Mowgli's neck again and again.

' Come back! ' she whispered. ' Son or no son, come back for I love thee—and look, he too grieves.'

The child was crying because the man with the shiny knife was going away.

' Come back again,' Messua repeated. ' By night or by day this door is never shut to thee.'

Mowgli's throat worked as though the cords in it were being pulled, and his voice seemed to be dragged from it as he answered, ' I will surely come back.'

' And now,' he said, as he put aside the head of the fawning wolf on the threshold, ' I have a little cry against thee, Gray Brother. Why came ye not, all Four, when I called so long ago? '

' So long ago? It was but last night. I—we—were singing in the Jungle, the new songs, for this is the Time of New Talk. Rememberest thou? '

' Truly, truly.'

' And as soon as the songs were sung,' Gray Brother went on earnestly, ' I followed thy trail. I ran from all the others and followed hot-foot. But, O Little Brother, what hast *thou* done—eating and sleeping with the Man-Pack? '

' If ye had come when I called this had never been,' said Mowgli, running much faster.

' And now what is to be? ' said Gray Brother.

Mowgli was going to answer when a girl in a white cloth came down some path that led from the outskirts of the village. Gray Brother dropped out of sight at once and Mowgli backed noiselessly into a field of high springing crops. He could almost have touched her with his hand when the warm green stalks closed before his face and he disappeared like a ghost. The girl screamed, for she thought she had seen a spirit, and then she gave a deep sigh. Mowgli parted the stalks with his hands and watched her till she was out of sight.

' And now I do not know,' he said, sighing in his turn. ' *Why* did ye not come when I called? '

' We follow thee—we follow thee,' Gray Brother mumbled, licking at Mowgli's heel. ' We follow thee always except in the Time of the New Talk.'

' And would ye follow me to the Man-Pack? ' Mowgli whispered.

' Did I not follow thee on the night that our old Pack cast thee out? Who waked thee lying among the crops? '

' Ay, but again? '

' Have I not followed thee to-night? '

' Ay, but again and again, and it may be again, Gray Brother.'

Gray Brother was silent. When he spoke he growled to himself, ' The Black One spoke truth.'

' And he said? '

' Man goes to Man at the last. Raksha our mother said—— '

' So also said Akela on the night of Red Dog,' Mowgli muttered.

' So also said Kaa, who is wiser than us all.'

' What dost thou say, Gray Brother? '

' They cast thee out once, with bad talk. They cut thy mouth with stones. They sent Buldeo to slay thee. They would have thrown thee into the Red Flower. Thou, and not I, hast said that they are evil and senseless. Thou and not I—I follow my own people—didst let in the Jungle upon them. Thou and not I didst make song against them more bitter even than our song against Red Dog.'

' I ask thee what *thou* sayest? '

They were talking as they ran. Gray Brother cantered on awhile without replying, and then he said between bound and bound as it were—' Man-cub—Master of the Jungle—Son of Raksha—Lair-brother to me—though I forget for a little while in the spring, thy trail is my trail, thy lair is my lair, thy kill is my kill, and thy death-fight is my death-fight. I speak for the Three. But what wilt thou say to the Jungle? '

' That is well thought. Between the sight and the kill it is not good to wait. Go before and cry them all to the Council Rock, and I will tell them what is in my stomach. But they may not come—in the Time of the New Talk they may forget me.'

' Hast thou then forgotten nothing? ' snapped Gray Brother over his shoulder, as he laid himself down to gallop, and Mowgli followed, thinking.

At any other season his news would have called all the Jungle together with bristling necks, but now they were busy hunting and fighting and kill-ing and singing. From one to another Gray Brother ran, crying, 'The Master of the Jungle goes back to Man. Come to the Council Rock! ' And the happy, eager people only answered, ' He will return in the summer heats. The Rains will drive him to lair. Run and sing with us, Gray Brother.'

' But the Master of the Jungle goes back to Man,' Gray Brother would repeat.

' Eee—Yowa? Is the Time of New Talk any less good for that? ' they would reply. So when Mowgli, heavy-hearted, came up through the well-remembered rocks to the place where he had been brought into the Pack, he found only the Four, Baloo, who was nearly blind with age, and the heavy, cold-blooded Kaa, coiled round Akela's empty seat.

' Thy trail ends here, then, Manling?' said Kaa, as Mowgli threw him-self down, his face in his hands. ' Cry thy cry. We be of one blood, thou and I—Man and Snake together.'

' Why was I not torn in two by Red Dog? ' the boy moaned. ' My strength is gone from me, and it is not the poison. By night and by day I hear a double step upon my trail. When I turn my head it is as though one had hidden himself from me that instant. I go to look behind the trees and he is not there. I call and none cry again, but it is as though one listened and kept back the answer. I lie down, but I do not rest. I run the spring-running, but I am not made still. I bathe, but I am not made cool. The

kill sickens me, but I have no heart to fight except I kill. The Red Flower is in my body, my bones are water—and—I know not what I know.'

'What need of talk?' said Baloo, slowly, turning his head to where Mowgli lay. 'Akela by the river said it, that Mowgli should drive Mowgli back to the Man-Pack. I said it. But who listens now to Baloo? Bagheera—where is Bagheera this night?—he knows also. It is the Law.'

'When we met at Cold Lairs, Manling, I knew it,' said Kaa, turning a little in his mighty coils. 'Man goes to Man at the last, though the Jungle does not cast him out.'

The four looked at one another and at Mowgli, puzzled but obedient.

'The Jungle does not cast me out, then?' Mowgli stammered.

Gray Brother and the Three growled furiously, beginning, 'So long as we live none shall dare—— ' But Baloo checked them.

'I taught thee the Law. It is for me to speak,' he said, 'and though I cannot now see the rocks before me, I see far. Little Frog, take thine own trail; make thy lair with thine own blood and pack and people; but when there is need of foot or tooth or eye or a word carried swiftly by night, remember, Master of the Jungle, the Jungle is thine at call.'

'The Middle Jungle is thine also,' said Kaa. 'I speak for no small people.'

'*Hai mai,* my brothers,' cried Mowgli, throwing up his arms with a sob. 'I know not what I know, I would not go, but I am drawn by both feet. How shall I leave these nights?'

'Nay, look up, Little Brother,' Baloo repeated. 'There is no shame in this hunting. When the honey is eaten we leave the empty hive.'

'Having cast the skin,' said Kaa, 'we may not creep into it afresh. It is the Law.'

'Listen, dearest of all to me,' said Baloo. 'There is neither word nor will here to hold thee back. Look up! Who may question the Master of the Jungle? I saw thee playing among the white pebbles yonder when thou wast a little frog; and Bagheera, that bought thee for the price of a young bull newly killed, saw thee also. Of that Looking Over we two only remain, for Raksha, thy lair-mother, is dead with thy lair-father; the old Wolf-Pack is long since dead; thou knowest whither Shere Khan went, and Akela died among the dholes, where but for thy wisdom and strength the second Seeonee Pack would also have died. There remain nothing but old bones. It is no longer the Man-cub that asks leave of his Pack, but the Master of the Jungle that changes his trail. Who shall question Man in his ways?'

'But Bagheera and the Bull that bought me,' said Mowgli. 'I would not—— '

His words were cut short by a roar and a crash in the thicket below, and Bagheera, light, strong, and terrible as always.

'*Therefore,*' he said, stretching out a dripping right paw, 'I did not come. It was a long hunt, but he lies dead in the bushes now—a bull in his second year—the Bull that frees thee, Little Brother. All debts are paid now.

For the rest, my word is Baloo's word.' He licked Mowgli's foot. ' Remember Bagheera loved thee,' he cried and bounded away. At the foot of the hill he cried again long and loud, ' Good hunting on a new trail, Master of the Jungle! Remember Bagheera loved thee.'

' Thou hast heard,' said Baloo. ' There is no more. Go now; but first come to me. O wise little Frog, come to me! '

' It is hard to cast the skin,' said Kaa, as Mowgli sobbed and sobbed with his head on the blind bear's side and his arms around his neck, while Baloo tried feebly to lick his feet.

' The stars are thin,' said Gray Brother snuffing at the dawn-wind. ' Where shall we lair to-day? for, from now we follow new trails.'

And this is the last of the Mowgli stories.

THE OUTSONG

This is the song that Mowgli heard behind him in the Jungle till he came to Messua's door again:

BALOO

For the sake of him who showed
One wise Frog the Jungle-Road,
Keep the Law the Man-Pack make—
For thy blind old Baloo's sake!
Clean or tainted, hot or stale,
Hold it as it were the trail,
Through the day and through the night,
Questing neither left nor right.
For the sake of him who loves
Thee beyond all else that moves,
When thy Pack would make thee pain,
Say: ' Tabaqui sings again.'
When thy Pack would work thee ill,
Say: ' Shere Khan is yet to kill.'
When the knife is drawn to slay,
Keep the Law and go thy way.
(Root and honey, palm and spathe,
Guard a cub from harm and scathe.)
Wood and Water, Wind and Tree,
Jungle-Favour go with thee!

KAA

Anger is the egg of Fear—
Only lidless eyes are clear.
Cobra-poison none may leech;
Even so with Cobra-speech.
Open talk shall call to thee
Strength whose mate is Courtesy.
Send no lunge beyond thy length;
Lend no rotten bough thy strength.
Gauge thy gape with buck or goat,
Lest thine eye should choke thy throat.
After gorging, wouldst thou sleep?
Look thy den is hid and deep,
Lest a wrong, by thee forgot,
Draw thy killer to the spot.
East and West and North and South,
Wash thy skin and close thy mouth.
(Pit and rift and blue pool-brim
Middle-Jungle follow him!)
Wood and Water, Wind and Tree,
Jungle-Favour go with thee!

BAGHEERA

In the cage my life began;
Well I know the ways of Man.
By the Broken Lock that freed—
Man-cub 'ware the Man-cub's breed!
Scenting-dew or starlight pale,
Choose no idle tree-cat trail.
Pack or council, hunt or den,
Cry no truce with Jackal-Men.
Feed them silence when they say:
' Come with us an easy way.'
Feed them silence when they seek
Help of thine to hurt the weak.
Make no *bandar's* boast of skill;
Hold thy peace above the kill.
Let nor call nor song nor sign
Turn thee from thy hunting-line.
(Morning mist or twilight clear
Serve him, Wardens of the Deer!)
Wood and Water, Wind and Tree,
Jungle-Favour go with thee!

THE THREE

On the trail that thou must tread
To the threshold of our dread,
Where the Flower blossoms red;
Through the nights when thou shalt lie
'Prisoned from our Mother-sky,
Hearing us, thy loves, go by;
In the dawns, when thou shalt wake
To the toil thou canst not break,
Heartsick for the Jungle's sake;
Wood and Water, Wind and Tree,
Jungle-Favour go with thee!

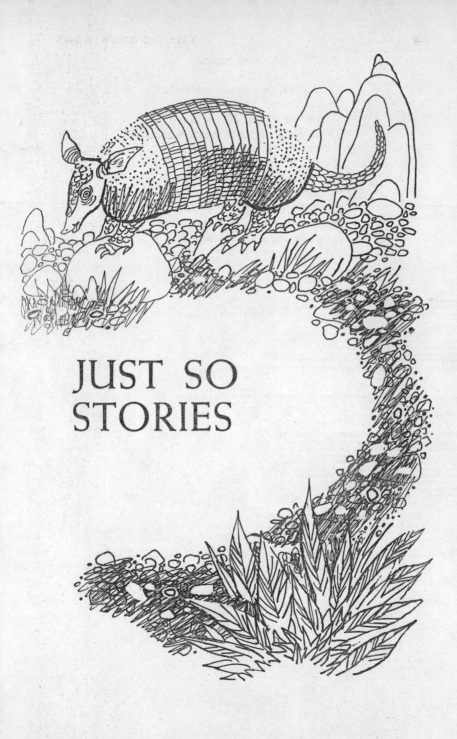

JUST SO
STORIES

JUST SO STORIES

HOW THE WHALE GOT HIS THROAT

IN THE SEA, once upon a time, O my Best Beloved, there was a Whale, and he ate fishes. He ate the starfish and the garfish, and the crab and the dab, and the plaice and the dace, and the skate and his mate, and the mackereel and the pickereel, and the really truly twirly-whirly eel. All the fishes he could find in all the sea he ate with his mouth—so! Till at last there was only one small fish left in all the sea, and he was a small 'Stute Fish, and he swam a little behind the Whale's right ear, so as to be out of harm's way. Then the Whale stood up on his tail and said, 'I'm hungry.' And the small 'Stute Fish said in a small 'stute voice, 'Noble and generous Cetacean, have you ever tasted Man?'

'No,' said the Whale. 'What is it like?'

'Nice,' said the small 'Stute Fish. 'Nice but nubbly.'

'Then fetch me some,' said the Whale, and he made the sea froth up with his tail.

'One at a time is enough,' said the 'Stute Fish. 'If you swim to latitude Fifty North, longitude Forty West (that is magic), you will find, sitting on a raft, in the middle of the sea, with nothing on but a pair of blue canvas breeches, a pair of suspenders (you must not forget the suspenders, Best Beloved), and a jack-knife, one shipwrecked Mariner, who, it is only fair to tell you, is a man of infinite-resource-and-sagacity.

So the Whale swam and swam to latitude Fifty North, longitude Forty West, as fast as he could swim, and on a raft, in the middle of the sea, with nothing to wear except a pair of blue canvas breeches, a pair of suspenders (you must particularly remember the suspenders, Best Beloved), and a jack-knife, he found one single, solitary shipwrecked Mariner, trailing his toes in the water. (He had his mummy's leave to paddle, or else he would never have done it because he was a man of infinite-resource-and-sagacity.)

Then the Whale opened his mouth back and back and back till it nearly touched his tail, and he swallowed the shipwrecked Mariner, and the raft he was sitting on, and his blue canvas breeches, and the suspenders (which you must not forget), and the jack-knife. He swallowed them all

down into his warm, dark, inside cupboards, and then he smacked his lips—so, and turned round three times on his tail.

But as soon as the Mariner, who was a man of infinite-resource-and-sagacity, found himself truly inside the Whale's warm, dark, inside cupboards, he stumped and he jumped and he thumped and he bumped, and he pranced and he danced, and he banged and he clanged, and he hit and he bit, and he leaped and he creeped, and he prowled and he howled, and he hopped and he dropped, and he cried and he sighed, and he crawled and he bawled, and he stepped and he lepped, and he danced hornpipes where he shouldn't, and the Whale felt most unhappy indeed. (*Have* you forgotten the suspenders?)

So he said to the 'Stute Fish, 'This man is very nubbly, and besides he is making me hiccough. What shall I do?'

'Tell him to come out,' said the 'Stute Fish.

So the Whale called down his own throat to the shipwrecked Mariner, 'Come out and behave yourself. I've got the hiccoughs.'

'Nay, nay!' said the Mariner. 'Not so, but far otherwise. Take me to my natal-shore and the white-cliffs-of-Albion, and I'll think about it.' And he began to dance more than ever.

'You had better take him home,' said the 'Stute Fish to the Whale. 'I ought to have warned you that he is a man of infinite-resource-and-sagacity.'

So the Whale swam and swam and swam, with both flippers and his tail, as hard as he could for the hiccoughs; and at last he saw the Mariner's natal-shore and the white-cliffs-of-Albion, and he rushed half-way up the beach, and opened his mouth wide and wide and wide, and said, 'Change here for Winchester, Ashuelot, Nashua, Keene, and stations on the *Fitch*-burg Road'; and just as he said 'Fitch' the Mariner walked out of his mouth. But while the Whale had been swimming, the Mariner, who was indeed a person of infinite-resource-and-sagacity, had taken his jack-knife and cut up the raft into a little square grating all running criss-cross, and he had tied it firm with his suspenders (*now* you know why you were not to forget the suspenders!), and he dragged that grating good and tight into the Whale's throat, and there it stuck! Then he recited the following *Sloka*, which, as you have not heard it, I will now proceed to relate—

> By means of a grating
> I have stopped your ating.

For the Mariner he was also an Hi-ber-ni-an. And he stepped out on the shingle, and went home to his mother, who had given him leave to trail his toes in the water; and he married and lived happily ever afterward. So did the Whale. But from that day on, the grating in his throat, which he could neither cough up nor swallow down, prevented him eating anything except very, very small fish; and that is the reason why whales nowadays never eat men or boys or little girls.

The small 'Stute Fish went and hid himself in the mud under the Door-sills of the Equator. He was afraid that the Whale might be angry with him.

The Sailor took the jack-knife home. He was wearing the blue canvas breeches when he walked out on the shingle. The suspenders were left behind, you see, to tie the grating with; and that is the end of *that* tale.

When the cabin port-holes are dark and green
 Because of the seas outside;
When the ship goes *wop* (with a wiggle between)
And the steward falls into the soup-tureen,
 And the trunks begin to slide;
When Nursey lies on the floor in a heap,
And Mummy tells you to let her sleep,
And you aren't waked or washed or dressed,
Why, then you will know (if you haven't guessed)
You're ' Fifty North and Forty West! '

HOW THE CAMEL GOT HIS HUMP

⌒§ NOW this is the next tale, and it tells how the Camel got his big hump. In the beginning of years, when the world was so new-and-all, and the Animals were just beginning to work for Man, there was a Camel, and he lived in the middle of a Howling Desert because he did not want to work; and besides, he was a Howler himself. So he ate sticks and thorns and tamarisks and milkweed and prickles, most 'scruciating idle; and when anybody spoke to him he said ' Humph! ' Just ' Humph! ' and no more.

Presently the Horse came to him on Monday morning, with a saddle on his back and a bit in his mouth, and said, ' Camel, O Camel, come out and trot like the rest of us.'

' Humph! ' said the Camel; and the Horse went away and told the Man.

Presently the Dog came to him, with a stick in his mouth, and said, ' Camel, O Camel, come and fetch and carry like the rest of us.'

' Humph! ' said the Camel; and the Dog went away and told the Man.

Presently the Ox came to him, with the yoke on his neck and said, ' Camel, O Camel, come and plough like the rest of us.'

' Humph! ' said the Camel; and the Ox went away and told the Man.

At the end of the day the Man called the Horse and the Dog and the Ox together, and said, ' Three, O Three, I'm very sorry for you (with the world so new-and-all); but that Humph-thing in the Desert can't work, or he would have been here by now, so I am going to leave him alone, and you must work double-time to make up for it.'

That made the Three very angry (with the world so new-and-all), and they held a palaver, and an *indaba*, and a *punchayet*, and a pow-wow on the edge of the Desert; and the Camel came chewing milkweed *most* 'scruciating idle, and laughed at them. Then he said ' Humph! ' and went away again.

Presently there came along the Djinn in charge of All Deserts, rolling in a cloud of dust (Djinns always travel that way because it is Magic), and he stopped to palaver and pow-wow with the Three.

' Djinn of All Deserts,' said the Horse, ' *is* it right for any one to be idle, with the world so new-and-all? '

' Certainly not,' said the Djinn.

' Well,' said the Horse, ' there's a thing in the middle of your Howling Desert (and he's a Howler himself) with a long neck and long legs, and he hasn't done a stroke of work since Monday morning. He won't trot.'

' Whew! ' said the Djinn, whistling, ' that's my Camel, for all the gold in Arabia! What does he say about it? '

'He says "Humph!"' said the Dog; 'and he won't fetch and carry.'

'Does he say anything else?'

'Only "Humph!"; and he won't plough,' said the Ox.

'Very good,' said the Djinn. 'I'll humph him if you will kindly wait a minute.'

The Djinn rolled himself up in his dust-cloak, and took a bearing across the desert, and found the Camel most 'scruciatingly idle, looking at his own reflection in a pool of water.

'My long and bubbling friend,' said the Djinn, 'what's this I hear of your doing no work, with the world so new-and-all?'

'Humph!' said the Camel.

The Djinn sat down, with his chin in his hand, and began to think a Great Magic, while the Camel looked at his own reflection in the pool of water.

'You've given the Three extra work ever since Monday morning, all on account of your 'scruciating idleness,' said the Djinn; and he went on thinking Magics, with his chin in his hand.

'Humph!' said the Camel.

'I shouldn't say that again if I were you,' said the Djinn; 'you might say it once too often. Bubbles, I want you to work.'

And the Camel said 'Humph!' again; but no sooner had he said it than he saw his back, that he was so proud of, puffing up and puffing up into a great big lolloping humph.

'Do you see that?' said the Djinn. 'That's your very own humph that you've brought upon your very own self by not working. To-day is Thursday, and you've done no work since Monday, when the work began. Now you are going to work.'

'How can I,' said the Camel, 'with this humph on my back?'

'That's made a-purpose,' said the Djinn, 'all because you missed those three days. You will be able to work now for three days without eating, because you can live on your humph; and don't you ever say I never did anything for you. Come out of the Desert and go to the Three, and behave. Humph yourself!'

And the Camel humphed himself, humph and all, and went away to join the Three. And from that day to this the Camel always wears a humph (we call it 'hump' now, not to hurt his feelings); but he has never yet caught up with the three days that he missed at the beginning of the world, and he has never yet learned how to behave.

> The Camel's hump is an ugly lump
> Which well you may see at the Zoo;
> But uglier yet is the hump we get
> From having too little to do.

Kiddie and grown-ups too-oo-oo,
If we haven't enough to do-oo-oo,
 We get the hump—
 Cameelious hump—
The hump that is black and blue!

We climb out of bed with a frouzly head
 And a snarly-yarly voice.
We shiver and scowl and we grunt and we growl
 At our bath and our boots and our toys;

And there ought to be a corner for me
(And I know there is one for you)
 When we get the hump—
 Cameelious hump—
The hump that is black and blue!

The cure for this ill is not to sit still,
 Or frowst with a book by the fire;
But to take a large hoe and a shovel also,
 And dig till you gently perspire;

And then you will find that the sun and the wind,
And the Djinn of the Garden too,
 Have lifted the hump—
 The horrible hump—
The hump that is black and blue!

I get it as well as you-oo-oo—
If I haven't enough to do-oo-oo—
 We all get hump—
 Cameelious hump—
Kiddies and grown-ups too!

HOW THE RHINOCEROS GOT HIS SKIN

ONCE upon a time, on an uninhabited island on the shores of the Red Sea, there lived a Parsee from whose hat the rays of the sun were reflected in more-than-oriental splendour. And the Parsee lived by the Red Sea with nothing but his hat and his knife and a cooking-stove of the kind that you must particularly never touch. And one day he took flour and water and currants and plums and sugar and things, and made himself one cake which was two feet across and three feet thick. It was indeed a Superior Comestible (*that's* magic), and he put it on the stove because *he* was allowed to cook on that stove, and he baked it and he baked it till it was all done brown and smelt most sentimental. But just as he was going to eat it there came down to the beach from the Altogether Uninhabited Interior one Rhinoceros with a horn on his nose, two piggy eyes, and few manners. In those days the Rhinoceros's skin fitted him quite tight. There were no wrinkles in it anywhere. He looked exactly like a Noah's Ark Rhinoceros, but of course much bigger. All the same, he had no manners then, and he has no manners now, and he never will have any manners. He said, ' How! ' and the Parsee left that cake and climbed to the top of a palm tree with nothing on but his hat, from which the rays of the sun were always reflected in more-than-oriental splendour. And the Rhinoceros upset the oil-stove with his nose, and the cake rolled on the sand, and he spiked that cake on the horn of his nose, and he ate it, and he went away, waving his tail, to the desolate and Exclusively Uninhabited Interior which abuts on the islands of Mazanderan, Socotra, and the Promontories of the Larger Equinox. Then the Parsee came down from his palm-tree and put the stove on its legs and recited the following *Sloka*, which, as you have not heard, I will now proceed to relate:—

> Them that takes cakes
> Which the Parsee-man bakes
> Makes dreadful mistakes.

And there was a great deal more in that than you would think.

Because, five weeks later, there was a heat-wave in the Red Sea, and everybody took off all the clothes they had. The Parsee took off his hat; but the Rhinoceros took off his skin and carried it over his shoulder as he came down to the beach to bathe. In those days it buttoned underneath with three buttons and looked like a waterproof. He said nothing whatever about the Parsee's cake, because he had eaten it all; and he never had any manners, then, since, or henceforward. He waddled straight into the water

and blew bubbles through his nose, leaving his skin on the beach.

Presently the Parsee came by and found the skin, and he smiled one smile that ran all round his face two times. Then he danced three times round the skin and rubbed his hands. Then he went to his camp and filled his hat with cake-crumbs, for the Parsee never ate anything but cake, and never swept out his camp. He took that skin, and he shook that skin, and he scrubbed that skin, and he rubbed that skin just as full of old, dry, stale, tickly cake-crumbs and some burned currants as ever it could *possibly* hold. Then he climbed to the top of his palm-tree and waited for the Rhinoceros to come out of the water and put it on.

And the Rhinoceros did. He buttoned it up with the three buttons, and it tickled like cake-crumbs in bed. Then he wanted to scratch, but that made it worse; and then he lay down on the sands and rolled and rolled and rolled, and every time he rolled the cake-crumbs tickled him worse and worse and worse. Then he ran to the palm-tree and rubbed and rubbed and rubbed himself against it. He rubbed so much and so hard that he rubbed his skin into a great fold over his shoulders, and another fold underneath, where the buttons used to be (but he rubbed the buttons off), and he rubbed some more folds over his legs. And it spoiled his temper, but it didn't make the least difference to the cake-crumbs. They were inside his skin and they tickled. So he went home, very angry indeed and horribly scratchy; and from that day to this every rhinoceros has great folds in his skin and a very bad temper, all on account of the cake-crumbs inside.

But the Parsee came down from his palm-tree, wearing his hat, from which the rays of the sun were reflected in more-than-oriental splendour, packed up his cooking-stove, and went away in the direction of Orotavo, Amygdala, the Upland Meadows of Anantarivo, and the Marshes of Sonaput.

> This Uninhabited Island
> Is off Cape Gardafui.
> By the Beaches of Socotra
> And the Pink Arabian Sea:
> But it's hot—too hot from Suez:
> For the likes of you and me
> Ever to go
> In a P. and O.
> And call on the Cake-Parsee!

HOW THE LEOPARD GOT HIS SPOTS

IN THE DAYS when everybody started fair, Best Beloved, the Leopard lived in a place called the High Veldt. 'Member it wasn't the Low Veldt, or the Bush Veldt, or the Sour Veldt, but the 'sclusively bare, hot, shiny High Veldt, where there was sand and sandy-coloured rock and 'sclusively tufts of sandy-yellowish grass. The Giraffe and the Zebra and the Eland and the Koodoo and the Hartebeest lived there; and they were 'sclusively sandy-yellow-brownish all over; but the Leopard, he was the 'sclusivest sandiest-yellowish-brownest of them all—a greyish-yellowish catty-shaped kind of beast, and he matched the 'sclusively yellowish-greyish-brownish colour of the High Veldt to one hair. This was very bad for the Giraffe and the Zebra and the rest of them; for he would lie down by a 'sclusively yellowish-greyish-brownish stone or clump of grass, and when the Giraffe or the Zebra or the Eland or the Koodoo or the Bush-Buck or the Bonte-Buck came by he would surprise them out of their jumpsome lives. He would indeed! And, also, there was an Ethiopian with bows and arrows (a 'sclusively greyish-brownish-yellowish man he was then), who lived on the High Veldt with the Leopard; and the two used to hunt together—the Ethiopian with his bows and arrows, and the Leopard 'sclusively with his teeth and claws—till the Giraffe and the Eland and the Koodoo and the Quagga and all the rest of them didn't know which way to jump, Best Beloved. They didn't indeed!

After a long time—things lived for ever so long in those days—they learned to avoid anything that looked like a Leopard or an Ethiopian; and bit by bit—the Giraffe began it, because his legs were the longest—they went away from the High Veldt. They scuttled for days and days and days till they came to a great forest, 'sclusively full of trees and bushes and stripy, speckly, patchy-blatchy shadows, and there they hid: and after another long time, what with standing half in the shade and half out of it, and what with the slippery-slidy shadows of the trees falling on them, the Giraffe grew blotchy, and the Zebra grew stripy, and the Eland and the Koodoo grew darker, with little wavy grey lines on their backs like bark on a tree trunk; and so, though you could hear them and smell them, you could very seldom see them, and then only when you knew precisely where to look. They had a beautiful time in the 'sclusively speckly-spickly shadows of the forest, while the Leopard and the Ethiopian ran about over the 'sclusively greyish-yellowish-reddish High Veldt outside, wondering where all their breakfasts and their dinners and their teas had gone. At last they were so hungry that they ate rats and beetles and rock-rabbits, the Leopard and the Ethiopian, and then they had the Big Tummy-ache, both together:

and then they met Baviaan—the dog-headed, barking Baboon, who is Quite the Wisest Animal in All South Africa.

Said Leopard to Baviaan (and it was a very hot day), 'Where has all the game gone?'

And Baviaan winked. *He* knew.

Said the Ethiopian to Baviaan, 'Can you tell me the present habitat of the aboriginal Fauna?' (That meant just the same thing, but the Ethiopian always used long words. He was a grown-up.)

And Baviaan winked. *He* knew.

Then said Baviaan, 'The game has gone into other spots; and my advice to you, Leopard, is to go into other spots as soon as you can.'

And the Ethiopian said, 'That is all very fine, but I wish to know whither the aboriginal Fauna has migrated.'

Then said Baviaan, 'The aboriginal Fauna has joined the aboriginal Flora because it was high time for a change; and my advice to you, Ethiopian, is to change as soon as you can.'

That puzzled the Leopard and the Ethiopian, but they set off to look for the aboriginal Flora, and presently, after ever so many days, they saw a great, high, tall forest full of tree trunks all 'sclusively speckled and sprottled and spotted, dotted and splashed and slashed and hatched and cross-hatched with shadows. (Say that quickly aloud, and you will see how *very* shadowy the forest must have been.)

'What is this,' said the Leopard, 'that is so 'sclusively dark, and yet so full of little pieces of light?'

'I don't know,' said the Ethiopian, 'but it ought to be the aboriginal Flora. I can smell Giraffe, and I can hear Giraffe, but I can't see Giraffe.'

'That's curious,' said the Leopard. 'I suppose it is because we have just come in out of the sunshine. I can smell Zebra, and I can hear Zebra, but I can't see Zebra.'

'Wait a bit,' said the Ethiopian. 'It's a long time since we've hunted 'em. Perhaps we've forgotten what they were like.'

'Fiddle!' said the Leopard. 'I remember them perfectly on the High Veldt, especially their marrow-bones. Giraffe is about seventeen feet high, of a 'sclusively fulvous golden-yellow from head to heel; and Zebra is about four and a half feet high, of a 'sclusively grey-fawn colour from head to heel.'

'Umm,' said the Ethiopian, looking into the speckly-spickly shadows of the aboriginal Flora-forest. 'Then they ought to show up in this dark place like ripe bananas in a smoke-house.'

But they didn't. The Leopard and the Ethiopian hunted all day; and though they could smell them and hear them, they never saw one of them.

'For goodness' sake,' said the Leopard at tea-time, 'let us wait till it gets dark. This daylight hunting is a perfect scandal.'

So they waited till dark, and then the Leopard heard something breathing sniffily in the starlight that fell all stripy through the branches, and he jumped at the noise, and it smelt like Zebra, and it felt like Zebra, and when he knocked it down it kicked like Zebra, but he couldn't see it. So he said, 'Be quiet, O you person without any form. I am going to sit on your head till morning, because there is something about you that I don't understand.'

Presently he heard a grunt and a crash and a scramble, and the Ethiopian called out, 'I've caught a thing that I can't see. It smells like Giraffe, and it kicks like Giraffe, but it hasn't any form.'

'Don't you trust it,' said the Leopard. 'Sit on its head till the

morning—same as me. They haven't any form—any of 'em.'

.

So they sat down on them hard till bright morning-time, and then Leopard said, 'What have you at your end of the table, Brother?'

The Ethiopian scratched his head and said, 'It ought to be 'sclusively a rich fulvous orange-tawny from head to heel, and it ought to be Giraffe; but it is covered all over with chestnut blotches. What have you at *your* end of the table, Brother?'

And the Leopard scratched his head and said, 'It ought to be 'sclusively a delicate greyish-fawn, and it ought to be Zebra; but it is covered all over with black and purple stripes. What in the world have you been doing to yourself, Zebra? Don't you know that if you were on the High Veldt I could see you ten miles off? You haven't any form.'

'Yes,' said the Zebra, 'but this isn't the High Veldt. Can't you see?'

'I can now,' said the Leopard. 'But I couldn't all yesterday. How is it done?'

'Let us up,' said the Zebra, 'and we will show you.'

They let the Zebra and the Giraffe get up; and Zebra moved away to some little thorn-bushes where the sunlight fell all stripy, and Giraffe moved off to some tallish trees where the shadows fell all blotchy.

'Now watch,' said the Zebra and the Giraffe. 'This is the way it's done. One—two—three! And where's your breakfast?'

Leopard stared, and Ethiopian stared, but all they could see were stripy shadows and blotched shadows in the forest, but never a sign of Zebra and Giraffe. They had just walked off and hidden themselves in the shadowy forest.

'Hi! Hi!' said the Ethiopian. 'That's a trick worth learning. Take a lesson by it, Leopard. You show up in this dark place like a bar of soap in a coal-scuttle.'

'Ho! Ho!' said the Leopard. 'Would it surprise you very much to know that you show up in this dark place like a mustard-plaster on a sack of coals?'

'Well, calling names won't catch dinner,' said the Ethiopian. 'The long and the little of it is that we don't match our backgrounds. I'm going to take Baviaan's advice. He told me I ought to change; and as I've nothing to change except my skin I'm going to change that.'

'What to?' said the Leopard, tremendously excited.

'To a nice working blackish-brownish colour, with a little purple in it, and touches of slaty-blue. It will be the very thing for hiding in hollows and behind trees.'

So he changed his skin then and there, and the Leopard was more excited than ever; he had never seen a man change his skin before.

'But what about me?' he said, when the Ethiopian had worked his last little finger into his fine new black skin.

'You take Baviaan's advice too. He told you to go into spots.'

' So I did,' said the Leopard. ' I went into other spots as fast as I could. I went into this spot with you, and a lot of good it has done me.'

' Oh,' said the Ethiopian, ' Baviaan didn't mean spots in South Africa. He meant spots on your skin.'

' What's the use of that? ' said the Leopard.

' Think of Giraffe,' said the Ethiopian. ' Or if you prefer stripes, think of Zebra. They find their spots and stripes give them per-fect satisfaction.'

' Umm,' said the Leopard. ' I wouldn't look like Zebra—not for ever so.'

' Well, make up your mind,' said the Ethiopian, ' because I'd hate to go hunting without you, but I must if you insist on looking like a sun-flower against a tarred fence.'

' I'll take spots, then,' said the Leopard; ' but don't make 'em too vulgar-big. I wouldn't look like Giraffe—not for ever so.'

' I'll make 'em with the tips of my fingers,' said the Ethiopian. ' There's plenty of black left on my skin still. Stand over! '

Then the Ethiopian put his five fingers close together (there was plenty of black left on his new skin still) and pressed them all over the Leopard, and wherever the five fingers touched they left five little black marks, all close together. You can see them on any Leopard's skin you like, Best Beloved. Sometimes the fingers slipped and the marks got a little blurred; but if you look closely at any Leopard now you will see that there are always five spots—off five fat black finger-tips.

' Now you *are* a beauty! ' said the Ethiopian. ' You can lie out on the bare ground and look like a heap of pebbles. You can lie out on the naked rocks and look like a piece of pudding-stone. You can lie out on a leafy branch and look like sunshine sifting through the leaves; and you can lie right across the centre of a path and look like nothing in particular. Think of that and purr! '

' But if I'm all this,' said the Leopard, ' why didn't you go spotty too? '

' Oh, plain black's best for a nigger,' said the Ethiopian. ' Now come along and we'll see if we can't get even with Mr. One-Two-Three-Where's-your-Breakfast! '

So they went away and lived happily ever afterward, Best Beloved. That is all.

Oh, now and then you will hear grown-ups say, ' Can the Ethiopian change his skin or the Leopard his spots? ' I don't think even grown-ups would keep on saying such a silly thing if the Leopard and the Ethiopian hadn't done it once—do you? But they will never do it again, Best Beloved. They are quite contented as they are.

I am the Most Wise Baviaan, saying in most wise tones,
' Let us melt into the landscape—just us two by our lones.'
People have come—in a carriage—calling. But Mummy is there . . .
Yes, I can go if you take me—Nurse say *she* don't care.

Let's go up to the pig-sties and sit on the farmyard rails!
Let's say things to the bunnies, and watch 'em skitter their tails!
Let's—oh, *anything*, Daddy, so long as it's you and me,
And going truly exploring, and not being in till tea!
Here's your boots (I've brought 'em), and here's your cap and stick
And here's your pipe and tobacco. Oh, come along out of it—quick.

THE SING-SONG OF OLD MAN KANGAROO

◆§ NOT always was the Kangaroo as now we do behold him, but a Different Animal with four short legs. He was grey and he was woolly, and his pride was inordinate: he danced on an outcrop in the middle of Australia, and he went to the Little God Nqa.

He went to Nqa at six before breakfast, saying, ' Make me different from all other animals by five this afternoon.'

Up jumped Nqa from his seat on the sand-flat and shouted, ' Go away! '

He was grey and he was woolly, and his pride was inordinate: he danced on a rock-ledge in the middle of Australia, and he went to the Middle God Nquing.

He went to Nquing at eight after breakfast, saying, ' Make me different from all other animals; make me, also, wonderfully popular by five this afternoon.'

Up jumped Nquing from his burrow in the spinifex and shouted, ' Go away! '

He was grey and he was woolly, and his pride was inordinate: he danced on a sandbank in the middle of Australia, and he went to the Big God Nqong.

He went to Nqong at ten before dinner-time, saying, ' Make me different from all other animals; make me popular and wonderfully run after by five this afternoon.'

Up jumped Nqong from his bath in the salt-pan and shouted, ' Yes, I will! '

Nqong called Dingo—Yellow-Dog Dingo—always hungry, dusty in the sunshine, and showed him Kangaroo. Nqong said, ' Dingo! Wake up, Dingo! Do you see that gentleman dancing on an ashpit? He wants to be popular and very truly run after. Dingo, make him so! '

Up jumped Dingo—Yellow-Dog Dingo—and said, ' What, *that* cat-rabbit? '

Off ran Dingo—Yellow-Dog Dingo—always hungry, grinning like a coal-scuttle,—ran after Kangaroo.

Off went the proud Kangaroo on his four little legs like a bunny.

This, O Beloved of mine, ends the first part of the tale!

He ran through the desert; he ran through the mountains; he ran through the salt-pans; he ran through the reed-beds; he ran through the blue gums; he ran through the spinifex; he ran till his front legs ached.

He had to!

Still ran Dingo—Yellow-Dog Dingo—always hungry, grinning like a

rat-trap, never getting nearer, never getting farther,—ran after Kangaroo.

He had to!

Still ran Kangaroo—Old Man Kangaroo. He ran through the ti-trees; he ran through the mulga; he ran through the long grass; he ran through the short grass; he ran through the Tropics of Capricorn and Cancer; he ran till his hind legs ached.

He had to!

Still ran Dingo—Yellow-Dog Dingo—hungrier and hungrier, grinning like a horse-collar, never getting nearer, never getting farther; and they came to the Wollgong River.

Now, there wasn't any bridge, and there wasn't any ferry-boat, and Kangaroo didn't know how to get over; so he stood on his legs and hopped.

He had to!

He hopped through the Flinders; he hopped through the Cinders; he hopped through the deserts in the middle of Australia. He hopped like a Kangaroo.

First he hopped one yard; then he hopped three yards; then he hopped five yards; his legs growing stronger; his legs growing longer. He hadn't any time for rest or refreshment, and he wanted them very much.

Still ran Dingo—Yellow-Dog Dingo—very much bewildered, very much hungry, and wondering what in the world or out of it made Old Man Kangaroo hop.

For he hopped like a cricket; like a pea in a saucepan; or a new rubber ball on a nursery floor.

He had to!

He tucked up his front legs; he hopped on his hind legs; he stuck out his tail for a balance-weight behind him; and he hopped through the Darling Downs.

He had to!

Still ran Dingo—Tired-Dog Dingo—hungrier and hungrier, very much bewildered, and wondering when in the world or out of it would Old Man Kangaroo stop.

Then came Nqong from his bath in the salt-pans, and said, ' It's five o'clock.'

Down sat Dingo—Poor-Dog Dingo—always hungry, dusky in the sunshine; hung out his tongue and howled.

Down sat Kangaroo—Old Man Kangaroo—stuck out his tail like a milking-stool behind him, and said, ' Thank goodness *that's* finished! '

Then said Nqong, who is always a gentleman, ' Why aren't you grateful to Yellow-Dog Dingo? Why don't you thank him for all he has done for you? '

Then said Kangaroo—Tired Old Kangaroo—' He's chased me out of the homes of my childhood; he's chased me out of my regular meal-times; he's altered my shape so I'll never get it back; and he's played Old Scratch with my legs.'

Then said Nqong, 'Perhaps I'm mistaken, but didn't you ask me to make you different from all other animals, as well as to make you very truly sought after? And now it is five o'clock.'

'Yes,' said Kangaroo. 'I wish that I hadn't. I thought you would do it by charms and incantations, but this is a practical joke.'

'Joke!' said Nqong from his bath in the blue gums. 'Say that again and I'll whistle up Dingo and run your hind legs off.'

'No,' said the Kangaroo. 'I must apologise. Legs are legs, and you needn't alter 'em so far as I am concerned. I only meant to explain to Your Lordliness that I've had nothing to eat since morning, and I'm very empty indeed.'

'Yes,' said Dingo—Yellow-Dog Dingo,—'I am just in the same situation. I've made him different from all other animals; but what may I have for my tea?'

Then said Nqong from his bath in the salt-pan, 'Come and ask me about it to-morrow, because I'm going to wash.'

So they were left in the middle of Australia, Old Man Kangaroo and Yellow-Dog Dingo, and each said, 'That's *your* fault.'

This is the mouth-filling song
Of the race that was run by a Boomer,
Run in a single burst—only event of its kind—
Started by big God Nqong from Warrigaborrigarooma—
Old Man Kangaroo first: Yellow-Dog Dingo behind.

Kangaroo bounded away,
His back-legs working like pistons—
Bounded from morning till dark,
Twenty-five feet to a bound.
Yellow-Dog Dingo lay
Like a yellow cloud in the distance—
Much too busy to bark.
My! but they covered the ground!

Nobody knows where they went,
Or followed the track that they flew in,
For that Continent
Hadn't been given a name.
They ran thirty degrees,
From Torres Straits to the Leeuwin
(Look at the Atlas, please),
And they ran back as they came.

S'posing you could trot
From Adelaide to the Pacific,
For an afternoon's run—
Half what these gentlmen did—
You would feel rather hot,
But your legs would develop terrific—
Yes, my importunate son,
You'd be a Marvellous Kid!

THE BEGINNING OF THE ARMADILLOS

~§ THIS, O Best Beloved, is another story of the High and Far-Off Times. In the very middle of those times was a Stickly-Prickly Hedgehog, and he lived on the banks of the turbid Amazon, eating shelly snails and things. And he had a friend, a Slow-Solid Tortoise, who lived on the banks of the turbid Amazon, eating green lettuces and things. And so *that* was all right, Best Beloved. Do you see?

But also, and at the same time, in those High and Far-Off Times, there was a Painted Jaguar, and he lived on the banks of the turbid Amazon too; and he ate everything that he could catch. When he could not catch deer or monkeys he would eat frogs and beetles; and when he could not catch frogs and beetles he went to his Mother Jaguar, and she told him how to eat hedgehogs and tortoises.

She said to him ever so many times, graciously waving her tail, 'My son, when you find a Hedgehog you must drop him into the water and then he will uncoil, and when you catch a Tortoise you must scoop him out of his shell with your paw.' And so that was all right, Best Beloved.

One beautiful night on the banks of the turbid Amazon, Painted Jaguar found Stickly-Prickly Hedgehog and Slow-Solid Tortoise sitting under the trunk of a fallen tree. They could not run away, and so Stickly-Prickly curled himself up into a ball, because he was a Hedgehog, and Slow-Solid Tortoise drew in his head and feet into his shell as far as they would go, because he was a Tortoise; and so *that* was all right, Best Beloved. Do you see?

'Now attend to me,' said Painted Jaguar, 'because this is very important. My mother said that when I meet a Hedgehog I am to drop him into the water and then he will uncoil, and when I meet a Tortoise I am to scoop him out of his shell with my paw. Now which of you is Hedgehog and which is Tortoise? Because, to save my spots, I can't tell.'

'Are you sure of what your Mummy told you?' said Stickly-Prickly Hedgehog. 'Are you quite sure? Perhaps she said that when you uncoil a Tortoise you must shell him out of the water with a scoop, and when you paw a Hedgehog you must drop him on the shell.'

'Are you sure of what your Mummy told you?' said Slow-and-Solid Tortoise. 'Are you quite sure? Perhaps she said that when you water a Hedgehog you must drop him into your paw, and when you meet a Tortoise you must shell him till he uncoils.'

'I don't think it was at all like that,' said Painted Jaguar, but he felt a little puzzled; 'but, please, say it again more distinctly.'

'When you scoop water with your paw you uncoil it with a Hedgehog,'

said Stickly-Prickly. 'Remember that, because it's important.'

'*But*,' said the Tortoise, 'when you paw your meat you drop it into a Tortoise with a scoop. Why can't you understand?'

'You are making my spots ache,' said Painted Jaguar; 'and besides, I didn't want your advice at all. I only wanted to know which of you is Hedgehog and which is Tortoise.'

'I shan't tell you,' said Stickly-Prickly. 'but you can scoop me out of my shell if you like.'

'Aha!' said Painted Jaguar. 'Now I know you're Tortoise. You thought I wouldn't! Now I will.' Painted Jaguar darted out his paddy-paw just as Stickly-Prickly curled himself up, and of course Jaguar's paddy-paw was just filled with prickles. Worse than that, he knocked Stickly-Prickly away and away into the woods and the bushes, where it was too dark to find him. Then he put his paddy-paw into his mouth, and of course the prickles hurt him worse than ever. As soon as he could speak he said, 'Now I know he isn't Tortoise at all. But '—and then he scratched his head with his un-prickly paw—'how do I know that this other is Tortoise?'

'But I *am* Tortoise,' said Slow-and-Solid. 'Your mother was quite right. She said that you were to scoop me out of my shell with your paw. Begin.'

'You didn't say she said that a minute ago,' said Painted Jaguar, sucking the prickles out of his paddy-paw. 'You said she said something quite different.'

'Well, suppose you say that I said that she said something quite different, I don't see that it makes any difference; because if she said what you said I said she said, it's just the same as if I said what she said she said. On the other hand, if you think she said that you were to uncoil me with a scoop, instead of pawing me into drops with a shell, I can't help that, can I?'

'But you said you wanted to be scooped out of your shell with my paw,' said Painted Jaguar.

'If you'll think again you'll find that I didn't say anything of the kind. I said that your mother said that you were to scoop me out of my shell,' said Slow-and-Solid.

'What will happen if I do?' said the Jaguar most sniffily and most cautious.

'I don't know, because I've never been scooped out of my shell before; but I tell you truly, if you want to see me swim away you've only got to drop me into the water.'

'I don't believe it,' said Painted Jaguar. 'You've mixed up all the things my mother told me to do with the things that you asked me whether I was sure that she didn't say, till I don't know whether I'm on my head or my painted tail; and now you come and tell me something I *can* understand, and it makes me more mixy than before. My mother told me that I was to drop one of you two into the water, and as you seem so anxious to be dropped I think you don't want to be dropped. So jump into the turbid

Amazon and be quick about it.'

'I warn you that your Mummy won't be pleased. Don't tell her I didn't tell you,' said Slow-Solid.

'If you say another word about what my mother said—' the Jaguar answered, but he had not finished the sentence before Slow-and-Solid quietly dived into the turbid Amazon, swam under water for a long way, and came out on the bank where Stickly-Prickly was waiting for him.

'That was a very narrow escape,' said Stickly-Prickly. 'I don't like Painted Jaguar. What did you tell him that you were?'

'I told him truthfully that I was a truthful Tortoise, but he wouldn't believe it, and he made me jump into the river to see if I was, and I was, and he is surprised. Now he's gone to tell his Mummy. Listen to him!'

They could hear Painted Jaguar roaring up and down among the trees and the bushes by the side of the turbid Amazon, till his Mummy came.

'Son, son!' said his mother ever so many times, graciously waving her tail, 'what have you been doing that you shouldn't have done?'

'I tried to scoop something that said it wanted to be scooped out of its shell with my paw, and my paw is full of per-ickles,' said Painted Jaguar.

'Son, son!' said his mother ever so many times, graciously waving her tail, 'by the prickles in your paddy-paw I see that that must have been a Hedgehog. You should have dropped him into the water.'

'I did that to the other thing; and he said he was a Tortoise, and I didn't believe him, and it was quite true, and he has dived under the turbid Amazon, and he won't come up again, and I haven't anything at all to eat, and I think we had better find lodgings somewhere else. They are too clever on the turbid Amazon for poor me!'

'Son, son!' said his mother ever so many times, graciously waving her tail, 'now attend to me and remember what I say. A Hedgehog curls himself up into a ball and his prickles stick out every which way at once. By this you may know the Hedgehog.'

'I don't like this old lady one little bit,' said Stickly-Prickly, under the shadow of a large leaf. 'I wonder what else she knows?'

'A Tortoise can't curl himself up,' Mother Jaguar went on, ever so many times, graciously waving her tail. 'He only draws his head and legs into his shell. By this you may know the Tortoise.'

'I don't like this old lady at all—at all,' said Slow-and-Solid Tortoise. 'Even Painted Jaguar can't forget those directions. It's a great pity that you can't swim, Stickly-Prickly.'

'Don't talk to me,' said Stickly-Prickly. 'Just think how much better it would be if you could curl up. This *is* a mess! Listen to Painted Jaguar.'

Painted Jaguar was sitting on the banks of the turbid Amazon sucking prickles out of his paws and saying to himself—

> 'Can't curl, but can swim—
> Slow-Solid, that's him!

> Curls up, but can't swim—
> Stickly-Prickly, that's him! '

' He'll never forget that this month of Sundays,' said Stickly-Prickly. ' Hold up my chin, Slow-and-Solid. I'm going to try to learn to swim. It may be useful.'

' Excellent! ' said Slow-and-Solid; and he held up Stickly-Prickly's chin, while Stickly-Prickly kicked in the waters of the turbid Amazon.

' You'll make a fine swimmer yet,' said Slow-and-Solid. ' Now, if you can unlace my back-plates a little, I'll see what I can do towards curling up. It may be useful.'

Stickly-Prickly helped to unlace Tortoise's back-plates, so that by twisting and straining Slow-and-Solid actually managed to curl up a tiddy wee bit.

' Excellent! ' said Stickly-Prickly; ' but I shouldn't do any more just now. It's making you black in the face. Kindly lead me into the water once again and I'll practise that side-stroke which you say is so easy.' And so Stickly-Prickly practised, and Slow-Solid swam alongside.

' Excellent! ' said Slow-and-Solid. ' A little more practice will make you a regular whale. Now, if I may trouble you to unlace my back and front plates two holes more, I'll try that fascinating bend that you say is so easy. Won't Painted Jaguar be surprised! '

' Excellent! ' said Stickly-Prickly, all wet from the turbid Amazon. ' I declare, I shouldn't know you from one of my own family. Two holes, I think, you said? A little more expression, please, and don't grunt quite so much, or Painted Jaguar may hear us. When you've finished, I want to try that long dive which you say is so easy. Won't Painted Jaguar be surprised! '

And so Stickly-Prickly dived, and Slow-and-Solid dived alongside.

' Excellent! ' said Slow-and-Solid. ' A leetle more attention to holding your breath and you will be able to keep house at the bottom of the turbid Amazon. Now I'll try that exercise of wrapping my hind legs round my ears which you say is so peculiarly comfortable. Won't Painted Jaguar be surprised! '

' Excellent! ' said Stickly-Prickly. ' But it's straining your back-plates a little. They are all overlapping now, instead of lying side by side.'

' Oh, that's the result of exercise,' said Slow-and-Solid. ' I've noticed that your prickles seem to be melting into one another, and that you're growing to look rather more like a pine-cone, and less like a chestnut-burr, than you used to.'

' Am I? ' said Stickly-Prickly. ' That comes from my soaking in the water. Oh, won't Painted Jaguar be surprised! '

They went on with their exercises, each helping the other, till morning came; and when the sun was high they rested and dried themselves. Then they saw that they were both of them quite different from what they had been.

' Stickly-Prickly,' said Tortoise after breakfast, ' I am not what I was

yesterday; but I think that I may yet amuse Painted Jaguar.'

'That was the very thing I was thinking just now,' said Stickly-Prickly. 'I think scales are a tremendous improvement on prickles—to say nothing of being able to swim. Oh, *won't* Painted Jaguar be surprised! Let's go and find him.'

By and by they found Painted Jaguar, still nursing his paddy-paw that had been hurt the night before. He was so astonished that he fell three times backward over his own painted tail without stopping.

'Good morning!' said Stickly-Prickly. 'And how is your dear gracious Mummy this morning?'

'She is quite well, thank you,' said Painted Jaguar; 'but you must forgive me if I do not at this precise moment recall your name.'

'That's unkind of you,' said Stickly-Prickly, 'seeing that this time yesterday you tried to scoop me out of my shell with your paw.'

'But you hadn't any shell. It was all prickles,' said Painted Jaguar. 'I know it was. Just look at my paw!'

'You told me to drop into the turbid Amazon and be drowned,' said Slow-Solid. 'Why are you so rude and forgetful to-day?'

'Don't you remember what your mother told you?' said Stickly-Prickly,—

> 'Can't curl, but can swim—
> Stickly-Prickly, that's him!
> Curls up, but can't swim—
> Slow-Solid, that's him!'

Then they both curled themselves up and rolled round and round Painted Jaguar till his eyes turned truly cart-wheels in his head.

Then he went to fetch his mother.

'Mother,' he said, 'there are two new animals in the woods to-day, and the one that you said couldn't swim, swims, and the one that you said couldn't curl up, curls; and they've gone shares in their prickles, I think, because both of them are scaly all over, instead of one being smooth and the other very prickly; and, besides that, they are rolling round and round in circles, and I don't feel comfy.'

'Son, son!' said Mother Jaguar ever so many times, graciously waving her tail, 'a Hedgehog is a Hedgehog, and can't be anything but a Hedgehog; and a Tortoise is a Tortoise, and can never be anything else.'

'But it isn't a Hedgehog, and it isn't a Tortoise. It's a little bit of both, and I don't know its proper name.'

'Nonsense!' said Mother Jaguar. 'Everything has its proper name. I should call it "Armadillo" till I found out the real one. And I should leave it alone.'

So Painted Jaguar did as he was told, especially about leaving them alone; but the curious thing is that from that day to this, O Best Beloved, no one on the banks of the turbid Amazon has ever called Stickly-Prickly

and Slow-Solid anything except Armadillo. There are Hedgehogs and Tortoises in other places, of course (there are some in my garden); but the real old and clever kind, with their scales lying lippety-lappety one over the other, like pine-cone scales, that lived on the banks of the turbid Amazon in the High and Far-Off Days, are always called Armadillos, because they were so clever.

So *that's* all right, Best Beloved. Do you see?

> I've never sailed the Amazon,
> I've never reached Brazil;
> But the *Don* and *Magdalena,*
> They can go there when they will!

>> Yes, weekly from Southampton,
>> Great steamers, white and gold,
>> Go rolling down to Rio
>> (Roll down—roll down to Rio!)
>> And I'd like to roll to Rio
>> Some day before I'm old!

> I've never seen a Jaguar,
> Nor yet an Armadill—
> O dilloing in his armour,
> And I s'pose I never will,

>> Unless I go to Rio
>> These wonders to behold—
>> Roll down—roll down to Rio—
>> Roll really down to Rio!
>> Oh, I'd love to roll to Rio
>> Some day before I'm old!

THE CRAB THAT PLAYED WITH THE SEA

BEFORE the High and Far-Off Times, O my Best Beloved, came the Time of the Very Beginnings; and that was in the days when the Eldest Magician was getting Things ready. First he got the Earth ready; then he got the Sea ready; and then he told all the Animals that they could come out and play. And the Animals said, ' O Eldest Magician, what shall we play at? ' and he said, ' I will show you.' He took the Elephant—All-the-Elephant-there-was—and said, ' Play at being an Elephant,' and All-the-Elephant-there-was played. He took the Beaver—All-the-Beaver-there-was—and said, ' Play at being a Beaver,' and All-the-Beaver-there-was played. He took the Cow—All-the-Cow-there-was—and said, ' Play at being a Cow,' and All-the-Cow-there-was played. He took the Turtle—All-the-Turtle-there-was—and said, ' Play at being a Turtle,' and All-the-Turtle-there-was played. One by one he took all the beasts and birds and fishes and told them what to play at.

But towards evening, when people and things grow restless and tired, there came up the Man (With his own little girl-daughter?)—Yes, with his own best beloved little girl-daughter sitting upon his shoulder, and he said, ' What is this play, Eldest Magician? ' And the Eldest Magician said, ' Ho, Son of Adam, this is the play of the Very Beginning; but you are too wise for this play.' And the Man saluted and said, ' Yes, I am too wise for this play; but see that you make all the Animals obedient to me.'

Now, while the two were talking together, Pau Amma the Crab, who was next in the game, scuttled off sideways and stepped into the sea, saying to himself, ' I will play my play alone in the deep waters, and I will never be obedient to this son of Adam.' Nobody saw him go away except the little girl-daughter where she leaned on the Man's shoulder. And the play went on till there were no more Animals left without orders; and the Eldest Magician wiped the fine dust off his hands and walked about the world to see how the Animals were playing.

He went North, Best Beloved, and he found All-the-Elephant-there-was digging with his tusks and stamping with his feet in the nice new clean earth that had been made ready for him.

' Kun? ' said All-the-Elephant-there-was, meaning, ' Is this right? '

' Payah kun,' said the Eldest Magician, meaning, ' That is quite right '; and he breathed upon the great rocks and lumps of earth that All-the-Elephant-there-was had thrown up, and they became the great Himalayan Mountains, and you can look them out on the map.

He went East, and he found All-the-Cow-there-was feeding in the field

that had been made ready for her, and she licked her tongue round a whole forest at a time, and swallowed it and sat down to chew her cud.

' *Kun?* ' said All-the-Cow-there-was.

' *Payah kun,*' said the Eldest Magician; and he breathed upon the bare patch where she had eaten, and upon the place where she had sat down, and one became the great Indian Desert, and the other became the Desert of Sahara, and you can look them out on the map.

He went West, and he found All-the-Beaver-there-was making a beaver-dam across the mouths of broad rivers that had been got ready for him.

' *Kun?* ' said All-the-Beaver-there-was.

' *Payah kun,*' said the Eldest Magician; and he breathed upon the fallen trees and the still water, and they became the Everglades in Florida, and you may look them out on the map.

Then he went South and found All-the-Turtle-there-was scratching with his flippers in the sand that had been got ready for him, and the sand and the rocks whirled through the air and fell far off into the sea.

' *Kun?* ' said All-the-Turtle-there-was.

' *Payah kun,*' said the Eldest Magician; and he breathed upon the sand and the rocks, where they had fallen in the sea, and they became the most beautiful islands of Borneo, Celebes, Sumatra, Java, and the rest of the Malay Archipelago, and you can look *them* out on the map!

By and by the Eldest Magician met the Man on the banks of the Perak river, and said, ' Ho! Son of Adam, are all the Animals obedient to you? '

' Yes,' said the Man.

' Is all the Earth obedient to you? '

' Yes,' said the Man.

' Is all the Sea obedient to you? '

' No,' said the Man. ' Once a day and once a night the Sea runs up the Perak river and drives the sweet-water back into the forest, so that my house is made wet; once a day and once a night it runs down the river and draws all the water after it, so that there is nothing left but mud, and my canoe is upset. Is that the play you told it to play? '

' No,' said the Eldest Magician. ' That is a new and a bad play.'

' Look! ' said the Man, and as he spoke the great Sea came up the mouth of the Perak river, driving the river backwards till it overflowed all the dark forests for miles and miles, and flooded the Man's house.

' This is wrong. Launch your canoe and we will find out who is playing with the Sea,' said the Eldest Magician. They stepped into the canoe; the little girl-daughter came with them; and the Man took his *kris*—a curving, wavy dagger with a blade like a flame,—and they pushed out on the Perak river. Then the Sea began to run back and back, and the canoe was sucked out of the mouth of the Perak river, past Selangor, past Malacca, past Singapore, out and out to the Island of Bingtang, as though it had been pulled by a string.

Then the Eldest Magician stood up and shouted, ' Ho! beasts, birds, and fishes, that I took between my hands at the Very Beginning and taught the play that you should play, which one of you is playing with the Sea? '

Then all the beasts, birds, and fishes said together, ' Eldest Magician, we play the plays that you taught us to play—we and our children's children. But not one of us plays with the Sea.'

Then the Moon rose big and full over the water, and the Eldest Magician said to the hunchbacked old man who sits in the Moon spinning a fishing-line with which he hopes one day to catch the world, ' Ho! Fisher of the Moon, are you playing with the Sea? '

' No,' said the Fisherman, ' I am spinning a line with which I shall some day catch the world; but I do not play with the Sea.' And he went on spinning his line.

Now there is also a Rat up in the Moon who always bites the old Fisherman's line as fast as it is made, and the Eldest Magician said to him, ' Ho! Rat of the Moon, are you playing with the Sea? '

And the Rat said, ' I am too busy biting through the line that this old Fisherman is spinning. I do not play with the Sea.' And he went on biting the line.

Then the little girl-daughter put up her little soft brown arms with the beautiful white shell bracelets and said, ' O Eldest Magician! when my father here talked to you at the Very Beginning, and I leaned upon his shoulder while the beasts were being taught their plays, one beast went away naughtily into the Sea before you had taught him his play.'

And the Eldest Magician said, ' How wise are little children who see and are silent! What was the beast like? '

And the little girl-daughter said, ' He was round and he was flat; and his eyes grew upon stalks; and he walked sideways like this; and he was covered with strong armour upon his back '

And the Eldest Magician said, ' How wise are little children who speak truth! Now I know where Pau Amma went. Give me the paddle! '

So he took the paddle; but there was no need to paddle, for the water flowed steadily past all the islands till they came to the place called Pusat Tasek—the Heart of the Sea—where the great hollow is that leads down to the heart of the world, and in that hollow grows the Wonderful Tree, Pauh Janggi, that bears the magic twin nuts. Then the Eldest Magician slid his arm up to the shoulder through the deep warm water, and under the roots of the Wonderful Tree he touched the broad back of Pau Amma the Crab. And Pau Amma settled down at the touch, and all the Sea rose up as water rises in a basin when you put your hand into it.

' Ah! ' said the Eldest Magician. ' Now I know who has been playing with the Sea '; and he called out, ' What are you doing, Pau Amma? '

And Pau Amma, deep down below, answered, ' Once a day and once a night I go out to look for my food. Once a day and once a night I return. Leave me alone.'

Then the Eldest Magician said, ' Listen, Pau Amma. When you go out from your cave the waters of the Sea pour down into Pusat Tasek, and all the beaches of all the islands are left bare, and the little fish die, and Raja Moyang Kaban, the King of the Elephants, his legs are made muddy. When you come back and sit in Pusat Tasek, the waters of the Sea rise, and half the little islands are drowned, and the Man's house is flooded, and Raja Abdullah, the King of the Crocodiles, his mouth is filled with the salt water.'

Then Pau Amma, deep down below, laughed and said, ' I did not know I was so important. Henceforward I will go out seven times a day, and the waters shall never be still.'

And the Eldest Magician said, ' I cannot make you play the play you were meant to play, Pau Amma, because you escaped me at the Very Beginning; but if you are not afraid, come up and we will talk about it.'

' I am not afraid,' said Pau Amma, and he rose to the top of the sea in the moonlight. There was nobody in the world so big as Pau Amma—for he was the King Crab of all Crabs. Not a common Crab, but a King Crab. One side of his great shell touched the beach at Sarawak; the other touched the beach at Pahang; and he was taller than the smoke of three volcanoes! As he rose up through the branches of the Wonderful Tree he tore off one of the great twin-fruits—the magic double-kernelled nuts that make people young,—and the little girl-daughter saw it bobbing alongside the canoe, and pulled it in and began to pick out the soft eyes of it with her little golden scissors.

' Now,' said the Magician, ' make a Magic, Pau Amma, to show that you are really important.'

Pau Amma rolled his eyes and waved his legs, but he could only stir up the Sea, because, though he was a King Crab, he was nothing more than a Crab, and the Eldest Magician laughed.

' You are not so important after all, Pau Amma,' he said. ' Now, let me try,' and he made a Magic with his left hand—with just the little finger of his left hand—and—lo and behold, Best Beloved, Pau Amma's hard, blue-green-black shell fell off him as a husk falls off a cocoa-nut, and Pau Amma was left all soft—soft as the little crabs that you sometimes find on the beach, Best Beloved.

' Indeed, you are very important,' said the Eldest Magician. ' Shall I ask the Man here to cut you with *kris*? Shall I send for Raja Moyang Kaban, the King of the Elephants, to pierce you with his tusks, or shall I call Raja Abdullah, the King of the Crocodiles, to bite you? '

And Pau Amma said, ' I am ashamed! Give me back my hard shell and let me go back to Pusat Tasek, and I will only stir out once a day and once a night to get my food.'

And the Eldest Magician said, ' No, Pau Amma, I will *not* give you back your shell, for you will grow bigger and prouder and stronger, and perhaps you will forget your promise, and you will play with the Sea once more.'

Then Pau Amma said, ' What shall I do? I am so big that I can only

hide in Pusat Tasek, and if I go anywhere else, all soft as I am now, the sharks and the dogfish will eat me. And if I go to Pusat Tasek, all soft as I am now, though I may be safe, I can never stir out to get my food, and so I shall die.' Then he waved his legs and lamented.

'Listen, Pau Amma,' said the Eldest Magician. 'I cannot make you play the play you were meant to play, because you escaped me at the Very Beginning; but if you choose, I can make every stone and every hole and every bunch of weed in all the seas a safe Pusat Tasek for you and your children for always.'

Then Pau Amma said, ' That is good, but I do not choose yet. Look! there is that Man who talked to you at the Very Beginning. If he had not taken up your attention I should not have grown tired of waiting and run away, and all this would never have happened. What will *he* do for me? '

And the Man said, ' If you choose, I will make a Magic, so that both the deep water and the dry ground will be a home for you and your children —so that you shall be able to hide both on the land and in the sea.'

And Pau Amma said, ' I do not choose yet. Look! there is that girl who saw me running away at the Very Beginning. If she had spoken then, the Eldest Magician would have called me back, and all this would never have happened. What will *she* do for me? '

And the little girl-daughter said, ' This is a good nut that I am eating. If you choose, I will make a Magic and I will give you this pair of scissors, very sharp and strong, so that you and your children can eat cocoa-nuts like this all day long when you come up from the Sea to the land; or you can dig a Pusat Tasek for yourself with the scissors that belong to you when there is no stone or hole near by; and when the earth is too hard, by the help of these same scissors you can run up a tree.'

And Pau Amma said, ' I do not choose yet, for, all soft as I am, these gifts would not help me. Give me back my shell, O Eldest Magician, and then I will play your play.'

And the Eldest Magician said, ' I will give it back, Pau Amma, for eleven months of the year; but on the twelfth month of every year it shall grow soft again, to remind you and all your children that I can make Magics, and to keep you humble, Pau Amma; for I see that if you can run both under the water and on land, you will grow too bold; and if you can climb trees and crack nuts and dig holes with your scissors, you will grow too greedy, Pau Amma.'

Then Pau Amma thought a little and said, ' I have made my choice. I will take all the gifts.'

Then the Eldest Magician made a Magic with the right hand, with all five fingers of his right hand, and lo and behold, Best Beloved, Pau Amma grew smaller and smaller and smaller, till at last there was only a little green crab swimming in the water alongside the canoe, crying in a very small voice, ' Give me the scissors! '

And the girl-daughter picked him up on the palm of her little brown

hand, and sat him in the bottom of the canoe and gave him her scissors, and he waved them in his little arms, and opened them and shut them and snapped them, and said, ' I can eat nuts. I can crack shells. I can dig holes. I can climb trees. I can breathe in the dry air, and I can find a safe Pusat Tasek under every stone. I did not know I was so important. *Kun?* ' (Is this right?)

' *Payah kun,*' said the Eldest Magician, and he laughed and gave him his blessing; and little Pau Amma scuttled over the side of the canoe into the water; and he was so tiny that he could have hidden under the shadow of a dry leaf on land or of a dead shell at the bottom of the sea.

' Was that well done? ' said the Eldest Magician.

' Yes,' said the Man. ' But now we must go back to Perak, and that is a weary way to paddle. If we had waited till Pau Amma had gone out of Pusat Tasek and come home, the water would have carried us there by itself.'

' You are lazy,' said the Eldest Magician. ' So your children shall be lazy. They shall be the laziest people in the world. They shall be called the Malazy—the lazy people '; and he held up his finger to the Moon and said, ' O Fisherman, here is the Man too lazy to row home. Pull his canoe home with your line, Fisherman.'

' No,' said the Man. ' If I am to be lazy all my days, let the Sea work for me twice a day for ever. That will save paddling.'

And the Eldest Magician laughed and said,

' *Payah kun*' (That is right).

And the Rat of the Moon stopped biting the line; and the Fisherman let his line down till it touched the Sea, and he pulled the whole deep Sea along, past the Island of Bintang, past Singapore, past Malacca, past Selangor, till the canoe whirled into the mouth of the Perak river again.

' *Kun?* ' said the Fisherman of the Moon.

' *Payah kun,*' said the Eldest Magician. ' See now that you pull the Sea twice a day and twice a night for ever, so that the Malazy fishermen may be saved paddling. But be careful not to do it too hard, or I shall make a Magic on you as I did to Pau Amma.'

Then they all went up the Perak river and went to bed, Best Beloved.

Now listen and attend!

From that day to this the Moon has always pulled the sea up and down and made what we called the tides. Sometimes the Fisher of the Sea pulls a little too hard, and then we get spring-tides; and sometimes he pulls a little too softly, and then we get what are called neap-tides; but nearly always he is careful, because of the Eldest Magician.

And Pau Amma? You can see when you go to the beach, how all Pau Ammas' babies make little Pusat Taseks for themselves under every stone and bunch of weed on the sands; you can see them waving their little scissors; and in some parts of the world they truly live on the dry land and run up the palm trees and eat cocoa-nuts, exactly as the girl-daughter promised.

But once a year all Pau Ammas must shake off their hard armour and be soft—to remind them of what the Eldest Magician could do. And so it isn't fair to kill or hunt Pau Ammas' babies just because old Pau Amma was stupidly rude a very long time ago.

Oh yes! And Pau Ammas' babies hate being taken out of their little Pusat Taseks and brought home in pickle-bottles. That is why they nip you with their scissors, and it serves you right!

China-going P. and O.'s
Pass Pau Amma's playground close,
And his Pusat Tasek lies
Near the track of most B.I.'s.
U.Y.K. and N.D.L.
Knows Pau Amma's home as well
As the fisher of the Sea knows
'Bens,' M.M.'s, and Rubattinos.
But (and this is rather queer)
A.T.L.'s can *not* come here;
O. and O. and D.O.A.
Must go round another way.
Orient, Anchor, Bibby, Hall,
Never go that way at all.
U.C.S. would have a fit
If it found itself on it.
And if 'Beavers' took their cargoes
To Penang instead of Lagos,
Or a fat Shaw-Savill bore
Passengers to Singapore,
Or a White Star were to try a
Little trip to Sourabaya,
Or a B.S.A. went on
Past Natal to Cheribon,
Then great Mr. Lloyds would come
With a wire and drag them home!

You'll know what my riddle means
When you've eaten mangosteens.

THE ELEPHANT'S CHILD

◦క IN THE HIGH and Far-Off Times the Elephant, O Best Beloved, had no trunk. He had only a blackish, bulgy nose, as big as a boot, that he could wriggle about from side to side; but he couldn't pick up things with it. But there was one Elephant—a new Elephant—an Elephant's Child— who was full of 'satiable curtiosity, and that means he asked ever so many questions. And he lived in Africa, and he filled all Africa with his 'satiable curtiosities. He asked his tall aunt, the Ostrich, why her tail-feathers grew just so, and his tall aunt the Ostrich spanked him with her hard, hard claw. He asked his tall uncle, the Giraffe, what made his skin spotty, and his tall uncle, the Giraffe, spanked him with his hard, hard hoof. And still he was full of 'satiable curtiosity! He asked his broad aunt, the Hippopotamus, why her eyes were red, and his broad aunt, the Hippopotamus, spanked him with her broad, broad hoof; and he asked his hairy uncle, the Baboon, why melons tasted just so, and his hairy uncle, the Baboon, spanked him with his hairy, hairy paw. And *still* he was full of 'satiable curtiosity! He asked questions about everything that he saw, or heard, or felt, or smelt, or touched, and all his uncles and his aunts spanked him. And still he was full of 'satiable curtiosity!

One fine morning in the middle of the Precession of the Equinoxes this 'satiable Elephant's Child asked a new fine question that he had never asked before. He asked, ' What does the Crocodile have for dinner? ' Then everybody said, ' Hush! ' in a loud and dretful tone, and they spanked him immediately and directly, without stopping, for a long time.

By and by, when that was finished, he came upon Kolokolo Bird sitting in the middle of a wait-a-bit thorn-bush, and he said, ' My father has spanked me, and my mother has spanked me; all my aunts and uncles have spanked me for my 'satiable curtiosity; and *still* I want to know what the Crocodile has for dinner! '

Then Kolokolo Bird said, with a mournful cry, ' Go to the banks of the great grey-green, greasy Limpopo River, all set about with fever-trees, and find out.'

That very next morning, when there was nothing left of the Equinoxes, because the Precession had preceded according to precedent, this 'satiable Elephant's Child took a hundred pounds of bananas (the little short red kind), and a hundred pounds of sugar-cane (the long purple kind), and seventeen melons (the greeny-crackly kind), and said to all his dear families, ' Good-bye. I am going to the great grey-green, greasy Limpopo River, all set about with fever-trees, to find out what the Crocodile has for dinner.'

And they all spanked him once more for luck, though he asked them most politely to stop.

Then he went away, a little warm, but not at all astonished, eating melons. and throwing the rind about, because he could not pick it up.

He went from Graham's Town to Kimberley, and from Kimberley to Khama's Country, and from Khama's Country he went east by north, eating melons all the time, till at last he came to the banks of the great grey-green, greasy Limpopo River, all set about with fever-trees, precisely as Kolokolo Bird had said.

Now you must know and understand, O Best Beloved, that till that very week, and day, and hour, and minute, this 'satiable Elephant's Child had never seen a Crocodile, and did not know what one was like. It was all his 'satiable curtiosity.

The first thing that he found was a Bi-Coloured-Python-Rock-Snake curled round a rock.

' 'Scuse me,' said the Elephant's Child most politely, ' but have you seen such a thing as a Crocodile in these promiscuous parts? '

' *Have* I seen a Crocodile? ' said the Bi-Coloured-Python-Rock-Snake, in a voice of dretful scorn. ' What will you ask me next? '

' 'Scuse me,' said the Elephant's Child, ' but could you kindly tell me what he has for dinner? '

Then the Bi-Coloured-Python-Rock-Snake uncoiled himself very quickly from the rock, and spanked the Elephant's Child with his scalesome, flailsome tail.

' That is odd,' said the Elephant's Child, ' because my father and my mother, and my uncle and my aunt, not to mention my other aunt, the Hippopotamus, and my other uncle, the Baboon, have all spanked me for my 'satiable curtiosity—and I suppose this is the same thing.'

So he said good-bye very politely to the Bi-Coloured-Python-Rock-Snake, and helped to coil him up on the rock again, and went on, a little warm, but not at all astonished, eating melons, and throwing the rind about, because he could not pick it up, till he trod on what he thought was a log of wood at the very edge of the great grey-green, greasy Limpopo River, all set about with fever-trees.

But it was really the Crocodile, O Best Beloved, and the Crocodile winked one eye—like this!

' 'Scuse me,' said the Elephant's Child most politely, ' but do you happen to have seen a Crocodile in these promiscuous parts? '

Then the Crocodile winked the other eye, and lifted half his tail out of the mud; and the Elephant's Child stepped back most politely, because he did not wish to be spanked again.

' Come hither, Little One,' said the Crocodile. ' Why do you ask such things? '

' 'Scuse me,' said the Elephant's Child most politely, ' but my father has spanked me, my mother has spanked me, not to mention my tall aunt,

the Ostrich, and my tall uncle, the Giraffe, who can kick ever so hard, as well as my broad aunt, the Hippopotamus, and my hairy uncle, the Baboon, *and* including the Bi-Coloured-Python-Rock-Snake, with the scalesome, flailsome tail, just up the bank, who spanks harder than any of them; and *so*, if it's quite all the same to you, I don't want to be spanked any more.'

'Come hither, Little One,' said the Crocodile, 'for I am the Crocodile,' and he wept crocodile-tears to show it was quite true.

Then the Elephant's Child grew all breathless, and panted, and kneeled down on the bank and said, 'You are the very person I have been looking for all these long days. Will you please tell me what you have for dinner?'

'Come hither, Little One,' said the Crocodile, 'and I'll whisper.'

Then the Elephant's Child put his head down close to the Crocodile's musky, tusky mouth, and the Crocodile caught him by his little nose, which up to that very week, day, hour, and minute, had been no bigger than a boot, though much more useful.

'I think,' said the Crocodile—and he said it between his teeth, like this—'I think to-day I will begin with Elephant's Child!'

At this, O Best Beloved, the Elephant's Child was much annoyed, and he said, speaking through his nose, like this, 'Led go! You are hurtig be!'

Then the Bi-Coloured-Python-Rock-Snake scuffled down from the bank and said, 'My young friend, if you do not now, immediately and instantly, pull as hard as ever you can, it is my opinion that your acquaintance in the large-pattern leather ulster' (and by this he meant the Crocodile) 'will jerk you into yonder limpid stream before you can say Jack Robinson.'

This is the way Bi-Coloured-Python-Rock-Snakes always talk.

Then the Elephant's Child sat back on his little haunches, and pulled, and pulled, and pulled, and his nose began to stretch. And the Crocodile floundered into the water, making it all creamy with great sweeps of his tail, and *he* pulled, and pulled, and pulled.

And the Elephant's Child's nose kept on stretching; and the Elephant's Child spread all his little four legs and pulled, and pulled, and pulled, and his nose kept on stretching; and the Crocodile threshed his tail like an oar, and *he* pulled, and pulled, and pulled, and at each pull the Elephant's Child's nose grew longer and longer—and it hurt him hijjus!

Then the Elephant's Child felt his legs slipping, and he said through his nose, which was now nearly five feet long, 'This is too butch for be!'

Then the Bi-Coloured-Python-Rock-Snake came down from the bank, and knotted himself in a double-clove-hitch round the Elephant's Child's hind legs, and said, 'Rash and inexperienced traveller, we will now seriously devote ourselves to a little high tension, because if we do not, it is my impression that yonder self-propelling man-of-war with the armour-plated upper deck' (and by this, O Best Beloved, he meant the Crocodile), 'will permanently vitiate your future career.'

That is the way all Bi-Coloured-Python-Rock-Snakes always talk.

So he pulled, and the Elephant's Child pulled, and the Crocodile

pulled; but the Elephant's Child and the Bi-Coloured-Python-Rock-Snake pulled hardest; and at last the Crocodile let go of the Elephant's Child's nose with a plop that you could hear all up and down the Limpopo.

Then the Elephant's Child sat down most hard and sudden; but first he was careful to say 'Thank you' to the Bi-Coloured-Python-Rock-Snake; and next he was kind to his poor pulled nose, and wrapped it all up in cool banana leaves, and hung it in the great grey-green, greasy Limpopo to cool.

'What are you doing that for?' said the Bi-Coloured-Python-Rock-Snake.

''Scuse me,' said the Elephant's Child, 'but my nose is badly out of shape, and I am waiting for it to shrink.'

'Then you will have to wait a long time,' said the Bi-Coloured-Python-

Rock-Snake. ' Some people do not know what is good for them.'

The Elephant's Child sat there for three days waiting for his nose to shrink. But it never grew any shorter, and, besides, it made him squint. For, O Best Beloved, you will see and understand that the Crocodile had pulled it out into a really truly trunk same as all Elephants have to-day.

At the end of the third day a fly came and stung him on the shoulder, and before he knew what he was doing he lifted up his trunk and hit that fly dead with the end of it.

' 'Vantage number one! ' said the Bi-Coloured-Python-Rock-Snake. ' You couldn't have done that with a mere-smear nose. Try and eat a little now.'

Before he thought what he was doing the Elephant's Child put out his trunk and plucked a large bundle of grass, dusted it clean against his fore-legs, and stuffed it into his own mouth.

' 'Vantage number two! ' said the Bi-Coloured-Python-Rock-Snake. ' You couldn't have done that with a mere-smear nose. Don't you think the sun is very hot here? '

' It is,' said the Elephant's Child, and before he thought what he was doing he schlooped up a schloop of mud from the banks of the great grey-green, greasy Limpopo, and slapped it on his head, where it made a cool schloopy-sloshy mud-cap all trickly behind his ears.

' 'Vantage number three! ' said the Bi-Coloured-Python-Rock-Snake. ' You couldn't have done that with a mere-smear nose. Now how do you feel about being spanked again? '

' 'Scuse me,' said the Elephant's Child, ' but I should not like it at all.'

' How would you like to spank somebody? ' said the Bi-Coloured-Python-Rock-Snake.

' I should like it very much indeed,' said the Elephant's Child.

' Well,' said the Bi-Coloured-Python-Rock-Snake, ' you will find that new nose of yours very useful to spank people with.'

' Thank you,' said the Elephant's Child, ' I'll remember that; and now I think I'll go home to all my dear families and try.'

So the Elephant's Child went home across Africa frisking and whisking his trunk. When he wanted fruit to eat he pulled fruit down from a tree, instead of waiting for it to fall as he used to do. When he wanted grass he plucked grass up from the ground, instead of going on his knees as he used to do. When the flies bit him he broke off the branch of a tree and used it as a fly-whisk; and he made himself a new, cool, slushy-squshy mud-cap whenever the sun was hot. When he felt lonely walking through Africa he sang to himself down his trunk, and the noise was louder than several brass bands. He went especially out of his way to find a broad Hippopotamus (she was no relation of his) , and he spanked her very hard, to make sure that the Bi-Coloured-Python-Rock-Snake had spoken the truth about his new trunk. The rest of the time he picked up the melon rinds that he had dropped on his way to the Limpopo—for he was a Tidy Pachyderm.

One dark evening he came back to all his dear families, and he coiled up his trunk and said, ' How do you do? ' They were very glad to see him, and immediately said, ' Come here and be spanked for your 'satiable curtiosity.'

' Pooh,' said the Elephant's Child. ' I don't think you peoples know anything about spanking; but I do, and I'll show you.'

Then he uncurled his trunk and knocked two of his dear brothers head over heels.

' O Bananas! ' said they. ' Where did you learn that trick, and what have you done to your nose? '

' I got a new one from the Crocodile on the banks of the great grey-green, greasy Limpopo River,' said the Elephant's Child. ' I asked him what he had for dinner, and he gave me this to keep.'

' It looks very ugly,' said his hairy uncle, the Baboon.

' It does,' said the Elephant's Child. ' But it's very useful,' and he picked up his hairy uncle, the Baboon, by one hairy leg, and hove him into a hornets' nest.

Then that bad Elephant's Child spanked all his dear families for a long time, till they were very warm and greatly astonished. He pulled out his tall Ostrich aunt's tail-feathers; and he caught his tall uncle, the Giraffe, by the hind-leg, and dragged him through a thorn-bush; and he shouted at his broad aunt, the Hippopotamus, and blew bubbles into her ear when she was sleeping in the water after meals; but he never let any one touch Kolokolo Bird.

At last things grew so exciting that his dear families went off one by one in a hurry to the banks of the great grey-green, greasy Limpopo River, all set about with fever-trees, to borrow new noses from the Crocodile. When they came back nobody spanked anybody any more; and ever since that day, O Best Beloved, all the Elephants you will ever see, besides all those that you won't, have trunks precisely like the trunk of the 'satiable Elephant's Child.

> I keep six honest serving-men;
> (They taught me all I knew)
> Their names are What and Where and When
> And How and Where and Who.
> I send them over land and sea,
> I send them east and west;
> But after they have worked for me,
> I give them all a rest.
>
> I let them rest from nine till five,
> For I am busy then,

As well as breakfast, lunch, and tea,
 For they are hungry men:
But different folk have different views:
 I know a person small—
She keeps ten million serving-men,
 Who get no rest at all!
She sends 'em abroad on her own affairs,
 From the second she opens her eyes—
One million Hows, two million Wheres,
 And seven million Whys!

THE CAT THAT WALKED BY HIMSELF

⚗ HEAR and attend and listen; for this befell and behappened and became and was, O my Best Beloved, when the Tame animals were wild. The Dog was wild, and the Horse was wild, and the Cow was wild, and the Sheep was wild, and the Pig was wild—as wild as wild could be—and they walked in the Wet Wild Woods by their wild lones. But the wildest of all the wild animals was the Cat. He walked by himself, and all places were alike to him.

Of course the Man was wild too. He was dreadfully wild. He didn't even begin to be tame till he met the Woman, and she told him that she did not like living in his wild ways. She picked out a nice dry Cave, instead of a heap of wet leaves, to lie down in; and she strewed clean sand on the floor; and she lit a nice fire of wood at the back of the Cave; and she hung a dried wild-horse skin, tail-down, across the opening of the Cave; and she said, 'Wipe your feet, dear, when you come in, and now we'll keep house.'

That night, Best Beloved, they ate wild sheep roasted on the hot stones, and flavoured with wild garlic and wild pepper; and wild duck stuffed with wild rice and wild fenugreek and wild coriander; and marrow-bones of wild oxen; and wild cherries, and wild grenadillas. Then the Man went to sleep in front of the fire ever so happy; but the Woman sat up, combing her hair. She took the bone of the shoulder of mutton—the big fat blade-bone—and she looked at the wonderful marks on it, and she threw more wood on the fire, and she made a Magic. She made the First Singing Magic in the world.

Out in the Wet Wild Woods all the wild animals gathered together where they could see the light of the fire a long way off, and they wondered what it meant.

Then Wild Horse stamped with his wild foot and said, 'O my Friends and O my Enemies, why have the Man and the Woman made that great light in that great Cave, and what harm will it do us?'

Wild Dog lifted up his wild nose and smelled the smell of roast mutton, and said, 'I will go up and see and look, and say; for I think it is good. Cat, come with me.'

'Nenni!' said the Cat. 'I am the Cat who walks by himself, and all places are alike to me. I will not come.'

'Then we can never be friends again,' said Wild Dog, and he trotted off to the Cave. But when he had gone a little way the Cat said to himself, 'All places are alike to me. Why should I not go too and see and look and come away at my own liking?' So he slipped after Wild Dog softly, very softly, and hid himself where he could hear everything.

When Wild Dog reached the mouth of the Cave he lifted up the dried

horse-skin with his nose and sniffed the beautiful smell of the roast mutton, and the Woman, looking at the blade-bone, heard him, and laughed, and said, ' Here comes the first. Wild Thing out of the Wild Woods, what do you want? '

Wild Dog said, ' O my Enemy and Wife of my Enemy, what is this that smells so good in the Wild Woods? '

Then the Woman picked up a roasted mutton-bone and threw it to Wild Dog, and said, ' Wild Thing out of the Wild Woods, taste and try.' Wild Dog gnawed the bone, and it was more delicious than anything he had ever tasted, and he said, ' O my Enemy and Wife of my Enemy, give me another.'

The Woman said, ' Wild Thing out of the Wild Woods, help my Man to hunt through the day and guard this Cave at night, and I will give you as many roast bones as you need.'

' Ah! ' said the Cat, listening. ' This is a very wise Woman, but she is not so wise as I am.'

Wild Dog crawled into the Cave and laid his head on the Woman's lap, and said, ' O my Friend and Wife of my Friend, I will help your Man to hunt through the day, and at night I will guard your Cave.'

' Ah! ' said the Cat, listening. ' That is a very foolish Dog.' And he went back through the Wet Wild Woods waving his wild tail, and walking by his wild lone. But he never told anybody.

When the Man waked up he said, ' What is Wild Dog doing here? ' And the Woman said, ' His name is not Wild Dog any more, but the First Friend, because he will be our friend for always and always and always. Take him with you when you go hunting.'

Next night the Woman cut great green armfuls of fresh grass from the water-meadows, and dried it before the fire, so that it smelt like new-mown hay, and she sat at the mouth of the Cave and plaited a halter out of horse-hide, and she looked at the shoulder of mutton-bone—at the big broad blade-bone—and she made a Magic. She made the Second Singing Magic in the world.

Out in the Wild Woods all the wild animals wondered what had happened to Wild Dog, and at last Wild Horse stamped with his foot and said, ' I will go and see and say why Wild Dog has not returned. Cat, come with me.'

' Nenni! ' said the Cat. ' I am the Cat who walks by himself, and all places are alike to me. I will not come.' But all the same he followed Wild Horse softly, very softly, and hid himself where he could hear everything.

When the Woman heard Wild Horse tripping and stumbling on his long mane, she laughed and said, ' Here comes the second. Wild Thing out of the Wild Woods, what do you want? '

Wild Horse said, ' O my Enemy and Wife of my Enemy, where is Wild Dog? '

The Woman laughed, and picked up the blade-bone and looked at it,

and said, 'Wild Thing out of the Wild Woods, you did not come here for Wild Dog, but for the sake of this good grass.'

And Wild Horse, tripping and stumbling on his long mane, said, 'That is true; give it me to eat.'

The Woman said, 'Wild Thing out of the Wild Woods, bend your wild head and wear what I give you, and you shall eat the wonderful grass three times a day.'

'Ah,' said the Cat, listening, 'this is a clever Woman, but she is not so clever as I am.'

Wild Horse bent his wild head, and the Woman slipped the plaited hide halter over it, and Wild Horse breathed on the Woman's feet and said, 'O my Mistress, and Wife of my Master, I will be your servant for the sake of the wonderful grass.'

'Ah,' said the Cat, listening, 'that is a very foolish horse.' And he went back through the Wet Wild Woods, waving his wild tail and walking by his wild lone. But he never told anybody.

When the Man and the Dog came back from hunting, the Man said, 'What is Wild Horse doing here?' And the Woman said, 'His name is not Wild Horse any more, but the First Servant, because he will carry us from place to place for always and always and always. Ride on his back when you go hunting.'

Next day, holding her wild head high that her wild horns should not catch in the wild trees, Wild Cow came up to the Cave, and the Cat followed, and hid himself just the same as before; and everything happened just the same as before; and the Cat said the same things as before, and when Wild Cow had promised to give her milk to the Woman every day in exchange for the wonderful grass, the Cat went back through the Wet Wild Woods waving his wild tail and walked by his wild lone, just the same as before. But he never told anybody. And when the Man and the Horse and the Dog came home from hunting and asked the same questions same as before, the Woman said, 'Her name is not Wild Cow any more, but the Giver of Good Food. She will give us the warm white milk for always and always and always, and I will take care of her while you and the First Friend and the First Servant go hunting.'

Next day the Cat waited to see if any other Wild thing would go up to the Cave, but no one moved in the Wet Wild Woods, so the Cat walked there by himself; and he saw the Woman milking the Cow, and he saw the light of the fire in the Cave, and he smelt the smell of the warm white milk.

Cat said, 'O my Enemy and Wife of my Enemy, where did Wild Cow go?'

The Woman laughed and said, 'Wild Thing out of the Wild Woods, go back to the Woods again, for I have braided up my hair, and I have put away the magic blade-bone, and we have no more need of either friends or servants in our cave.'

Cat said, 'I am not a friend, and I am not a servant. I am the Cat who

walks by himself, and I wish to come into your cave.'

Woman said, 'Then why did you not come with First Friend on the first night?'

Cat grew very angry and said, 'Has Wild Dog told tales of me?'

Then the Woman laughed and said, 'You are the Cat who walks by himself, and all places are alike to you. You are neither a friend nor a servant. You have said it yourself. Go away and walk by yourself in all places alike.'

Then Cat pretended to be sorry and said, 'Must I never come into the Cave? Must I never sit by the warm fire? Must I never drink the warm white milk? You are very wise and very beautiful. You should not be cruel even to a Cat.'

Woman said, 'I knew I was wise, but I did not know I was beautiful. So I will make a bargain with you. If ever I say one word in your praise you may come into the Cave.'

'And if you say two words in my praise?' said the Cat.

'I never shall,' said the Woman, 'but if I say two words in your praise, you may sit by the fire in the Cave.'

'And if you say three words?' said the Cat.

'I never shall,' said the Woman, 'but if I say three words in your praise, you may drink the warm white milk three times a day for always and always and always.'

Then the Cat arched his back and said, 'Now let the Curtain at the mouth of the Cave, and the Fire at the back of the Cave, and the Milk-pots that stand beside the Fire, remember what my Enemy and the Wife of my Enemy has said.' And he went away through the Wet Wild Woods waving his wild tail and walking by his wild lone.

That night when the Man and the Horse and the Dog came home from hunting, the Woman did not tell them of the bargain that she had made with the Cat, because she was afraid that they might not like it.

Cat went far and far away and hid himself in the Wet Wild Woods by his wild lone for a long time till the Woman forgot all about him. Only the Bat—the little upside-down Bat—that hung inside the Cave, knew where Cat hid; and every evening Bat would fly to Cat with news of what was happening.

One evening Bat said, 'There is a Baby in the Cave. He is new and pink and fat and small, and the Woman is very fond of him.'

'Ah,' said the Cat, listening, 'but what is the Baby fond of?'

'He is fond of things that are soft and tickle,' said the Bat. 'He is fond of warm things to hold in his arms when he goes to sleep. He is fond of being played with. He is fond of all those things.'

'Ah,' said the Cat, listening, 'then my time has come.'

Next night Cat walked through the Wet Wild Woods and hid very near the Cave till morning-time, and Man and Dog and Horse went hunting. The Woman was busy cooking that morning, and the Baby cried and interrupted. So she carried him outside the Cave and gave him a handful of peb-

bles to play with. But still the Baby cried.

Then the Cat put out his paddy paw and patted the Baby on the cheek, and it cooed; and the Cat rubbed against its fat knees and tickled it under its fat chin with his tail. And the Baby laughed and the Woman heard him and smiled.

Then the Bat—the little upside-down Bat—that hung in the mouth of the Cave said, ' O my Hostess and Wife of my Host and Mother of my Host's Son, a Wild Thing from the Wild Woods is most beautifully playing with your Baby.'

' A blessing on that Wild Thing whoever he may be,' said the Woman, straightening her back, ' for I was a busy woman this morning and he has done me a service.'

The very minute and second, Best Beloved, the dried horse-skin Curtain that was stretched tail-down at the mouth of the Cave fell down—*woosh!*—because it remembered the bargain she had made with the Cat, and when the Woman went to pick it up—lo and behold!—the Cat was sitting quite comfy inside the Cave.

' O my Enemy and Wife of my Enemy and Mother of my Enemy,' said the Cat, ' it is I: for you have spoken a word in my praise, and now I can sit within the Cave for always and always and always. But still I am the Cat who walks by himself, and all places are alike to me.'

The Woman was very angry, and shut her lips tight and took up her spinning-wheel and began to spin.

But the Baby cried because the Cat had gone away, and the Woman could not hush it, for it struggled and kicked and grew black in the face.

' O my Enemy and Wife of my Enemy and Mother of my Enemy,' said the Cat, ' take a strand of the wire that you are spinning and tie it to your spinning-whorl and drag it along the floor, and I will show you a Magic that shall make your Baby laugh as loudly as he is now crying.'

' I will do so,' said the Woman, ' because I am at my wits' end; but I will not thank you for it.'

She tied the thread to the little clay spindle-whorl and drew it across the floor, and the Cat ran after it and patted it with his paws and rolled head over heels, and tossed it backward over his shoulder and chased it between his hind-legs and pretended to lose it, and pounced down upon it again, till the Baby laughed as loudly as it had been crying, and scrambled after the Cat and frolicked all over the Cave till it grew tired and settled down to sleep with the Cat in its arms.

' Now,' said the Cat, ' I will sing the Baby a song that shall keep him asleep for an hour.' And he began to purr, loud and low, low and loud, till the Baby fell fast asleep. The Woman smiled as she looked down upon the two of them and said, ' That was wonderfully done. No question but you are very clever, O Cat.'

That very minute and second, Best Beloved, the smoke of the fire at the back of the Cave came down in clouds from the roof—*puff!*—because

it remembered the bargain she had made with the Cat, and when it had cleared away—lo and behold!—the Cat was sitting quite comfy close to the fire.

'O my Enemy and Wife of my Enemy and Mother of my Enemy,' said the Cat, ' it is I, for you have spoken a second word in my praise, and now I can sit by the warm fire at the back of the Cave for always and always and always. But still I am the Cat who walks by himself, and all places are alike to me.'

Then the Woman was very very angry, and let down her hair and put more wood on the fire and brought out the broad blade-bone of the shoulder of mutton and began to make a Magic that should prevent her from saying a third word in praise of the Cat. It was not a Singing Magic, Best Beloved, it was a Still Magic; and by and by the Cave grew so still that a little wee-wee mouse crept out of a corner and ran across the floor.

'O my Enemy and Wife of my Enemy and Mother of my Enemy,' said the Cat, ' is that little mouse part of your magic? '

' Ouh! Chee! No indeed! ' said the Woman, and she dropped the blade-bone and jumped upon the footstool in front of the fire and braided up her hair very quick for fear that the mouse should run up it.

' Ah,' said the Cat, watching, ' then the mouse will do me no harm if I eat it? '

' No,' said the Woman, braiding up her hair, ' eat it quickly and I will ever be grateful to you.'

Cat made one jump and caught the little mouse, and the Woman said, ' A hundred thanks. Even the First Friend is not quick enough to catch little mice as you have done. You must be very wise.'

That very moment and second, O Best Beloved, the Milk-pot that stood by the fire cracked in two pieces—*ffft*—because it remembered the bargain she had made with the Cat, and when the Woman jumped down from the footstool—lo and behold!—the Cat was lapping up the warm white milk that lay in one of the broken pieces.

'O my Enemy and Wife of my Enemy and Mother of my Enemy,' said the Cat, ' it is I; for you have spoken three words in my praise, and now I can drink the warm white milk three times a day for always and always and always. But *still* I am the Cat who walks by himself, and all places are alike to me.'

Then the Woman laughed and set the Cat a bowl of the warm white milk and said, ' O Cat, you are as clever as a man, but remember that your bargain was not made with the Man or the Dog, and I do not know what they will do when they come home.'

' What is that to me? ' said the Cat. ' If I have my place in the Cave by the fire and my warm white milk three times a day I do not care what the Man or the Dog can do.'

That evening when the Man and the Dog came into the Cave, the Woman told them all the story of the bargain while the Cat sat by the fire

and smiled. Then the Man said, ' Yes, but he has not made a bargain with *me* or with all proper Men after me.' Then he took off his two leather boots and he took up his little stone axe (that makes three) and he fetched a piece of wood and a hatchet (that is five altogether), and he set them out in a row and he said, ' Now we will make *our* bargain. If you do not catch mice when you are in the Cave for always and always and always, I will throw these five things at you whenever I see you, and so shall all proper Men do after me.'

' Ah,' said the Woman, listening, ' this is a very clever Cat, but he is not so clever as my Man.'

The Cat counted the five things (and they looked very knobby) and he said, ' I will catch mice when I am in the Cave for always and always and always; but *still* I am the Cat who walks by himself, and all places are alike to me.'

' Not when I am near,' said the Man. ' If you had not said that last I would have put all these things away for always and always and always; but I am now going to throw my two boots and my little stone axe (that makes three) at you whenever I meet you. And so shall all proper Men do after me! '

Then the Dog said, ' Wait a minute. He has not made a bargain with *me* or with all proper Dogs after me.' And he showed his teeth and said, ' If you are not kind to the Baby while I am in the Cave for always and always and always, I will hunt you till I catch you, and when I catch you I will bite you. And so shall all proper Dogs do after me.'

' Ah,' said the Woman, listening, ' this is a very clever Cat, but he is not so clever as the Dog.'

Cat counted the Dog's teeth (and they looked very pointed) and he said, ' I will be kind to the Baby while I am in the Cave, as long as he does not pull my tail too hard, for always and always and always. But *still* I am the Cat that walks by himself, and all places are alike to me.'

' Not when I am near,' said the Dog. ' If you had not said that last I would have shut my mouth for always and always and always; but *now* I am going to hunt you up a tree whenever I meet you. And so shall all proper Dogs do after me.'

Then the Man threw his two boots and his little stone axe (that makes three) at the Cat, and the Cat ran out of the Cave and the Dog chased him up a tree; and from that day to this, Best Beloved, three proper Men out of five will always throw things at a Cat whenever they meet him, and all proper Dogs will chase him up a tree. But the Cat keeps his side of the bargain too. He will kill mice and he will be kind to Babies when he is in the house, just as long as they do not pull his tail too hard. But when he has done that, and between times, and when the moon gets up and night comes, he is the Cat that walks by himself, and all places are alike to him. Then he goes out to the Wet Wild Woods or up the Wet Wild

Trees or on the Wet Wild Roofs, waving his wild tail and walking by his
wild lone.

Pussy can sit by the fire and sing,
 Pussy can climb a tree,
Or play with a silly old cork and string
 To 'muse herself, not me.
But I like *Binkie* my dog, because
 He knows how to behave;
So, *Binkie's* the same as the First Friend was
 And I am the Man in the Cave.

Pussy will play man-Friday till
 It's time to wet her paw
And make her walk on the window-sill
 (For the footprint Crusoe saw);
Then she fluffles her tail and mews,
 And scratches and won't attend.
But *Binkie* will play whatever I choose,
 And he is my true First Friend.

Pussy will rub my knees with her head
 Pretending she loves me hard;
But the very minute I go to my bed
 Pussy runs out in the yard,
And there she stays till the morning-light;
 So I know it is only pretend;
But *Binkie*, he snores at my feet all night,
 And he is my Firstest Friend!

THE BUTTERFLY THAT STAMPED

꿏 THIS, O my Best Beloved, is a story—a new and a wonderful story—a story quite different from the other stories—a story about The Most Wise Sovereign Suleiman-bin-Daoud—Solomon the Son of David.

There are three hundred and fifty-five stories about Suleiman-bin-Daoud; but this was not one of them. It is not the story of the Lapwing who found the Water; or the Hoopoe who shaded Suleiman-bin-Daoud from the heat. It is not the story of the Glass Pavement, or the Ruby with the Crooked Hole, or the Gold Bars of Balkis. It is the story of the Butterfly that Stamped.

Now attend all over again and listen!

Suleiman-bin-Daoud was wise. He understood what the beasts said, what the birds said, what the fishes said, and what the insects said. He understood what the rocks said deep under the earth when they bowed in towards each other and groaned; and he understood what the trees said when they rustled in the middle of the morning. He understood everything, from the bishop on the bench to the hyssop on the wall, and Balkis, his Head Queen, the Most Beautiful Queen Balkis, was nearly as wise as he was.

Suleiman-bin-Daoud was strong. Upon the third finger of the right hand he wore a ring. When he turned it once, Afrits and Djinns came out of the earth to do whatever he told them. When he turned it twice, Fairies came down from the sky to do whatever he told them; and when he turned it three times, the very great angel Azrael of the Sword came dressed as a water-carrier, and told him the news of the three worlds,—Above—Below—and Here.

And yet Suleiman-bin-Daoud was not proud. He very seldom showed off, and when he did he was sorry for it. Once he tried to feed all the animals in all the world in one day, but when the food was ready an Animal came out of the deep sea and ate it up in three mouthfuls. Suleiman-bin-Daoud was very surprised and said, ' O Animal, who are you? ' And the Animal said, ' O King, live for ever! I am the smallest of thirty thousand brothers, and our home is at the bottom of the sea. We heard that you were going to feed all the animals in all the world, and my brothers sent me to ask when dinner would be ready.' Suleiman-bin-Daoud was more surprised than ever and said, ' O Animal, you have eaten all the dinner that I made ready for all the animals in the world.' And the Animal said, ' O King, live for ever, but do you really call that a dinner? Where I come from we each eat twice as much as that between meals.' Then Suleiman-bin-Daoud fell flat on his

face and said, ' O Animal! I gave that dinner to show what a great and rich king I was, and not because I really wanted to be kind to the animals. Now I am ashamed, and it serves me right.' Suleiman-bin-Daoud was a really truly wise man, Best Beloved. After that he never forgot that it was silly to show off; and now the real story part of my story begins.

He married ever so many wives. He married nine hundred and ninety-nine wives, besides the Most Beautiful Balkis; and they all lived in a great golden palace in the middle of a lovely garden with fountains. He didn't really want nine hundred and ninety-nine wives, but in those days everybody married ever so many wives, and of course the King had to marry ever so many more just to show that he was the King.

Some of the wives were nice, but some were simply horrid, and the horrid ones quarrelled with the nice ones and made them horrid too, and then they would all quarrel with Suleiman-bin-Daoud, and that was horrid for him. But Balkis the Most Beautiful never quarrelled with Suleiman-bin-Daoud. She loved him too much. She sat in her rooms in the Golden Palace, or walked in the Palace garden, and was truly sorry for him.

Of course if he had chosen to turn his ring on his finger and call up the Djinns and Afrits they would have magicked all those nine hundred and ninety-nine quarrelsome wives into white mules of the desert or greyhounds or pomegranate seeds; but Suleiman-bin-Daoud thought that that would be showing off. So, when they quarrelled too much, he only walked by himself in one part of the beautiful Palace gardens and wished he had never been born.

One day, when they had quarrelled for three weeks—all nine hundred and ninety-nine wives together—Suleiman-bin-Daoud went out for peace and quiet as usual; and among the orange trees he met Balkis the Most Beautiful, very sorrowful because Suleiman-bin-Daoud was so worried. And she said to him, ' O my Lord and Light of my Eyes, turn the ring upon your finger and show these Queens of Egypt and Mesopotamia and Persia and China that you are the great and terrible King.' But Suleiman-bin-Daoud shook his head and said, ' O my lady and Delight of my Life, remember the Animal that came out of the sea and made me ashamed before all the animals in all the world because I showed off. Now, if I showed off before these Queens of Persia and Egypt and Abyssinia and China, merely because they worry me, I might be made even more ashamed than I have been.'

And Balkis the Most Beautiful said, ' O my Lord and Treasure of my Soul, what will you do?'

And Suleiman-bin-Daoud said, ' O my Lady and Content of my Heart, I shall continue to endure my fate at the hands of these nine hundred and ninety-nine Queens who vex me with their continual quarrelling.'

So he went on between the lilies and the loquats and the roses and the cannas and the heavy-scented ginger-plants that grew in the garden, till he came to the great camphor-tree that was called the Camphor Tree of Sulei-man-bin-Daoud. But Balkis hid among the tall irises and the spotted bam-

boos and the red lilies behind the camphor-tree, so as to be near her own true love, Suleiman-bin-Daoud.

Presently two Butterflies flew under the tree, quarrelling.

Suleiman-bin-Daoud heard one say to the other, ' I wonder at your presumption in talking like this to me. Don't you know that if I stamped with my foot all Suleiman-bin-Daoud's Palace and his garden here would immediately vanish in a clap of thunder? '

Then Suleiman-bin-Daoud forgot his nine hundred and ninety-nine bothersome wives, and laughed, till the camphor-tree shook, at the Butterfly's boast. And he held out his finger and said, ' Little man, come here.'

The Butterfly was dreadfully frightened, but he managed to fly up to the hand of Suleiman-bin-Daoud, and clung there, fanning himself. Suleiman-bin-Daoud bent his head and whispered very softly, ' Little man, you know that all your stamping wouldn't bend one blade of grass. What made you tell that awful fib to your wife?—for doubtless she is your wife.'

The Butterfly looked at Suleiman-bin-Daoud and saw the most wise King's eyes twinkle like stars on a frosty night, and he picked up his courage with both wings, and he put his head on one side and said, ' O King, live for ever. She *is* my wife; and you know what wives are like.'

Suleiman-bin-Daoud smiled in his beard and said, ' Yes, I know, little brother.'

' One must keep them in order somehow,' said the Butterfly, ' and she has been quarrelling with me all the morning. I said that to quiet her.'

And Suleiman-bin-Daoud said, ' May it quiet her. Go back to your wife, little brother, and let me hear what you say.'

Back flew the Butterfly to his wife, who was all of a twitter behind a leaf, and she said, ' He heard you! Suleiman-bin-Daoud himself heard you! '

' Heard me! ' said the Butterfly. ' Of course he did. I meant him to hear me.'

' And what did he say? Oh, what did he say? '

' Well,' said the Butterfly, fanning himself most importantly, ' between you and me, my dear—of course I don't blame him, because his Palace must have cost a great deal and the oranges are just ripening,—he asked me not to stamp, and I promised I wouldn't.'

' Gracious! ' said his wife, and sat quite quiet; but Suleiman-bin-Daoud laughed till the tears ran down his face at the impudence of the bad little Butterfly.

Balkis the Most Beautiful stood up behind the tree among the red lilies and smiled to herself, for she had heard all this talk. She thought, ' If I am wise I can yet save my Lord from the persecutions of these quarrelsome Queens,' and she held out her finger and whispered softly to the Butterfly's Wife, ' Little woman, come here.' Up flew the Butterfly's Wife, very frightened, and clung to Balkis's white hand.

Balkis bent her beautiful head down and whispered, ' Little woman, do you believe what your husband has just said? '

The Butterfly's Wife looked at Balkis, and saw the most beautiful Queen's eyes shining like deep pools with starlight on them, and she picked up her courage with both wings and said, ' O Queen, be lovely for ever. You know what men-folk are like.'

And the Queen Balkis, the Wise Balkis of Sheba, put her hand to her lips to hide a smile and said, ' Little sister, I know.'

' They get angry,' said the Butterfly's Wife, fanning herself quickly, ' over nothing at all, but we must humour them, O Queen. They never mean half they say. If it pleases my husband to believe that I believe he can make Suleiman-bin-Daoud's Palace disappear by stamping his foot, I'm sure I don't care. He'll forget all about it to-morrow.'

' Little sister,' said Balkis, ' you are quite right; but next time he begins to boast, take him at his word. Ask him to stamp, and see what will happen. We know what men-folk are like, don't we? He'll be very much ashamed.'

Away flew the Butterfly's Wife to her husband, and in five minutes they were quarrelling worse than ever.

' Remember! ' said the Butterfly. ' Remember what I can do if I stamp my foot.'

' I don't believe you one little bit,' said the Butterfly's Wife. ' I should very much like to see it done. Suppose you stamp now.'

' I promised Suleiman-bin-Daoud that I wouldn't,' said the Butterfly, ' and I don't want to break my promise.'

' It wouldn't matter if you did,' said his wife. ' You couldn't bend a blade of grass with your stamping. I dare you to do it,' she said. ' Stamp! Stamp! Stamp! '

Suleiman-bin-Daoud, sitting under the camphor-tree, heard every word of this, and he laughed as he had never laughed in his life before. He forgot all about his Queens; he forgot all about the Animal that came out of the sea; he forgot about showing off. He just laughed with joy, and Balkis, on the other side of the tree, smiled because her own true love was so joyful.

Presently the Butterfly, very hot and puffy, came whirling back under the shadow of the camphor-tree and said to Suleiman, ' She wants me to stamp! She wants to see what will happen, O Suleiman-bin-Daoud! You know I can't do it, and now she'll never believe a word I say. She'll laugh at me to the end of my days! '

' No, little brother,' said Suleiman-bin-Daoud, ' she will never laugh at you again,' and he turned the ring on his finger—just for the little Butterfly's sake, not for the sake of showing off,—and, lo and behold, four huge Djinns came out of the earth!

' Slaves,' said Suleiman-bin-Daoud, ' when this gentleman on my finger' (that was where the impudent Butterfly was sitting) ' stamps his left front forefoot you will make my Palace and these gardens disappear in a clap of thunder. When he stamps again you will bring them back carefully.

' Now, little brother,' he said, ' go back to your wife and stamp all you've a mind to.'

Away flew the Butterfly to his wife, who was crying, 'I dare you to do it! I dare you to do it! Stamp! Stamp now! Stamp!' Balkis saw the four vast Djinns stoop down to the four corners of the gardens with the Palace in the middle, and she clapped her hands softly and said, 'At last Suleiman-bin-Daoud will do for the sake of a Butterfly what he ought to have done long ago for his own sake, and the quarrelsome Queens will be frightened!'

Then the Butterfly stamped. The Djinns jerked the Palace and the gardens a thousand miles into the air: there was a most awful thunder-clap, and everything grew inky-black. The Butterfly's Wife fluttered about in the dark, crying, 'Oh, I'll be good! I'm so sorry I spoke. Only bring the gardens back, my dear darling husband, and I'll never contradict again.'

The Butterfly was nearly as frightened as his wife, and Suleiman-bin-Daoud laughed so much that it was several minutes before he found breath enough to whisper to the Butterfly, 'Stamp again, little brother. Give me back my Palace, most great magician.'

'Yes, give him back his Palace,' said the Butterfly's Wife, still flying about in the dark like a moth. 'Give him back his Palace, and don't let's have any more horrid magic.'

'Well, my dear,' said the Butterfly as bravely as he could, 'you see what your nagging has led to. Of course it doesn't make any difference to *me*—I'm used to this kind of thing—but as a favour to you and to Suleiman-bin-Daoud I don't mind putting things right.'

So he stamped once more, and that instant the Djinns let down the Palace and the gardens, without even a bump. The sun shone on the dark-green orange leaves; the fountains played among the pink Egyptian lilies; the birds went on singing, and the Butterfly's Wife lay on her side under the camphor-tree waggling her wings and panting, 'Oh, I'll be good! I'll be good!'

Suleiman-bin-Daoud could hardly speak for laughing. He leaned back all weak and hiccoughy, and shook his finger at the Butterfly and said, 'O great wizard, what is the sense of returning to me my Palace if at the same time you slay me with mirth!'

Then came a terrible noise, for all the nine hundred and ninety-nine Queens ran out of the Palace shrieking and shouting and calling for their babies. They hurried down the great marble steps below the fountain, one hundred abreast, and the Most Wise Balkis went statelily forward to meet them and said, 'What is your trouble, O Queens?'

They stood on the marble steps one hundred abreast and shouted, '*What* is our trouble? We were living peacefully in our golden palace, as is our custom, when upon a sudden the Palace disappeared, and we were left sitting in a thick and noisome darkness; and it thundered, and Djinns and Afrits moved about in the darkness! *That* is our trouble, O Head Queen, and we are most extremely troubled on account of that trouble, for it was a troublesome trouble, unlike any trouble we have known.'

Then Balkis the Most Beautiful Queen—Suleiman-bin-Daoud's Very

Best Beloved—Queen that was of Sheba and Sabie and the Rivers of the Gold of the South—from the Desert of Zinn to the Towers of Zimbabwe—Balkis, almost as wise as the Most Wise Suleiman-bin-Daoud himself, said, ' It is nothing, O Queens! A Butterfly has made complaint against his wife because she quarrelled with him, and it has pleased our Lord Suleiman-bin-Daoud to teach her a lesson in low-speaking and humbleness, for that is counted a virtue among the wives of the butterflies.'

Then up and spoke an Egyptian Queen—the daughter of a Pharaoh—and she said, ' Our Palace cannot be plucked up by the roots like a leek for the sake of a little insect. No! Suleiman-bin-Daoud must be dead, and what we heard and saw was the earth thundering and darkening at the news.'

Then Balkis beckoned that bold Queen without looking at her, and said to her and to the others, ' Come and see.'

They came down the marble steps, one hundred abreast, and beneath his camphor-tree, still weak with laughing, they saw the Most Wise King Suleiman-bin-Daoud rocking back and forth with a Butterfly on either hand, and they heard him say, ' O wife of my brother in the air, remember after this, to please your husband in all things, lest he be provoked to stamp his foot yet again; for he has said that he is used to this magic, and he is most eminently a great magician—one who steals away the very Palace of Suleiman-bin-Daoud himself. Go in peace, little folk! ' And he kissed them on the wings, and they flew away.

Then all the Queens except Balkis—the Most Beautiful and Splendid Balkis, who stood apart smiling—fell flat on their faces, for they said, ' If these things are done when a Butterfly is displeased with his wife, what shall be done to us who have vexed our King with our loud-speaking and open quarrelling through many days? '

Then they put their veils over their heads, and they put their hands over their mouths, and they tiptoed back to the Palace most mousy-quiet.

Then Balkis—The Most Beautiful and Excellent Balkis—went forward through the red lilies into the shade of the camphor-tree and laid her hand upon Suleiman-bin-Daoud's shoulder and said, ' O my Lord and Treasure of my Soul, rejoice, for we have taught the Queens of Egypt and Ethiopia and Abyssinia and Persia and India and China with a great and a memorable teaching.'

And Suleiman-bin-Daoud, still looking after the Butterflies where they played in the sunlight, said, ' O my Lady and Jewel of my Felicity, when did this happen? For I have been jesting with a Butterfly ever since I came into the garden.' And he told Balkis what he had done.

Balkis—The Tender and Most Lovely Balkis—said, ' O my Lord and Regent of my Existence, I hid behind the camphor-tree and saw it all. It was I who told the Butterfly's Wife to ask the Butterfly to stamp, because I hoped that for the sake of the jest my Lord would make some great magic and that the Queens would see it and be frightened.' And she told him what the Queens had said and seen and thought.

Then Suleiman-bin-Daoud rose up from his seat under the camphor-tree, and stretched his arms and rejoiced and said, ' O my Lady and Sweetener of my Days, know that if I had made a magic against my Queens for the sake of pride or anger, as I made that feast for all the animals, I should certainly have been put to shame. But by means of your wisdom I made the magic for the sake of a jest and for the sake of a little Butterfly, and—behold—it has also delivered me from the vexations of my vexatious wives! Tell me, therefore, O my Lady and Heart of my Heart, how did you come to be so wise? '

And Balkis the Queen, beautiful and tall, looked up into Suleiman-bin-Daoud's eyes and put her head a little on one side, just like the Butterfly, and said, ' First, O my Lord, because I love you; and secondly, O my Lord, because I know what women-folk are.'

Then they went up to the Palace and lived happily ever afterwards. But wasn't it clever of Balkis?

There was never a Queen like Balkis,
 From here to the wide world's end;
But Balkis talked to a butterfly
 As you would talk to a friend.

There was never a King like Solomon,
 Not since the world began;
But Solomon talked to a butterfly
 As a man would talk to a man.

She was Queen of Sabæa—
 And *he* was Asia's Lord—
But they both of 'em talked to butterflies
 When they took their walks abroad!

PUCK OF POOK'S

HILL

PUCK OF POOK'S HILL

PUCK'S SONG

See you the dimpled track that runs,
 All hollow through the wheat?
O that was where they hauled the guns
 That smote King Philip's fleet.

See you our little mill that clacks,
 So busy by the brook?
She has ground her corn and paid her tax
 Ever since Domesday Book.

See you our stilly woods of oak,
 And the dread ditch beside?
O that was where the Saxons broke,
 On the day that Harold died.

See you the windy levels spread
 About the gates of Rye?
O that was where the Northmen fled,
 When Alfred's ships came by.

See you our pastures wide and lone,
 Where the red oxen browse?
O there was a City thronged and known,
 Ere London boasted a house.

And see you, after rain, the trace
 Of mound and ditch and wall?
O that was a Legion's camping-place,
 When Cæsar sailed from Gaul.

And see you marks that show and fade,
 Like shadows on the Downs?

O they are the lines the Flint Men made,
 To guard their wondrous towns.

Trackway and Camp and City lost,
 Salt Marsh where now is corn;
Old Wars, old Peace, old Arts that cease,
 And so was England born!

She is not any common Earth,
 Water or wood or air,
But Merlin's Isle of Gramarye,
 Where you and I will fare.

WELAND'S SWORD

~§ THE children were at the Theatre, acting to Three Cows as much as they could remember of *Midsummer Night's Dream*. Their father had made them a small play out of the big Shakespeare one, and they had rehearsed it with him and with their mother till they could say it by heart. They began where Nick Bottom the weaver comes out of the bushes with a donkey's head on his shoulder, and finds Titania Queen of the Fairies asleep. Then they skipped to the part where Bottom asks three little Fairies to scratch his head and bring him honey, and they ended where he falls asleep in Titania's arms. Dan was Puck and Nick Bottom, as well as all three Fairies. He wore a pointy-eared cloth cap for Puck, and a paper donkey's head out of a Christmas cracker—but it tore if you were not careful—for Bottom. Una was Titania, with a wreath of columbines and a fox-glove wand.

The Theatre lay in a meadow called the Long Slip. A little mill-stream, carrying water to a mill two or three fields away, bent round one corner of it, and in the middle of the bend lay a large old Fairy Ring of darkened grass, which was the stage. The mill-stream banks, overgrown with willow, hazel, and guelder-rose, made convenient places to wait in till your turn came; and a grown-up who had seen it said that Shakespeare himself could not have imagined a more suitable setting for his play. They were not, of course, allowed to act on Midsummer Night itself, but they went down after tea on Midsummer Eve, when the shadows were growing, and they took their supper—hard-boiled eggs, Bath Oliver biscuits, and salt in an envelope—with them. Three Cows had been milked and were grazing steadily with a tearing noise that one could hear all down the meadow; and the noise of the mill at work sounded like bare feet running on hard ground. A cuckoo sat on a gate-post singing his broken June tune, ' cuckoo-cuk,' while a busy kingfisher crossed from the mill-stream to the brook which ran on the other side of the meadow. Everything else was a sort of thick, sleepy stillness smelling of meadow-sweet and dry grass.

Their play went beautifully. Dan remembered all his parts—Puck, Bottom, and the three Fairies—and Una never forgot a word of Titania—not even the difficult piece where she tells the Fairies how to feed Bottom with ' apricocks, ripe figs, and dewberries,' and all the lines end in ' ies.' They were both so pleased that they acted it three times over from beginning to end before they sat down in the unthistly centre of the Ring to eat eggs and Bath Olivers. This was when they heard a whistle among the alders on the bank, and they jumped.

The bushes parted. In the very spot where Dan had stood as Puck they saw a small, brown, broad-shouldered, pointy-eared person with a snub nose, slanting blue eyes, and a grin that ran right across his freckled face. He shaded his forehead as though he were watching Quince, Snout, Bottom, and the others rehearsing *Pyramis and Thisbe*, and, in a voice as deep as Three Cows asking to be milked, he began:

> ' What hempen homespuns have we swaggering here,
> So near the cradle of our fairy Queen? '

He stopped, hollowed one hand round his ear, and with a wicked twinkle in his eye, went on:

> ' What, a play toward? I'll be auditor,
> An actor too, perhaps, if I see cause.'

The children looked and gasped. The small thing—he was no taller than Dan's shoulder—stepped quietly into the Ring.

' I'm rather out of practice,' said he; ' but that's the way my part ought to be played.'

Still the children stared at him—from his dark blue cap, like a big columbine flower, to his bare, hairy feet. At last he laughed.

' Please don't look like that. It isn't my fault. What else could you expect? ' he said.

' We didn't expect any one,' Dan answered, slowly. ' This is our field.'

' Is it? ' said their visitor, sitting down. ' Then what on Human Earth made you act *Midsummer Night's Dream* three times over, on Midsummer Eve, in the middle of a Ring, and under—right under one of my oldest hills in Old England? Pook's Hill—Puck's Hill—Puck's Hill—Pook's Hill! It's as plain as the nose on my face.'

He pointed to the bare, fern-covered slope of Pook's Hill that runs up from the far side of the mill-stream to a dark wood. Beyond that wood the ground rises and rises for five hundred feet, till at last you climb out on the bare top of Beacon Hill, to look over the Pevensey Levels and the Channel and half the naked South Downs.

' By Oak, Ash, and Thorn! ' he cried, still laughing. ' If this had happened a few hundred years ago you'd have had all the People of the Hills out like bees in June! '

' We didn't know it was wrong,' said Dan.

' Wrong! ' The little fellow shook with laughter. ' Indeed, it isn't wrong. You've done something that Kings and Knights and Scholars in old days would have given their crowns and spurs and books to find out. If Merlin himself had helped you, you couldn't have managed better! You've broken the Hills—you've broken the Hills! It hasn't happened in a thousand years.'

' We—we didn't mean to,' said Una.

' Of course you didn't! That's just why you did it. Unluckily the Hills

are empty now, and all the People of the Hills are gone. I'm the only one left. I'm Puck, the oldest Old Thing in England, very much at your service if—if you care to have anything to do with me. If you don't, of course you've only to say so, and I'll go.'

He looked at the children and the children looked at him for quite half a minute. His eyes did not twinkle any more. They were very kind, and there was the beginning of a good smile on his lips.

Una put out her hand. ' Don't go,' she said. ' We like you.'

' Have a Bath Oliver,' said Dan, and he passed over the squashy envelope with the eggs.

' By Oak, Ash, and Thorn,' cried Puck, taking off his blue cap, ' I like you too. Sprinkle a plenty salt on the biscuit, Dan, and I'll eat it with you. That'll show you the sort of person I am. Some of us '—he went on, with his mouth full—' couldn't abide Salt, or Horseshoes over a door, or Moun-tain-ash berries, or Running Water, or Cold Iron, or the sound of Church Bells. But I'm Puck! '

He brushed the crumbs carefully from his doublet and shook hands.

' We always said, Dan and I,' Una stammered, ' that if it ever happened we'd know ex-actly what to do; but—but now it seems all different some-how.'

' She means meeting a fairy,' said Dan. ' I never believed in 'em—not after I was six, anyhow.'

' I did,' said Una. ' At least, I sort of half believed till we learned " Farewell Rewards." Do you know " Farewell Rewards and Fairies "? '

' Do you mean this? ' said Puck. He threw his big head back and began at the second line:—

> ' Good housewives now may say,
> For now foul sluts in dairies
> Do fare as well as they;
> For though they sweep their hearths no less

(' Join in, Una! ')

> Than maids were wont to do,
> Yet who of late for cleanliness
> Finds sixpence in her shoe? '

The echoes flapped all along the flat meadow.

' Of course I know it,' he said.

' And then there's the verse about the Rings,' said Dan. ' When I was little it always made me feel unhappy in my inside.'

' " Witness those rings and roundelays," do you mean? ' boomed Puck, with a voice like a great church organ.

> ' Of theirs which yet remain,
> Were footed in Queen Mary's days
> On many a grassy plain.

But since of late Elizabeth,
And, later, James came in,
Are never seen on any heath
As when the time hath been.

'It's some time since I heard that sung, but there's no good beating about the bush: it's true. The People of the Hills have all left. I saw them come into Old England and I saw them go. Giants, trolls, kelpies, brownies, goblins, imps; wood, tree, mound, and water-spirits; heath-people, hill-watchers, treasure-guards, good people, little people, pishogues, leprechauns, night-riders, pixies, nixies, gnomes, and the rest—gone, all gone! I came into England with Oak, Ash, and Thorn, and when Oak, Ash, and Thorn are gone I shall go too.'

Dan looked round the meadow—at Una's oak by the lower gate, at the line of ash trees that overhang Otter Pool where the mill-stream spills over when the mill does not need it, and at the gnarled old white-thorn where Three Cows scratched their necks.

'It's all right,' he said; and added, ' I'm planting a lot of acorns this autumn too.'

'Then aren't you most awfully old?' said Una.

'Not old—fairly long-lived, as folk say hereabouts. Let me see—my friends used to set my dish of cream for me o' nights when Stonehenge was new. Yes, before the Flint Men made the Dewpond under Chanctonbury Ring.'

Una clasped her hands, cried 'Oh!' and nodded her head.

'She's thought a plan,' Dan explained. ' She always does like that when she thinks a plan.'

'I was thinking—suppose we saved some of our porridge and put it in the attic for you. They'd notice if we left it in the nursery.'

'Schoolroom,' said Dan, quickly, and Una flushed, because they had made a solemn treaty that summer not to call the schoolroom the nursery any more.

'Bless your heart o' gold!' said Puck. ' You'll make a fine considering wench some market-day. I really don't want you to put out a bowl for me; but if ever I need a bite, be sure I'll tell you.'

He stretched himself at length on the dry grass, and the children stretched out beside him, their bare legs waving happily in the air. They felt they could not be afraid of him any more than of their particular friend old Hobden the hedger. He did not bother them with grown-up questions, or laugh at the donkey's head, but lay and smiled to himself in the most sensible way.

'Have you a knife on you?' he said at last.

Dan handed over his big one-bladed outdoor knife, and Puck began to carve a piece of turf from the centre of the Ring.

'What's that for—Magic?' said Una, as he pressed up the square of chocolate loam that cut like so much cheese.

'One of my little magics,' he answered, and cut another. 'You see, I can't let you into the Hills because the People of the Hills have gone; but if you care to take seizin from me, I may be able to show you something out of the common here on Human Earth. You certainly deserve it.'

'What's taking seizin?' said Dan, cautiously.

'It's an old custom the people had when they bought and sold land. They used to cut out a clod and hand it over to the buyer, and you weren't lawfully seized of your land—it didn't really belong to you—till the other fellow had actually given you a piece of it—like this.' He held out the turves.

'But it's our own meadow,' said Dan, drawing back. 'Are you going to magic it away?'

Puck laughed. 'I know it's your meadow, but there's a great deal more in it than you or your father ever guessed. Try!'

He turned his eyes on Una.

'I'll do it,' she said. Dan followed her example at once.

'Now are you two lawfully seized and possessed of all Old England,' began Puck, in a sing-song voice. 'By Right of Oak, Ash, and Thorn are you free to come and go and look and know where I shall show or best you please. You shall see What you shall see and you shall hear What you shall hear, though It shall have happened three thousand year; and you shall know neither Doubt nor Fear. Fast! Hold fast all I give you.'

The children shut their eyes, but nothing happened.

'Well?' said Una, disappointedly opening them. 'I thought there would be dragons.'

'"Though It shall have happened three thousand year,"' said Puck, and counted on his fingers. 'No; I'm afraid there were no dragons three thousand years ago.'

'But there hasn't happened anything at all,' said Dan.

'Wait awhile,' said Puck. 'You don't grow an oak in a year—and Old England's older than twenty oaks. Let's sit down again and think. I can do that for a century at a time.'

'Ah, but you're a fairy,' said Dan.

'Have you ever heard me use that word yet?' said Puck, quickly.

'No. You talk about "the People of the Hills," but you never say "fairies,"' said Una. 'I was wondering at that. Don't you like it?'

'How would you like to be called "mortal" or "human being" all the time?' said Puck; 'or "son of Adam" or "daughter of Eve"?'

'I shouldn't like it at all,' said Dan. 'That's how the Djinns and Afrits talk in the *Arabian Nights*.'

'And that's how I feel about saying—that word that I don't say. Besides, what you call them are made-up things the People of the Hills have never heard of—little buzzflies with butterfly wings and gauze petticoats, and shiny stars in their hair, and a wand like a school-teacher's cane for punishing bad boys and rewarding good ones. I know 'em!'

'We don't mean that sort,' said Dan. 'We hate 'em too.'

'Exactly,' said Puck. 'Can you wonder that the People of the Hills don't care to be confused with that painty-winged, wand-waving, sugar-and-shake-your-head set of impostors? Butterfly wings, indeed! I've seen Sir Huon and a troop of his people setting off from Tintagel Castle for Hy-Brasil in the teeth of a sou'-westerly gale, with the spray flying all over the Castle, and the Horses of the Hill wild with fright. Out they'd go in a lull, scream-ing like gulls, and back they'd be driven five good miles inland before they could come head to wind again. Butterfly-wings! It was Magic—Magic as black as Merlin could make it, and the whole sea was green fire and white foam, with singing mermaids in it. And the Horses of the Hill picked their way from one wave to another by the lightning flashes! That was how it was in the old days!'

'Splendid,' said Dan, but Una shuddered.

'I'm glad they're gone, then; but what made the People of the Hills go away?' Una asked.

'Different things. I'll tell you one of them some day—the thing that made the biggest flit of any,' said Puck. 'But they didn't all flit at once. They dropped off, one by one, through the centuries. Most of them were foreigners who couldn't stand our climate. They flitted early.'

'How early?' said Dan.

'A couple of thousand years or more. The fact is they began as Gods. The Phœnicians brought some over when they came to buy tin; and the Gauls, and the Jutes, and the Danes, and the Frisians, and the Angles brought more when they landed. They were always landing in those days, or being driven back to their ships, and they always brought their Gods with them. England is a bad country for Gods. Now, I began as I mean to go on. A bowl of porridge, a dish of milk, and a little quiet fun with the country-folk in the lanes was enough for me then, as it is now. I belong here, you see, and I have been mixed up with people all my days. But most of the others insisted on being Gods, and having temples, and altars, and priests, and sacrifices of their own.'

'People burned in wicker baskets?' said Dan. 'Like Miss Blake tells us about?'

'All sorts of sacrifices,' said Puck. 'If it wasn't men, it was horses, or cattle, or pigs, or metheglin—that's a sticky, sweet sort of beer. I never liked it. They were a stiff-necked, extravagant set of idols, the Old Things. But what was the result? Men don't like being sacrificed at the best of times; they don't even like sacrificing their farm-horses. After a while men simply left the Old Things alone, and the roofs of their temples fell in, and the Old Things had to scuttle out and pick up a living as they could. Some of them took to hanging about trees, and hiding in graves and groaning o' nights. If they groaned loud enough and long enough they might frighten a poor countryman into sacrificing a hen, or leaving a pound of butter for them. I remember one Goddess called Belisama. She became a common

wet water-spirit somewhere in Lancashire. And there were hundreds of other friends of mine. First they were Gods. Then they were People of the Hills, and then they flitted to other places because they couldn't get on with the English for one reason or another. There was only one Old Thing, I remember, who honestly worked for his living after he came down in the world. He was called Weland, and he was a smith to some Gods. I've forgotten their names, but he used to make them swords and spears. I think he claimed kin with Thor of the Scandinavians.'

'*Heroes of Asgard* Thor?' said Una. She had been reading the book.

'Perhaps,' answered Puck. 'None the less, when bad times came, he didn't beg or steal. He worked; and I was lucky enough to be able to do him a good turn.'

'Tell us about it,' said Dan. 'I think I like hearing of Old Things.'

They rearranged themselves comfortably, each chewing a grass stem. Puck propped himself on one strong arm and went on:

'Let's think! I met Weland first on a November afternoon in a sleet storm, on Pevensey Level— '

'Pevensey? Over the hill, you mean?' Dan pointed south.

'Yes; but it was all marsh in those days, right up to Horsebridge and Hydeneye. I was on Beacon Hill—they called it Brunanburgh then—when I saw the pale flame that burning thatch makes, and I went down to look. Some pirates—I think they must have been Peofn's men—were burning a village on the Levels, and Weland's image—a big, black wooden thing with amber beads round its neck—lay in the bows of a black thirty-two-oar galley that they had just beached. Bitter cold it was! There were icicles hanging from her deck and the oars were glazed over with ice, and there was ice on Weland's lips. When he saw me he began a long chant in his own tongue, telling me how he was going to rule England, and how I should smell the smoke of his altars from Lincolnshire to the Isle of Wight. I didn't care! I'd seen too many Gods charging into Old England to be upset about it. I let him sing himself out while his men were burning the village, and then I said (I don't know what put it into my head), " Smith of the Gods," I said, " the time comes when I shall meet you plying your trade for hire by the wayside." '

'What did Weland say?' said Una. 'Was he angry?'

'He called me names and rolled his eyes, and I went away to wake up the people inland. But the pirates conquered the country, and for centuries Weland was a most important God. He had temples everywhere —from Lincolnshire to the Isle of Wight, as he said—and his sacrifices were simply scandalous. To do him justice, he preferred horses to men; but men or horses, I knew that presently he'd have to come down in the world— like the other Old Things. I gave him lots of time—I gave him about a thousand years—and at the end of 'em I went into one of his temples near Andover to see how he prospered. There was his altar, and there was his image, and there were his priests, and there were the congregation, and

everybody seemed quite happy, except Weland and the priests. In the old days the congregation were unhappy until the priests had chosen their sacrifices; and so would you have been. When the service began a priest rushed out, dragged a man up to the altar, pretended to hit him on the head with a little gilt axe, and the man fell down and pretended to die. Then everybody shouted: " A sacrifice to Weland! A sacrifice to Weland! " '

' And the man wasn't really dead? ' said Una.

' Not a bit. All as much pretence as a dolls' tea-party. Then they brought out a splendid white horse, and the priest cut some hair from its mane and tail and burned it on the altar, shouting, " A sacrifice! " That counted the same as if a man and a horse had been killed. I saw poor Weland's face through the smoke, and I couldn't help laughing. He looked so disgusted and so hungry, and all he had to satisfy himself was a horrid smell of burning hair. Just a dolls' tea-party!

' I judged it better not to say anything then ('twouldn't have been fair), and the next time I came to Andover, a few hundred years later, Weland and his temple were gone, and there was a Christian bishop in a church there. None of the People of the Hills could tell me anything about him, and I supposed that he had left England.' Puck turned; lay on the other elbow, and thought for a long time.

' Let's see,' he said at last. ' It must have been some few years later— a year or two before the Conquest, I think—that I came back to Pook's Hill here, and one evening I heard old Hobden talking about Weland's Ford.'

' If you mean old Hobden the hedger, he's only seventy-two. He told me so himself,' said Dan. ' He's a intimate friend of ours.'

' You're quite right,' Puck replied. ' I meant old Hobden's ninth great-grandfather. He was a free man and burned charcoal hereabouts. I've known the family, father and son, so long that I get confused sometimes. Hob of the Dene was my Hobden's name, and he lived at the Forge cottage. Of course, I pricked up my ears when I heard Weland mentioned, and I scuttled through the woods to the Ford just beyond Bog Wood yonder.' He jerked his head westward, where the valley narrows between wooded hills and steep hop-fields.

' Why, that's Willingford Bridge,' said Una. ' We go there for walks often. There's a kingfisher there.'

' It was Weland's Ford then, dearie. A road led down to it from the Beacon on the top of the hill—a shocking bad road it was—and all the hillside was thick, thick oak-forest, with deer in it. There was no trace of Weland, but presently I saw a fat old farmer riding down from the Beacon under the greenwood tree. His horse had cast a shoe in the clay, and when he came to the Ford he dismounted, took a penny out of his purse, laid it on a stone, tied the old horse to an oak, and called out: " Smith, Smith, here is work for you! " Then he sat down and went to sleep. You can imagine how I felt when I saw a white-bearded, bent old blacksmith in a leather

apron creep out from behind the oak and begin to shoe the horse. It was Weland himself. I was so astonished that I jumped out and said: " What on Human Earth are you doing here, Weland? " '

' Poor Weland! ' sighed Una.

' He pushed the long hair back from his forehead (he didn't recognise me at first). Then he said: " You ought to know. You foretold it, Old Thing. I'm shoeing horses for hire. I'm not even Weland now," he said. " They call me Wayland-Smith." '

' Poor chap! ' said Dan. ' What did you say? '

' What could I say? He looked up, with the horse's foot on his lap, and he said, smiling, " I remember the time when I wouldn't have accepted this old bag of bones as a sacrifice, and now I'm glad enough to shoe him for a penny."

' " Isn't there any way for you to get back to Valhalla, or wherever you come from? " I said.

' " I'm afraid not," he said, rasping away at the hoof. He had a wonderful touch with horses. The old beast was whinnying on his shoulder. " You may remember that I was not a gentle God in my Day and my Time and my Power. I shall never be released till some human being truly wishes me well."

' " Surely," said I, " the farmer can't do less than that. You're shoeing the horse all round for him."

' " Yes," said he, " and my nails will hold a shoe from one full moon to the next. But farmers and Weald clay," said he, " are both uncommon cold and sour."

' Would you believe it, that when that farmer woke and found his horse shod he rode away without one word of thanks? I was so angry that I wheeled his horse right round and walked him back three miles to the Beacon, just to teach the old sinner politeness.'

' Were you invisible? ' said Una. Puck nodded, gravely.

' The Beacon was always laid in those days ready to light, in case the French landed at Pevensey; and I walked the horse about and about it that lee-long summer night. The farmer thought he was bewitched—well, he was, of course—and began to pray and shout. I didn't care! I was as good a Christian as he any fair-day in the County, and about four o'clock in the morning a young novice came along from the monastery that used to stand on the top of Beacon hill.'

' What's a novice? ' said Dan.

' It really means a man who is beginning to be a monk, but in those days people sent their sons to a monastery just the same as a school. This young fellow had been to a monastery in France for a few months every year, and he was finishing his studies in the monastery close to his home here. Hugh was his name, and he had got up to go fishing hereabouts. His people owned all this valley. Hugh heard the farmer shouting, and asked him what in the world he meant. The old man spun him a wonderful tale about

fairies and goblins and witches; and I know he hadn't seen a thing except rabbits and red deer all that night. (The People of the Hills are like otters —they don't show except when they choose.) But the novice wasn't a fool. He looked down at the horse's feet, and saw the new shoes fastened as only Weland knew how to fasten 'em. (Weland had a way of turning down the nails that folks called the Smith's Clinch.)

'"H'm!" said the novice. "Where did you get your horse shod?"

'The farmer wouldn't tell him at first, because the priests never liked their people to have any dealings with the Old Things. At last he confessed that the Smith had done it. "What did you pay him?" said the novice. "Penny," said the farmer, very sulkily. "That's less than a Christian would have charged," said the novice. "I hope you threw a 'Thank you' into the bargain." "No," said the farmer; "Wayland-Smith's a heathen." "Heathen or no heathen," said the novice, "you took his help, and where you get help there you must give thanks." "What?" said the farmer—he was in a furious temper because I was walking the old horse in circles all this time—"What, you young jackanapes?" said he. "Then by your reasoning I ought to say 'Thank you' to Satan if he helped me?" "Don't roll about up there splitting reasons with me," said the novice. "Come back to the Ford and thank the Smith, or you'll be sorry."

'Back the farmer had to go. I led the horse, though no one saw me, and the novice walked beside us, his gown swishing through the shiny dew and his fishing-rod across his shoulders spear-wise. When we reached the Ford again—it was five o'clock and misty still under the oaks—the farmer simply wouldn't say "Thank you." He said he'd tell the Abbot that the novice wanted him to worship heathen gods. Then Hugh the novice lost his temper. He just cried, "Out!" put his arm under the farmer's fat leg, and heaved him from his saddle on to the turf, and before he could rise he caught him by the back of the neck and shook him like a rat till the farmer growled, "Thank you, Wayland-Smith."'

'Did Weland see all this?' said Dan.

'Oh, yes, and he shouted his old war-cry when the farmer thudded on to the ground. He was delighted. Then the novice turned to the oak tree and said, "Ho! Smith of the Gods, I am ashamed of this rude farmer; but for all you have done in kindness and charity to him and to others of our people, I thank you and wish you well." Then he picked up his fishing-rod—it looked more like a tall spear than ever—and tramped off down your valley.'

'And what did poor Weland do?' said Una.

'He laughed and he cried with joy, because he had been released at last, and could go away. But he was an honest Old Thing. He had worked for his living and he paid his debts before he left. "I shall give that novice a gift," said Weland. "A gift that shall do him good the wide world over and Old England after him. Blow up my fire, Old Thing, while I get the iron for my last task." Then he made a sword—a dark gray, wavy-lined sword

—and I blew the fire while he hammered. By Oak, Ash, and Thorn, I tell you, Weland was a Smith of the Gods! He cooled that sword in running water twice, and the third time he cooled it in the evening dew, and he laid it out in the moonlight and said Runes (that's charms) over it, and he carved Runes of Prophecy on the blade. " Old Thing," he said to me, wiping his forehead, " this is the best blade that Weland ever made. Even the user will never know how good it is. Come to the monastery."

'We went to the dormitory where the monks slept, we saw the novice fast asleep in his cot, and Weland put the sword into his hand, and I remember the young fellow gripped it in his sleep. Then Weland strode as far as he dared into the Chapel and threw down all his shoeing-tools—his hammer, and pincers, and rasps—to show that he had done with them for ever. It sounded like suits of armour falling, and the sleepy monks ran in, for they thought the monastery had been attacked by the French. The novice came first of all, waving his new sword and shouting Saxon battle-cries. When they saw the shoeing-tools they were very bewildered, till the novice asked leave to speak, and told what he had done to the farmer, and what he had said to Wayland-Smith, and how, though the dormitory light was burning, he had found the wonderful rune-carved sword in his cot.

'The Abbot shook his head at first, and then he laughed and said to the novice: " Son Hugh, it needed no sign from a heathen God to show me that you will never be a monk. Take your sword, and keep your sword, and go with your sword, and be as gentle as you are strong and courteous. We will hang up the Smith's tools before the Altar," he said, " because, whatever the Smith of the Gods may have been in the old days, we know that he worked honestly for his living and made gifts to Mother Church." Then they went to bed again, all except the novice, and he sat up in the garth playing with his sword. Then Weland said to me by the stables: " Farewell, Old Thing; you had the right of it. You saw me come to England, and you see me go. Farewell! "

'With that he strode down the hill to the corner of the Great Woods—Woods Corner, you call it now—to the very place where he had first landed—and I heard him moving through the thickets towards Horsebridge for a little, and then he was gone. That was how it happened. I saw it.'

Both children drew a long breath.

'But what happened to Hugh the novice?' said Una.

'And the sword?' said Dan.

Puck looked down the meadow that lay all quiet and cool in the shadow of Pook's Hill. A corncrake jarred in a hay-field near by, and the small trouts of the brook began to jump. A big white moth flew unsteadily from the alders and flapped round the children's heads, and the least little haze of water-mist rose from the brook.

'Do you really want to know?' Puck said.

'We do,' cried the children. 'Awfully!'

'Very good. I promised you that you shall see What you shall see,

and you shall hear What you shall hear, though It shall have happened three thousand year; but just now it seems to me that, unless you go back to the house, people will be looking for you. I'll walk with you as far as the gate.'

'Will you be here when we come again?' they asked.

'Surely, sure-ly,' said Puck. 'I've been here some time already. One minute first, please.'

He gave them each three leaves—one of Oak, one of Ash, and one of Thorn.

'Bite these,' said he. 'Otherwise you might be talking at home of what you've seen and heard, and—if I know human beings—they'd send for the doctor. Bite!'

They bit hard, and found themselves walking side by side to the lower gate. Their father was leaning over it.

'And how did your play go?' he asked.

'Oh, splendidly,' said Dan. 'Only afterwards, I think, we went to sleep. It was very hot and quiet. Don't you remember, Una?'

Una shook her head and said nothing.

'I see,' said her father.

> 'Late—late in the evening Kilmeny came home,
> For Kilmeny had been she could not tell where,
> And Kilmeny had seen what she could not declare.

But why are you chewing leaves at your time of life, daughter? For fun?'

'No. It was for something, but I can't azactly remember,' said Una.

And neither of them could till—

A TREE SONG

Of all the trees that grow so fair,
 Old England to adorn,
Greater are none beneath the Sun,
 Than Oak, and Ash, and Thorn.
Sing Oak, and Ash, and Thorn, good Sirs
 (All of a Midsummer morn)!
Surely we sing no little thing,
 In Oak, and Ash, and Thorn!

Oak of the Clay lived many a day,
 Or ever Æneas began;
Ash of the Loam was a lady at home,
 When Brut was an outlaw man;
Thorn of the Down saw New Troy Town

(From which was London born);
Witness hereby the ancientry
 Of Oak, and Ash, and Thorn!

Yew that is old in churchyard mould,
 He breedeth a mighty bow;
Alder for shoes do wise men choose,
 And beech for cups also.
But when ye have killed, and your bowl is spilled,
 And your shoes are clean outworn,
Back ye must speed for all that ye need,
 To Oak, and Ash, and Thorn!

Ellum she hateth mankind, and waiteth
 Till every gust be laid,
To drop a limb on the head of him,
 That anyway trusts her shade:
But whether a lad be sober or sad,
 Or mellow with ale from the horn,
He will take no wrong when he lieth along
 'Neath Oak, and Ash, and Thorn!

Oh, do not tell the Priest our plight,
 Or he would call it a sin;
But—we have been out in the woods all night,
 A-conjuring Summer in!
And we bring you news by word of mouth—
 Good news for cattle and corn—
Now is the Sun come up from the South,
 With Oak, and Ash, and Thorn!

Sing Oak, and Ash, and Thorn, good Sirs
 (All of a Midsummer morn)!
England shall bide till Judgment Tide,
 By Oak, and Ash, and Thorn!

YOUNG MEN AT THE MANOR

৵ৡ THEY were fishing, a few days later, in the bed of the brook that for centuries had cut deep into the soft valley soil. The trees closing overhead made long tunnels through which the sunshine worked in blobs and patches. Down in the tunnels were bars of sand and gravel, old roots and trunks covered with moss or painted red by the irony water; foxgloves growing lean and pale towards the light; clumps of fern and thirsty shy flowers who could not live away from moisture and shade. In the pools you could see the wave thrown up by the trouts as they charged hither and yon, and the pools were joined to each other—except in flood time, when all was one brown rush—by sheets of thin broken water that poured themselves chuckling round the darkness of the next bend.

This was one of the children's most secret hunting-grounds, and their particular friend, old Hobden the hedger, had shown them how to use it. Except for the click of a rod hitting a low willow, or a switch and tussle among the young ash-leaves as a line hung up for the minute, nobody in the hot pasture could have guessed what game was going on among the trouts below the banks.

'We's got half-a-dozen,' said Dan, after a warm, wet hour. 'I vote we go up to Stone Bay and try Long Pool.'

Una nodded—most of her talk was by nods—and they crept from the gloom of the tunnels towards the tiny weir that turns the brook into the mill-stream. Here the banks are low and bare, and the glare of the afternoon sun on the Long Pool below the weir makes your eyes ache.

When they were in the open they nearly fell down with astonishment. A huge gray horse, whose tail-hairs crinkled the glassy water, was drinking in the pool, and the ripples about his muzzle flashed like melted gold. On his back sat an old, white-haired man dressed in a loose glimmery gown of chain-mail. He was bare-headed, and a nut-shaped iron helmet hung at his saddle-bow. His reins were of red leather, five or six inches deep, scalloped at the edges, and his high padded saddle with its red girths was held fore and aft by a red leather breastband and crupper.

'Look!' said Una, as though Dan were not staring his very eyes out. 'It's like the picture in your room—" Sir Isumbras at the Ford."'

The rider turned towards them, and his thin, long face was just as sweet and gentle as that of the knight who carries the children in that picture.

'They should be here now, Sir Richard,' said Puck's deep voice among the willow-herb.

'They are here,' the knight said, and he smiled at Dan with the string of trouts in his hand. 'There seems no great change in boys since mine fished this water.'

'If your horse has drunk, we shall be more at ease in the Ring,' said Puck; and he nodded to the children as though he had never magicked away their memories a week before.

The great horse turned and hoisted himself into the pasture with a kick and a scramble that tore the clods down rattling.

'Your pardon!' said Sir Richard to Dan. 'When these lands were mine, I never loved that mounted men should cross the brook except by the paved ford. But my Swallow here was thirsty, and I wished to meet you.'

'We're very glad you've come, sir,' said Dan. 'It doesn't matter in the least about the banks.'

He trotted across the pasture on the sword side of the mighty horse, and it was a mighty iron-handled sword that swung from Sir Richard's belt. Una walked behind with Puck. She remembered everything now.

'I'm sorry about the Leaves,' he said, 'but it would never have done if you had gone home and told, would it?'

'I s'pose not,' Una answered. 'But you said that all the fair—People of the Hills had left England.'

'So they have; but I told you that you should come and go and look and know, didn't I? The knight isn't a fairy. He's Sir Richard Dalyngridge, a very old friend of mine. He came over with William the Conqueror, and he wants to see you particularly.'

'What for?' said Una.

'On account of your great wisdom and learning,' Puck replied, without a twinkle.

'Us?' said Una. 'Why, I don't know my Nine Times—not to say it dodging, and Dan makes the most awful mess of fractions. He can't mean us!'

'Una!' Dan called back. 'Sir Richard says he is going to tell what happened to Weland's sword. He's got it. Isn't it splendid?'

'Nay—nay,' said Sir Richard, dismounting as they reached the Ring, in the bend of the mill-stream bank. 'It is you that must tell me, for I hear the youngest child in our England to-day is as wise as our wisest clerk.' He slipped the bit out of Swallow's mouth, dropped the ruby-red reins over his head, and the wise horse moved off to graze.

Sir Richard (they noticed he limped a little) unslung his great sword.

'That's it,' Dan whispered to Una.

'This is the sword that Brother Hugh had from Wayland-Smith,' Sir Richard said. 'Once he gave it me, but I would not take it; but at the last it became mine after such a fight as never christened man fought. See!' He half drew it from its sheath and turned it before them. On either side just below the handle, where the Runic letters shivered as though they were alive, were two deep gouges in the dull, deadly steel. 'Now, what Thing

made those? ' said he. ' I know not, but you, perhaps, can say.'

' Tell them all the tale, Sir Richard,' said Puck. ' It concerns their land somewhat.'

'.Yes, from the very beginning,' Una pleaded, for the knight's good face and the smile on it more than ever reminded her of ' Sir Isumbras at the Ford.'

They settled down to listen, Sir Richard bare-headed to the sunshine, dandling the sword in both hands, while the gray horse cropped outside the Ring, and the helmet on the saddle-bow clinged softly each time he jerked his head.

' From the beginning, then,' Sir Richard said, ' since it concerns your land, I will tell the tale. When our Duke came out of Normandy to take his England, great knights (have ye heard?) came and strove hard to serve the Duke, because he promised them lands here, and small knights followed the great ones. My folk in Normandy were poor; but a great knight, Enger-rard of the Eagle—Engenulf De Aquila—who was kin to my father, followed the Earl of Mortain, who followed William the Duke, and I followed De Aquila. Yes, with thirty men-at-arms out of my father's house and a new sword, I set out to conquer England three days after I was made knight. I did not then know that England would conquer me. We went up to Santlache with the rest—a very great host of us.'

' Does that mean the Battle of Hastings—Ten Sixty-Six? ' Una whis-pered, and Puck nodded, so as not to interrupt.

' At Santlache, over the hill yonder '—he pointed south-eastward to-wards Fairlight—' we found Harold's men. We fought. At the day's end they ran. My men went with De Aquila's to chase and plunder, and in that chase Engerrard of the Eagle was slain, and his son Gilbert took his banner and his men forward. This I did not know till after, for Swallow here was cut in the flank, so I stayed to wash the wound at a brook by a thorn. There a single Saxon cried out to me in French, and we fought together. I should have known his voice, but we fought together. For a long time neither had any advantage, till by pure ill-fortune his foot slipped and his sword flew from his hand. Now I had but newly been made knight, and wished, above all, to be courteous and fameworthy, so I forbore to strike and bade him get his sword again. " A plague on my sword," said he. " It has lost me my first fight. You have spared my life. Take my sword." He held it out to me, but as I stretched my hand the sword groaned like a stricken man, and I leaped back crying, " Sorcery! "

[The children looked at the sword as though it might speak again.]

' Suddenly a clump of Saxons ran out upon me and, seeing a Norman alone, would have killed me, but my Saxon cried out that I was his prisoner, and beat them off. Thus, see you, he saved my life. He put me on my horse and led me through the woods ten long miles to this valley.'

' To here, d'you mean? ' said Una.

' To this very valley. We came in by the Lower Ford under the King's

Hill yonder '—he pointed eastward where the valley widens.

' And was that Saxon Hugh the novice? ' Dan asked.

' Yes, and more than that. He had been for three years at the monastery at Bec by Rouen, where '—Sir Richard chuckled—' the Abbot Herluin would not suffer me to remain.'

' Why wouldn't he? ' said Dan.

' Because I rode my horse into the refectory, when the scholars were at meat, to show the Saxon boys we Normans were not afraid of an abbot. It was that very Saxon Hugh tempted me to do it, and we had not met since that day. I thought I knew his voice even inside my helmet, and, for all that our Lords fought, we each rejoiced we had not slain the other. He walked by my side, and he told me how a Heathen God, as he believed, had given him his sword, but he said he had never heard it sing before. I remember I warned him to beware of sorcery and quick enchantments.' Sir Richard smiled to himself. ' I was very young—very young!

' When we came to his house here we had almost forgotten that we had been at blows. It was near midnight, and the Great Hall was full of men and women waiting news. There I first saw his sister, the Lady Ælueva, of whom he had spoken to us in France. She cried out fiercely at me, and would have had me hanged in that hour, but her brother said that I had spared his life—he said not how he saved mine from the Saxons—and that our Duke had won the day; and even while they wrangled over my poor body, of a sudden he fell down in a swoon from his wounds.

' " This is thy fault," said the Lady Ælueva to me, and she kneeled above him and called for wine and cloths.

' " If I had known," I answered, " he should have ridden and I walked. But he set me on my horse; he made no complaint; he walked beside me and spoke merrily throughout. I pray I have done him no harm."

' " Thou hast need to pray," she said, catching up her underlip. " If he dies, thou shalt hang."

' They bore off Hugh to his chamber; but three tall men of the house bound me and set me under the beam of the Great Hall with a rope round my neck. The end of the rope they flung over the beam, and they sat them down by the fire to wait word whether Hugh lived or died. They cracked nuts with their knife-hilts the while.'

' And how did you feel? ' said Dan.

' Very weary; but I did heartily pray for my school-mate Hugh his health. About noon I heard horses in the valley, and the three men loosed my ropes and fled out, and De Aquila's men rode up. Gilbert de Aquila came with them, for it was his boast that, like his father, he forgot no man that served him. He was little, like his father, but terrible, with a nose like an eagle's nose and yellow eyes like an eagle. He rode tall war-horses—roans, which he bred himself—and he could never abide to be helped into the saddle. He saw the rope hanging from the beam and laughed, and his men laughed, for I was too stiff to rise.

'"This is poor entertainment for a Norman knight," he said, "but, such as it is let us be grateful. Show me, boy, to whom thou owest most, and we will pay them out of hand."'

'What did he mean? To kill 'em?' said Dan.

'Assuredly. But I looked at the Lady Ælueva where she stood among her maids, and her brother beside her. De Aquila's men had driven them all into the Great Hall.'

'Was she pretty?' said Una.

'In all my long life I have never seen woman fit to strew rushes before my Lady Ælueva,' the knight replied, quite simply and quietly. 'As I looked at her I thought I might save her and her house by a jest.

'"Seeing that I came somewhat hastily and without warning," said I to De Aquila, "I have no fault to find with the courtesy that these Saxons have shown me." But my voice shook. It is—it was not good to jest with that little man.

'All were silent awhile, till De Aquila laughed. "Look, men—a miracle," said he. "The fight is scarce sped, my father is not yet buried, and here we find our youngest knight already set down in his Manor, while his Saxons —ye can see it in their fat faces—have paid him homage and service! By the Saints," he said, rubbing his nose, "I never thought England would be so easy won! Surely I can do no less than give the lad what he had taken. This Manor shall be thine, boy," he said, "till I come again, or till thou art slain. Now, mount, men, and ride. We follow our Duke into Kent to make him King of England."

'He drew me with him to the door while they brought his horse—a lean roan, taller than my Swallow here, but not so well girthed.

'"Hark to me," he said, fretting with his great war-gloves. "I have given thee this Manor, which is a Saxon hornets' nest, and I think thou wilt be slain in a month—as my father was slain. Yet if thou canst keep the roof on the hall, the thatch on the barn, and the plough in the furrow till I come back, thou shalt hold the Manor from me; for the Duke has promised our Earl Mortain all the lands by Pevensey, and Mortain will give me of them what he would have given my father. God knows if thou or I shall live till England is won; but remember, boy, that here and now fighting is foolishness and "—he reached for the reins—"craft and cunning is all."

'"Alas, I have no cunning," said I.

'"Not yet," said he, hopping abroad, foot in stirrup, and poking his horse in the belly with his toe. "Not yet, but I think thou hast a good teacher. Farewell! Hold the Manor and live. Lose the Manor and hang," he said, and spurred out, his shield-straps squeaking behind him.

'So, children, here was I, little more than a boy, and Santlache fight not two days old, left alone with my thirty men-at-arms, in a land I knew not, among a people whose tongue I could not speak, to hold down the land which I had taken from them.'

'And that was here at home?' said Una.

'Yes, here. See! From the Upper Ford, Weland's Ford, to the Lower Ford, by the Belle Allee, west and east it ran half a league. From the Beacon of Brunanburgh behind us here, south and north it ran a full league— and all the woods were full of broken men from Santlache, Saxon thieves, Norman plunderers, robbers, and deer-stealers. A hornets' nest indeed!

'When De Aquila had gone, Hugh would have thanked me for saving their lives; but the Lady Ælueva said that I had done it only for the sake of receiving the Manor.

'"How could I know that De Aquila would give it me?" I said. "If I had told him I had spent my night in your halter he would have burned the place twice over by now."

'"If any man had put my neck in a rope," she said, "I would have seen his house burned thrice over before I would have made terms."

'"But it was a woman," I said; and I laughed, and she wept and said that I mocked her in her captivity.

'"Lady," said I, "there is no captive in this valley except one, and he is not a Saxon."

'At this she cried that I was a Norman thief, who came with false, sweet words, having intended from the first to turn her out in the fields to beg her bread. Into the fields! She had never seen the face of war!

'I was angry, and answered, "This much at least I can disprove, for I swear "—and on my sword-hilt I swore it in that place—"I swear I will never set foot in the Great Hall till the Lady Ælueva herself shall summon me there."

'She went away, saying nothing, and I walked out, and Hugh limped after me, whistling dolorously (that is a custom of the English), and we came upon the three Saxons that had bound me. They were now bound by my men-at-arms, and behind them stood some fifty stark and sullen churls of the House and the Manor, waiting to see what should fall. We heard De Aquila's trumpets blow thin through the woods Kentward.

'"Shall we hang these? " said my men.

'"Then my churls will fight," said Hugh, beneath his breath; but I bade him ask the three what mercy they hoped for.

'"None," said they all. "She bade us hang thee if our master died. And we would have hanged thee. There is no more to it."

'As I stood doubting a woman ran down from the oak wood above the King's Hill yonder, and cried out that some Normans were driving off the swine there.

'"Norman or Saxon," said I, "we must beat them back, or they will rob us every day. Out at them with any arms ye have! " So I loosed those three carles and we ran together, my men-at-arms and the Saxons with bills and bows which they had hidden in the thatch of their huts, and Hugh led them. Half-way up the King's Hill we found a false fellow from Picardy— a sutler that sold wine in the Duke's camp—with a dead knight's shield on his arm, a stolen horse under him, and some ten or twelve wastrels at his

tail, all cutting and slashing at the pigs. We beat them off, and saved our pork. One hundred and seventy pigs we saved in that great battle.' Sir Richard laughed.

'That, then, was our first work together, and I bade Hugh tell his folk that so would I deal with any man, knight or churl, Norman or Saxon, who stole as much as one egg from our valley. Said he to me, riding home: " Thou hast gone far to conquer England this evening." I answered: " England must be thine and mine, then. Help me, Hugh, to deal aright with these people. Make them to know that if they slay me De Aquila will surely send to slay them, and he will put a worse man in my place." " That may well be true," said he, and gave me his hand. " Better the devil we know than the devil we know not, till we can pack you Normans home." And so, too, said his Saxons; and they laughed as we drove the pigs downhill. But I think some of them, even then, began not to hate me.'

' I like Brother Hugh,' said Una, softly.

' Beyond question he was the most perfect, courteous, valiant, tender, and wise knight that ever drew breath,' said Sir Richard, caressing the sword. ' He hung up his sword—this sword—on the wall of the Great Hall, because he said it was fairly mine, and never he took it down till De Aquila returned, as I shall presently show. For three months his men and mine guarded the valley, till all robbers and nightwalkers learned there was nothing to get from us save hard tack and a hanging. Side by side we fought against all who came—thrice a week sometimes we fought—against thieves and landless knights looking for good manors. Then we were in some peace, and I made shift by Hugh's help to govern the valley—for all this valley of yours was my Manor—as a knight should. I kept the roof on the hall and the thatch on the barn, but . . . The English are a bold people. His Saxons would laugh and jest with Hugh, and Hugh with them, and—this was mar- vellous to me—if even the meanest of them said that such and such a thing was the Custom of the Manor, then straightway would Hugh and such old men of the Manor as might be near forsake everything else to debate the matter—I have seen them stop the mill with the corn half ground—and if the custom or usage were proven to be as it was said, why, that was the end of it, even though it were flat against Hugh, his wish and command. Wonderful! '

' Aye,' said Puck, breaking in for the first time. ' The Custom of Old England was here before your Norman knights came, and it outlasted them, though they fought against it cruel.'

' Not I,' said Sir Richard. ' I let the Saxons go their stubborn way, but when my own men-at-arms, Normans not six months in England, stood up and told me what was the custom of the country, then I was angry. Ah, good days! Ah, wonderful people! And I loved them all.'

The knight lifted his arms as though he would hug the whole dear valley, and Swallow, hearing the chink of his chain-mail, looked up and whinnied softly.

'At last,' he went on, 'after a year of striving and contriving and some little driving, De Aquila came to the valley, alone and without warning. I saw him first at the Lower Ford, with a swineherd's brat on his saddle-bow.

' " There is no need for thee to give any account of thy stewardship," said he. " I have it all from the child here." And he told me how the young thing had stopped his tall horse at the Ford, by waving of a branch, and crying that the way was barred. " And if one bold, bare babe be enough to guard the Ford in these days, thou hast done well," said he, and puffed and wiped his head.

' He pinched the child's cheek, and looked at our cattle in the flat by the river.

' " Both fat," said he, rubbing his nose. " This is craft and cunning such as I love. What did I tell thee when I rode away, boy? "

' " Hold the Manor or hang," said I. I had never forgotten it.

' " True. And thou hast held." He clambered from his saddle and with his sword's point cut out a turf from the bank and gave it me where I kneeled.'

Dan looked at Una, and Una looked at Dan.

' That's seizin,' said Puck, in a whisper.

' " Now thou art lawfully seized of the Manor, Sir Richard," said he— 'twas the first time he ever called me that—" thou and thy heirs for ever. This must serve till the King's clerks write out thy title on a parchment. England is all ours—if we can hold it."

' " What service shall I pay? " I asked, and I remember I was proud beyond words.

' " Knight's fee, boy, knight's fee! " said he, hopping round his horse on one foot. (Have I said he was little, and could not endure to be helped to his saddle?) " Six mounted men or twelve archers thou shalt send me whenever I call for them, and—where got you that corn? " said he, for it was near harvest, and our corn stood well. " I have never seen such bright straw. Send me three bags of the same seed yearly, and furthermore, in memory of our last meeting—with the rope round thy neck—entertain me and my men for two days of each year in the Great Hall of thy Manor."

' " Alas! " said I, " then my Manor is already forfeit. I am under vow not to enter the Great Hall." And I told him what I had sworn to the Lady Ælueva.'

' And hadn't you ever been into the house since? ' said Una.

' Never,' Sir Richard answered smiling. ' I had made me a little hut of wood up the hill, and there I did justice and slept. . . . De Aquila wheeled aside, and his shield shook on his back. " No matter, boy," said he. " I will remit the homage for a year." '

' He meant Sir Richard needn't give him dinner there the first year,' Puck explained.

' De Aquila stayed with me in the hut, and Hugh, who could read and write and cast accounts, showed him the Roll of the Manor, in which were

written all the names of our fields and men, and he asked a thousand questions touching the land, the timber, the grazing, the mill, and the fish-ponds, and the worth of every man in the valley. But never he named the Lady Ælueva's name, nor went he near the Great Hall. By night he drank with us in the hut. Yes, he sat on the straw like an eagle ruffled in her feathers, his yellow eyes rolling above the cup, and he pounced in his talk like an eagle, swooping from one thing to another, but always binding fast. Yes; he would lie still awhile, and then rustle in the straw, and speak some-times as though he were King William himself, and anon he would speak in parables and tales, and if at once we saw not his meaning he would yerk us in the ribs with his scabbarded sword.

'"Look you, boys," said he, "I am born out of my due time. Five hundred years ago I would have made all England such an England as neither Dane, Saxon, nor Norman should have conquered. Five hundred years hence I should have been such a councillor to Kings as the world hath never dreamed of. 'Tis all here," said he, tapping his big head, "but it hath no play in this black age. Now Hugh here is a better man than thou art, Rich-ard." He had made his voice harsh and croaking, like a raven's.

'"Truth," said I. "But for Hugh, his help and patience and long-suffering, I could never have kept the Manor."

'"Nor thy life either," said De Aquila. "Hugh has saved thee not once, but a hundred times. Be still, Hugh!" he said. "Dost thou know, Richard, why Hugh slept, and why he still sleeps, among thy Norman men-at-arms?"

'"To be near me," said I, for I thought this was truth.

'"Fool!" said De Aquila. "It is because his Saxons have begged him to rise against thee, and to sweep every Norman out of the valley. No matter how I know. It is truth. Therefore Hugh hath made himself an hostage for thy life, well knowing that if any harm befell thee from his Saxons thy Normans would slay him without remedy. And this his Saxons know. Is it true, Hugh?"

'"In some sort," said Hugh, shamefacedly; "at least, it was true half a year ago. My Saxons would not harm Richard now—I think they know him—but I judged it best to make sure."

'Look, children, what that man had done—and I had never guessed it! Night after night had he lain down among my men-at-arms, knowing that if one Saxon had lifted knife against me his life would have answered for mine.

'"Yes," said De Aquila. "And he is a swordless man." He pointed to Hugh's belt, for Hugh had put away his sword—did I tell you?—the day after it flew from his hand at Santlache. He carried only the short knife and the long-bow. "Swordless and landless art thou, Hugh; and they call thee kin to Earl Goodwin." (Hugh was indeed of Goodwin's blood.) "The Manor that was thine is given to this boy and to his children for ever. Sit up and beg, for he can turn thee out like a dog, Hugh."

'Hugh said nothing, but I heard his teeth grind, and I bade De Aquila, my own overlord, hold his peace, or I would stuff his words down his throat. Then De Aquila laughed till the tears ran down his face.

'"I warned the King," said he, "what would come of giving England to us Norman thieves. Here art thou, Richard, less than two days confirmed in thy Manor, and already thou hast risen against thy overlord. What shall we do to him, Sir Hugh?"

'"I am a swordless man," said Hugh. "Do not jest with me," and he laid his head on his knees and groaned.

'"The greater fool thou," said De Aquila, and all his voice changed; "for I have given thee the Manor of Dallington up the hill this half-hour since," and he yerked at Hugh with his scabbard across the straw.

'"To me?" said Hugh. "I am a Saxon, and, except that I love Richard here, I have not sworn fealty to any Norman."

'"In God's good time, which because of my sins I shall not live to see, there will be neither Saxon nor Norman in England," said De Aquila. "If I know men, thou art more faithful unsworn than a score of Normans I could name. Take Dallington, and join Sir Richard to fight me to-morrow, if it please thee!"

'"Nay," said Hugh. "I am no child. Where I take a gift, there I render service"; and he put his hands between De Aquila's, and swore to be faithful, and, as I remember, I kissed him, and De Aquila kissed us both.

'We sat afterwards outside the hut while the sun rose, and De Aquila marked our churls going to their work in the fields, and talked of holy things, and how we should govern our manors in time to come, and of hunting and of horse-breeding, and of the King's wisdom and unwisdom; for he spoke to us as though we were in all sorts now his brothers. Anon a churl stole up to me—he was one of the three I had not hanged a year ago—and he bellowed—which is the Saxon for whispering—that the Lady Ælueva would speak to me at the Great House. She walked abroad daily in the Manor, and it was her custom to send me word whither she went, that I might set an archer or two behind and in front to guard her. Very often I myself lay up in the woods and watched on her also.

'I went swiftly, and as I passed the great door it opened from within, and there stood my Lady Ælueva, and she said to me: "Sir Richard, will it please you enter your Great Hall?" Then she wept, but we were alone.'

The knight was silent for a long time, his face turned across the valley, smiling.

'Oh, well done!' said Una, and clapped her hands very softly. 'She was sorry, and she said so.'

'Aye, she was sorry, and she said so,' said Sir Richard, coming back with a little start. 'Very soon—but he said it was two full hours later—De Aquila rode to the door, with his shield new scoured (Hugh had cleansed it), and demanded entertainment, and called me a false knight, that would starve his overlord to death. Then Hugh cried out that no man should work in the

valley that day, and our Saxons blew horns, and set about feasting and drinking, and running of races, and dancing and singing; and De Aquila climbed upon a horse-block and spoke to them in what he swore was good Saxon, but no man understood it. At night we feasted in the Great Hall, and when the harpers and the singers were gone we four sat late at the high table. As I remember, it was a warm night with a full moon, and De Aquila bade Hugh take down his sword from the wall again, for the honour of the Manor of Dallington, and Hugh took it gladly enough. Dust lay on the hilt, for I saw him blow it off.

'She and I sat talking a little apart, and at first we thought the harpers had come back, for the Great Hall was filled with a rushing noise of music. De Aquila leaped up; but there was only the moonlight fretty on the floor.

'"Hearken!" said Hugh. "It is my sword," and as he belted it on the music ceased.

'"Over Gods, forbid that I should ever belt blade like that," said De Aquila. "What does it foretell?"

'"The Gods that made it may know. Last time it spoke was at Hastings, when I lost all my lands. Belike it sings now that I have new lands and am a man again," said Hugh.

'He loosed the blade a little and drove it back happily into the sheath, and the sword answered him low and crooningly, as—as a woman would speak to a man, her head on his shoulder.

'Now that was the second time in all my life I heard this Sword sing.' . . .

'Look!' said Una. 'There's mother coming down the Long Slip. What will she say to Sir Richard? She can't help seeing him.'

'And Puck can't magic us this time,' said Dan.

'Are you sure?' said Puck; and he leaned forward and whispered to Sir Richard, who, smiling, bowed his head.

'But what befell the sword and my brother Hugh I will tell on another time,' said he, rising. 'Ohe, Swallow!'

The great horse cantered up from the far end of the meadow, close to mother.

They heard mother say: 'Children, Gleason's old horse has broken into the meadow again. Where did he get through?'

'Just below Stone Bay,' said Dan. 'He tore down simple flobs of the bank! We noticed it just now. And we've caught no end of fish. We've been at it all the afternoon.'

And they honestly believed that they had. They never noticed the Oak, Ash, and Thorn leaves that Puck had slyly thrown into their laps.

SIR RICHARD'S SONG

I followed my Duke ere I was a lover,
 To take from England fief and fee;
But now this game is the other way over—
 But now England hath taken me!

I had my horse, my shield and banner,
 And a boy's heart, so whole and free;
But now I sing in another manner—
 But now England hath taken me!

As for my Father in his tower,
 Asking news of my ship at sea;
He will remember his own hour—
 Tell him England hath taken me!

As for my Mother in her bower,
 That rules my Father so cunningly;
She will remember a maiden's power—
 Tell her England hath taken me!

As for my Brother in Rouen city,
 A nimble and naughty page is he;
But he will come to suffer and pity—
 Tell him England hath taken me!

As for my little Sister waiting
 In the pleasant orchards of Normandie;
Tell her youth is the time for mating—
 Tell her England hath taken me!

As for my Comrades in camp and highway,
 That lift their eyebrows scornfully;
Tell them their way is not my way—
 Tell them England hath taken me!

Kings and Princes and Barons famed,
 Knights and Captains in your degree;
Hear me a little before I am blamed—
 Seeing England hath taken me!

Howso great man's strength be reckoned,
 There are two things he cannot flee;
Love is the first, and Death is the second—
 And Love, in England, hath taken me!

THE KNIGHTS OF THE JOYOUS VENTURE

HARP SONG OF THE DANE WOMEN

What is a woman that you forsake her,
And the hearth-fire and the home-acre,
To go with the old gray Widow-maker?

She has no house to lay a guest in—
But one chill bed for all to rest in,
That the pale suns and the stray bergs nest in.

She has no strong white arms to fold you,
But the ten-times-fingering weed to hold you
Bound on the rocks where the tide has rolled you.

Yet, when the signs of summer thicken,
And the ice breaks, and the birch-buds quicken,
Yearly you turn from our side, and sicken—

Sicken again for the shouts and the slaughters,—
You steal away to the lapping waters,
And look at your ship in her winter quarters.

You forget our mirth, and talk at the tables,
The kine in the shed and the horse in the stables—
To pitch her sides and go over her cables!

Then you drive out where the storm-clouds swallow:
And the sound of your oar-blades falling hollow,
Is all we have left through the months to follow.

Ah, what is Woman that you forsake her,
And the hearth-fire and the home-acre,
To go with the old gray Widow-maker?

IT WAS too hot to run about in the open, so Dan asked their friend, old Hobden, to take their own dinghy from the pond and put her on the brook at the bottom of the garden. Her painted name was the *Daisy*, but

for exploring expeditions she was the *Golden Hind* or the *Long Serpent*, or some such suitable name. Dan hiked and howked with a boat-hook (the brook was too narrow for sculls), and Una punted with a piece of hop-pole. When they came to a very shallow place (the *Golden Hind* drew quite three inches of water) they disembarked and scuffled her over the gravel by her tow-rope, and when they reached the overgrown banks beyond the garden they pulled themselves up stream by the low branches.

That day they intended to discover the North Cape like 'Othere, the old sea-captain,' in the book of verses which Una had brought with her; but on account of the heat they changed it to a voyage up the Amazon and the sources of the Nile. Even on the shaded water the air was hot and heavy with drowsy scents, while outside, through breaks in the trees, the sunshine burned the pasture like fire. The kingfisher was asleep on his watching-branch, and the blackbirds scarcely took the trouble to dive into the next bush. Dragonflies wheeling and clashing were the only things at work, except the moor-hens and a big Red Admiral, who flapped down out of the sunshine for a drink.

When they reached Otter Pool the *Golden Hind* grounded comfortably on a shallow, and they lay beneath a roof of close green, watching the water trickle over the flood-gates down the mossy brick chute from the mill-stream to the brook. A big trout—the children knew him well—rolled head and shoulders at some fly that sailed round the bend, while once in just so often the brook rose a fraction of an inch against all the wet pebbles, and they watched the slow draw and shiver of a breath of air through the tree-tops. Then the little voices of the slipping water began again.

'It's like the shadows talking, isn't it?' said Una. She had given up trying to read. Dan lay over the bows, trailing his hands in the current. They heard feet on the gravel-bar that runs half across the pool and saw Sir Richard Dalyngridge standing over them.

'Was yours a dangerous voyage?' he asked, smiling.

'She bumped a lot, sir,' said Dan. 'There's hardly any water this summer.'

'Ah, the brook was deeper and wider when my children played at Danish pirates. Are you pirate-folk?'

'Oh, no. We gave up being pirates years ago,' explained Una. 'We're nearly always explorers now. Sailing round the world, you know.'

'Round?' said Sir Richard. He sat him in the comfortable crotch of an old ash-root on the bank. 'How can it be round?'

'Wasn't it in your books?' Dan suggested. He had been doing geography at his last lesson.

'I can neither write nor read,' he replied. 'Canst thou read, child?'

'Yes,' said Dan, 'barring the very long words.'

'Wonderful! Read to me, that I may hear for myself.'

Dan flushed, but opened the book and began—gabbling a little—at 'The Discoverer of the North Cape.'

> ' Othere, the old sea-captain,
> Who dwelt in Helgoland,
> To Alfred, lover of truth,
> Brought a snow-white walrus tooth,
> That he held in his right hand.'

' But—but—this I know! This is an old song! This I have heard sung! This is a miracle,' Sir Richard interrupted. ' Nay, do not stop! ' He leaned forward, and the shadows of the leaves slipped and slid upon his chain-mail.

> ' I ploughed the land with horses,
> But my heart was ill at ease,
> For the old sea-faring men
> Came to me now and then
> With their Sagas of the Seas.'

His hand fell on the hilt of the great sword. ' This is truth,' he cried, ' for so did it happen to me,' and he beat time delightedly to the tramp of verse after verse.

> ' " And now the land," said Othere,
> " Bent southward suddenly,
> And I followed the curving shore,
> And ever southward bore
> Into a nameless sea." '

' A nameless sea! ' he repeated. ' So did I—so did Hugh and I.'

' Where did you go? Tell us,' said Una.

' Wait. Let me hear all first.' So Dan read to the poem's very end.

' Good,' said the knight. ' That is Othere's tale—even as I have heard the men in the Dane ships sing it. Not in those same valiant words, but something like to them.'

' Have you ever explored North? ' Dan shut the book.

' Nay. My venture was South. Farther South than any man has fared, Hugh and I went down with Witta and his heathen.' He jerked the tall sword forward, and leaned on it with both hands; but his eyes looked long past them.

' I thought you always lived here,' said Una, timidly.

' Yes; while my Lady Ælueva lived. But she died. She died. Then, my eldest son being a man, I asked De Aquila's leave that he should hold the Manor while I went on some journey or pilgrimage—to forget. De Aquila, whom the Second William had made Warden of Pevensey in Earl Mortain's place, was very old then, but still he rode his tall roan horses, and in the saddle he looked like a little white falcon. When Hugh, at Dallington over yonder, heard what I did, he sent for my second son, whom being unmarried he had ever looked upon as his own child, and, by De Aquila's leave, gave him the Manor of Dallington to hold till he should return. Then Hugh came with me.'

' When did this happen? ' said Dan.

'That I can answer to the very day, for as we rode with De Aquila by
Pevensey—have I said that he was Lord of Pevensey and of the Honour of
the Eagle?—to the Bordeaux ship that fetched him his wines yearly out
of France, a Marsh man ran to us crying that he had seen a great black
goat which bore on his back the body of the King, and that the goat had
spoken to him. On that same day Red William our King, the Conqueror's
son, died of a secret arrow while he hunted in a forest. "This is a cross
matter," said De Aquila, "to meet on the threshold of a journey. If Red
William be dead I may have to fight for my lands. Wait a little."

'My Lady being dead, I cared nothing for signs and omens, nor Hugh
either. We took that wine-ship to go to Bordeaux; but the wind failed while
we were yet in sight of Pevensey, a thick mist hid us, and we drifted with
the tide along the cliffs to the west. Our company was, for the most part,
merchants returning to France, and we were laden with wool and there were
three couple of tall hunting-dogs chained to the rail. Their master was a
knight of Artois. His name I never learned, but his shield bore gold pieces
on a red ground, and he limped, much as I do, from a wound which he had
got in his youth at Mantes siege. He served the Duke of Burgundy against
the Moors in Spain, and was returning to that war with his dogs. He sang
us strange Moorish songs that first night, and half persuaded us to go with
him. I was on pilgrimage to forget—which is what no pilgrimage brings. I
think I would have gone, but . . .

'Look you how the life and fortune of man changes! Towards morning
a Dane ship, rowing silently, struck against us in the mist, and while we
rolled hither and yon Hugh, leaning over the rail, fell outboard. I leaped
after him, and we two tumbled aboard the Dane, and were caught and
bound ere we could rise. Our own ship was swallowed up in the mist. I judge
the Knight of the Gold Pieces muzzled his dogs with his cloak, lest they
should give tongue and betray the merchants, for I heard their baying sud-
denly stop.

'We lay bound among the benches till morning, when the Danes dragged
us to the high deck by the steering-place, and their captain—Witta, he was
called—turned us over with his foot. Bracelets of gold from elbow to armpit
he wore, and his red hair was long as a woman's, and came down in plaited
locks on his shoulder. He was stout, with bowed legs and long arms. He
spoiled us of all we had, but when he laid hand on Hugh's sword and saw
the runes on the blade hastily he thrust it back. Yet his covetousness over-
came him and he tried again and again, and the third time the Sword sang
loud and angrily, so that the rowers leaned on their oars to listen. Here they
all spoke together, screaming like gulls, and a Yellow Man, such as I have
never seen, came to the high deck and cut our bonds. He was yellow—not
from sickness, but by nature—yellow as honey, and his eyes stood endwise
in his head.'

'How do you mean?' said Una, her chin on her hand.

'Thus,' said Sir Richard. He put a finger to the corner of each eye,
and pushed it up till his eyes narrowed to slits.

'Why, you look just like a Chinaman!' cried Dan. 'Was the man a Chinaman?'

'I know not what that may be. Witta had found him half dead among ice on the shores of Muscovy. We thought he was a devil. He crawled before us and brought food in a silver dish which these sea-wolves had robbed from some rich abbey, and Witta with his own hands gave us wine. He spoke a little in French, a little in South Saxon, and much in the Northman's tongue. We asked him to set us ashore, promising to pay him better ransom than he would get price if he sold us to the Moors—as once befell a knight of my acquaintance sailing from Flushing.

'"Not by my father Guthrum's head," said he. "The Gods sent ye into my ship for a luck-offering."

'At this I quaked, for I knew it was still the Danes' custom to sacrifice captives to their gods for fair weather.

'"A plague on thy four long bones!" said Hugh. "What profit canst thou make of poor old pilgrims that can neither work nor fight?"

' " Gods forbid I should fight against thee, poor Pilgrim with the Sing-
ing Sword," said he. " Come with us and be poor no more. Thy teeth are
far apart, which is a sure sign thou wilt travel and grow rich."

' " What if we will not come? " said Hugh.

' " Swim to England or France," said Witta. " We are midway be-
tween the two. Unless ye choose to drown yourselves no hair of your head
will be harmed here aboard. We think ye bring us luck, and I myself know
the runes on that Sword are good." He turned and bade them hoist sail.

' Hereafter all made way for us as we walked about the ship, and the
ship was full of wonders.'

' What was she like? ' said Dan.

' Long, low, and narrow, bearing one mast with a red sail, and rowed
by fifteen oars a-side,' the knight answered. ' At her bows was a deck under
which men might lie, and at her stern another shut off by a painted door
from the rowers' benches. Here Hugh and I slept, with Witta and the Yel-
low Man, upon tapestries as soft as wool. I remember '—he laughed to him-
self—' when first we entered there a loud voice cried, " Out swords! Out
swords! Kill, kill! " Seeing us start, Witta laughed, and showed us it was but
a great-beaked gray bird with a red tail. He sat her on his shoulder, and she
called for bread and wine hoarsely, and prayed him to kiss her. Yet she was
no more than a silly bird. But—ye knew this? ' He looked at their smiling
faces.

' We weren't laughing at you,' said Una. ' That must have been a parrot.
It's just what Pollies do.'

' So we learned later. But here is another marvel. The Yellow Man,
whose name was Kitai, had with him a brown box. In the box was a blue
bowl with red marks upon the rim, and within the bowl, hanging from a
fine thread, was a piece of iron no thicker than that grass stem, and as long,
maybe, as my spur, but straight. In this iron, said Witta, abode an Evil Spirit
which Kitai, the Yellow Man, had brought by Art Magic out of his own
country that lay three years' journey southward. The Evil Spirit strove day
and night to return to his country, and therefore, look you, the iron needle
pointed continually to the South.'

' South? ' said Dan, suddenly, and put his hand into his pocket.

' With my own eyes I saw it. Every day and all day long, though the
ship rolled, though the sun and the moon and the stars were hid, this blind
Spirit in the iron knew whither it would go, and strained to the South. Witta
called it the Wise Iron, because it showed him his way across the unknow-
able seas.' Again Sir Richard looked keenly at the children. ' How think ye?
Was it sorcery? '

' Was it anything like this? ' Dan fished out his old brass pocket-com-
pass, that generally lived with his knife and key-ring. ' The glass has got
cracked, but the needle waggles all right, sir.'

The knight drew a long breath of wonder. ' Yes, yes. The Wise Iron
shook and swung in just this fashion. Now it is still. Now it points to the
South.'

'North,' said Dan.

'Nay, South! There is the South,' said Sir Richard. Then they both laughed, for naturally when one end of a straight compass-needle points to the North, the other must point to the South.

'Te,' said Sir Richard, clicking his tongue. 'There can be no sorcery if a child carries it. Wherefore does it point South—or North?'

'Father says that nobody knows,' said Una.

Sir Richard looked relieved. 'Then it may still be magic. It was magic to us. And so we voyaged. When the wind served we hoisted sail, and lay all up along the windward rail, our shields on our backs to break the spray. When it failed, they rowed with long oars; the Yellow Man sat by the Wise Iron, and Witta steered. At first I feared the great white-flowering waves, but as I saw how wisely Witta led his ship among them I grew bolder. Hugh liked it well from the first. My skill is not upon the water; and rocks, and whirlpools such as we saw by the West Isles of France, where an oar caught on a rock and broke, are much against my stomach. We sailed South across a stormy sea, where by moonlight, between clouds, we saw a Flanders ship roll clean over and sink. Again, though Hugh laboured with Witta all night, I lay under the deck with the Talking Bird, and cared not whether I lived or died. There is a sickness of the sea which for three days is pure death! When we next saw land Witta said it was Spain, and we stood out to sea. That coast was full of ships busy in the Duke's war against the Moors, and we feared to be hanged by the Duke's men or sold into slavery by the Moors. So we put into a small harbour which Witta knew. At night men came down with loaded mules, and Witta exchanged amber out of the North against little wedges of iron and packets of beads in earthen pots. The pots he put under the decks, and the wedges of iron he laid on the bottom of the ship after he had cast out the stones and shingle which till then had been our ballast. Wine, too, he bought for lumps of sweet-smelling gray amber—a little morsel no bigger than a thumbnail purchased a cask of wine. But I speak like a merchant.'

'No, no. Tell us what you had to eat,' cried Dan.

'Meat dried in the sun, and dried fish and ground beans, Witta took in; and corded frails of a certain sweet, soft fruit, which the Moors use, which is like paste of figs, but with thin, long stones. Aha! Dates is the name.

'"Now," said Witta, when the ship was loaded, "I counsel you strangers to pray to your gods, for, from here on, our road is No Man's road." He and his men killed a black goat for sacrifice on the bows; and the Yellow Man brought out a small, smiling image of dull-green stone and burned incense before it. Hugh and I commended ourselves to God, and Saint Barnabas, and Our Lady of the Assumption who was specially dear to my Lady. We were not young, but I think no shame to say whenas we drove out of that secret harbour at sunrise over a still sea, we two rejoiced and sang as did the knights of old when they followed our great Duke to England. Yet was our leader an heathen pirate; all our proud fleet but one galley perilously overloaded; for guidance we leaned on a pagan sorcerer;

and our port was beyond the world's end. Witta told us that his father Guthrum had once in his life rowed along the shores of Africa to a land where naked men sold gold for iron and beads. There had he bought much gold, and no few elephants' teeth, and thither by help of the Wise Iron would Witta go. Witta feared nothing—except to be poor.

' " My father told me," said Witta, " that a great Shoal runs three days' sail out from that land, and south of the shoal lies a Forest which grows in the sea. South and east of the Forest my father came to a place where the men hid gold in their hair; but all that country, he said, was full of Devils who lived in trees, and tore folk limb from limb. How think ye? "

' " Gold or no gold," said Hugh, fingering his sword, " it is a joyous venture. Have at these devils of thine, Witta! "

' " Venture! " said Witta, sourly. " I am only a poor sea-thief. I do not set my life adrift on a plank for joy, or the venture. Once I beach ship again at Stavanger, and feel the wife's arms round my neck, I'll seek no more ventures. A ship is heavier care than a wife or cattle."

' He leaped down among the rowers, chiding them for their little strength and their great stomachs. Yet Witta was a wolf in fight, and a very fox in cunning.

' We were driven South by a storm, and for three days and three nights he took the stern-oar, and threddled the long-ship through the sea. When it rose beyond measure he brake a pot of whale's oil upon the water, which wonderfully smoothed it, and in that anointed patch he turned her head to the wind and threw out oars at the end of a rope, to make, he said, an anchor at which we lay rolling sorely, but dry. This craft his father Guthrum had shown him. He knew, too, all the Leech-Book of Bald, who was a wise doctor, and he knew the Ship-Book of Hlaf the Woman, who robbed Egypt. He knew all the care of a ship.

' After the storm we saw a mountain whose top was covered with snow and pierced the clouds. The grasses under this mountain, boiled and eaten, are a good cure for soreness of the gums and swelled ankles. We lay there eight days, till men in skins threw stones at us. When the heat increased Witta spread a cloth on bent sticks above the rowers, for the wind failed between the Island of the Mountain and the shore of Africa, which is east of it. That shore is sandy, and we rowed along it within three bowshots. Here we saw whales, and fish in the shape of shields, but longer than our ship. Some slept, some opened their mouths at us, and some danced on the hot waters. The water was hot to the hand, and the sky was hidden by hot, gray mists, out of which blew a fine dust that whitened our hair and beards of a morning. Here, too, were fish that flew in the air like birds. They would fall on the laps of the rowers, and when we went ashore we would roast and eat them.'

The knight paused to see if the children doubted him, but they only nodded and said, ' Go on.'

' The yellow land lay on our left, the gray sea on our right. Knight though

I was, I pulled my oar amongst the rowers. I caught seaweed and dried it, and stuffed it between the pots of beads lest they should break. Knighthood is for the land. At sea, look you, a man is but a spurless rider on a bridleless horse. I learned to make strong knots in ropes—yes, and to join two ropes end to end, so that even Witta could scarcely see where they had been married. But Hugh had tenfold more sea-cunning than I. Witta gave him charge of the rowers of the left side. Thorkild of Borkum, a man with a broken nose, that wore a Norman steel cap, had the rowers of the right, and each side rowed and sang against the other. They saw that no man was idle. Truly, as Hugh said, and Witta would laugh at him, a ship is all more care than a Manor.

'How? Thus. There was water to fetch from the shore when we could find it, as well as wild fruit and grasses, and sand for scrubbing of the decks and benches to keep them sweet. Also we hauled the ship out on low islands and emptied all her gear, even to the iron wedges, and burned off the weed, that had grown on her, with torches of rush, and smoked below the decks with rushes dampened in salt water, as Hlaf the Woman orders in her Ship-Book. Once when we were thus stripped, and the ship lay propped on her keel, the bird cried, " Out swords! " as though she saw an enemy. Witta vowed he would wring her neck.'

'Poor Polly! Did he?' said Una.

'Nay. She was the ship's bird. She could call all the rowers by name. . . . Those were good days—for a wifeless man—with Witta and his heathen—beyond the world's end. . . . After many weeks we came on the Great Shoal which stretched, as Witta's father had said, far out to sea. We skirted it till we were giddy with the sight and dizzy with the sound of bars and breakers, and when we reached land again we found a naked black people dwelling among woods, who for one wedge of iron loaded us with fruits and grasses and eggs. Witta scratched his head at them in sign he would buy gold. They had no gold, but they understood the sign (all the gold-traders hide their gold in their thick hair), for they pointed along the coast. They beat, too, on their chests with their clenched hands, and that, if we had known it, was an evil sign.'

'What did it mean?' said Dan.

'Patience. Ye shall hear. We followed the coast eastward sixteen days (counting time by sword-cuts on the helm-rail) till we came to the Forest in the Sea. Trees grew there out of mud, arched upon lean and high roots, and many muddy waterways ran all whither into darkness under the trees. Here we lost the sun. We followed the winding channels between the trees, and where we could not row we laid hold of the crusted roots and hauled ourselves along. The water was foul, and great glittering flies tormented us. Morning and evening a blue mist covered the mud, which bred fevers. Four of our rowers sickened, and were bound to their benches, lest they should leap overboard and be eaten by the monsters of the mud. The Yellow Man lay sick beside the Wise Iron, rolling his head and talking in his own tongue.'

Only the Bird throve. She sat on Witta's shoulder and screamed in that noisome, silent darkness. Yes; I think it was the silence we most feared.'

He paused to listen to the comfortable home noises of the brook.

'When we had lost count of time among those black gullies and swashes we heard, as it were, a drum beat far off, and following it we broke into a broad, brown river by a hut in a clearing among fields of pumpkins. We thanked God to see the sun again. The people of the village gave the good welcome, and Witta scratched his head at them (for gold), and showed them our iron and beads. They ran to the bank—we were still in the ship—and pointed to our swords and bows, for always when near shore we lay armed. Soon they fetched store of gold in bars and in dust from their huts, and some great blackened elephant teeth. These they piled on the bank, as though to tempt us, and made signs of dealing blows in battle, and pointed up to the tree-tops, and to the forest behind. Their captain or chief sorcerer then beat on his chest with his fists, and gnashed his teeth.

'Said Thorkild of Borkum: "Do they mean we must fight for all this gear?" and he half drew sword.

'"Nay," said Hugh. "I think they ask us to league against some enemy."

'"I like this not," said Witta, of a sudden. "Back into mid-stream."

'So we did, and sat still all, watching the black folk and the gold they piled on the bank. Again we heard drums beat in the forest, and the people fled to their huts, leaving the gold unguarded.

'Then Hugh, at the bows, pointed without speech, and we saw a great Devil come out of the forest. He shaded his brows with his hand, and moistened his pink tongue between his lips—thus.'

'A Devil!' said Dan, delightfully horrified.

'Yea. Taller than a man; covered with reddish hair. When he had well regarded our ship, he beat on his chest with his fists till it sounded like rolling drums, and came to the bank swinging all his body between his long arms, and gnashed his teeth at us. Hugh loosed arrow, and pierced him through the throat. He fell roaring, and three other Devils ran out of the forest and hauled him into a tall tree out of sight. Anon they cast down the blood-stained arrow, and lamented together among the leaves. Witta saw the gold on the bank; he was loath to leave it. "Sirs," said he (no man had spoken till then), "yonder is what we have come so far and so painfully to find, laid out to our very hand. Let us row in while these Devils bewail themselves, and at least bear off what we may."

'Bold as a wolf, cunning as a fox was Witta! He set four archers on the foredeck to shoot the Devils if they should leap from the tree, which was close to the bank. He manned ten oars a-side, and bade them watch his hand to row in or back out, and so coaxed he them towards the bank. But none would set foot ashore, though the gold was within ten paces. No man is hasty to his hanging! They whimpered at their oars like beaten hounds, and Witta bit his fingers for rage.

'Said Hugh of a sudden, "Hark!" At first we thought it was the buzzing of the glittering flies on the water; but it grew loud and fierce, so that all men heard.'

'What?' said Dan and Una.

'It was the sword.' Sir Richard patted the smooth hilt. 'It sang as a Dane sings before battle. "I go," said Hugh, and he leaped from the bows and fell among the gold. I was afraid to my four bones' marrow, but for shame's sake I followed, and Thorkild of Borkum leaped after me. None other came. "Blame me not," cried Witta behind us, "I must abide by my ship." We three had no time to blame or praise. We stooped to the gold and threw it back over our shoulders, one hand on our swords and one eye on the tree, which nigh over-hung us.

'I know not how the Devils leaped down, or how the fight began. I heard Hugh cry: "Out! out!" as though he were at Santlache again; I saw Thorkild's steel cap smitten off his head by a great hairy hand, and I felt an arrow from the ship whistle past my ear. They say that till Witta took his sword to the rowers he could not bring his ship inshore; and each one of the four archers said afterwards that he alone had pierced the Devil that fought me. I do not know. I went to it in my mail-shirt, which saved my skin. With longsword and belt-dagger I fought for the life against a Devil whose very feet were hands, and who whirled me back and forth like a dead branch. He had me by the waist, my arms to my side, when an arrow from the ship pierced him between the shoulders, and he loosened grip. I passed my sword twice through him, and he crutched himself away between his long arms, coughing and moaning. Next, as I remember, I saw Thorkild of Borkum bare-headed and smiling, leaping up and down before a Devil that leaped and gnashed his teeth. Then Hugh passed, his sword shifted to his left hand, and I wondered why I had not known that Hugh was a left-handed man; and thereafter I remembered nothing till I felt spray on my face, and we were in sunshine on the open sea. That was twenty days after.'

'What had happened? Did Hugh die?' the children asked.

'Never was such a fight fought by christened man,' said Sir Richard. 'An arrow from the ship had saved me from my Devil, and Thorkild of Borkum had given back before his Devil, till the bowmen on the ship could shoot it all full of arrows from near by; but Hugh's Devil was cunning, and had kept behind trees, where no arrow could reach. Body to body there, by stark strength of sword and hand, had Hugh slain him, and, dying, the Thing had clenched his teeth on the sword. Judge what teeth they were!'

Sir Richard turned the sword again that the children might see the two great chiselled gouges on either side of the blade.

'Those same teeth met in Hugh's right arm and side,' Sir Richard went on. 'I? Oh, I had no more than a broken foot and a fever. Thorkild's ear was bitten, but Hugh's arm and side clean withered away. I saw him where he lay along, sucking a fruit in his left hand. His flesh was wasted off his bones, his hair was patched with white, and his hand was blue-veined

like a woman's. He put his left hand round my neck and whispered, "Take my sword. It has been thine since Hastings, O my brother, but I can never hold hilt again." We lay there on the high deck talking of Santlache, and, I think, of every day since Santlache, and it came so that we both wept. I was weak, and he little more than a shadow.

'"Nay—nay," said Witta, at the helm-rail. "Gold is a good right arm to any man. Look—look at the gold!" He bade Thorkild show us the gold and the elephants' teeth, as though we had been children. He had brought away all the gold on the bank, and twice as much more, that the people of the village gave him for slaying the Devils. They worshipped us as gods, Thorkild told me: it was one of their old women healed up Hugh's poor arm.'

'How much gold did you get?' asked Dan.

'How can I say? Where we came out with wedges of iron under the rowers' feet we returned with wedges of gold hidden beneath planks. There was dust of gold in packages where we slept and along the side, and cross-wise under the benches we lashed the blackened elephants' teeth.

'"I had sooner have my right arm," said Hugh, when he had seen all.

'"Ahai! That was my fault," said Witta. "I should have taken ransom and landed you in France when first you came aboard, ten months ago."

'"It is over-late now," said Hugh, laughing.

'Witta plucked at his long shoulder-lock. "But think!" said he. "If I had let ye go—which I swear I would never have done, for I love ye more than brothers—if I had let ye go, by now ye might have been horribly slain by some mere Moor in the Duke of Burgundy's war, or ye might have been murdered by land-thieves, or ye might have died of the plague at an inn. Think of this and do not blame me overmuch, Hugh. See! I will only take a half of the gold."

'"I blame thee not at all, Witta," said Hugh. "It was a joyous venture, and we thirty-five here have done what never men have done. If I live till England, I will build me a stout keep over Dallington out of my share."

'"I will buy cattle and amber and warm red cloth for the wife," said Witta, "and I will hold all the land at the head of Stavanger Fiord. Many will fight for me now. But first we must turn North, and with this honest treasure aboard I pray we meet no pirate ships."

'We did not laugh. We were careful. We were afraid lest we should lose one grain of our gold, for which we had fought Devils.

'"Where is the Sorcerer?" said I, for Witta was looking at the Wise Iron in the box, and I could not see the Yellow Man.

'"He has gone to his own country," said he. "He rose up in the night while we were beating out of that forest in the mud, and said that he could see it behind the trees. He leaped out on to the mud, and did not answer when we called; so we called no more. He left the Wise Iron, which is all that I care for—and see, the Spirit still points to the South."

'We were troubled for fear that the Wise Iron should fail us now that

its Yellow Man had gone, and when we saw the Spirit still served us we grew afraid of too strong winds, and of shoals, and of careless leaping fish, and of all the people on all the shores where we landed.'

' Why? ' said Dan.

' Because of the gold—because of our gold. Gold changes men altogether. Thorkild of Borkum did not change. He laughed at Witta for his fears, and at us for our counselling Witta to furl sail when the ship pitched at all.

' " Better be drowned out of hand," said Thorkild of Borkum, " than go tied to a deck-load of yellow dust."

' He was a landless man, and had been slave to some King in the East. He would have beaten out the gold into deep bands to put round the oars, and round the prow.

' Yet, though he vexed himself for the gold, Witta waited upon Hugh like a woman, lending him his shoulder when the ship rolled, and tying of ropes from side to side that Hugh might hold by them. But for Hugh, he said—and so did all his men—they would never have won the gold. I remember Witta made a little, thin gold ring for our Bird to swing in.

' Three months we rowed and sailed and went ashore for fruits or to clean the ship. When we saw wild horsemen, riding among sand-dunes, flourishing spears, we knew we were on the Moors' coast, and stood over north to Spain; and a strong south-west wind bore us in ten days to a coast of high red rocks, where we heard a hunting-horn blow among the yellow gorse and knew it was England.

' " Now find ye Pevensey yourselves," said Witta. " I love not these narrow ship-filled seas."

' He set the dried, salted head of the Devil, which Hugh had killed, high on our prow, and all boats fled us. Yet, for our gold's sake, we were more afraid than they. We crept along the coast by night till we came to the chalk cliffs, and so east to Pevensey. Witta would not come ashore with us, though Hugh promised him wine at Dallington enough to swim in. He was on fire to see his wife, and ran into the Marsh after sunset, and there he left us and our share of gold, and backed out on the same tide. He made no promise; he swore no oath; he looked for no thanks; but to Hugh, an armless man, and to me, an old cripple whom he could have flung into the sea, he passed over wedge upon wedge, packet upon packet of gold and dust of gold, and only ceased when we would take no more. As he stooped from the rail to bid us farewell he stripped off his right-arm bracelets and put them all on Hugh's left, and he kissed Hugh on the cheek. I think when Thorkild of Borkum bade the rowers give way we were near weeping. It is true that Witta was an heathen and a pirate; true it is he held us by force many months in his ship, but I loved that bow-legged, blue-eyed man for his great boldness, his cunning, his skill, and, beyond all, for his simplicity.'

' Did he get home all right? ' said Dan.

'I never knew. We saw him hoist sail under the moon-track and stand away. I have prayed that he found his wife and the children.'

'And what did you do?'

'We waited on the Marsh till the day. Then I sat by the gold, all tied in an old sail, while Hugh went to Pevensey, and De Aquila sent us horses.'

Sir Richard crossed hands on his sword-hilt, and stared down stream through the soft warm shadows.

'A whole shipload of gold!' said Una, looking at the little *Golden Hind*. 'But I'm glad I didn't see the Devils.'

'I don't believe they were Devils,' Dan whispered back.

'Eh?' said Sir Richard. 'Witta's father warned him they were unquestionable Devils. One must believe one's father, and not one's children. What were my Devils, then?'

Dan flushed all over. 'I—I only thought,' he stammered; 'I've got a book called *The Gorilla Hunters*—it's a continuation of *Coral Island*, sir —and it says there that the gorillas (they're big monkeys, you know) were always chewing iron up.'

'Not always,' said Una. 'Only twice.' They had been reading *The Gorilla Hunters* in the orchard.

'Well, anyhow, they always drummed on their chests, like Sir Richard's did, before they went for people. And they built houses in trees, too.'

'Ha!' Sir Richard opened his eyes. 'Houses like flat nests did our Devils make, where their imps lay and looked at us. I did not see them (I was sick after the fight), but Witta told me, and, lo, ye know it also? Wonderful! Were our Devils only nest-building apes? Is there no sorcery left in the world?'

'I don't know,' answered Dan, uncomfortably. 'I've seen a man take rabbits out of a hat, and he told us we could see how he did it, if we watched hard. And we did.'

'But we didn't,' said Una, sighing. 'Oh! there's Puck!'

The little fellow, brown and smiling, peered between two stems of an ash, nodded, and slid down the bank into the cool beside them.

'No sorcery, Sir Richard?' he laughed, and blew on a full dandelion head he had picked.

'They tell me that Witta's Wise Iron was a toy. The boy carries such an iron with him. They tell me our Devils were apes, called gorillas!' said Sir Richard, indignantly.

'That is the sorcery of books,' said Puck. 'I warned thee they were wise children. All people can be wise by reading of books.'

'But are the books true?' Sir Richard frowned. 'I like not all this reading and writing.'

'Ye-es,' said Puck, holding the naked dandelion head at arm's length. 'But if we hang all fellows who write falsely, why did De Aquila not begin with Gilbert, the Clerk? He was false enough.'

'Poor false Gilbert. Yet, in his fashion, he was bold,' said Sir Richard.
'What did he do?' said Dan.
'He wrote,' said Sir Richard. 'Is the tale meet for children, think you?'
He looked at Puck; but 'Tell us! Tell us!' cried Dan and Una together.

THORKILD'S SONG

There's no wind along these seas,
　　Out oars for Stavanger!
　　Forward all for Stavanger!
So we must wake the white-ash breeze,
　　Let fall for Stavanger!
　　A long pull for Stavanger!

Oh, hear the benches creak and strain!
　　(A long pull for Stavanger!)
She thinks she smells the Northland rain!
　　(A long pull for Stavanger!)

She thinks she smells the Northland snow,
And she's as glad as we to go.

She thinks she smells the Northland rime,
And the dear dark nights of winter-time.

Her very bolts are sick for shore,
And we—we want it ten times more!

So all you Gods that love brave men,
Send us a three-reef gale again!

Send us a gale, and watch us come,
With close-cropped canvas slashing home!

But—there's no wind in all these seas,
　　A long pull for Stavanger!
So we must wake the white-ash breeze,
　　A long pull for Stavanger!

OLD MEN AT PEVENSEY

❦ IT HAS nought to do with apes or devils,' Sir Richard went on, in an undertone. 'It concerns De Aquila, than whom there was never bolder nor craftier, nor more hardy knight born. And remember he was an old, old man at that time.'

'When?' said Dan.

'When we came back from sailing with Witta.'

'What did you do with your gold?' said Dan.

'Have patience. Link by link is chain-mail made. I will tell all in its place. We bore the gold to Pevensey on horseback—three loads of it—and then up to the north chamber, above the Great Hall of Pevensey Castle, where De Aquila lay in winter. He sat on his bed like a little white falcon, turning his head swiftly from one to the other as we told our tale. Jehan the Crab, an old sour man-at-arms, guarded the stairway, but De Aquila bade him wait at the stair-foot, and let down both leather curtains over the door. It was Jehan whom De Aquila had sent to us with the horses, and only Jehan had loaded the gold. When our story was told, De Aquila gave us the news of England, for we were as men waked from a year-long sleep. The Red King was dead—slain (ye remember?) the day we set sail—and Henry, his younger brother, had made himself King of England over the head of Robert of Normandy. This was the very thing that William the Red King had done to Robert when our Great William died. Then Robert of Normandy, mad, as De Aquila said, at twice missing of this kingdom, had sent an army against England, which army had been well beaten back to their ships at Portsmouth. A little earlier, and Witta's ship would have rowed through them.

'"And now," said De Aquila, "half the great Barons of the north and west are out against the King between Salisbury and Shrewsbury, and half the other half wait to see which way the game shall go. They say Henry is overly English for their stomachs, because he hath married an English wife and she hath coaxed him to give back their old laws to our Saxons. (Better ride a horse on the bit he knows, I say.) But that is only a cloak to their falsehood." He cracked his finger on the table where the wine was spilt, and thus he spoke:—

'"William crammed us Norman barons full of good English acres after Santlache. I had my share too," he said, and clapped Hugh on the shoulder; "but I warned him—I warned him before Odo rebelled—that he should have bidden the Barons give up their lands and lordships in Normandy if they would be English lords. Now they are all but princes both in England

and Normandy—trencher-fed hounds, with a foot in one trough and both eyes on the other! Robert of Normandy has sent them word that if they do not fight for him in England he will sack and harry out their lands in Normandy. Therefore Clare has risen, FitzOsborne has risen, Montgomery has risen—whom our First William made an English earl. Even D'Arcy is out with his men, whose father I remember a little hedge-sparrow knight nearby Caen. If Henry wins, the Barons can still flee to Normandy, where Robert will welcome them. If Henry loses, Robert, he says, will give them more lands in England. Oh, a pest—a pest on Normandy, for she will be our England's curse this many a long year!"

' "Amen," said Hugh. "But will the war come our ways, think you?"

' "Not from the north," said De Aquila. "But the sea is always open. If the Barons gain the upper hand Robert will send another army into England for sure, and this time I think he will land there—where his father, the Conqueror, landed. Ye have brought your pigs to a pretty market! Half England alight, and gold enough on the ground "—he stamped on the bars beneath the table—" to set every sword in Christendom fighting."

' "What is to do?" said Hugh. " I have no keep at Dallington; and if we buried it, whom could we trust?"

' " Me," said De Aquila. " Pevensey walls are strong. No man but Jehan, who is my dog, knows what is between them." He drew a curtain by the shot-window and showed us the shaft of a well in the thickness of the wall.

' " I made it for a drinking-well," he said, " but we found salt water, and it rises and falls with the tide. Hark!" We heard the water whistle and blow at the bottom. " Will it serve?" said he.

' "Needs must," said Hugh. " Our lives are in thy hands." So we lowered all the gold down except one small chest of it by De Aquila's bed, which we kept as much for his delight in its weight and colour as for any our needs.

' In the morning, ere we rode to our Manors, he said: " I do not say farewell; because ye will return and bide here. Not for love nor for sorrow, but to be with the gold. Have a care," he said, laughing, " lest I use it to make myself Pope. Trust me not, but return!" '

Sir Richard paused, and smiled sadly.

' In seven days, then, we returned from our Manors—from the Manors which had been ours.'

' And were the children quite well?' said Una.

' My sons were young. Land and governance belong by right to young men.' Sir Richard was talking to himself. ' It would have broken their hearts if we had taken back our Manors. They made us great welcome, but we could see—Hugh and I could see—that our day was done. I was a cripple and he a one-armed man. No!' He shook his head. ' And therefore '—he raised his voice—' we rode back to Pevensey.'

' I'm sorry,' said Una, for the knight seemed very sorrowful.

' Little maid, it all passed long ago. They were young; we were old.

We let them rule the Manors. " Aha! " cried De Aquila from his shot-window, when we dismounted. " Back again to earth, old foxes? " but when we were in his chamber above the Hall he puts his arms about us and says, " Welcome, ghosts! Welcome, poor ghosts! " . . . Thus it fell out that we were rich beyond belief, and lonely. And lonely! '

' What did you do? ' said Dan.

' We watched for Robert of Normandy,' said the knight. ' De Aquila was like Witta. He suffered no idleness. In fair weather we would ride along between Bexlei on the one side, to Cuckmere on the other—sometimes with hawk, sometimes with hound (there are stout hares both on the Marsh and the Downland), but always with an eye to the sea, for fear of fleets from Normandy. In foul weather he would walk on the top of his tower, frowning against the rain—peering here and pointing there. It always vexed him to think how Witta's ship had come and gone without his knowledge. When the wind ceased and ships anchored, to the wharf's edge he would go and, leaning on his sword among the stinking fish, would call to the mariners for their news from France. His other eye he kept landward for word of Henry's war against the Barons.

' Many brought him news—jongleurs, harpers, pedlars, sutlers, priests, and the like; and, though he was secret enough in small things, yet, if their news misliked him, then, regarding neither time nor place nor people, would he curse our King Henry for a fool or a babe. I have heard him cry aloud by the fishing-boats: " If I were King of England I would do thus and thus " ; and when I rode out to see that the warning-beacons were laid and dry, he hath often called to me from the shot-window: " Look to it, Richard! Do not copy our blind King, but see with thine own eyes and feel with thine own hands." I do not think he knew any sort of fear. And so we lived at Pevensey, in the little chamber above the Hall.

' One foul night came word that a messenger of the King waited below. We were chilled after a long riding in the fog towards Bexlei, which is an easy place for ships to land. De Aquila sent word the man might either eat with us or wait till we had fed. Anon Jehan, at the stair-head, cried that he had called for horse, and was gone. " Pest on him! " said De Aquila. " I have more to do than to shiver in the Great Hall for every gadling the King sends. Left he no word? "

' " None," said Jehan, " except "—he had been with De Aquila at Santlache—" except he said that if an old dog could not learn new tricks it was time to sweep out the kennel."

' " Oho! " said De Aquila, rubbing his nose, " to whom did he say that? "

' " To his beard, chiefly, but some to his horse's flank as he was girthing up. I followed him out," said Jehan the Crab.

' " What was his shield-mark? "

' " Gold horseshoes on black," said the Crab.

' " That is one of Fulke's men," said De Aquila.'

Puck broke in very gently, ' Gold horseshoes on black is not the Fulkes' shield. The Fulkes' arms are— '

The knight waved one hand statelily.

' Thou knowest that evil man's true name,' he replied, ' but I have chosen to call him Fulke because I promised him I would not tell the story of his wickedness so that any man might guess it. I have changed all the names in my tale. His children's children may be still alive.'

' True—true,' said Puck, smiling softly. ' It is knightly to keep faith—even after a thousand years.'

Sir Richard bowed a little and went on:—

' " Gold horseshoes on black? " said De Aquila. " I had heard Fulke had joined the Barons, but if this is true our King must be of the upper hand. No matter, all Fulkes are faithless. Still, I would not have sent the man away empty."

' " He fed," said Jehan. " Gilbert the Clerk fetched him meat and wine from the kitchens. He ate at Gilbert's table."

' This Gilbert was a clerk from Battle Abbey, who kept the accounts of the Manor of Pevensey. He was tall and pale-coloured, and carried those new-fashioned beads for counting the prayers. They were large brown nuts or seeds, and hanging from his girdle with his penner and inkhorn they clashed when he walked. His place was in the great fireplace. There was his table of accounts, and there he lay o' nights. He feared the hounds in the Hall that came nosing after bones or to sleep on the warm ashes, and would slash at them with his beads—like a woman. When De Aquila sat in Hall to do justice, take fines, or grant lands, Gilbert would so write it in the Manor-roll. But it was none of his work to feed our guests, or to let them depart without his lord's knowledge.

' Said De Aquila, after Jehan was gone down the stair: " Hugh, hast thou ever told my Gilbert thou canst read Latin hand-of-write? "

' " No," said Hugh. " He is no friend to me, or to Odo my hound either." " No matter," said De Aquila. " Let him never know thou canst tell one letter from its fellow, and "—here he yerked us in the ribs with his scabbard—" watch him both of ye. There be devils in Africa, as I have heard, but by the Saints there be greater devils in Pevensey! " And that was all he would say.

' It chanced, some small while afterwards, a Norman man-at-arms would wed a Saxon wench of the Manor, and Gilbert (we had watched him well since De Aquila spoke) doubted whether her folk were free or slave. Since De Aquila would give them a field of good land, if she were free, the matter came up at the justice in Great Hall before De Aquila. First the wench's father spoke; then her mother; then all together, till the Hall rang and the hounds bayed. De Aquila held up his hands. " Write her free," he called to Gilbert by the fireplace. " A' God's Name write her free, before she deafens me! Yes, yes," he said to the wench that was on her knees at him; " thou art Cerdic's sister, and own cousin to the Lady of Mercia, if thou

wilt be silent. In fifty years there will be neither Norman nor Saxon, but all English," said he, " and these are the men that do our work! " He clapped the man-at-arms, that was Jehan's nephew, on the shoulder, and kissed the wench, and fretted with his feet among the rushes to show it was finished. (The Great Hall is always bitter cold.) I stood at his side; Hugh was behind Gilbert in the fire-place making to play with wise rough Odo. He signed to De Aquila, who bade Gilbert measure the new field for the new couple. Out then runs our Gilbert between man and maid, his beads clashing at his waist, and the Hall being empty, we three sit by the fire.

' Said Hugh, leaning down to the hearthstones, " I saw this stone move under Gilbert's foot when Odo snuffed at it. Look! " De Aquila digged in the ashes with his sword; the stone tilted; beneath it lay a parchment folden, and the writing atop was: " Words spoken against the King by our Lord of Pevensey—the second part."

' Here was set out (Hugh read it us whispering) every jest De Aquila had made to us touching the King; every time he had called out to me from the shot-window; and every time he had said what he would do if he were King of England. Yes, day by day had his daily speech, which he never stinted, been set down by Gilbert, tricked out and twisted from its true meaning, yet withal so cunningly that none could deny who knew him that De Aquila had in some sort spoken those words. Ye see? '

Dan and Una nodded.

' Yes,' said Una, gravely. ' It isn't what you say so much. It's what you mean when you say it. Like calling Dan a beast in fun. Only grown-ups don't always understand.'

' " He hath done this day by day before our very face? " said De Aquila.

' " Nay, hour by hour," said Hugh. " When De Aquila spoke even now, in the Hall, of Saxons and Normans, I saw Gilbert write on a parchment, which he kept beside the Manor-roll, that De Aquila said soon there would be no Normans left in England if his men-at-arms did their work aright."

' " Bones of the Saints! " said De Aquila. " What avail is honour or a sword against a pen? Where did Gilbert hide that writing? He shall eat it."

' " In his breast when he ran out," said Hugh. " Which made me look to see where he kept his finished stuff. When Odo scratched at this stone here, I saw his face change. So I was sure."

' " He is bold," said De Aquila. " Do him justice. In his own fashion, my Gilbert is bold."

' " Overbold," said Hugh. " Hearken here," and he read: " Upon the Feast of St. Agatha, our Lord of Pevensey, lying in his upper chamber, being clothed in his second fur gown reversed with rabbit— "

' " Pest on him! He is not my tire-woman! " said De Aquila, and Hugh and I laughed.

' " Reversed with rabbit, seeing a fog over the marshes, did wake Sir Richard Dalyngridge, his drunken cup-mate " (here they laughed at me)

" and said, ' Peer out, old fox, for God is on the Duke of Normandy's side.' "

' " So did I. It was a black fog. Robert could have landed ten thousand men, and we none the wiser. Does he tell how we were out all day riding the marsh, and how I near perished in a quicksand, and coughed like a sick ewe for ten days after? " cried De Aquila.

' " No," said Hugh. " But here is the prayer of Gilbert himself to his master Fulke."

' " Ah," said De Aquila. " Well I knew it was Fulke. What is the price of my blood? "

' " Gilbert prayeth that when our Lord of Pevensey is stripped of his lands on this evidence which Gilbert hath, with fear and pains, collected— "

' " Fear and pains is a true word," said De Aquila, and sucked in his cheeks. " But how excellent a weapon is a pen! I must learn it."

' " He prays that Fulke will advance him from his present service to that honour in the Church which Fulke promised him. And lest Fulke should forget, he has written below, ' To be Sacristan of Battle.' "

' At this De Aquila whistled. " A man who can plot against one lord can plot against another. When I am stripped of my lands Fulke will whip off my Gilbert's foolish head. None the less Battle needs a new Sacristan. They tell me the Abbot Henry keeps no sort of rule there."

' " Let the Abbot wait," said Hugh. " It is our heads and our lands that are in danger. This parchment is the second part of the tale. The first has gone to Fulke, and so to the King, who will hold us traitors."

' " Assuredly," said De Aquila. " Fulke's man took the first part that evening when Gilbert fed him, and our King is so beset by his brother and his Barons (small blame, too!) that he is mad with mistrust. Fulke has his ear, and pours poison into it. Presently the King gives him my land and yours. This is old," and he leaned back and yawned.

' " And thou wilt surrender Pevensey without word or blow? " said Hugh. " We Saxons will fight your King then. I will go warn my nephew at Dallington. Give me a horse! "

' " Give thee a toy and a rattle," said De Aquila. " Put back the parchment, and rake over the ashes. If Fulke is given my Pevensey, which is England's gate, what will he do with it? He is Norman at heart, and his heart is in Normandy, where he can kill peasants at his pleasure. He will open England's gate to our sleepy Robert, as Odo and Mortain tried to do, and then there will be another landing and another Santlache. Therefore I cannot give up Pevensey."

' " Good," said we two.

' " Ah, but wait! If my King be made, on Gilbert's evidence, to mistrust me, he will send his men against me here, and, while we fight, England's gate is left unguarded. Who will be the first to come through thereby? Even Robert of Normandy. Therefore I cannot fight my King." He nursed his sword—thus.

' " This is saying and unsaying like a Norman," said Hugh " What of our Manors? "

' "I do not think for myself," said De Aquila, "nor for our King, nor for your lands. I think for England, for whom neither King nor Baron thinks. I am not Norman, Sir Richard, nor Saxon, Sir Hugh. English am I."

' "Saxon, Norman, or English," said Hugh, "our lives are thine, however the game goes. When do we hang Gilbert?"

' "Never," said De Aquila. "Who knows he may yet be Sacristan of Battle, for, to do him justice, he is a good writer. Dead men make dumb witnesses. Wait."

' "But the King may give Pevensey to Fulke. And our Manors go with it," said I. "Shall we tell our sons?"

' "No. The King will not wake up a hornets' nest in the south till he has smoked out the bees in the north. He may hold me a traitor; but at least he sees I am not fighting against him, and every day that I lie still is so much gain to him while he fights the Barons. If he were wise he would wait till that war were over before he made new enemies. But I think Fulke will play upon him to send for me, and if I do not obey the summons that will, to Henry's mind, be proof of my treason. But mere talk, such as Gilbert sends, is no proof nowadays. We Barons follow the Church, and, like Anselm, we speak what we please. Let us go about our day's dealings, and say naught to Gilbert."

' "Then we do nothing?" said Hugh.

' "We wait," said De Aquila. "I am old, but still I find that the most grievous work I know."

' And so we found it, but in the end De Aquila was right.

' A little later in the year, armed men rode over the hill, the Golden Horseshoes flying behind the King's banner. Said De Aquila, at the window of our chamber: "How did I tell you? Here comes Fulke himself to spy out his new lands which our King hath promised him if he can bring proof of my treason."

' "How dost thou know?" said Hugh.

' "Because that is what I would do if I were Fulke, but I should have brought more men. My roan horse to your old shoes," said he, "Fulke brings me the King's Summons to leave Pevensey and join the war." He sucked in his cheeks and drummed on the edge of the shaft, where the water sounded all hollow.

' "Shall we go?" said I.

' "Go! At this time of year? Stark madness," said he. "Take me from Pevensey to fisk and flyte through fern and forest, and in three days Robert's keels would be lying on Pevensey mud with ten thousand men! Who would stop them—Fulke?"

' The horns blew without, and anon Fulke cried the King's Summons at the great door that De Aquila with all men and horse should join the King's camp at Salisbury.

' "How did I tell you?" said De Aquila. "There are twenty Barons 'twixt here and Salisbury could give King Henry good land service, but he

has been worked upon by Fulke to send south and call me—me!—off the Gate of England, when his enemies stand about to batter it in. See that Fulke's men lie in the big south barn," said he. " Give them drink, and when Fulke has eaten we will drink in my chamber. The Great Hall is too cold for old bones."

' As soon as he was off-horse Fulke went to the chapel with Gilbert to give thanks for his safe coming, and when he had eaten—he was a fat man, and rolled his eyes greedily at our good roast Sussex wheatears—we led him to the little upper chamber, whither Gilbert had already gone with the Manor-roll. I remember when Fulke heard the tide blow and whistle in the shaft he leaped back, and his long down-turned stirrup-shoes caught in the rushes and he stumbled, so that Jehan behind him found it easy to knock his head against the wall.'

' Did you know it was going to happen? ' said Dan.

' Assuredly,' said Sir Richard, with a sweet smile. ' I put my foot on his sword and plucked away his dagger, but he knew not whether it was day or night for awhile. He lay rolling his eyes and bubbling with his mouth, and Jehan roped him like a calf. He was cased all in that new-fangled armour which we call lizard-mail. Not rings like my hauberk here '—Sir Richard tapped his chest—' but little pieces of dagger-proof steel overlapping on stout leather. We stripped it off (no need to spoil good harness by wetting it), and in the neckpiece De Aquila found the same folden piece of parchment which we had put back under the hearthstone.

' At this Gilbert would have run out. I laid my hand on his shoulder. It sufficed. He fell to trembling and praying on his beads.

' " Gilbert," said De Aquila, " here be more notable sayings and doings of our Lord of Pevensey for thee to write down. Take penner and inkhorn, Gilbert. We cannot all be Sacristans of Battle."

' Said Fulke from the floor, " Ye have bound a King's messenger. Pevensey shall burn for this."

' " Maybe. I have seen it besieged once," said De Aquila, " but heart up, Fulke. I promise thee that thou shalt be hanged in the middle of the flames at the end of that siege, if I have to share my last loaf with thee; and that is more than Odo would have done when we starved out him and Mortain."

' Then Fulke sat up and looked long and cunningly at De Aquila.

' " By the Saints," said he, " why didst thou not say thou wast on Duke Robert's side at the first? "

' " Am I? " said De Aquila.

' Fulke laughed and said, " No man who serves King Henry dare do this much to his messenger. When didst thou come over to the Duke? Let me up and we can smooth it out together." And he smiled and becked and winked.

' " Yes, we will smooth it out," said De Aquila. He nodded to me, and Jehan and I heaved up Fulke—he was a heavy man—and lowered him

into the shaft by a rope, not so as to stand on our gold, but dangling by his shoulders a little above. It was turn of ebb, and the water came to his knees. He said nothing, but shivered somewhat.

'Then Jehan of a sudden beat down Gilbert's wrist with his sheathed dagger. " Stop! " he said. " He swallows his beads."

' " Poison, belike," said De Aquila. " It is good for men who know too much. I have carried it these thirty years. Give me! "

'Then Gilbert wept and howled. De Aquila ran the beads through his fingers. The last one—I have said they were large nuts—opened in two halves on a pin, and there was a small folded parchment within. On it was written: " The Old Dog goes to Salisbury to be beaten. I have his Kennel. Come quickly."

' " This is worse than poison," said De Aquila, very softly, and sucked in his cheeks. Then Gilbert grovelled in the rushes, and told us all he knew. The letter, as we guessed, was from Fulke to the Duke (and not the first that had passed between them); Fulke had given it to Gilbert in the chapel, and Gilbert thought to have taken it by morning to a certain fishing-boat at the wharf, which trafficked between Pevensey and the French shore. Gilbert was a false fellow, but he found time between his quakings and shakings to swear that the master of the boat knew nothing of the matter.

' " He hath called me shaved head," said Gilbert, " and he hath thrown haddock-guts at me; but for all that, he is no traitor."

' " I will have no clerk of mine mishandled or miscalled," said De Aquila. " That seaman shall be whipped at his own mast. Write me first a letter, and thou shalt bear it, with the order for the whipping, to-morrow to the boat."

'At this Gilbert would have kissed De Aquila's hand—he had not hoped to live until the morning—and when he trembled less he wrote a letter as from Fulke to the Duke, saying that the Kennel, which signified Pevensey, was shut, and that the Old Dog (which was De Aquila) sat outside it, and, moreover, that all had been betrayed.

' " Write to any man that all is betrayed," said De Aquila, " and even the Pope himself would sleep uneasily. Eh, Jehan? If one told thee all was betrayed, what wouldst thou do? "

' " I would run away," said Jehan. " It might be true."

' " Well said," quoth De Aquila. " Write, Gilbert, that Montgomery, the great Earl, hath made his peace with the King, and that little D'Arcy, whom I hate, hath been hanged by the heels. We will give Robert full measure to chew upon. Write also that Fulke himself is sick to death of a dropsy."

' " Nay! " cried Fulke, hanging in the well-shaft. " Drown me out of hand, but do not make a jest of me."

' " Jest? I? " said De Aquila. " I am but fighting for life and lands with a pen, as thou hast shown me, Fulke."

'Then Fulke groaned, for he was cold, and, " Let me confess," said he.

' " Now, this is right neighbourly," said De Aquila, leaning over the shaft. " Thou hast read my sayings and doings—or at least the first part of them—and thou art minded to repay me with thy own doings and sayings. Take penner and inkhorn, Gilbert. Here is work that will not irk thee."

' " Let my men go without hurt, and I will confess my treason against the King," said Fulke.

' " Now, why has he grown so tender of his men of a sudden? " said Hugh to me; for Fulke had no name for mercy to his men. Plunder he gave them, but pity, none.

' " Te! Te! " said De Aquila. " Thy treason was all confessed long ago by Gilbert. It would be enough to hang Montgomery himself."

' " Nay; but spare my men," said Fulke; and we heard him splash like a fish in a pond, for the tide was rising.

' " All in good time," said De Aquila. " The night is young; the wine is old; and we need only the merry tale. Begin the story of thy life since when thou wast a lad at Tours. Tell it nimbly! "

' " Ye shame me to my soul," said Fulke.

' " Then I have done what neither King nor Duke could do," said De Aquila. " But begin, and forget nothing."

' " Send thy man Jehan away then," said Fulke.

' " That much can I do," said De Aquila. " But, remember, I am like the Danes' King; I cannot turn the tide."

' " How long will it rise? " said Fulke, and splashed anew.

' " For three hours," said De Aquila. " Time to tell all thy good deeds. Begin, and Gilbert—I have heard thou art somewhat careless—do not twist his words from their true meaning."

' So—fear of death in the dark being upon him—Fulke began, and Gilbert, not knowing what his fate might be, wrote it word by word. I have heard many tales, but never heard I aught to match the tale of Fulke, his black life, as Fulke told it hollowly, hanging in the shaft.'

' Was it bad? ' said Dan, awestruck.

' Beyond belief,' Sir Richard answered. ' None the less, there was that in it which forced even Gilbert to laugh. We three laughed till we ached. At one place his teeth so chattered that we could not well hear, and we reached him down a cup of wine. Then he warmed to it, and smoothly set out all his shifts, malices, and treacheries, his extreme boldnesses (he was desperate bold); his retreats, shufflings, and counterfeitings (he was also inconceivably a coward); his lack of gear and honour; his despair at their loss; his remedies, and well-coloured contrivances. Yes, he waved the filthy rags of his life before us, as though they had been some proud banner. When he ceased, we saw by torches that the tide stood at the corners of his mouth, and he breathed strongly through his nose.

' We had him out, and rubbed him; we wrapped him in a cloak, and gave him wine, and we leaned and looked upon him, the while he drank. He was shivering, but shameless.

'Of a sudden we heard Jehan at the stairway wake, but a boy pushed past him, and stood before us, the hall rushes in his hair, all slubbered with sleep. "My father! My father! I dreamed of treachery," he cried, and babbled thickly.

' "There is no treachery here," said Fulke. "Go," and the boy turned, even then not fully awake, and Jehan led him by the hand to the Great Hall.

' "Thy only son! " said De Aquila. "Why didst thou bring the child here? "

' "He is my heir. I dared not trust him to my brother," said Fulke, and now he was ashamed. De Aquila said nothing, but sat weighing a wine-cup in his two hands—thus. Anon, Fulke touched him on the knee.

' "Let the boy escape to Normandy," said he, "and do with me at thy pleasure. Yea, hang me to-morrow, with my letter to Robert round my neck, but let the boy go."

' "Be still," said De Aquila. "I think for England."

' So we waited what our Lord of Pevensey should devise; and the sweat ran down Fulke's forehead.

' At last said De Aquila: "I am too old to judge, or to trust any man. I do not covet thy lands, as thou hast coveted mine; and whether thou art any better or any worse than any other black Angevin thief, it is for thy King to find out. Therefore, go back to thy King, Fulke."

' "And thou wilt say nothing of what has passed? " said Fulke.

' "Why should I? Thy son will stay with me. If the King calls me again to leave Pevensey, which I must guard against England's enemies; if the King sends his men against me for a traitor; or if I hear that the King in his bed thinks any evil of me or of my two knights, thy son will be hanged from out this window, Fulke." '

' But it hadn't anything to do with his son,' cried Una, startled.

' How could we have hanged Fulke? ' said Sir Richard. ' We needed him to make our peace with the King. He would have betrayed half England for the boy's sake. Of that we were sure.'

' I don't understand,' said Una. ' But I think it was simply awful.'

' So did not Fulke. He was well pleased.'

' What? Because his son was going to be killed? '

' Nay. Because De Aquila had shown him how he might save the boy's life and his own lands and honours. "I will do it," he said. "I swear I will do it. I will tell the King thou art no traitor, but the most excellent, valiant, and perfect of us all. Yes, I will save thee."

' De Aquila looked still into the bottom of the cup, rolling the wine-dregs to and fro.

' "Ay," he said. "If I had a son, I would, I think, save him. But do not by any means tell me how thou wilt go about it."

' "Nay, nay," said Fulke, nodding his bald head wisely. "That is my secret. But rest at ease, De Aquila, no hair of thy head nor rood of thy land shall be forfeited," and he smiled like one planning great good deeds.

' " And henceforward," said De Aquila, " I counsel thee to serve one master—not two."

' " What? " said Fulke. " Can I work no more honest trading between the two sides these troublous times? "

' " Serve Robert or the King—England or Normandy," said De Aquila. " I care not which it is, but make thy choice here and now."

' " The King, then," said Fulke, " for I see he is better served than Robert. Shall I swear it? "

' " No need," said De Aquila, and he laid his hand on the parchments which Gilbert had written. " It shall be some part of my Gilbert's penance to copy out the savoury tale of thy life, till we have made ten, twenty, an hundred, maybe, copies. How many cattle, think you, would the Bishop of Tours give for that tale? Or thy brother? Or the Monks of Blois? Minstrels will turn it into songs which thy own Saxon serfs shall sing behind their plough-stilts, and men-at-arms riding through thy Norman towns. From here to Rome, Fulke, men will make very merry over that tale, and how Fulke told it, hanging in a well, like a drowned puppy. This shall be thy punishment, if ever I find thee double-dealing with thy King any more. Meantime, the parchments stay here with thy son. Him I will return to thee when thou hast made my peace with the King. The parchments never."

' Fulke hid his face and groaned.

' " Bones of the Saints! " said De Aquila, laughing. " The pen cuts deep. I could never have fetched that grunt out of thee with any sword."

' " But so long as I do not anger thee, my tale will be secret? " said Fulke.

' " Just so long. Does that comfort thee, Fulke? " said De Aquila.

' " What other comfort have ye left me? " he said, and of a sudden he wept hopelessly like a child, dropping his face on his knees.'

' Poor Fulke,' said Una.

' I pitied him also,' said Sir Richard.

' " After the spur, corn," said De Aquila, and he threw Fulke three wedges of gold that he had taken from our little chest by the bedplace.

' " If I had known this," said Fulke, catching his breath, " I would never have lifted hand against Pevensey. Only lack of this yellow stuff has made me so unlucky in my dealings."

' It was dawn then, and they stirred in the Great Hall below. We sent down Fulke's mail to be scoured, and when he rode away at noon under his own and the King's banner very splendid and stately did he show. He smoothed his long beard, and called his son to his stirrup and kissed him. De Aquila rode with him as far as the New Mill landward. We thought the night had been all a dream.'

' But did he make it right with the King? ' Dan asked. ' About your not being traitors, I mean? '

Sir Richard smiled. ' The King sent no second summons to Pevensey, nor did he ask why De Aquila had not obeyed the first. Yes, that was Fulke's

work. I know not how he did it, but it was well and swiftly done.'

'Then you didn't do anything to his son?' said Una.

'The boy? Oh, he was an imp. He turned the keep doors out of dortoirs while we had him. He sang foul songs, learned in the Barons' camps—poor fool; he set the hounds fighting in hall; he lit the rushes to drive out, as he said, the fleas; he drew his dagger on Jehan, who threw him down the stairway for it; and he rode his horse through crops and among sheep. But when we had beaten him, and showed him wolf and deer, he followed us old men like a young, eager hound, and called us "uncle." His father came the summer's end to take him away, but the boy had no lust to go, because of the otter-hunting, and he stayed on till the fox-hunting. I gave him a bittern's claw to bring him good luck at shooting. An imp, if ever there was!'

'And what happened to Gilbert?' said Dan.

'Not even a whipping. De Aquila said he would sooner a clerk, however false, that knew the Manor-roll than a fool, however true, that must be taught his work afresh. Moreover, after that night I think Gilbert loved as much as he feared De Aquila. At least he would not leave us—not even when Vivian, the King's Clerk, would have made him Sacristan of Battle Abbey. A false fellow, but, in his fashion, bold.'

'Did Robert ever land in Pevensey after all?' Dan went on.

'We guarded the coast too well while Henry was fighting his Barons; and three or four years later, when England had peace, Henry crossed to Normandy and showed his brother some work at Tenchebrai that cured Robert of fighting. Many of Henry's men sailed from Pevensey to that war. Fulke came, I remember, and we all four lay in the little chamber once again, and drank together. De Aquila was right. One should not judge men. Fulke was merry. Yes, always merry—with a catch in his breath.'

'And what did you do afterwards?' said Una.

'We talked together of times past. That is all men can do when they grow old, little maid.'

The bell for tea rang faintly across the meadows. Dan lay in the bows of the *Golden Hind*; Una in the stern, the book of verses open in her lap, was reading from *The Slave's Dream*:—

> 'Again in the mist and shadow of sleep
> He saw his native land.'

'I don't know when you began that,' said Dan, sleepily.

On the middle thwart of the boat, beside Una's sun-bonnet, lay an Oak leaf, an Ash leaf, and a Thorn leaf, that must have dropped down from the trees above; and the brook giggled as though it had just seen some joke.

THE RUNES ON WELAND'S SWORD

A Smith makes me
To betray my Man
In my first fight.

To gather Gold
At the world's end
I am sent.

The Gold I gather
Comes into England
Out of deep Water.

Like a shining Fish
Then it descends
Into deep Water.

It is not given
For goods or gear,
But for The Thing.

The Gold I gather
A King covets
For an ill use.

The Gold I gather
Is drawn up
Out of deep Water.

Like a shining Fish
Then it descends
Into deep Water.

It is not given
For goods or gear,
But for The Thing.

A CENTURION OF THE THIRTIETH

Cities and Thrones and Powers,
 Stand in Time's eye,
Almost as long as flowers,
 Which daily die:
But, as new buds put forth,
 To glad new men,
Out of the spent and unconsidered Earth,
 The Cities rise again.

This season's Daffodil,
 She never hears,
What change, what chance, what chill,
 Cut down last year's:
But with bold countenance,
 And knowledge small,
Esteems her seven days' continuance
 To be perpetual.

So Time that is o'er-kind,
 To all that be,
Ordains us e'en as blind,
 As bold as she:
That in our very death,
 And burial sure,
Shadow to shadow, well-persuaded, saith,
 ' See how our works endure! '

❦ DAN had come to grief over his Latin, and was kept in; so Una went alone to Far Wood. Dan's big catapult and the lead bullets that Hobden had made for him were hidden in an old hollow beech-stub on the west of the wood. They had named the place out of the verse in *Lays of Ancient Rome*.

From lordly Volaterrae,
 Where scowls the far-famed hold,
Piled by the hands of giants
 For Godlike Kings of old.

They were the 'Godlike Kings,' and when old Hobden piled some comfortable brushwood between the big wooden knees of Volaterrae, they called him 'Hands of Giants.'

Una slipped through their private gap in the fence, and sat still awhile, scowling as scowlily and lordlily as she knew how; for 'Volaterrae' is an important watch-tower that juts out of Far Wood just as Far Wood juts out of the hillside. Pook's Hill lay below her, and all the turns of the brook as it wanders out of the Willingford Woods, between hop-gardens, to old Hobden's cottage at the Forge. The Sou'-West wind (there is always a wind by Volaterrae) blew from the bare ridge where Cherry Clack Windmill stands.

Now wind prowling through woods sounds like exciting things going to happen, and that is why on blowy days you stand up in Volaterrae and shout bits of the 'Lays' to suit its noises.

Una took Dan's catapult from its secret place, and made ready to meet Lars Porsena's army stealing through the wind-whitened aspens by the brook. A gust boomed up the valley, and Una chanted sorrowfully:

> 'Verbenna down to Ostia
> Hath wasted all the plain;
> Astur hath stormed Janiculum
> And the stout guards are slain.'

But the wind, not charging fair to the wood, started aside and shook a single oak in Gleason's pasture. Here it made itself all small and crouched among the grasses, waving the tips of them as a cat waves the tip of her tail before she springs.

'Now welcome—welcome Sextus,' sang Una, loading the catapult—

> 'Now welcome to thy home,
> Why dost thou stay and turn away?
> Here lies the road to Rome.'

She fired into the face of the lull, to wake up the cowardly wind, and heard a grunt from behind a thorn in the pasture.

'Oh, my Winkie!' she said aloud, and that was something she had picked up from Dan. 'I b'lieve I've tickled up a Gleason cow.'

'You little painted beast!' a voice cried. 'I'll teach you to sling your masters!'

She looked down most cautiously, and saw a young man covered with hoopy bronze armour all glowing among the late broom. But what Una admired beyond all was his great bronze helmet with a red horse-tail that flicked in the wind. She could hear the long hairs rasp on his shimmery shoulder-plates.

'What does the Faun mean,' he said, half aloud to himself, 'by telling

me that the Painted People have changed? ' IIe caught sight of Una's yellow head. ' Have you seen a painted lead-slinger? ' he called.

' No-o,' said Una. ' But if you've seen a bullet— '

' Seen? ' cried the man. ' It passed within a hair's breadth of my ear.'

' Well, that was me. I'm most awfully sorry.'

' Didn't the Faun tell you I was coming? ' He smiled.

' Not if you mean Puck. I thought you were a Gleason cow. I—I didn't know you were a—a— What are you? '

He laughed outright, showing a set of splendid teeth. His face and eyes were dark, and his eyebrows met above his big nose in one bushy black bar.

' They call me Parnesius. I have been a Centurion of the Seventh Cohort of the Thirtieth Legion—the Ulpia Victrix. Did you sling that bullet? '

' I did. I was using Dan's catapult,' said Una.

' Catapults! ' said he. ' I ought to know something about them. Show me! '

He leaped the rough fence with a rattle of spear, shield, and armour, and hoisted himself into Volaterrae as quickly as a shadow.

' A sling on a forked stick. I understand! ' he cried, and pulled at the elastic. ' But what wonderful beast yields this stretching leather? '

' It's laccy—elastic. You put the bullet into that loop, and then you pull hard.'

The man pulled, and hit himself square on his thumbnail.

' Each to his own weapon,' he said, gravely, handing it back. ' I am better with the bigger machine, little maiden. But it's a pretty toy. A wolf would laugh at it. Aren't you afraid of wolves? '

' There aren't any,' said Una.

' Never believe it! A wolf's like a Winged Hat. He comes when he isn't expected. Don't they hunt wolves here? '

' We don't hunt,' said Una, remembering what she had heard from grown-ups. ' We preserve—pheasants. Do you know them? '

' I ought to,' said the young man, smiling again, and he imitated the cry of the cock-pheasant so perfectly that a bird answered out of the wood.

' What a big painted clucking fool is a pheasant,' he said. ' Just like some Romans! '

' But you're a Roman yourself, aren't you? ' said Una.

' Ye-es and no. I'm one of a good few thousands who have never seen Rome except in a picture. My people have lived at Vectis for generations. Vectis. That island West yonder that you can see from so far in clear weather.'

' Do you mean the Isle of Wight? It lifts up just before rain, and you see it from the Downs.'

' Very likely. Our Villa's on the South edge of the Island, by the Broken Cliffs. Most of it is three hundred years old, but the cow-stables, where our first ancestor lived, must be a hundred years older. Oh, quite

that, because the founder of our family had his land given him by Agricola at the Settlement. It's not a bad little place for its size. In spring-time violets grown down to the very beach. I've gathered sea-weeds for myself and violets for my Mother many a time with our old nurse.'

' Was your nurse a—a Romaness too? '

' No, a Numidian. Gods be good to her! A dear, fat, brown thing with a tongue like a cow-bell. She was a free woman. By the way, are you free, maiden? '

' Oh, quite,' said Una. ' At least, till tea-time; and in summer our governess doesn't say much if we're late.'

The young man laughed again—a proper understanding laugh.

' I see,' said he. ' That accounts for your being in the wood. We hid among the cliffs.'

' Did you have a governess, then? '

' Did we not? A Greek, too. She had a way of clutching her dress when she hunted us among the gorse-bushes that made us laugh. Then she'd say she'd get us whipped. She never did, though, bless her! Aglaia was a thorough sportswoman, for all her learning.'

' But what lessons did you do—when—when you were little? '

' Ancient history, the Classics, arithmetic, and so on,' he answered. ' My sister and I were thick-heads, but my two brothers (I'm the middle one) liked those things, and, of course, Mother was clever enough for any six. She was nearly as tall as I am, and she looked like the new statue on the Western Road—the Demeter of the Baskets, you know. And funny! Roma Dea! How Mother could make us laugh! '

' What at? '

' Little jokes and sayings that every family has. Don't you know? '

' I know we have, but I didn't know other people had them too,' said Una. ' Tell me about all your family, please.'

' Good families are very much alike. Mother would sit spinning of evenings while Aglaia read in her corner, and Father did accounts, and we four romped about the passages. When our noise grew too loud the Pater would say, " Less tumult! Less tumult! Have you never heard of a Father's right over his children? He can slay them, my loves—slay them dead, and the Gods highly approve of the action! " Then Mother would prim up her dear mouth over the wheel and answer: " H'm! I'm afraid there can't be much of the Roman Father about you! " Then the Pater would roll up his accounts, and say, " I'll show you! " and then—then, he'd be worse than any of us! '

' Fathers can—if they like,' said Una, her eyes dancing.

' Didn't I say all good families are very much the same? '

' What did you do in summer? ' said Una. ' Play about, like us? '

' Yes, and we visited our friends. There are no wolves in Vectis. We had many friends, and as many ponies as we wished.'

' It must have been lovely,' said Una. ' I hope it lasted for ever.'

'Not quite, little maid. When I was about sixteen or seventeen, the Father felt gouty, and we all went to the Waters.'

'What waters?'

'At Aquac Sulis. Every one goes there. You ought to get your Father to take you some day.'

'But where? I don't know,' said Una.

The young man looked astonished for a moment. 'Aquae Sulis,' he repeated. 'The best baths in Britain. Just as good, I'm told, as Rome. All the old gluttons sit in hot water, and talk scandal and politics. And the Generals come through the streets with their guards behind them; and the magistrates come in their chairs with their stiff guards behind them; and you meet fortune-tellers, and goldsmiths, and merchants, and philosophers, and feather-sellers, and ultra-Roman Britons, and ultra-British Romans, and tame tribesmen pretending to be civilised, and Jew lecturers, and—oh, everybody interesting. We young people, of course, took no interest in politics. We had not the gout: there were many of our age like us. We did not find life sad.

'But while we were enjoying ourselves without thinking, my sister met the son of a magistrate in the west—and a year afterwards she was married to him. My young brother, who was always interested in plants and roots, met the First Doctor of a Legion from the City of the Legions, and he decided that he would be an Army doctor. I do not think it is a profession for a well-born man, but then—I'm not my brother. He went to Rome to study medicine, and now he's First Doctor of a Legion in Egypt—at Antinoe, I think, but I have not heard from him for some time.

'My eldest brother came across a Greek philosopher, and told my Father that he intended to settle down on the estate as a farmer and a philosopher. You see'—the young man's eyes twinkled—'his philosopher was a long-haired one!'

'I thought philosophers were bald,' said Una.

'Not all. She was very pretty. I don't blame him. Nothing could have suited me better than my eldest brother's doing this, for I was only too keen to join the Army. I had always feared I should have to stay at home and look after the estate while my brother took this.'

He rapped on his great glistening shield that never seemed to be in his way.

'So we were well contented—we young people—and we rode back to Clausentum along the Wood Road very quietly. But when we reached home, Aglaia, our governess, saw what had come to us. I remember her at the door, the torch over her head, watching us climb the cliff-path from the boat. "Aie! Aie!" she said. "Children you went away. Men and a woman you return!" Then she kissed Mother, and Mother wept. Thus our visit to the Waters settled our fates for each of us, maiden.'

He rose to his feet and listened, leaning on the shield-rim.

'I think that's Dan—my brother,' said Una.

'Yes; and the Faun is with him,' he replied, as Dan with Puck stumbled through the copse.

'We should have come sooner,' Puck called, 'but the beauties of your native tongue, O Parnesius, have enthralled this young citizen.'

Parnesius looked bewildered, even when Una explained.

'Dan said the plural of "dominus" was "dominoes," and when Miss Blake said it wasn't he said he supposed it was "backgammon," and so he had to write it out twice—for cheek, you know.'

Dan had climbed into Volaterrae, hot and panting.

'I've run nearly all the way,' he gasped, 'and then Puck met me. How do you do, Sir?'

'I am in good health,' Parnesius answered. 'See! I have tried to bend the bow of Ulysses, but—' He held up his thumb.

'I'm sorry. You must have pulled off too soon,' said Dan. 'But Puck said you were telling Una a story.'

'Continue, O Parnesius,' said Puck, who had perched himself on a dead branch above them. 'I will be chorus. Has he puzzled you much, Una?'

'Not a bit, except—I didn't know where Ak—Ak something was,' she answered.

'Oh, Aquae Sulis. That's Bath, where the buns come from. Let the hero tell his own tale.'

Parnesius pretended to thrust his spear at Puck's legs, but Puck reached down, caught at the horse-tail plume, and pulled off the tall helmet.

'Thanks, jester,' said Parnesius, shaking his curly dark head. 'That is cooler. Now hang it up for me. . . .

'I was telling your sister how I joined the Army,' he said to Dan.

'Did you have to pass an Exam?' Dan asked, eagerly.

'No. I went to my Father, and said I should like to enter the Dacian Horse (I had seen some at Aquae Sulis); but he said I had better begin service in a regular Legion from Rome. Now, like many of our youngsters, I was not too fond of anything Roman. The Roman-born officers and magistrates looked down on us British-born as though we were barbarians. I told my Father so.

'"I know they do," he said; "but remember, after all, we are the people of the Old Stock, and our duty is to the Empire."

'"To which Empire?" I asked. "We split the Eagle before I was born."

'"What thieves' talk is that?" said my Father. He hated slang.

'"Well, Sir," I said, "we've one Emperor in Rome, and I don't know how many Emperors the outlying Provinces have set up from time to time. Which am I to follow?"

'"Gratian," said he. "At least he's a sportsman."

'"He's all that," I said. "Hasn't he turned himself into a raw-beef-eating Scythian?"

'"Where did you hear of it?" said the Pater.

' "At Aquae Sulis," I said. It was perfectly true. This precious Emperor Gratian of ours had a bodyguard of fur-cloaked Scythians, and he was so crazy about them that he dressed like them. In Rome of all places in the world! It was as bad as if my own Father had painted himself blue!

' "No matter for the clothes," said the Pater. "They are only the fringe of the trouble. It began before your time or mine. Rome has forsaken her Gods, and must be punished. The great war with the Painted People broke out in the very year the temples of our Gods were destroyed. We beat the Painted People in the very year our temples were rebuilt. Go back farther still." . . . He went back to the time of Diocletian; and to listen to him you would have thought Eternal Rome herself was on the edge of destruction, just because a few people had become a little large-minded.

' I knew nothing about it. Aglaia never taught us the history of our own country. She was so full of her ancient Greeks.

' "There is no hope for Rome," said the Pater, at last. "She has forsaken her Gods, but if the Gods forgive us here, we may save Britain. To do that, we must keep the Painted People back. Therefore, I tell you, Parnesius, as a Father, that if your heart is set on service, your place is among men on the Wall—and not with women among the cities." '

' What Wall? ' asked Dan and Una at once.

' Father meant the one we call Hadrian's Wall. I'll tell you about it later. It was built long ago, across North Britain, to keep out the Painted People—Picts you call them. Father had fought in the great Pict War that lasted more than twenty years, and he knew what fighting meant. Theodosius, one of our great Generals, had chased the little beasts back far into the North before I was born: down at Vectis of course we never troubled our heads about them. But when my Father spoke as he did, I kissed his hand, and waited for orders. We British-born Romans know what is due to our parents.'

' If I kissed my Father's hand, he'd laugh,' said Dan.

' Customs change; but if you do not obey your father, the Gods remember it. You may be quite sure of that.

' After our talk, seeing I was in earnest, the Pater sent me over to Clausentum to learn my foot-drill in a barrack full of foreign auxiliaries—as unwashed and unshaved a mob of mixed barbarians as ever scrubbed a breastplate. It was your stick in their stomachs and your shield in their faces to push them into any sort of formation. When I had learned my work the Instructor gave me a handful—and they were a handful!—of Gauls and Iberians to polish up till they were sent to their stations up-country. I did my best, and one night a villa in the suburbs caught fire, and I had my handful out and at work before any of the other troops. I noticed a quiet-looking man on the lawn, leaning on a stick. He watched us passing buckets from the pond, and at last he said to me: "Who are you?"

' "A probationer, waiting for a command," I answered. I didn't know who he was from Deucalion!

' " Born in Britain? " he said.

' " Yes, if you were born in Spain," I said, for he neighed his words like an Iberian mule.

' " And what might you call yourself when you are at home? " he said, laughing.

' " That depends," I answered; " sometimes one thing and sometimes another. But now I'm busy."

' He said no more till we had saved the family gods (they were respectable householders), and then he grunted across the laurels: " Listen, young sometimes-one-thing-and-sometimes-another. In future call yourself Centurion of the Seventh Cohort to the Thirtieth, the Ulpia Victrix. That will help me to remember you. Your Father and a few other people call me Maximus."

' He tossed me the polished stick he was leaning on, and went away. You might have knocked me down with it! '

' Who was he? ' said Dan.

' Maximus himself, our great General! The General of Britain who had been Theodosius's right hand in the Pict War! Not only had he given me my Centurion's stick direct, but three steps in a good Legion as well! A new man generally begins in the Tenth Cohort of his Legion, and works up.'

' And were you pleased? ' said Una.

' Very. I thought Maximus had chosen me for my good looks and fine style in marching, but, when I went home, the Pater told me he had served under Maximus in the great Pict War, and had asked him to befriend me.'

' A child you were! ' said Puck, from above.

' I was,' said Parnesius. ' Don't begrudge it me, Faun. Afterwards—the Gods know I put aside the games! ' And Puck nodded, brown chin on brown hand, his big eyes still.

' The night before I left we sacrificed to our ancestors—the usual little Home Sacrifice—but I never prayed so earnestly to all the Good Shades, and then I went with my Father by boat to Regnum, and across the chalk castwards to Anderida yonder.'

' Regnum? Anderida? ' The children turned their faces to Puck.

' Regnum's Chichester,' he said, pointing towards Cherry Clack, and— he threw his arm South behind him—' Anderida's Pevensey.'

' Pevensey again! ' said Dan. ' Where Weland landed? '

' Weland and a few others,' said Puck. ' Pevensey isn't young—even compared to me! '

' The headquarters of the Thirtieth lay at Anderida in summer, but my own Cohort, the Seventh, was on the Wall up North. Maximus was inspecting Auxiliaries—the Abulci, I think—at Anderida, and we stayed with him, for he and my Father were very old friends. I was only there ten days when I was ordered to go up with thirty men to my Cohort.' He

laughed merrily. 'A man never forgets his first march. I was happier than any Emperor when I led my handful through the North Gate of the Camp, and we saluted the guard and the Altar of Victory there.'

'How? How?' said Dan and Una.

Parnesius smiled, and stood up, flashing in his armour.

'So!' said he; and he moved slowly through the beautiful movements of the Roman Salute, that ends with a hollow clang of the shield coming into its place between the shoulders.

'Hail!' said Puck. 'That sets one thinking!'

'We went out fully armed,' said Parnesius, sitting down; 'but as soon as the road entered the Great Forest, my men expected the pack-horses to hang their shields on. "No!" I said; "you can dress like women in Anderida, but while you're with me you will carry your own weapons and armour."

'"But it's hot," said one of them, "and we haven't a doctor. Suppose we get sunstroke, or a fever?"

'"Then die," I said, "and a good riddance to Rome! Up shield—up spears, and tighten your foot-wear!"

'"Don't think yourself Emperor of Britain already," a fellow shouted. I knocked him over with the butt of my spear, and explained to these Roman-born Romans that, if there were any further trouble, we should go on with one man short. And, by the Light of the Sun, I meant it too! My raw Gauls at Clausentum had never treated me so.

'Then, quietly as a cloud, Maximus rode out of the fern (my Father behind him), and reined up across the road. He wore the Purple, as though he were already Emperor; his leggings were of white buckskin laced with gold.

'My men dropped like—like partridges.

'He said nothing for some time, only looked, with his eyes puckered. Then he crooked his forefinger, and my men walked—crawled, I mean—to one side.

'"Stand in the sun, children," he said, and they formed up on the hard road.

'"What would you have done?" he said to me, "if I had not been here?"

' " I should have killed that man," I answered.

' " Kill him now," he said. " He will not move a limb."

' " No," I said. " You've taken my men out of my command. I should only be your butcher if I killed him now." Do you see what I meant? ' Parnesius turned to Dan.

' Yes,' said Dan. ' It wouldn't have been fair, somehow.'

' That was what I thought,' said Parnesius. ' But Maximus frowned. " You'll never be an Emperor," he said. " Not even a General will you be."

' I was silent, but my Father seemed pleased.

' " I came here to see the last of you," he said.

' " You have seen it," said Maximus. " I shall never need your son any more. He will live and he will die an officer of a Legion—and he might have been Prefect of one of my Provinces. Now eat and drink with us," he said. " Your men will wait till you have finished."

' My miserable thirty stood like wine-skins glistening in the hot sun, and Maximus led us to where his people had set a meal. Himself he mixed the wine.

' " A year from now," he said, " you will remember that you have sat with the Emperor of Britain—and Gaul."

' " Yes," said the Pater, " you can drive two mules—Gaul and Britain."

' " Five years hence you will remember that you have drunk "—he passed me the cup and there was blue borage in it—" with the Emperor of Rome! "

' " No; you can't drive three mules; they will tear you in pieces," said my Father.

' " And you on the Wall, among the heather, will weep because your notion of justice was more to you than the favour of the Emperor of Rome."

' I sat quite still. One does not answer a General who wears the Purple.

' " I am not angry with you," he went on; " I owe too much to your Father— "

' " You owe me nothing but advice that you never took," said the Pater.

' " —to be unjust to any of your family. Indeed, I say you may make a good Tribune; but, so far as I am concerned, on the Wall you will live, and on the Wall you will die," said Maximus.

' " Very like," said my Father. " But we shall have the Picts and their friends breaking through before long. You cannot move all troops out of Britain to make you Emperor, and expect the North to sit quiet."

' " I follow my destiny," said Maximus.

' " Follow it, then," said my Father, pulling up a fern root; " and die as Theodosius died."

' " Ah! " said Maximus. " My old General was killed because he served the Empire too well. I may be killed, but not for that reason," and he smiled a little pale gray smile that made my blood run cold.

' " Then I had better follow my destiny," I said, " and take my men to the Wall."

' He looked at me a long time, and bowed his head slanting like a Spaniard. " Follow it, boy," he said. That was all. I was only too glad to get away, though I had many messages for home. I found my men standing as they had been put—they had not even shifted their feet in the dust, and off I marched, still feeling that terrific smile like an east wind up my back. I never halted them till sunset, and '—he turned about and looked at Pook's Hill below him—' then I halted yonder.' He pointed to the broken, bracken-covered shoulder of the Forge Hill behind old Hobden's cottage.

' There? Why, that's only the old Forge—where they made iron once,' said Dan.

' Very good stuff it was too,' said Parnesius, calmly. ' We mended three shoulder-straps here and had a spear-head riveted. The forge was rented from the Government by a one-eyed smith from Carthage. I remember we called him Cyclops. He sold me a beaver-skin rug for my sister's room.'

' But it couldn't have been here,' Dan insisted.

' But it was! From the Altar of Victory at Anderida to the First Forge in the Forest here is twelve miles seven hundred paces. It is all in the Road Book. A man doesn't forget his first march. I think I could tell you every

station between this and—' He leaned forward, but his eye was caught by the setting sun.

It had come down to the top of Cherry Clack Hill, and the light poured in between the tree trunks so that you could see red and gold and black deep into the heart of Far Wood; and Parnesius in his armour shone as though he had been afire.

'Wait,' he said, lifting a hand, and the sunlight jinked on his glass bracelet. 'Wait! I pray to Mithras!'

He rose and stretched his arms westward, with deep, splendid-sounding words.

Then Puck began to sing too, in a voice like bells tolling, and as he sang he slipped from Volaterrae to the ground, and beckoned the children to follow. They obeyed; it seemed as though the voices were pushing them along; and through the goldy-brown light on the beech leaves they walked, while Puck between them chanted something like this:—

> 'Cur mundus militat sub vana gloria
> Cujus prosperitas est transitoria?
> Tam cito labitur ejus potentia
> Quam vasa figuli quæ sunt fragilia.'

They found themselves at the little locked gates of the wood.

> 'Quo Cæsar abiit celsus imperio?
> Vel Dives splendidus totus in prandio?
> Dic ubi Tullius—'

Still singing, he took Dan's hand and wheeled him round to face Una as she came out of the gate. It shut behind her, at the same time as Puck threw the momory-magicking Oak, Ash, and Thorn leaves over their heads.

'Well, you are jolly late,' said Una. 'Couldn't you get away before?'

'I did,' said Dan. 'I got away in lots of time, but—but I didn't know it was so late. Where've you been?'

'In Volaterrae—waiting for you.'

'Sorry,' said Dan. 'It was all that beastly Latin.'

A BRITISH-ROMAN SONG

(A. D. 406)

My father's father saw it not,
 And I, belike, shall never come,
To look on that so-holy spot—
 The very Rome—

Crowned by all Time, all Art, all Might,
 The equal work of Gods and Man,
City beneath whose oldest height—
 The Race began!

Soon to send forth again a brood,
 Unshakeable, we pray, that clings,
To Rome's thrice-hammered hardihood—
 In arduous things.

Strong heart with triple armour bound,
 Beat strongly, for thy life-blood runs,
Age after Age, the Empire round—
 In us thy Sons,

Who, distant from the Seven Hills,
 Loving and serving much, require
Thee,—thee to guard 'gainst home-born ills,
 The Imperial Fire!

ON THE GREAT WALL

'When I left Rome for Lalage's sake
 By the Legions' Road to Rimini,
She vowed her heart was mine to take
 With me and my shield to Rimini—
 (Till the Eagles flew from Rimini!)
 And I've tramped Britain and I've tramped Gaul
 And the Pontic shore where the snow-flakes fall
 As white as the neck of Lalage—
 As cold as the heart of Lalage!
 And I've lost Britain and I've lost Gaul,'

(the voice seemed very cheerful about it),

 'And I've lost Rome, and worst of all,
 I've lost Lalage!'

⁀§ THEY were standing by the gate to Far Wood when they heard this song. Without a word they hurried to their private gap and wriggled through the hedge almost atop of a jay that was feeding from Puck's hand.

'Gently!' said Puck. 'What are you looking for?'

'Parnesius, of course,' Dan answered. 'We've only just remembered yesterday. It isn't fair.'

Puck chuckled as he rose. 'I'm sorry, but children who spend the afternoon with me and a Roman Centurion need a little settling dose of Magic before they go to tea with their governess. Ohe, Parnesius!' he called.

'Here, Faun!' came the answer from Volaterrae. They could see the shimmer of bronze armour in the beech crotch, and the friendly flash of the great shield uplifted.

'I have driven out the Britons.' Parnesius laughed like a boy. 'I occupy their high forts. But Rome is merciful! You may come up.' And up they three all scrambled.

'What was the song you were singing just now?' said Una, as soon as she had settled herself.

'That? Oh, Rimini. It's one of the tunes that are always being born somewhere in the Empire. They run like a pestilence for six months or a year, till another one pleases the Legions, and then they march to that.'

'Tell them about the marching, Parnesius. Few people nowadays walk from end to end of this country,' said Puck.

'The greater their loss. I know nothing better than the Long March when your feet are hardened. You begin after the mists have risen, and you

end, perhaps, an hour after sun-down.'

' And what do you have to eat? ' Dan asked, promptly.

' Fat bacon, beans, and bread, and whatever wine happens to be in the rest-houses. But soldiers are born grumblers. Their very first day out, my men complained of our water-ground British corn. They said it wasn't so filling as the rough stuff that is ground in the Roman ox-mills. However, they had to fetch and eat it.'

' Fetch it? Where from? ' said Una.

' From that newly-invented water-mill below the Forge.'

' That's Forge Mill—our Mill! ' Una looked at Puck.

' Yes; yours,' Puck put in. ' How old did you think it was? '

' I don't know. Didn't Sir Richard Dalyngridge talk about it? '

' He did, and it was old in his day,' Puck answered. ' Hundreds of years old.'

' It was new in mine,' said Parnesius. ' My men looked at the flour in their helmets as though it had been a nest of adders. They did it to try my patience. But I—addressed them, and we became friends. To tell the truth, they taught me the Roman Step. You see, I'd only served with quick-marching Auxiliaries. A Legion's pace is altogether different. It is a long, slow stride, that never varies from sunrise to sunset. " Rome's Race—Rome's Pace," as the proverb says. Twenty-four miles in eight hours, neither more nor less. Head and spear up, shield on your back, cuirass collar open one hand's breadth—and that's how you take the Eagles through Britain.'

' And did you meet any adventures? ' said Dan.

' There are no adventures South the Wall,' said Parnesius. ' The worst thing that happened me was having to appear before a magistrate up North, where a wandering philosopher had jeered at the Eagles. I was able to show that the old man had deliberately blocked our road; and the magistrate told him, out of his own Book, I believe, that, whatever his Gods might be, he should pay proper respect to Cæsar.'

' What did you do? ' said Dan.

' Went on. Why should I care for such things, my business being to reach my station? It took me twenty days.

' Of course, the farther North you go the emptier are the roads. At last you fetch clear of the forests and climb bare hills, where wolves howl in the ruins of our cities that have been. No more pretty girls; no more jolly magistrates who knew your Father when he was young, and invite you to stay with them; no news at the temples and way-stations except bad news of wild beasts. There's where you meet hunters, and trappers for the Circuses, prodding along chained bears and muzzled wolves. Your pony shies at them, and your men laugh.

' The houses change from gardened villas to shut forts with watch-towers of gray stone, and great stone-walled sheepfolds, guarded by armed Britons of the North Shore. In the naked hills beyond the naked houses, where the shadows of the clouds play like cavalry charging, you see puffs of

black smoke from the mines. The hard road goes on and on—and the wind sings through your helmet-plume—past altars to Legions and Generals forgotten, and broken statues of Gods and Heroes, and thousands of graves where the mountain foxes and hares peep at you. Red-hot in summer, freezing in winter, is that big, purple heather country of broken stone.

' Just when you think you are at the world's end, you see a smoke from East to West as far as the eye can turn, and then, under it, also as far as the eye can stretch, houses and temples, shops and theatres, barracks and granaries, trickling along like dice behind—always behind—one long, low, rising and falling, and hiding and showing line of towers. And that is the Wall! '

' Ah! ' said the children, taking breath.

' You may well,' said Parnesius. ' Old men who have followed the Eagles since boyhood say nothing in the Empire is more wonderful than first sight of the Wall! '

' Is it just a Wall? Like the one round the kitchen-garden? ' said Dan.

' No, no! It is the Wall. Along the top are towers with guard-houses, small towers, between. Even on the narrowest part of it three men with shields can walk abreast, from guard-house to guard-house. A little curtain wall, no higher than a man's neck, runs along the top of the thick wall, so that from a distance you see the helmets of the sentries sliding back and forth like beads. Thirty feet high is the Wall, and on the Picts' side, the North, is a ditch, strewn with blades of old swords and spear-heads set in wood, and tyres of wheels joined by chains. The Little People come there to steal iron for their arrow-heads.

' But the Wall itself is not more wonderful than the town behind it. Long ago there were great ramparts and ditches on the South side, and no one was allowed to build there. Now the ramparts are partly pulled down and built over, from end to end of the Wall; making a thin town eighty miles long. Think of it! One roaring, rioting, cock-fighting, wolf-baiting, horse-racing town, from Ituna on the West to Segedunum on the cold eastern beach! On one side heather, woods and ruins where Picts hide, and on the other, a vast town—long like a snake, and wicked like a snake. Yes, a snake basking beside a warm wall!

' My Cohort, I was told, lay at Hunno, where the Great North Road runs through the Wall into the Province of Valentia.' Parnesius laughed scornfully. ' The Province of Valentia! We followed the road, therefore, into Hunno town, and stood astonished. The place was a fair—a fair of peoples from every corner of the Empire. Some were racing horses: some sat in wine-shops: some watched dogs baiting bears, and many gathered in a ditch to see cocks fight. A boy not much older than myself, but I could see he was an officer, reined up before me and asked what I wanted.

' " My station," I said, and showed him my shield. Parnesius held up his broad shield with its three X's like letters on a beer-cask.

' " Lucky omen! " said he. " Your Cohort's the next tower to us, but

they're all at the cock-fight. This is a happy place. Come and wet the Eagles." He meant to offer me a drink.

' " When I've handed over my men," I said. I felt angry and ashamed.

' " Oh, you'll soon outgrow that sort of nonsense," he answered. " But don't let me interfere with your hopes. Go on to the Statue of Roma Dea. You can't miss it. The main road into Valentia! " and he laughed and rode off. I could see the statue not a quarter of a mile away, and there I went. At some time or other the Great North Road ran under it into Valentia; but the far end had been blocked up because of the Picts, and on the plaster a man had scratched, " Finish! " It was like marching into a cave. We grounded spears together, my little thirty, and it echoed in the barrel of the arch, but none came. There was a door at one side painted with our number. We prowled in, and I found a cook asleep, and ordered him to give us food. Then I climbed to the top of the Wall, and looked out over the Pict country, and I—thought,' said Parnesius. ' The bricked-up arch with " Finish! " on the plaster was what shook me, for I was not much more than a boy.'

' What a shame! ' said Una. ' But did you feel happy after you'd had a good— ' Dan stopped her with a nudge.

' Happy? ' said Parnesius. ' When the men of the Cohort I was to command came back unhelmeted from the cock-fight, their birds under their arms, and asked me who I was? No, I was not happy; but I made my new Cohort unhappy too. . . . I wrote my Mother I was happy, but, oh, my friends '—he stretched arms over bare knees—' I would not wish my worst enemy to suffer as I suffered through my first months on the Wall. Remember this: among the officers was scarcely one, except myself (and I thought I had lost the favour of Maximus my General), scarcely one who had not done something of wrong or folly. Either he had killed a man, or taken money, or insulted the magistrates, or blasphemed the Gods, and so had been sent to the Wall as a hiding-place from shame or fear. And the men were as the officers. Remember, also, that the Wall was manned by every breed and race in the Empire. No two towers spoke the same tongue, or worshipped the same Gods. In one thing only we were all equal. No matter what arms we had used before we came to the Wall, on the Wall we were all archers, like the Scythians. The Pict cannot run away from the arrow, or crawl under it. He is a bowman himself. He knows! '

' I suppose you were fighting Picts all the time,' said Dan.

' Picts seldom fight. I never saw a fighting Pict for half a year. The tame Picts told us they had all gone North.'

' What is a tame Pict? ' said Dan.

' A Pict—there were many such—who speaks a few words of our tongue, and slips across the Wall to sell ponies and wolf-hounds. Without a horse and a dog, and a friend, man would perish. The Gods gave me all three, and there is no gift like friendship. Remember this '—Parnesius turned to Dan—' when you become a young man. For your fate will turn on the first true friend you make.'

'He means,' said Puck, grinning, 'that if you try to make yourself a decent chap when you're young, you'll make rather decent friends when you grow up. If you're a beast, you'll have beastly friends. Listen to the Pious Parnesius on Friendship!'

'I am not pious,' Parnesius answered, 'but I know what goodness means; and my friend, though he was without hope, was ten thousand times better than I. Stop laughing, Faun!'

'Oh Youth Eternal and All-believing,' cried Puck, as he rocked on the branch above. 'Tell them about your Pertinax.'

'He was that friend the Gods sent me—the boy who spoke to me when I first came. Little older than myself, commanding the Augusta Victoria Cohort on the tower next to us and the Numidians. In virtue he was far my superior.'

'Then why was he on the Wall?' Una asked, quickly. 'They'd all done something bad. You said so yourself.'

'He was the nephew, his Father had died, of a great rich man in Gaul who was not always kind to his Mother. When Pertinax grew up he discovered this, and so his uncle shipped him off, by trickery and force, to the Wall. We came to know each other at a ceremony in our Temple—in the dark. It was the Bull Killing,' Parnesius explained to Puck.

'I see,' said Puck, and turned to the children. 'That's something you wouldn't quite understand. Parnesius means he met Pertinax in church.'

'Yes—in the Cave we first met, and we were both raised to the Degree of Gryphons together.' Parnesius lifted his hand towards his neck for an instant. 'He had been on the Wall two years, and knew the Picts well. He taught me first how to take Heather.'

'What's that?' said Dan.

'Going out hunting in the Pict country with a tame Pict. You are quite safe so long as you are his guest, and wear a sprig of heather where it can be seen. If you went alone you would surely be killed, if you were not smothered first in the bogs. Only the Picts know their way about those black and hidden bogs. Old Allo, the one-eyed, withered little Pict from whom we bought our ponies, was our special friend. At first we went only to escape from the terrible town, and to talk together about our homes. Then he showed us how to hunt wolves and those great red deer with horns like Jewish candlesticks. The Roman-born officers rather looked down on us for doing this, but we preferred the heather to their amusements. Believe me,' Parnesius turned again to Dan, 'a boy is safe from all things that really harm when he is astride a pony or after a deer. Do you remember, O Faun,' he turned to Puck, 'the little altar I built to the Sylvan Pan by the pine-forest beyond the brook?'

'Which? The stone one with the line from Xenophon?' said Puck, in quite a new voice.

'No. What do I know of Xenophon? That was Pertinax—after he had shot his first mountain-hare with an arrow—by chance! Mine I made of

round pebbles in memory of my first bear. It took me one happy day to build.' Parnesius faced the children quickly.

'And that was how we lived on the Wall for two years—a little scuffling with the Picts, and a great deal of hunting with old Allo in the Pict country. He called us his children sometimes, and we were fond of him and his barbarians, though we never let them paint us Pict fashion. The marks endure till you die.'

'How's it done?' said Dan. 'Anything like tattooing?'

'They prick the skin till the blood runs, and rub in coloured juices. Allo was painted blue, green, and red from his forehead to his ankles. He said it was part of his religion. He told us about his religion (Pertinax was always interested in such things), and as we came to know him well, he told us what was happening in Britain behind the Wall. Many things took place behind us in those days. And by the Light of the Sun,' said Parnesius, earnestly, 'there was not much that those little people did not know! He told me when Maximus crossed over to Gaul, after he made himself Emperor of Britain, and what troops and emigrants he had taken with him. We did not get the news on the Wall till fifteen days later. He told me what troops Maximus was taking out of Britain every month to help him to conquer Gaul; and I always found the numbers were as he said. Wonderful! And I tell another strange thing!'

He jointed his hands across his knees, and leaned his head on the curve of the shield behind him.

'Late in the summer, when the first frosts begin and the Picts kill their bees, we three rode out after wolf with some new hounds. Rutilianus, our General, had given us ten days' leave, and we had pushed beyond the Second Wall—beyond the Province of Valentia—into the higher hills, where there are not even any of Rome's old ruins. We killed a she-wolf before noon, and while Allo was skinning her he looked up and said to me, "When you are Captain of the Wall, my child, you won't be able to do this any more!"

'I might as well have been made Prefect of Lower Gaul, so I laughed and said, "Wait till I am Captain." "No, don't wait," said Allo. "Take my advice and go home—both of you." "We have no homes," said Pertinax. "You know that as well as we do. We're finished men—thumbs down against both of us. Only men without hope would risk their necks on your ponies." The old man laughed one of those short Pict laughs—like a fox barking on a frosty night. "I'm fond of you two," he said. "Besides, I've taught you what little you know about hunting. Take my advice and go home."

'"We can't," I said. "I'm out of favour with my General, for one thing; and for another, Pertinax has an uncle."

'"I don't know about his uncle," said Allo, "but the trouble with you, Parnesius, is that your General thinks well of you."

'"Roma Dea!" said Pertinax, sitting up. "What can you guess what Maximus thinks, you old horse-coper?"

'Just then (you know how near the brutes creep when one is eating?) a great dog-wolf jumped out behind us, and away our rested hounds tore after him, with us at their tails. He ran us far out of any country we'd ever heard of, straight as an arrow till sunset, towards the sunset. We came at last to long capes stretching into winding waters, and on a gray beach below us we saw ships drawn up. Forty-seven we counted—not Roman galleys but the raven-winged ships from the North where Rome does not rule. Men moved in the ships, and the sun flashed on their helmets—winged helmets of the red-haired men from the North where Rome does not rule. We watched, and we counted, and we wondered, for though we had heard rumours concerning these Winged Hats, as the Picts called them, never before had we looked upon them.

'" Come away! come away! " said Allo. " My Heather won't protect you here. We shall all be killed! " His legs trembled like his voice. Back we went—back across the heather under the moon, till it was nearly morning, and our poor beasts stumbled on some ruins.

'When we woke, very stiff and cold, Allo was mixing the meal and water. One does not light fires in the Pict country except near a village. The little men are always signalling to each other with smokes, and a strange smoke brings them out buzzing like bees. They can sting, too!

'" What we saw last night was a trading-station," said Allo. " Nothing but a trading-station."

" I do not like lies on an empty stomach," said Pertinax. " I suppose " (he had eyes like an eagle's)—" I suppose that is a trading-station also? " He pointed to a smoke far off on a hill-top, ascending in what we call the Picts' Call:—Puff—double-puff: double-puff—puff! They make it by raising and dropping a wet hide on a fire.

'" No," said Allo, pushing the platter back into the bag. " That is for you and me. Your fate is fixed. Come."

'We came. When one takes Heather, one must obey one's Pict—but that wretched smoke was twenty miles distant, well over on the east coast, and the day was as hot as a bath.

'" Whatever happens," said Allo, while our ponies grunted along, " I want you to remember me."

'" I shall not forget," said Pertinax. " You have cheated me out of my breakfast."

'" What is a handful of crushed oats to a Roman? " he said. Then he laughed his laugh that was not a laugh. " What would you do if you were a handful of oats being crushed between the upper and lower stones of a mill? "

'" I'm Pertinax, not a riddle-guesser," said Pertinax.

'" You're a fool," said Allo. " Your Gods and my Gods are threatened by strange Gods, and all you can do is to laugh."

'" Threatened men live long," I said.

' " I pray the Gods that may be true," he said. " But I ask you again not to forget me."

' We climbed the last hot hill and looked out on the eastern sea, three or four miles off. There was a small sailing-galley of the North Gaul pattern at anchor, her landing-plank down and her sail half up; and below us, alone in a hollow, holding his pony, sat Maximus, Emperor of Britain! He was dressed like a hunter, and he leaned on his little stick; but I knew that back as far as I could see it, and I told Pertinax.

' " You're madder than Allo! " he said. " It must be the sun! "

' Maximus never stirred till we stood before him. Then he looked me up and down, and said: " Hungry again? It seems to be my destiny to feed you whenever we meet. I have food here. Allo shall cook it."

' " No," said Allo. " A Prince in his own land does not wait on wandering Emperors. I feed my two children without asking your leave." He began to blow up the ashes.

' " I was wrong," said Pertinax. " We are all mad. Speak up, O Madman called Emperor! "

' Maximus smiled his terrible tight-lipped smile, but two years on the Wall do not make a man afraid of mere looks. So I was not afraid.

' " I meant you, Parnesius, to live and die a Centurion of the Wall," said Maximus. " But it seems from these," he fumbled in his breast, " you can think as well as draw." He pulled out a roll of letters I had written to my people, full of drawings of Picts, and bears, and men I had met on the Wall. Mother and my sister always liked my pictures.

' He handed me one that I had called " Maximus's Soldiers." It showed a row of fat wine-skins, and our old Doctor of the Hunno hospital snuffing at them. Each time that Maximus had taken troops out of Britain to help him to conquer Gaul, he used to send the garrisons more wine—to keep them quiet, I suppose. On the Wall, we always called a wine-skin a " Maximus." Oh, yes; and I had drawn them in Imperial helmets.

' "Not long since," he went on, " men's names were sent up to Cæsar for smaller jokes than this."

' " True, Cæsar," said Pertinax; " but you forget that was before I, your friend's friend, became such a good spear-thrower."

' He did not actually point his hunting spear at Maximus, but balanced it on his palm—so!

' " I was speaking of time past," said Maximus, never fluttering an eyelid. " Nowadays one is only too pleased to find boys who can think for themselves, and their friends." He nodded at Pertinax. " Your Father lent me the letters, Parnesius, so you run no risk from me."

' " None whatever," said Pertinax, and rubbed the spear-point on his sleeve.

' " I have been forced to reduce the garrisons in Britain, because I need troops in Gaul. Now I come to take troops from the Wall itself," said he.

' " I wish you joy of us," said Pertinax. " We're the last sweepings of

the Empire—the men without hope. Myself, I'd sooner trust condemned criminals."

' " You think so? " he said, quite seriously. " But it will only be till I win Gaul. One must always risk one's life, or one's soul, or one's peace—or some little thing."

' Allo passed round the fire with the sizzling deer's meat. He served us two first.

' " Ah! " said Maximus, waiting his turn. " I perceive you are in your own country. Well, you deserve it. They tell me you have quite a following among the Picts, Parnesius."

' " I have hunted with them," I said. " Maybe I have a few friends among the Heather."

' " He is the only armoured man of you all who understands us," said Allo, and he began a long speech about our virtues, and how we had saved one of his grand-children from a wolf the year before.'

' Had you? ' said Una.

' Yes; but that was neither here nor there. The little green man orated like a—like Cicero. He made us out to be magnificent fellows. Maximus never took his eyes off our faces.

' " Enough," he said. " I have heard Allo on you. I wish to hear you on the Picts."

' I told him as much as I knew, and Pertinax helped me out. There is never harm in a Pict if you but take the trouble to find out what he wants. Their real grievance against us came from our burning their heather. The whole garrison of the Wall moved out twice a year, and solemnly burned the heather for ten miles North. Rutilianus, our General, called it clearing the country. The Picts, of course, scampered away, and all we did was to destroy their bee-bloom in the summer, and ruin their sheep-food in the spring.

' " True, quite true," said Allo. " How can we make our holy heather-wine, if you burn our bee-pasture? "

' We talked long, Maximus asking keen questions that showed he knew much and had thought more about the Picts. He said presently to me: " If I gave you the old Province of Valentia to govern, could you keep the Picts contented till I won Gaul? Stand away, so that you do not see Allo's face; and speak your own thoughts."

' " No," I said. " You cannot remake that Province. The Picts have been free too long."

' " Leave them their village councils, and let them furnish their own soldiers," he said. " You, I am sure, would hold the reins very lightly."

' " Even then, no," I said. " At least not now. They have been too oppressed by us to trust anything with a Roman name for years and years."

' I heard old Allo behind me mutter: " Good child! "

' " Then what do you recommend," said Maximus, " to keep the North quiet till I win Gaul? "

' " Leave the Picts alone," I said. " Stop the heather-burning at once, and—they are improvident little animals—send them a shipload or two of corn now and then."

' " Their own men must distribute it—not some cheating Greek accountant," said Pertinax.

' " Yes, and allow them to come to our hospitals when they are sick," I said.

' " Surely they would die first," said Maximus.

' " Not if Parnesius brought them in," said Allo. " I could show you twenty wolf-bitten, bear-clawed Picts within twenty miles of here. But Parnesius must stay with them in Hospital, else they would go mad with fear."

' " I see," said Maximus. " Like everything else in the world, it is one man's work. You, I think, are that one man."

' " Pertinax and I are one," I said.

' " As you please, so long as you work. Now, Allo, you know that I mean your people no harm. Leave us to talk together," said Maximus.

' " No need! " said Allo. " I am the corn between the upper and lower millstones. I must know what the lower millstone means to do. These boys have spoken the truth as far as they know it. I, a Prince, will tell you the rest. I am troubled about the Men of the North." He squatted like a hare in the heather, and looked over his shoulder.

' " I also," said Maximus, " or I should not be here."

' " Listen," said Allo. " Long and long ago the Winged Hats "—he meant the Northmen—" came to our beaches and said, ' Rome falls! Push her down! ' We fought you. You sent men. We were beaten. After that we said to the Winged Hats, ' You are liars! Make our men alive that Rome killed, and we will believe you.' They went away ashamed. Now they come back bold, and they tell the old tale, which we begin to believe—that Rome falls! "

' " Give me three years' peace on the Wall," cried Maximus, " and I will show you and all the ravens how they lie! "

' " Ah, I wish it too! I wish to save what is left of the corn from the millstones. But you shoot us Picts when we come to borrow a little iron from the Iron Ditch; you burn our heather, which is all our crop; you trouble us with your great catapults. Then you hide behind the Wall, and scorch us with Greek fire. How can I keep my young men from listening to the Winged Hats—in winter especially, when we are hungry? My young men will say, ' Rome can neither fight nor rule. She is taking her men out of Britain. The Winged Hats will help us to push down the Wall. Let us show them the secret roads across the bogs.' Do I want that? No! " He spat like an adder. " I would keep the secrets of my people though I were burned alive. My two children here have spoken truth. Leave us Picts alone. Comfort us, and cherish us, and feed us from far off—with the hand behind your back. Parnesius understands us. Let him have rule on the Wall, and I will

hold my young men quiet for "—he ticked it off on his fingers—" one year easily: the next year not so easily: the third year, perhaps! See, I give you three years. If then you do not show us that Rome is strong in men and terrible in arms, the Winged Hats, I tell you, will sweep down the Wall from either sea till they meet in the middle, and you will go. I shall not grieve over that, but well I know tribe never helps tribe except for one price. We Picts will go too. The Winged Hats will grind us to this! " He tossed a handful of dust in the air.

'" Oh, Roma Dea! " said Maximus, half aloud. " It is always one man's work—always and everywhere! "

'" And one man's life," said Allo. " You are Emperor, but not a God. You may die."

'" I have thought of that too," said he. " Very good. If this wind holds, I shall be at the East end of the Wall by morning. To-morrow, then, I shall see you two when I inspect, and I will make you Captains of the Wall for this work."

'" One instant, Cæsar," said Pertinax. " All men have their price. I am not bought yet."

'" Do you also begin to bargain so early? " said Maximus. " Well? "

'" Give me justice against my uncle Icenus, the Duumvir of Divio in Gaul," he said.

'" Only a life? I thought it would be money or an office. Certainly you shall have him. Write his name on these tablets—on the red side; the other is for the living! " And Maximus held out his tablets.

'" He is of no use to me dead," said Pertinax. " My mother is a widow. I am far off. I am not sure he pays her all her dowry."

'" No matter. My arm is reasonably long. We will look through your uncle's accounts in due time. Now, farewell till to-morrow, O Captains of the Wall! "

' We saw him grow small across the heather as he walked to the galley. There were Picts, scores, each side of him, hidden behind stones. He never looked left or right. He sailed away southerly, full spread before the evening breeze, and when we had watched him out to sea, we were silent. We understood that Earth bred few men like to this man.

' Presently Allo brought the ponies and held them for us to mount—a thing he had never done before.

'" Wait awhile," said Pertinax, and he made a little altar of cut turf, and strewed heather-bloom atop, and laid upon it a letter from a girl in Gaul.

'" What do you do, O my friend? " I said.

'" I sacrifice to my dead youth," he answered, and, when the flames had consumed the letter, he ground them out with his heel. Then we rode back to that Wall of which we were to be Captains.'

Parnesius stopped. The children sat still, not even asking if that were all the tale. Puck beckoned, and pointed the way out of the wood. ' Sorry,' he whispered, ' but you must go now.'

'We haven't made him angry, have we?' said Una. 'He looks so far off, and—and—thinky.'

'Bless your heart, no. Wait till to-morrow. It won't be long. Remember, you've been playing *Lays of Ancient Rome*.'

And as soon as they had scrambled through their gap where Oak, Ash, and Thorn grew, that was all they remembered.

A SONG TO MITHRAS

Mithras, God of the Morning, our trumpets waken the wall!
'Rome is above the Nations, but Thou art over all!'
Now as the names are answered, and the guards are marched away,
Mithras, also a soldier, give us strength for the day!

Mithras, God of the Noontide, the heather swims in the heat,
Our helmets scorch our foreheads; our sandals burn our feet.
Now in the ungirt hour; now ere we blink and drowse,
Mithras, also a soldier, keep us true to our vows!

Mithras, God of the Sunset, low on the Western main,
Thou descending immortal, immortal to rise again!
Now when the watch is ended, now when the wine is drawn,
Mithras, also a soldier, keep us pure till the dawn!

Mithras, God of the Midnight, here where the great bull dies,
Look on thy children in darkness. Oh take our sacrifice!
Many roads Thou hast fashioned: all of them lead to the Light,
Mithras, also a soldier, teach us to die aright!

THE WINGED HATS

THE next day happened to be what they called a Wild Afternoon. Father and Mother went out to pay calls; Miss Blake went for a ride on her bicycle, and they were left all alone till eight o'clock.

When they had seen their dear parents and their dear preceptress politely off the premises they got a cabbage-leaf full of raspberries from the gardener, and a Wild Tea from Ellen. They ate the raspberries to prevent their squashing, and they meant to divide the cabbage-leaf with Three Cows down at the Theatre, but they came across a dead hedgehog which they simply had to bury, and the leaf was too useful to waste.

Then they went on to the Forge and found old Hobden the hedger at home with his son, the Bee Boy who is not quite right in his head, but who can pick up swarms of bees in his naked hands; and the Bee Boy told them the rhyme about the slow-worm:—

'If I had eyes as I could see,
No mortal man would trouble me.'

They all had tea together by the hives, and Hobden said the loaf-cake which Ellen had given them was almost as good as what his wife used to make, and he showed them how to set a wire at the right height for hares. They knew about rabbits already.

Then they climbed up Long Ditch into the lower end of Far Wood. This is sadder and darker than the Volaterrae end because of an old marlpit full of black water, where weepy, hairy moss hangs round the stumps of the willows and alders. But the birds come to perch on the dead branches, and Hobden says that the bitter willow-water is a sort of medicine for sick animals.

They sat down on a felled oak-trunk in the shadows of the beech undergrowth, and were looping the wires Hobden had given them, when they saw Parnesius.

'How quietly you came!' said Una, moving up to make room. 'Where's Puck?'

'The Faun and I have disputed whether it is better that I should tell you all my tale, or leave it untold,' he replied.

'I only said that if he told it as it happened you wouldn't understand it,' said Puck, jumping up like a squirrel from behind the log.

'I don't understand all of it,' said Una, 'but I like hearing about the little Picts.'

'What I can't understand,' said Dan, ' is how Maximus knew all about the Picts when he was over in Gaul.'

'He who makes himself Emperor anywhere must know everything, everywhere,' said Parnesius. 'We had this much from Maximus's mouth after the Games.'

'Games? What Games?' said Dan.

Parnesius stretched his arm out stiffly, thumb pointed to the ground. 'Gladiators! That sort of game,' he said. 'There were two days' Games in his honour when he landed all unexpected at Segedunum on the East end of the Wall. Yes, the day after we had met him we held two days' Games; but I think the greatest risk was run, not by the poor wretches on the sand, but by Maximus. In the old days the Legions kept silence before their Emperor. So did not we! You could hear the solid roar run West along the Wall as his chair was carried rocking through the crowds. The garrison beat round him—clamouring, clowning, asking for pay, for change of quarters, for anything that came into their wild heads. That chair was like a little boat among waves, dipping and falling, but always rising again after one had shut the eyes.' Parnesius shivered.

'Were they angry with him?' said Dan.

'No more angry than wolves in a cage when their trainer walks among them. If he had turned his back an instant, or for an instant had ceased to hold their eyes, there would have been another Emperor made on the Wall that hour. Was it not so, Faun?'

'So it was. So it always will be,' said Puck.

'Late in the evening his messenger came for us, and we followed to the Temple of Victory, where he lodged with Rutilianus, the General of the Wall. I had hardly seen the General before, but he always gave me leave when I wished to take Heather. He was a great glutton, and kept five Asian cooks, and he came of a family that believed in oracles. We could smell his good dinner when we entered, but the tables were empty. He lay snorting on a couch. Maximus sat apart among long rolls of accounts. Then the doors were shut.

'"These are your men," said Maximus to the General, who propped his eye-corners open with his gouty fingers, and stared at us like a fish.

'"I shall know them again, Cæsar," said Rutilianus.

'"Very good," said Maximus. "Now hear! You are not to move man or shield on the Wall except as these boys shall tell you. You will do nothing, except eat, without their permission. They are the head and arms. You are the belly!"

'"As Cæsar pleases," the old man grunted. "If my pay and profits are not cut, you may make my Ancestors' Oracle my master. Rome has been! Rome has been!" Then he turned on his side to sleep.

'"He has it," said Maximus. "We will get to what I need."

'He unrolled full copies of the number of men and supplies on the Wall—down to the sick that very day in Hunno Hospital. Oh, but I groaned when his pen marked off detachment after detachment of our best—of our least worthless men! He took two towers of our Scythians, two of our North

British auxiliaries, two Numidian cohorts, the Dacians all, and half the Belgians. It was like an eagle pecking a carcass.

' " And now, how many catapults have you? " He turned up a new list, but Pertinax laid his open hand there.

' " No, Cæsar," said he. " Do not tempt the Gods too far. Take men, or engines, but not both; else we refuse." '

' Engines? ' said Una.

' The catapults of the Wall—huge things forty feet high to the head—firing nets of raw stone or forged bolts. Nothing can stand against them. He left us our catapults at last, but he took a Cæsar's half of our men without pity. We were a shell when he rolled up the lists!

' " Hail, Cæsar! We, about to die, salute you! " said Pertinax, laughing. " If any enemy even leans against the Wall now, it will tumble."

' " Give me the three years Allo spoke of," he answered, " and you shall have twenty thousand men of your own choosing up here. But now it is a gamble—a game played against the Gods, and the stakes are Britain, Gaul, and perhaps, Rome. You play on my side? "

' " We will play, Cæsar," I said, for I had never met a man like this man.

' " Good. To-morrow," said he, " I proclaim you Captains of the Wall before the troops."

' So we went into the moonlight, where they were cleaning the ground after the Games. We saw great Roma Dea atop of the Wall, the frost on her helmet, and her spear pointed towards the North Star. We saw the twinkle of night-fires all along the guard towers, and the line of the black catapults growing smaller and smaller in the distance. All these things we knew till we were weary; but that night they seemed very strange to us, because the next day we knew we were to be their masters.

' The men took the news well; but when Maximus went away with half our strength, and we had to spread ourselves into the emptied towers, and the townspeople complained that trade would be ruined, and the Autumn gales blew—it was dark days for us two. Here Pertinax was more than my right hand. Being born and bred among the great country-houses in Gaul, he knew the proper words to address to all—from Roman-born Centurions to those dogs of the Third—the Libyans. And he spoke to each as though that man were as high-minded as himself. Now I saw so strongly what things were needed to be done, that I forgot things are easily accomplished by means of men. That was a mistake.

' I feared nothing from the Picts, at least for that year, but Allo warned me that the Winged Hats would soon come in from the sea at each end of the Wall to prove to the Picts how weak we were. So I made ready in haste, and none too soon. I shifted our best men to the ends of the Wall, and set up screened catapults by the beach. The Winged Hats would drive in before the snow-squalls—ten or twenty boats at a time—on Segedunum or Ituna, according as the wind blew.

'Now a ship coming in to land men must furl her sail. If you wait till you see her men gather up the sail's foot, your catapults can jerk a net of loose stones (bolts only cut through the cloth) into the bag of it. Then she turns over, and the sea makes everything clean again. A few men may come ashore, but very few. . . . It was not hard work, except the waiting on the beach in blowing sand and snow. And that was how we dealt with the Winged Hats that winter.

'Early in the Spring, when the East winds blow like skinning-knives, they gathered again off Segedunum with many ships. Allo told me they would never rest till they had taken a tower in open fight. Certainly they fought in the open. We dealt with them thoroughly through a long day: and when all was finished, one man dived clear of the wreckage of his ship, and swam towards shore. I waited, and a wave tumbled him at my feet.

'As I stooped, I saw he wore such a medal as I wear.' Parnesius raised his hand to his neck. 'Therefore, when he could speak, I addressed him a certain Question which can only be answered in a certain manner. He answered with the necessary Word—the Word that belongs to the Degree of Gryphons in the science of Mithras my God. I put my shield over him till he could stand up. You see I am not short, but he was a head taller than I. He said: "What now?" I said: "At your pleasure, my brother, to stay or go."

'He looked out across the surf. There remained one ship unhurt, beyond range of our catapults. I checked the catapults and he waved her in. She came as a hound comes to a master. When she was yet a hundred paces from the beach, he flung back his hair, and swam out. They hauled him in, and went away. I knew that those who worship Mithras are many and of all races, so I did not think much more upon the matter.

'A month later I saw Allo with his horses—by the Temple of Pan, O Faun—and he gave me a great necklace of gold studded with coral.

'At first I thought it was a bribe from some tradesman in the town— meant for old Rutilianus. "Nay," said Allo. "This is a gift from Amal, that Winged Hat whom you saved on the beach. He says you are a Man."

'"He is a Man, too. Tell him I can wear his gift," I answered.

'"Oh, Amal is a young fool; but, speaking as sensible men, your Emperor is doing such great things in Gaul that the Winged Hats are anxious to be his friends, or, better still, the friends of his servants. They think you and Pertinax could lead them to victories." Allo looked at me like a one-eyed raven.

'"Allo," I said, "you are the corn between the two millstones. Be content if they grind evenly, and don't thrust your hand between them."

'"I?" said Allo. "I hate Rome and the Winged Hats equally; but if the Winged Hats thought that some day you and Pertinax might join them against Maximus, they would leave you in peace while you considered. Time is what we need—you and I and Maximus. Let me carry a pleasant message back to the Winged Hats—something for them to make a council over. We

barbarians are all alike. We sit up half the night to discuss anything a Roman says. Eh? "

' " We have no men. We must fight with words," said Pertinax. " Leave it to Allo and me."

' So Allo carried word back to the Winged Hats that we would not fight them if they did not fight us; and they (I think they were a little tired of losing men in the sea) agreed to a sort of truce. I believe Allo, who being a horse-dealer loved lies, also told them we might some day rise against Maximus as Maximus had risen against Rome.

' Indeed, they permitted the corn-ships which I sent to the Picts to pass North that season without harm. Therefore the Picts were well fed that winter, and since they were in some sort my children, I was glad of it. We had only two thousand men on the Wall, and I wrote many times to Maximus and begged—prayed—him to send me only one cohort of my old North British troops. He could not spare them. He needed them to win more victories in Gaul.

' Then came news that he had defeated and slain the Emperor Gratian, and thinking he must now be secure, I wrote again for men. He answered: " *You will learn that I have at last settled accounts with the pup Gratian. There was no need that he should have died, but he became confused and lost his head, which is a bad thing to befall any Emperor. Tell your Father I am content to drive two mules only; for unless my old General's son thinks himself destined to destroy me, I shall rest Emperor of Gaul and Britain, and then you, my two children, will presently get all the men you need. Just now I can spare none.*" '

' What did he mean by his General's son? ' said Dan.

' He meant Theodosius Emperor of Rome, who was the son of Theodosius the General under whom Maximus had fought in the old Pict War. The two men never loved each other, and when Gratian made the younger Theodosius Emperor of the East (at least, so I've heard), Maximus carried on the war to the second generation. It was his fate, and it was his fall. But Theodosius the Emperor is a good man. As I know.' Parnesius was silent for a moment and then continued.

' I wrote back to Maximus that, though we had peace on the Wall, I should be happier with a few more men and some new catapults. He answered: " *You must live a little longer under the shadow of my victories, till I can see what young Theodosius intends. He may welcome me as a brother-Emperor, or he may be preparing an army. In either case I cannot spare men just now.*" '

' But he was always saying that,' cried Una.

' It was true. He did not make excuses; but thanks, as he said, to the news of his victories, we had no trouble on the Wall for a long, long time. The Picts grew fat as their own sheep among the heather, and as many of my men as lived were well exercised in their weapons. Yes, the Wall looked strong. For myself, I knew how weak we were. I knew that if even a false

rumour of any defeat to Maximus broke loose among the Winged Hats, they might come down in earnest, and then—the Wall must go! For the Picts I never cared, but in those years I learned something of the strength of the Winged Hats. They increased their strength every day, but I could not increase my men. Maximus had emptied Britain behind us, and I felt myself to be a man with a rotten stick standing before a broken fence to turn bulls.

'Thus, my friends, we lived on the Wall, waiting—waiting—waiting for the men that Maximus never sent.

'Presently he wrote that he was preparing an army against Theodosius. He wrote—and Pertinax read it over my shoulder in our quarters: "*Tell your Father that my destiny orders me to drive three mules or be torn in pieces by them. I hope within a year to finish with Theodosius, son of Theodosius, once and for all. Then you shall have Britain to rule, and Pertinax, if he chooses, Gaul. To-day I wish strongly you were with me to beat my Auxiliaries into shape. Do not, I pray you, believe any rumour of my sickness. I have a little evil in my old body which I shall cure by riding swiftly into Rome.*"

'Said Pertinax: "It is finished with Maximus. He writes as a man without hope. I, a man without hope, can see this. What does he add at the bottom of the roll? '*Tell Pertinax I have met his late Uncle, the Duumvir of Divio, and that he accounted to me quite truthfully for all his Mother's monies. I have sent her with a fitting escort, for she is the mother of a hero, to Nicaea, where the climate is warm.*'

'"That is proof," said Pertinax. "Nicaea is not far by sea from Rome. A woman there could take ship and fly to Rome in time of war. Yes, Maximus foresees his death, and is fulfilling his promises one by one. But I am glad my Uncle met him."

'"You think blackly to-day?" I asked.

'"I think truth. The Gods weary of the play we have played against them. Theodosius will destroy Maximus. It is finished!"

'"Will you write him that?" I said.

'"See what I shall write," he answered, and he took pen and wrote a letter cheerful as the light of day, tender as a woman's and full of jests. Even I, reading over his shoulder, took comfort from it till—I saw his face!

'"And now," he said, sealing it, "we be two dead men, my brother. Let us go to the Temple."

'We prayed awhile to Mithras, where we had many times prayed before. After that, we lived day by day among evil rumours till winter came again.

'It happened one morning that we rode to the East shore, and found on the beach a fair-haired man, half frozen, bound to some broken planks. Turning him over, we saw by his belt-buckle that he was a Goth of an Eastern Legion. Suddenly he opened his eyes and cried loudly, "He is dead! The letters were with me, but the Winged Hats sank the ship." So saying, he died between our hands.

'We asked not who was dead. We knew! We raced before the driving snow to Hunno, thinking perhaps Allo might be there. We found him already at our stables, and he saw by our faces what we had heard.

' " It was in a tent by the sea," he stammered. " He was beheaded by Theodosius. He sent a letter to you, written while he waited to be slain. The Winged Hats met the ship and took it. The news is running through the heather like fire. Blame me not! I cannot hold back my young men any more."

' " I would we could say as much for our men," said Pertinax, laughing. " But, Gods be praised, they cannot run away."

' " What do you do? " said Allo. " I bring an order—a message—from the Winged Hats that you join them with your men, and march South to plunder Britain."

' " It grieves me," said Pertinax, " but we are stationed here to stop that thing."

' " If I carry back such an answer they will kill me," said Allo. " I always promised the Winged Hats that you would rise when Maximus fell. I—I did not think he could fall."

' " Alas! my poor barbarian," said Pertinax, still laughing. " Well, you have sold us too many good ponies to be thrown back to your friends. We will make you a prisoner, although you are an ambassador."

' " Yes, that will be best," said Allo, holding out a halter. We bound him lightly, for he was an old man.

' " Presently the Winged Hats may come to look for you, and that will give us more time. See how the habit of playing for time sticks to a man! " said Pertinax, as he tied the rope.

' " No," I said. " Time may help. If Maximus wrote us a letter while he was a prisoner, Theodosius must have sent the ship that brought it. If he can send ships, he can send men."

' " How will that profit us? " said Pertinax. " We serve Maximus, not Theodosius. Even if by some miracle of the Gods Theodosius down South sent and saved the Wall, we could not expect more than the death Maximus died."

' " It concerns us to defend the Wall, no matter what Emperor dies, or makes die," I said.

' " That is worthy of your brother the philosopher," said Pertinax. " Myself I am without hope, so I do not say solemn and stupid things! Rouse the Wall! "

'We armed the Wall from end to end; we told the officers that there was a rumour of Maximus's death which might bring down the Winged Hats, but we were sure, even if it were true, that Theodosius, for the sake of Britain, would send us help. Therefore, we must stand fast. . . . My friends, it is above all things strange to see how men bear ill news! Often the strongest till then become the weakest, while the weakest, as it were, reach up and steal strength from the Gods. So it was with us. Yet my Perti-

nax by his jests and his courtesy and his labours had put heart and training into our poor numbers during the past years—more than I should have thought possible. Even our Libyan cohort—the Third—stood up in their padded cuirasses and did not whimper.

' In three days came seven chiefs and elders of the Winged Hats. Among them was that tall young man, Amal, whom I had met on the beach, and he smiled when he saw my necklace. We made them welcome, for they were ambassadors. We showed them Allo, alive but bound. They thought we had killed him, and I saw it would not have vexed them if we had. Allo saw it too, and it vexed him. Then in our quarters at Hunno we came to Council.

' They said that Rome was falling, and that we must join them. They offered me all South Britain to govern after they had taken a tribute out of it.

' I answered, " Patience. This Wall is not weighed off like plunder. Give me proof that my General is dead."

' " Nay," said one elder, " prove to us that he lives " ; and another said, cunningly, " What will you give us if we read you his last words? "

' " We are not merchants to bargain," cried Amal. " Moreover, I owe this man my life. He shall have his proof." He threw across to me a letter (well I knew the seal) from Maximus.

' " We took this out of the ship we sank," he cried. " I cannot read, but I know one sign, at least, which makes me believe." He showed me a dark stain on the outer roll that my heavy heart perceived was the valiant blood of Maximus.

' " Read! " said Amal. " Read, and then let us hear whose servants you are! "

' Said Pertinax, very softly, after he had looked through it: " I will read it all. Listen, barbarians! " He read that which I have carried next my heart ever since.'

Parnesius drew from his neck a folded and spotted piece of parchment, and began in a hushed voice:—

' "*To Parnesius and Pertinax, the not unworthy Captains of the Wall, from Maximus, once Emperor of Gaul and Britain, now prisoner waiting death by the sea in the camp of Theodosius—Greeting and Good-bye!* "

' " Enough," said young Amal; " there is your proof! You must join us now! "

' Pertinax looked long and silently at him, till that fair man blushed like a girl. Then read Pertinax:—

' " *I have joyfully done much evil in my life to those who have wished me evil, but if ever I did any evil to you two I repent, and I ask your forgiveness. The three mules which I strove to drive have torn me in pieces as your Father prophesied. The naked swords wait at the tent door to give me the death I gave to Gratian. Therefore I, your General and your Emperor, send you free and honourable dismissal from my service, which you entered,*

*not for money or office, but, as it makes me warm to believe, because you
loved me!"*

'"By the Light of the Sun," Amal broke in. "This was in some sort
a Man! We may have been mistaken in his servants!"

'And Pertinax read on: "*You gave me the time for which I asked.
If I have failed to use it, do not lament. We have gambled very splendidly
against the Gods, but they hold weighted dice, and I must pay the forfeit.
Remember, I have been; but Rome is; and Rome will be. Tell Pertinax his
Mother is in safety at Nicaea, and her monies are in charge of the Prefect
at Antipolis. Make my remembrances to your Father and to your Mother,
whose friendship was great gain to me. Give also to my little Picts and to
the Winged Hats such messages as their thick heads can understand. I would
have sent you three Legions this very day if all had gone aright. Do not
forget me. We have worked together. Farewell! Farewell! Farewell!"*

'Now, that was my Emperor's last letter.' (The children heard the
parchment crackle as Parnesius returned it to its place.)

'"I was mistaken," said Amal. "The servants of such a man will sell
nothing except over the sword. I am glad of it." He held out his hand to me.

'"But Maximus has given you your dismissal," said an elder. "You
are certainly free to serve—or to rule—whom you please. Join—do not fol-
low—join us!"

'"We thank you," said Pertinax. "But Maximus tells us to give you
such messages as—pardon me, but I use his words—your thick heads can
understand." He pointed through the door to the foot of a catapult wound
up.

'"We understand," said an elder. "The Wall must be won at a price?"

'"It grieves me," said Pertinax, laughing, "but so it must be won,"
and he gave them of our best Southern wine.

'They drank, and wiped their yellow beards in silence till they rose
to go.

'Said Amal, stretching himself (for they were barbarians), "We be
a goodly company; I wonder what the ravens and the dogfish will make of
some of us before this snow melts."

'"Think rather what Theodosius may send," I answered; and though
they laughed, I saw that my chance shot troubled them.

'Only old Allo lingered behind a little.

'"You see," he said, winking and blinking, "I am no more than their
dog. When I have shown their men the secret short ways across our bogs,
they will kick me like one."

'"Then I should not be in haste to show them those ways," said Perti-
nax, "till I was sure that Rome could not save the Wall."

'"You think so? Woe is me!" said the old man. "I only wanted peace
for my people," and he went out stumbling through the snow behind the
tall Winged Hats.

'In this fashion then, slowly, a day at a time, which is very bad for

doubting troops, the War came upon us. At first the Winged Hats swept in from the sea as they had done before, and there we met them as before— with the catapults; and they sickened of it. Yet for a long time they would not trust their duck-legs on land, and I think when it came to revealing the secrets of the tribe, the little Picts were afraid or ashamed to show them all the roads across the heather. I had this from a Pict prisoner. They were as much our spies as our enemies, for the Winged Hats oppressed them, and took their winter stores. Ah, foolish Little People!

'Then the Winged Hats began to roll us up from each end of the Wall. I sent runners Southward to see what the news might be in Britain, but the wolves were very bold that winter, among the deserted stations where the troops had once been, and none came back. We had trouble too with the forage for the ponies along the Wall. I kept ten, and so did Pertinax. We lived and slept in the saddle, riding east or west, and we ate our worn-out ponies. The people of the town also made us some trouble till I gathered them all in one quarter behind Hunno. We broke down the Wall on either side of it to make as it were a citadel. Our men fought better in close order.

'By the end of the second month we were deep in the War as a man is deep in a snowdrift or in a dream. I think we fought in our sleep. At least I know I have gone on the Wall and come off again, remembering nothing between, though my throat was harsh with giving orders, and my sword, I could see, had been used.

'The Winged Hats fought like wolves—all in a pack. Where they had suffered most, there they charged in most hotly. This was hard for the defender, but it held them from sweeping on into Britain.

'In those days Pertinax and I wrote on the plaster of the bricked arch-way into Valentia the names of the towers, and the days on which they fell one by one. We wished for some record.

'And the fighting? The fight was always hottest to left and right of the great statue of Roma Dea, near to Rutilianus's house. By the Light of the Sun, that old fat man, whom we had not considered at all, grew young again among the trumpets! I remember he said his sword was an oracle! "Let us consult the Oracle," he would say, and put the handle against his ear, and shake his head wisely. "And this day is allowed Rutilianus to live," he would say, and, tucking up his cloak, he would puff and pant and fight well. Oh, there were jests in plenty on the Wall to take the place of food!

'We endured for two months and seventeen days—always being pressed from three sides into a smaller space. Several times Allo sent in word that help was at hand. We did not believe it, but it cheered our men.

'The end came not with shoutings of joy, but, like the rest, as in a dream. The Winged Hats suddenly left us in peace for one night, and the next day; which is too long for spent men. We slept at first lightly, expecting to be roused, and then like logs, each where he lay. May you never need such sleep! When I waked, our towers were full of strange,

armed men, who watched us snoring. I roused Pertinax, and we leaped up together.

'"What?" said a young man in clean armour. "Do you fight against Theodosius? Look!"

'North we looked over the red snow. No Winged Hats were there. South we looked over the white snow, and behold there were the Eagles of two strong Legions encamped. East and west we saw flame and fighting, but by Hunno all was still.

'"Trouble no more," said the young man. "Rome's arm is long. Where are the Captains of the Wall?"

'We said we were those men.

'"But you are old and gray-haired," he cried. "Maximus said that they were boys."

'"Yes, that was true some years ago," said Pertinax. "What is our fate to be, you fine and well-fed child?"

'"I am called Ambrosius, a secretary of the Emperor," he answered. "Show me a certain letter which Maximus wrote from a tent at Aquileia, and perhaps I will believe."

'I took it from my breast, and when he had read it he saluted us, saying: "Your fate is in your own hands. If you choose to serve Theodosius, he will give you a Legion. If it suits you to go to your homes, we will give you a Triumph."

'"I would like better a bath, wine, food, razors, soaps, oils, and scents," said Pertinax, laughing.

'"Oh, I see you are a boy," said Ambrosius. "And you?" turning to me.

'"We bear no ill-will against Theodosius, but in War—" I began.

'"In War it is as it is in Love," said Pertinax. "Whether she be good or bad, one gives one's best once, to one only. That given, there remains no second worth giving or taking."

'"That is true," said Ambrosius. "I was with Maximus before he died. He warned Theodosius that you would never serve him, and frankly I say I am sorry for my Emperor."

'"He has Rome to console him," said Pertinax. "I ask you of your kindness to let us go to our homes and get this smell out of our nostrils."

'None the less they gave us a Triumph!'

'It was well earned,' said Puck, throwing some leaves into the still water of the marlpit. The black, oily circles spread dizzily as the children watched them.

'I want to know, oh, ever so many things,' said Dan. 'What happened to old Allo? Did the Winged Hats ever come back? And what did Amal do?'

'And what happened to the fat old General with the five cooks?' said Una. 'And what did your Mother say when you came home? . . .'

'She'd say you're settin' too long over this old pit, so late as 'tis al-

ready,' said old Hobden's voice behind them. ' Hst! ' he whispered.

He stood still, for not twenty paces away a magnificent dog-fox sat on his haunches and looked at the children as though he were an old friend of theirs.

' Oh, Mus' Reynolds, Mus' Reynolds! ' said Hobden, under his breath. ' If I knowed all was inside your head, I'd know something wuth knowin'. Mus' Dan an' Miss Una, come along o' me while I lock up my liddle hen-house.'

A PICT SONG

Rome never looks where she treads,
 Always her heavy hooves fall,
On our stomachs, our hearts or our heads;
 And Rome never heeds when we bawl.
Her sentries pass on—that is all,
 And we gather behind them in hordes,
And plot to reconquer the Wall,
 With only our tongues for our swords.

We are the Little Folk—we!
 Too little to love or to hate.
Leave us alone and you'll see
 How we can drag down the Great!
We are the worm in the wood?
 We are the rot at the root!
We are the germ in the blood!
 We are the thorn in the foot!

Mistletoe killing an oak—
 Rats gnawing cables in two—
Moths making holes in a cloak—
 How they must love what they do!
Yes,—and we Little Folk too,
 We are as busy as they—
Working our works out of view—
 Watch, and you'll see it some day!

No indeed! We are not strong,
 But we know Peoples that are.
Yes, and we'll guide them along,
 To smash and destroy you in War!
We shall be slaves just the same?

Yes, we have always been slaves,
But you—you will die of the shame,
And then we shall dance on your graves!

We are the Little Folk, we, etc.

HAL O' THE DRAFT

Prophets have honour all over the Earth,
 Except in the village where they were born;
Where such as knew them boys from birth,
 Nature-ally hold 'em in scorn.

When Prophets are naughty and young and vain,
 They make a won'erful grievance of it;
(You can see by their writings how they complain),
 But O, 'tis won'erful good for the Prophet!

There's nothing Nineveh Town can give
 (Nor being swallowed by whales between),
Makes up for the place where a man's folk live,
 That don't care nothing what he has been.
He might ha' been that, or he might ha' been this,
But they love and they hate him for what he is.

 A RAINY afternoon drove Dan and Una over to play pirates in the Little Mill. If you don't mind rats on the rafters and oats in your shoes, the mill-attic, with its trap-doors and inscriptions on the beams about floods and sweethearts, is a splendid place. It is lighted by a foot-square window, called Duck Window, that looks across to Little Lindens Farm, and the spot where Jack Cade was killed.

 When they had climbed the attic ladder (they called it ' the mainmast-tree,' out of the ballad of Sir Andrew Barton, and Dan ' swarved it with might and main,' as the ballad says) they saw a man sitting on Duck Window-sill. He was dressed in a plum-coloured doublet and tight plum-coloured hose, and he drew busily in a red-edged book.

 ' Sit ye! Sit ye! ' Puck cried from a rafter overhead. ' See what it is to be beautiful! Sir Harry Dawe—pardon, Hal—says I am the very image of a head for a gargoyle.'

 The man laughed and raised his dark velvet cap to the children, and his grizzled hair bristled out in a stormy fringe. He was old—forty at least—but his eyes were young, with funny little wrinkles all round them. A satchel of embroidered leather hung from his broad belt, which looked interesting.

 ' May we see? ' said Una, coming forward.

 ' Surely—sure-ly! ' he said, moving up on the window-seat, and returned to his work with a silver-pointed pencil. Puck sat as though the grin were

fixed for ever on his broad face, while they watched the quick, certain fingers that copied it. Presently the man took a reed pen from his satchel, and trimmed it with a little ivory knife, carved in the semblance of a fish.

' Oh, what a beauty! ' cried Dan.

' 'Ware fingers! That blade is perilous sharp. I made it myself of the best Low Country cross-bow steel. And so, too, this fish. When his back-fin travels to his tail—so—he swallows up the blade, even as the whale swallowed Gaffer Jonah. . . . Yes, and that's my ink-horn. I made the four silver saints round it. Press Barnabas's head. It opens, and then— ' He dipped the trimmed pen, and with careful boldness began to put in the essential lines of Puck's rugged face, that had been but faintly revealed by the silverpoint.

The children gasped, for it fairly leaped from the page.

As he worked, and the rain fell on the tiles, he talked—now clearly, now muttering, now breaking off to frown or smile at his work. He told them he was born at Little Lindens Farm, and his father used to beat him for drawing things instead of doing things, till an old priest called Father Roger, who drew illuminated letters in rich people's books, coaxed the parents to let him take the boy as a sort of painter's apprentice. Then he went with Father Roger to Oxford, where he cleaned plates and carried cloaks and shoes for the scholars of a College called Merton.

' Didn't you hate that? ' said Dan after a great many other questions.

' I never thought on't. Half Oxford was building new colleges or beautifying the old, and she had called to her aid the master-craftsman of all Christendie—kings in their trade and honoured of Kings. I knew them. I worked for them: that was enough. No wonder— ' He stopped and laughed.

' You became a great man, Hal,' said Puck.

' They said so, Robin. Even Bramante said so.'

' Why? What did you do? ' Dan asked.

The artist looked at him queerly. ' Things in stone and such, up and down England. You would not have heard of 'em. To come nearer home, I rebuilded this little St. Barnabas' Church of ours. It cost me more trouble and sorrow than aught I've touched in my life. But 'twas a sound lesson.'

' Um,' said Dan. ' We've had lessons this morning.'

' I'll not afflict ye, lad,' said Hal, while Puck roared. ' Only 'tis strange to think how that little church was re-built, re-roofed, and made glorious, thanks to some few godly Sussex ironmasters, a Bristow sailor lad, a proud ass called Hal o' the Draft because, d'you see, he was always drawing and drafting; and '—he dragged the words slowly—' and a Scotch pirate.'

' Pirate? ' said Dan. He wriggled like a hooked fish.

' Even that Andrew Barton you were singing of on the stair just now.' He dipped again in the ink-well, and held his breath over a sweeping line, as though he had forgotten everything else.

' Pirates don't build churches, do they? ' said Dan. ' Or do they? '

'They help mightily,' Hal laughed. 'But you were at your lessons this morn, Jack Scholar.'

'Oh, pirates aren't lessons. It was only Bruce and his silly old spider,' said Una. 'Why did Sir Andrew Barton help you?'

'I question if he ever knew it,' said Hal, twinkling. 'Robin, how a' mischief's name am I to tell these innocents what comes of sinful pride?'

'Oh, we know all about that,' said Una pertly. 'If you get too beany— that's cheeky—you get sat upon, of course.'

Hal considered a moment, pen in air, and Puck said some long words.

'Aha! that was my case too,' he cried. 'Beany—you say—but certainly I did not conduct myself well. I was proud of—of such things as porches— a Galilee porch at Lincoln for choice—proud of one Torrigiano's arm on my shoulder, proud in some sort of my knighthood when I made the gilt scroll-work for the *Sovereign*—our King's ship. But Father Roger sitting in Merton College Library, he did not forget me. At the top of my pride, when I and no other should have builded the porch at Lincoln, he laid it on me with his terrible fore-finger to go back to my Sussex clays and re-build, at my own charges, my own church, where us Dawes have been buried for six generations. "Out! Son of my Art!" said he. "Fight the Devil at home ere you call yourself a man and a craftsman." And I quaked, and I went. . . . How's yon, Robin?' He flourished the finished sketch before Puck.

'Me! Me past peradventure,' said Puck, smirking like a man at a mirror. 'Ah, see! The rain has took off! I hate housen in daylight.'

'Whoop! Holiday!' cried Hal, leaping up. 'Who's for my Little Lindens? We can talk there.'

They tumbled downstairs, and turned past the dripping willows by the sunny mill-dam.

'Body o' me,' said Hal, staring at the hop-garden, where the hops were just ready to blossom. 'What are these? Vines? No, not vines, and they twine the wrong way to beans.' He began to draw in his ready book.

'Hops. New since your day,' said Puck. 'They're an herb of Mars, and their flowers dried flavour ale. We say—

"Turkeys, Heresy, Hops, and Beer
Came into England all in one year."'

'Heresy I know. I've seen Hops—God be praised for their beauty! What is your Turkis?'

The children laughed. They knew the Lindens turkeys, and as soon as they reached Lindens orchard on the hill the full flock charged at them.

Out came Hal's book at once. 'Hoity-toity!' he cried. 'Here's Pride in purple feathers! Here's wrathy contempt and the Pomps of the Flesh! How d'you call them?'

'Turkeys! Turkeys!' the children shouted, as the old gobbler raved and flamed against Hal's plum-coloured hose.

''Save Your Magnificence!' he said. 'I've drafted two good new things to-day.' And he doffed his cap to the bubbling bird.

Then they walked through the grass to the knoll where Little Lindens stands. The old farmhouse, weather-tiled to the ground, took almost the colour of a blood-ruby in the afternoon light. The pigeons pecked at the mortar in the chimney-stacks; the bees that had lived under the tiles since it was built filled the hot August air with their booming; and the smell of the box-tree by the dairy-window mixed with the smell of earth after rain, bread after baking, and a tickle of wood-smoke.

The farmer's wife came to the door, baby on arm, shaded her brows against the sun, stooped to pluck a sprig of rosemary, and turned down the orchard. The old spaniel in his barrel barked once or twice to show he was in charge of the empty house. Puck clicked back the garden-gate.

'D'you marvel that I love it?' said Hal, in a whisper. 'What can town folk know of the nature of housen—or land?'

They perched themselves arow on the old hacked oak bench in Lindens garden, looking across the valley of the brook at the fern-covered dimples and hollows of the Forge behind Hobden's cottage. The old man was cutting a faggot in his garden by the hives. It was quite a second after his chopper fell that the chump of the blow reached their lazy ears.

'Eh—yeh!' said Hal. 'I mind when where that old gaffer stands was Nether Forge—Master John Collins's foundry. Many a night has his big trip-hammer shook me in my bed here. "Boom-bitty! Boom-bitty!" If the wind was east, I could hear Master Tom Collins's forge at Stockens answering his brother, "Boom-oop! Boom-oop!" and midway between, Sir John Pelham's sledge-hammers at Brightling would strike in like a pack o' scholars, and "Hic-haec-hoc" they'd say, "Hic-haec-hoc," till I fell asleep. Yes. The valley was as full o' forges and fineries as a May shaw o' cuckoos. All gone to grass now!'

'What did they make?' said Dan.

'Guns for the King's ships—and for others. Serpentines and cannon mostly. When the guns were cast, down would come the King's Officers, and take our plough-oxen to haul them to the coast. Look! Here's one of the first and finest craftsmen of the Sea!'

He fluttered back a page of his book, and showed them a young man's head. Underneath was written: 'Sebastianus.'

'He came down with a King's Order on Master John Collins for twenty serpentines (wicked little cannon they be!) to furnish a venture of ships. I drafted him thus sitting by our fire telling Mother of the new lands he'd find the far side of the world. And he found them, too! There's a nose to cleave through unknown seas! Cabot was his name—a Bristol lad—half a foreigner. I set a heap by him. He helped me to my church-building.'

'I thought that was Sir Andrew Barton,' said Dan.

'Ay, but foundations before roofs,' Hal answered. 'Sebastian first put me in the way of it. I had come down here, not to serve God as a craftsman

should, but to show my people how great a craftsman I was. They cared not, and it served me right, one split straw for my craft or my greatness. What a murrain call had I, they said, to mell with old St. Barnabas '? Ruinous the church had been since the Black Death, and ruinous she should remain; and I could hang myself in my new scaffold-ropes! Gentle and simple, high and low—the Hayes, the Fowles, the Fenners, the Collinses—they were all in a tale against me. Only Sir John Pelham up yonder at Brightling bade me heart-up and go on. Yet how could I? Did I ask Master Collins for his timber-tug to haul beams? The oxen had gone to Lewes after lime. Did he promise me a set of iron cramps or ties for the roof? They never came to hand, or else they were spaulty or cracked. So with everything. Nothing said, but naught done except I stood by them, and then done amiss. I thought the country-side was fair bewitched.'

' It was, sure-ly,' said Puck, knees under chin. ' Did you never suspect ary one? '

' Not till Sebastian came for his guns, and John Collins played him the same dog's tricks as he'd played me with my ironwork. Week in, week out, two of three serpentines would be flawed in the casting, and only fit, they said, to be remelted. Then John Collins would shake his head, and vow he could pass no cannon for the King's service that were not perfect. Saints! How Sebastian stormed! I know, for we sat on this bench sharing our sorrows inter-common.

' When Sebastian had fumed away six weeks at Lindens and gotten just six serpentines, Dirk Brenzett, Master of the *Cygnet* hoy, sends me word that the block of stone he was fetching me from France for our new font he'd hove overboard to lighten his ship, chased by Andrew Barton up to Rye Port.'

' Ah! The pirate! ' said Dan.

' Yes. And while I am tearing my hair over this, Ticehurst Will, my best mason, comes to me shaking, and vowing that the Devil, horned, tailed, and chained, has run out on him from the church-tower, and the men would work there no more. So I took 'em off the foundations, which we were strengthening, and went into the Bell Tavern for a cup of ale. Says Master John Collins: " Have it your own way, lad; but if I was you, I'd take the sinnification o' the sign, and leave old Barnabas' Church alone! " And they all wagged their sinful heads, and agreed. Less afraid of the Devil than of me—as I saw later.

' When I brought my sweet news to Lindens, Sebastian was limewash-ing the kitchen-beams for Mother. He loved her like a son.

' " Cheer up, lad," he says. " God's where He was. Only you and I chance to be pure pute asses. We've been tricked, Hal, and more shame to me, a sailor, that I did not guess it before! You must leave your belfry alone, forsooth, because the Devil is adrift there; and I cannot get my serpentines because John Collins cannot cast them aright. Meantime Andrew Barton hawks off the Port of Rye. And why? To take those very serpentines

which poor Cabot must whistle for; the said serpentines, I'll wager my share of new Continents, being now hid away in St. Barnabas' church-tower. Clear as the Irish coast at noonday! "

' " They'd sure never dare to do it," I said; " and, for another thing, selling cannon to the King's enemies is black treason—hanging and fine."

' " It is sure, large profit. Men'll dare any gallows for that. I have been a trader myself," says he. " We must be upsides with 'em for the honour of Bristol."

' Then he hatched a plot, sitting on the limewash bucket. We gave out to ride o' Tuesday to London and made a show of taking farewells of our friends—especially of Master John Collins. But at Wadhurst Woods we turned; rode home to the water-meadows; hid our horses in a willow-tot at the foot of the glebe, and, come night, stole a-tiptoe up hill to Barnabas' Church again. A thick mist, and a moon striking through.

' I had no sooner locked the tower-door behind us than over goes Sebastian full length in the dark.

' " Pest! " he says. " Step high and feel low, Hal. I've stumbled over guns before."

' I groped, and one by one—the tower was pitchy dark—I counted the lither barrels of twenty serpentines laid out on pease straw. No conceal at all!

' " There's two demi-cannon my end," says Sebastian, slapping metal. " They'll be for Andrew Barton's lower deck. Honest—honest John Collins! So this is his warehouse, his arsenal, his armoury! Now, see you why your pokings and pryings have raised the Devil in Sussex? You've hindered John's lawful trade for months," and he laughed where he lay.

' A clay-cold tower is no fireside at midnight, so we climbed the belfry stairs, and there Sebastian trips over a cow-hide with its horns and tail.

' " Aha! Your Devil has left his doublet! Does it become me, Hal? " He draws it on and capers in the slits of window-moonlight—won'erful devilish-like. Then he sits on the stairs, rapping with his tail on a board, and his back-aspect was dreader than his front, and a howlet lit in, and screeched at the horns of him.

' " If you'd keep out the Devil, shut the door," he whispered. " And that's another false proverb, Hal, for I can hear your tower-door opening."

' " I locked it. Who a-plague has another key, then? " I said.

' " All the congregation, to judge by their feet," he says, and peers into the blackness. " Still! Still, Hal! Hear 'em grunt! That's more o' my serpentines, I'll be bound. One—two—three—four they bear in! Faith, Andrew equips himself like an admiral! Twenty-four serpentines in all! "

' As if it had been an echo, we heard John Collins's voice come up all hollow: " Twenty-four serpentines and two demi-cannon. That's the full tally for Sir Andrew Barton."

' " Courtesy costs naught," whispers Sebastian. " Shall I drop my dagger on his head? "

' " They go over to Rye o' Thursday in the wool-wains, hid under the wool packs. Dirk Brenzett meets them at Udimore, as before," says John.

' " Lord! What a worn, handsmooth trade it is! " says Sebastian. " I lay we are the sole two babes in the village that have not our lawful share in the venture."

' There was a full score folk below, talking like all Robertsbridge Market. We counted them by voice.

' Master John Collins pipes: " The guns for the French carrack must lie here next month. Will, when does your young fool (me, so please you!) come back from Lunnon? "

' " No odds," I heard Ticehurst Will answer. " Lay 'em just where you've a mind, Mus' Collins. We're all too afraid o' the Devil to mell with the tower now." And the long knave laughed.

' " Ah! 'tis easy enow for you to raise the Devil, Will," says another —Ralph Hobden of the Forge.

' " Aaa-men! " roars Sebastian, and ere I could hold him, he leaps down the stairs—won'erful devilish-like—howling no bounds. He had scarce time to lay out for the nearest than they ran. Saints, how they ran! We heard them pound on the door of the Bell Tavern, and then we ran too.

' " What's next? " says Sebastian, looping up his cow-tail as he leaped the briars. " I've broke honest John's face."

' " Ride to Sir John Pelham's," I said. " He is the only one that ever stood by me."

' We rode to Brightling, and past Sir John's lodges, where the keepers would have shot at us for deer-stealers, and we had Sir John down into his Justice's chair, and when we had told him our tale and showed him the cow-

hide which Sebastian wore still girt about him, he laughed till the tears ran.

' " Wel-a-well! " he says. " I'll see justice done before daylight. What's your complaint? Master Collins is my old friend."

' " He's none of mine," I cried. " When I think how he and his likes have baulked and dozened and cozened me at every turn over the church " —and I choked at the thought.

' " Ah, but ye see now they needed it for another use," says he, smoothly.

' " So they did my serpentines," Sebastian cries. " I should be half across the Western Ocean by now if my guns had been ready. But they're sold to a Scotch pirate by your old friend."

' " Where's your proof? " says Sir John, stroking his beard.

' " I broke my shins over them not an hour since, and I heard John give order where they were to be taken," says Sebastian.

' " Words! Words only," says Sir John. " Master Collins is somewhat of a liar at best."

' He carried it so gravely that, for the moment, I thought he was dipped in this secret traffick too, and that there was not an honest ironmaster in Sussex.

' " Name o' Reason! " says Sebastian, and raps with his cow-tail on the table, " whose guns are they, then? "

' " Yours, manifestly," says Sir John. " You come with the King's Order for 'em, and Master Collins casts them in his foundry. If he chooses to bring them up from Nether Forge and lay 'em out in the church-tower, why they are e'en so much the nearer to the main road, and you are saved a day's hauling. What a coil to make of a mere act of neighbourly kindness, lad! "

' " I fear I have requited him very scurvily," says Sebastian, looking at his knuckles. " But what of the demi-cannon? I could do with 'em well, but they are not in the King's Order."

' " Kindness—loving-kindness," says Sir John. " Questionless, in his zeal for the King and his love for you, John adds those two cannon as a gift. 'Tis plain as this coming daylight, ye stockfish! "

' " So it is," says Sebastian. " Oh, Sir John, Sir John, why did you never use the sea? You are lost ashore." And he looked on him with great love.

' " I do my best in my station." Sir John strokes his beard again and rolls forth his deep drumming Justice's voice thus: " But—suffer me!—you two lads, on some midnight frolic into which I probe not, roystering around the taverns, surprise Master Collins at his "—he thinks a moment—" at his good deeds done by stealth. Ye surprise him, I say, cruelly."

' " Truth, Sir John. If you had seen him run! " says Sebastian.

' " On this you ride breakneck to me with a tale of pirates, and wool-wains, and cow-hides, which, though it hath moved my mirth as a man, offendeth my reason as a magistrate. So I will e'en accompany you back to

the tower with, perhaps, some few of my own people, and three-four wagons, and I'll be your warrant that Master John Collins will freely give you your guns and your demi-cannon, Master Sebastian." He breaks into his proper voice—" I warned the old tod and his neighbours long ago that they'd come to trouble with their side-sellings and bye-dealings; but we cannot have half Sussex hanged for a little gun-running. Are ye content, lads? "

' " I'd commit any treason for two demi-cannon," said Sebastian, and rubs his hands.

' " Ye have just compounded with rank treason-felony for the same bribe," says Sir John. " Wherefore to horse, and get the guns." '

' But Master Collins meant the guns for Sir Andrew Barton all along, didn't he? ' said Dan.

' Questionless, that he did,' said Hal. ' But he lost them. We poured into the village on the red edge of dawn, Sir John horsed, in half-armour, his pennon flying; behind him thirty stout Brightling knaves, five abreast; behind them four wool-wains, and behind them four trumpets to triumph over the jest, blowing: " Our King went forth to Normandie." When we halted and rolled the ringing guns out of the tower, 'twas for all the world like Friar Roger's picture of the French siege in the Queen's Missal-book.'

' And what did we—I mean, what did our village do? ' said Dan.

' Oh! Bore it nobly—nobly,' cried Hal. ' Though they had tricked me, I was proud of them. They came out of their housen, looked at that little army as though it had been a post, and went their shut-mouthed way. Never a sign! Never a word! They'd ha' perished sooner than let Brightling overcrow us. Even that villain, Ticehurst Will, coming out of the Bell for his morning ale, he all but runs under Sir John's horse.

' " 'Ware, Sirrah Devil! " cries Sir John, reining back.

' " Oh! " says Will. " Market day, is it? And all the bullocks from Brightling here? "

' I spared him his belting for that—the brazen knave!

' But John Collins was our masterpiece! He happened along-street (his jaw tied up where Sebastian had clouted him) when we were trundling the first demi-cannon through the lych-gate.

' " I reckon you'll find her middlin' heavy," he says. " If you've a mind to pay, I'll loan ye my timber-tug. She won't lie easy on ary wool-wain."

' That was the one time I ever saw Sebastian taken flat aback. He opened and shut his mouth, fishy-like.

' " No offence," says Master John. " You've got her reasonable good cheap. I thought ye might not grudge me a groat if I helped move her." Ah, he was a masterpiece! They say that morning's work cost our John two hundred pounds, and he never winked an eyelid, not even when he saw the guns all carted off to Lewes.'

' Neither then nor later? ' said Puck.

' Once. 'Twas after he gave St. Barnabas' the new chime of bells. (Oh, there was nothing the Collinses, or the Hayes, or the Fowles, or the

Fenners would not do for the church then! "Ask and have" was their
song.) We had rung 'em in, and he was in the tower with Black Nick
Fowle, that gave us our rood-screen. The old man pinches the bell-rope one
hand and scratches his neck with t'other. "'Sooner she was pulling yon
clapper than my neck," he says. That was all! That was Sussex—seely
Sussex for everlastin'! '

'And what happened after?' said Una.

'I went back into England,' said Hal, slowly. 'I'd had my lesson
against pride. But they tell me I left St. Barnabas' a jewel—justabout a
jewel! Wel-a-well! 'Twas done for and among my own people, and—Father
Roger was right—I never knew such trouble or such triumph since. That's
the nature o' things. A dear—dear land.' He dropped his chin on his chest.

'There's your Father at the Forge. What's he talking to old Hobden
about?' said Puck, opening his hand with three leaves in it.

Dan looked towards the cottage.

'Oh, I know. It's that old oak lying across the brook. Pater always
wants it grubbed.'

In the still valley they could hear old Hobden's deep tones.

'Have it as you've a mind to,' he was saying. 'But the vivers of her
roots they hold the bank together. If you grub her out, the bank she'll
all come tearin' down, an' next floods the brook'll swarve up. But have it
as you've a mind. The mistuss she sets a heap by the ferns on her trunk.'

'Oh! I'll think it over,' said the Pater.

Una laughed a little bubbling chuckle.

'What Devil's in that belfry?' said Hal, with a lazy laugh. 'That
should be a Hobden by his voice.'

'Why, the oak is the regular bridge for all the rabbits between the
Three Acre and our meadow. The best place for wires on the farm, Hobden
says. He's got two there now,' Una answered. 'He won't ever let it be
grubbed!'

'Ah, Sussex! Silly Sussex for everlastin',' murmured Hal; and the next
moment their Father's voice calling across to Little Lindens broke the spell
as little St. Barnabas' clock struck five.

A SMUGGLER'S SONG

If you wake at midnight, and hear a horse's feet,
Don't go drawing back the blind, or looking in the street.
Them that asks no questions isn't told a lie.
Watch the wall, my darling, while the Gentlemen go by!

Five and twenty ponies,
Trotting through the dark—
Brandy for the Parson,

'Baccy for the Clerk;
Laces for a lady; letters for a spy;

And watch the wall, my darling, while the Gentlemen go by!

Running round the woodlump if you chance to find
Little barrels, roped and tarred, all full of brandy-wine;
Don't you shout to come and look, nor take 'em for your play;
Put the brishwood back again,—and they'll be gone next day!

If you see the stableyard setting open wide;
If you see a tired horse lying down inside;
If your mother mends a coat cut about and tore;
If the lining's wet and warm—don't you ask no more!

If you meet King George's men, dressed in blue and red,
You be careful what you say, and mindful what is said.
If they call you ' pretty maid,' and chuck you 'neath the chin,
Don't you tell where no one is, nor yet where no one's been!

Knocks and footsteps round the house—whistles after dark—
You've no call for running out till the house-dogs bark.
Trusty's here, and Pincher's here, and see how dumb they lie!
They don't fret to follow when the Gentlemen go by!

If you do as you've been told, 'likely there's a chance,
You'll be give a dainty doll, all the way from France,
With a cap of Valenciennes, and a velvet hood—
A present from the Gentlemen, along o' being good!

Five and twenty ponies,
Trotting through the dark—
Brandy for the Parson,
'Baccy for the Clerk.

Them that asks no questions isn't told a lie—
Watch the wall, my darling, while the Gentlemen go by!

'DYMCHURCH FLIT'

THE BEE BOY'S SONG

Bees! Bees! Hark to your bees!
' Hide from your neighbours as much as you please,
But all that has happened, to us you must tell,
Or else we will give you no honey to sell! '

A maiden in her glory,
 Upon her wedding-day,
Must tell her Bees the story,
 Or else they'll fly away.
 Fly away—die away—
 Dwindle down and leave you!
 But if you don't deceive your Bees,
 Your Bees will not deceive you.

Marriage, birth or buryin',
 News across the seas,
All you're sad or merry in,
 You must tell the Bees.
 Tell 'em coming in an' out,
 Where the Fanners fan,
 'Cause the Bees are justabout
 As curious as a man.

Don't you wait where trees are,
 When the lightnings play;
Nor don't you hate where Bees are,
 Or else they'll pine away.
 Pine away—dwine away—
 Anything to leave you!
 But if you never grieve your Bees,
 Your Bees'll never grieve you.

JUST at dusk, a soft September rain began to fall on the hop-pickers. The mothers wheeled the bouncing perambulators out of the gardens; bins were put away, and tally-books made up. The young couples strolled home, two to each umbrella, and the single men walked behind them laughing. Dan and Una, who had been picking after their lessons, marched off to roast potatoes at the oast-house, where old Hobden, with Blue-eyed Bess, his lurcher dog, lived all the month through, drying the hops.

They settled themselves, as usual, on the sack-strewn cot in front of the fires, and, when Hobden drew up the shutter, stared, as usual, at the flameless bed of coals spouting its heat up the dark well of the old-fashioned roundel. Slowly he cracked off a few fresh pieces of coal, packed them, with fingers that never flinched, exactly where they would do most good; slowly he reached behind him till Dan tilted the potatoes into his iron scoop of a hand; carefully he arranged them round the fire, and then stood for a moment, black against the glare. As he closed the shutter, the oast-house seemed dark before the day's end, and he lit the candle in the lanthorn. The children liked all these things because they knew them so well.

The Bee Boy, Hobden's son, who is not quite right in his head, though he can do anything with bees, slipped in like a shadow. They only guessed it when Bess's stump-tail wagged against them.

A big voice began singing outside in the drizzle:—

' Old Mother Laidinwool had nigh twelve months been dead,
She heard the hops were doing well, and then popped up her head.'

' There can't be two people made to holler like that! ' cried old Hobden, wheeling round.

' For, says she, " The boys I've picked with when I was young and fair,
They're bound to be at hoppin', and I'm— " '

A man showed at the doorway.

' Well, well! They do say hoppin'll draw the very deadest, and now I belieft 'em. You, Tom? Tom Shoesmith! ' Hobden lowered his lanthorn.

' You're a hem of a time makin' your mind to it, Ralph! ' The stranger strode in—three full inches taller than Hobden, a gray-whiskered, brown-faced giant with clear blue eyes. They shook hands, and the children could hear the hard palms rasp together.

' You ain't lost none o' your grip,' said Hobden. ' Was it thirty or forty year back you broke my head at Peasmarsh Fair? '

' Only thirty an' no odds 'tween us regardin' heads, neither. You had it back at me with a hop-pole. How did we get home that night? Swimmin'? '

' Same way the pheasant come into Gubbs's pocket—by a little luck an' a deal o' conjurin'.' Old Hobden laughed in his deep chest.

' I see you've not forgot your way about the woods. D'ye do any o' this still? ' The stranger pretended to look along a gun.

Hobden answered with a quick movement of the hand as though he were pegging down a rabbit-wire.

' No. That's all that's left me now. Age she must as Age she can. An' what's your news since all these years? '

' Oh, I've bin to Plymouth, I've bin to Dover—
I've bin ramblin', boys, the wide world over,'

the man answered cheerily. ' I reckon I know as much of Old England as most.' He turned towards the children and winked boldly.

' I lay they told you a sight o' lies, then. I've been into England fur as Wiltsheer once. I was cheated proper over a pair of hedging-gloves,' said Hobden.

' There's fancy-talkin' everywhere. You've cleaved to your own parts pretty middlin' close, Ralph.'

' Can't shift an old tree 'thout it dyin',' Hobden chuckled. ' An' I be no more anxious to die than you look to be to help me with my hops to-night.'

The great man leaned against the brick-work of the roundel, and swung his arms abroad. ' Hire me! ' was all he said, and they stumped upstairs laughing.

The children heard their shovels rasp on the cloth where the yellow hops lie drying above the fires, and all the oast-house filled with the sweet, sleepy smell as they were turned.

' Who is it? ' Una whispered to the Bee Boy.

' Dunno, no more'n you—if you dunno,' said he, and smiled.

The voices on the drying-floor talked and chuckled together, and the heavy footsteps moved back and forth. Presently a hop-pocket dropped through the press-hole overhead, and stiffened and fattened as they shovelled it full. ' Clank! ' went the press, and rammed the loose stuff into tight cake.

' Gentle! ' they heard Hobden cry. ' You'll bust her crop if you lay on so. You be as careless as Gleason's bull, Tom. Come an' sit by the fires. She'll do now.'

They came down, and as Hobden opened the shutter to see if the potatoes were done Tom Shoesmith said to the children, ' Put a plenty salt on 'em. That'll show you the sort o' man I be.' Again he winked, and again the Bee Boy laughed and Una stared at Dan.

' I know what sort o' man you be,' old Hobden grunted, groping for the potatoes round the fire.

' Do ye? ' Tom went on behind his back. ' Some of us can't abide Horseshoes, or Church Bells, or Running Water; an', talkin' o' runnin' water '—he turned to Hobden, who was backing out of the roundel—' d'you mind the great floods at Robertsbridge, when the miller's man was drowned in the street? '

' Middlin' well.' Old Hobden let himself down on the coals by the fire door. ' I was courtin' my woman on the Marsh that year. Carter to Mus' Plum I was, gettin' ten shillin's week. Mine was a Marsh woman.'

' Won'erful odd-gates place—Romney Marsh,' said Tom Shoesmith. ' I've heard say the world's divided like into Europe, Ashy, Afriky, Ameriky, Australy, an' Romney Marsh.'

' The Marsh folk think so,' said Hobden. ' I had a hem o' trouble to get my woman to leave it.'

' Where did she come out of? I've forgot, Ralph.'

'Dymchurch under the Wall,' Hobden answered, a potato in his hand.

'Then she'd be a Pett—or a Whitgift, would she?'

'Whitgift.' Hobden broke open the potato and ate it with the curious neatness of men who make most of their meals in the blowy open. 'She growed to be quite reasonable-like after livin' in the Weald awhile, but our first twenty year or two she was odd-fashioned, no bounds. And she was a won'erful hand with bees.' He cut away a little piece of potato and threw it out to the door.

'Ah! I've heard say the Whitgifts could see farther through a millstone than most,' said Shoesmith. 'Did she, now?'

'She was honest-innocent of any nigromancin',' said Hobden. 'Only she'd read signs and sinnifications out o' birds flyin', stars fallin', bees hivin', and such. An' she'd lie awake—listenin' for calls, she said.'

'That don't prove naught,' said Tom. 'All Marsh folk has been smugglers since time everlastin'. 'Twould be in her blood to listen out o' nights.'

'Nature-ally,' old Hobden replied, smiling. 'I mind when there was smugglin' a sight nearer us than what the Marsh be. But that wasn't my woman's trouble. 'Twas a passel o' no-sense talk,' he dropped his voice, 'about Pharisees.'

'Yes. I've heard Marsh men belieft in 'em.' Tom looked straight at the wide-eyed children beside Bess.

'Pharisees?' cried Una. 'Fairies? Oh, I see!'

'People o' the Hills,' said the Bee Boy, throwing half of his potato towards the door.

'There you be!' said Hobden, pointing at him. 'My boy, he has her eyes and her out-gate senses. That's what she called 'em!'

'And what did you think of it all?'

'Um—um,' Hobden rumbled. 'A man that uses fields an' shaws after dark as much as I've done, he don't go out of his road excep' for keepers.'

'But settin' that aside?' said Tom, coaxingly. 'I saw ye throw the Good Piece out-at-doors just now. Do ye believe or—do ye?'

'There was a great black eye to that tater,' said Hobden, indignantly.

'My liddle eye didn't see un, then. It looked as if you meant it for— for Any One that might need it. But settin' that aside. D'ye believe or —do ye?'

'I ain't sayin' nothin', because I've heard naught, an' I've seen naught. But if you was to say there was more things after dark in the shaws than men, or fur, or feather, or fin, I dunno as I'd go far about to call you a liar. Now turn again, Tom. What's your say?'

'I'm like you. I say nothin'. But I'll tell you a tale, an' you can fit it as how you please.'

'Passel o' no-sense stuff,' growled Hobden, but he filled his pipe.

'The Marsh men they call it Dymchurch Flit,' Tom went on slowly. 'Hap you have heard it?'

'My woman she've told it me scores o' times. Dunno as I didn't end by belieftin' it—sometimes.'

Hobden crossed over as he spoke, and sucked with his pipe at the yellow lanthorn flame. Tom rested one great elbow on one great knee, where he sat among the coal.

'Have you ever bin in the Marsh?' he said to Dan.

'Only as far as Rye, once,' Dan answered.

'Ah, that's but the edge. Back behind of her there's steeples settin' beside churches, an' wise women settin' beside their doors, an' the sea settin' above the land, an' ducks herdin' wild in the diks' (he meant ditches). 'The Marsh is justabout riddled with diks an' sluices, an' tide-gates an' water-lets. You can hear 'em bubblin' an' grummelin' when the tide works in 'em, an' then you hear the sea rangin' left and right-handed all up along the Wall. You've seen how flat she is—the Marsh? You'd think nothin' easier than to walk eend-on acrost her? Ah, but the diks an' the water-lets, they twists the roads about as ravelly as witch-yarn on the spindles. So ye get all turned round in broad daylight.'

'That's because they've dreened the waters into the diks,' said Hobden. 'When I courted my woman the rushes was green—Eh me! the rushes was green—an' the Bailiff o' the Marshes, he rode up and down as free as the fog.'

'Who was he?' said Dan.

'Why, the Marsh fever an' ague. He've clapped me on the shoulder once or twice till I shook proper. But now the dreenin' off of the waters have done away with the fevers; so they make a joke, like, that the Bailiff o' the Marshes broke his neck in a dik. A won'erful place for bees an' ducks 'tis too.'

'An' old,' Tom went on. 'Flesh an' Blood have been there since Time Everlastin' Beyond. Well, now, speakin' among themselves, the Marsh men say that from Time Everlastin' Beyond, the Pharisees favoured the Marsh above the rest of Old England. I lay the Marsh men ought to know. They've been out after dark, father an' son, smugglin' some one thing or t'other, since ever wool grew to sheep's backs. They say there was always a middlin' few Pharisees to be seen on the Marsh. Impident as rabbits, they was. They'd dance on the nakid roads in the nakid daytime; they'd flash their liddle green lights along the diks, comin' an' goin', like honest smugglers. Yes, an' times they'd lock the church doors against parson an' clerk of Sundays.'

'That 'ud be smugglers layin' in the lace or the brandy till they could run it out o' the Marsh. I've told my woman so,' said Hobden.

'I'll lay she didn't belieft it, then—not if she was a Whitgift. A won'erful choice place for Pharisees, the Marsh, by all accounts, till Queen Bess's father he come in with his Reformatories.'

'Would that be a Act o' Parliament like?' Hobden asked.

'Sure-ly. 'Can't do nothing in Old England without Act, Warrant, an' Summons. He got his Act allowed him, an', they say, Queen Bess's father

he used the parish churches something shameful. Justabout tore the gizzards out of I dunnamany. Some folk in England they held with 'en; but some they saw it different, an' it eended in 'em takin' sides an' burnin' each other no bounds, accordin' which side was top, time bein'. That tarrified the Pharisees: for Good-will among Flesh an' Blood is meat an' drink to 'em, an' ill-will is poison.'

'Same as bees,' said the Bee Boy. 'Bees won't stay by a house where there's hating.'

'True,' said Tom. 'This Reformations tarrified the Pharisees same as the reaper goin' round a last stand o' wheat tarrifies rabbits. They packed into the Marsh from all parts, and they says, "Fair or foul, we must flit out o' this, for Merry England's done with, an' we're reckoned among the Images."'

'Did they all see it that way?' said Hobden.

'All but one that was called Robin—if you've heard of him. What are you laughing at?' Tom turned to Dan. 'The Pharisees's trouble didn't tech Robin, because he'd cleaved middlin' close to people like. No more he never meant to go out of Old England—not he; so he was sent messagin' for help among Flesh an' Blood. But Flesh an' Blood must always think of their own concerns, an' Robin couldn't get through at 'em, ye see. They thought it was tide-echoes off the Marsh.'

'What did you—what did the fai—Pharisees want?' Una asked.

'A boat, to be sure. Their liddle wings could no more cross Channel than so many tired butterflies. A boat an' a crew they desired to sail 'em over to France, where yet awhile folks hadn't tore down the Images. They couldn't abide cruel Canterbury Bells ringin' to Bulverhithe for more pore men an' women to be burnded, nor the King's proud messenger ridin' through the land givin' orders to tear down the Images. They couldn't abide it no shape. Nor yet they couldn't get their boat an' crew to flit by without Leave an' Good-will from Flesh an' Blood; an' Flesh an' Blood came an' went about its own business the while the Marsh was swarvin' up, an' swarvin' up with Pharisees from all England over, striving all means to get through at Flesh an' Blood to tell 'em their sore need. . . . I don't know as you've ever heard say Pharisees are like chickens?'

'My woman used to say that too,' said Hobden, folding his brown arms.

'They be. You run too many chickens together, an' the ground sickens like, an' you get a squat, an' your chickens die. 'Same way, you crowd Pharisees all in one place—they don't die, but Flesh an' Blood walkin' among 'em is apt to sick up an' pine off. They don't mean it, an' Flesh an' Blood don't know it, but that's the truth—as I've heard. The Pharisees through bein' all stenched up an' frighted, an' tryin' to come through with their supplications, they nature-ally changed the thin airs and humours in Flesh an' Blood. It lay on the Marsh like thunder. Men saw their churches ablaze with the wildfire in the windows after dark; they saw their cattle scatterin' and no man scarin'; their sheep flockin' and no man drivin'; their horses

latherin' an' no man leadin'; they saw the liddle low green lights more than ever in the dik-sides; they heard the liddle feet patterin' more than ever round the houses; an' night an' day, day an' night, 'twas all as though they were bein' creeped up on, and hinted at by Some One or other that couldn't rightly shape their trouble. Oh, I lay they sweated! Man an' maid, woman an' child, their Nature done 'em no service all the weeks while the Marsh was swarvin' up with Pharisees. But they was Flesh an' Blood, an' Marsh men before all. They reckoned the signs sinnified trouble for the Marsh. Or that the sea 'ud rear up against Dymchurch Wall an' they'd be drownded like Old Winchelsea; or that the Plague was comin'. So they looked for the meanin' in the sea or in the clouds—far an' high up. They never thought to look near an' knee-high, where they could see naught.

' Now there was a poor widow at Dymchurch under the Wall, which, lacking man or property, she had the more time for feeling; and she come to feel there was a Trouble outside her doorstep bigger an' heavier than aught she'd ever carried over it. She had two sons—one born blind, and t'other struck dumb through fallin' off the Wall when he was liddle. They was men grown, but not wage-earnin', an' she worked for 'em, keepin' bees and answerin' Questions.'

' What sort of questions? ' said Dan.

' Like where lost things might be found, an' what to put about a crooked baby's neck, an' how to join parted sweethearts. She felt the Trouble on the Marsh same as eels feel thunder. She was a wise woman.'

' My woman was won'erful weather-tender, too,' said Hobden. 'I've seen her brish sparks like off a anvil out of her hair in thunderstorms. But she never laid out to answer Questions.'

' This woman was a Seeker like, an' Seekers they sometimes find. One night, while she lay abed, hot an' aching, there come a Dream an' tapped at her window, and " Widow Whitgift," it said, " Widow Whitgift! "

' First, by the wings an' the whistling, she thought it was peewits, but last she arose an' dressed herself, an' opened her door to the Marsh, an' she felt the Trouble an' the Groaning all about her, strong as fever an' ague, an' she calls: " What is it? Oh, what is it? "

' Then 'twas all like the frogs in the diks peeping: then 'twas all like the reeds in the diks clip-clapping; an' then the great Tide-wave rummelled along the Wall, an' she couldn't hear proper.

' Three times she called, an' three times the Tide-wave did her down. But she catched the quiet between, an' she cries out, " What is the Trouble on the Marsh that's been lying down with my heart an' arising with my body this month gone? " She felt a liddle hand lay hold on her gown-hem, an' she stooped to the pull o' that liddle hand.'

Tom Shoesmith spread his huge fist before the fire and smiled at it as he went on.

' " Will the sea drown the Marsh? " she says. She was a Marsh-woman first an' foremost.

' "No," says the liddle voice. " Sleep sound for all o' that."

' " Is the Plague comin' to the Marsh? " she says. Them was all the ills she knowed.

' " No. Sleep sound for all o' that," says Robin.

' She turned about, half mindful to go in, but the liddle voices grieved that shrill an' sorrowful she turns back, an' she cries: " If it is not a Trouble of Flesh an' Blood, what can I do? "

' The Pharisees cried out upon her from all round to fetch them a boat to sail to France, an' come back no more.

' " There's a boat on the Wall," she says, " but I can't push it down to the sea, nor sail it when 'tis there."

' " Lend us your sons," says all the Pharisees. " Give 'em Leave an' Good-will to sail it for us, Mother—O Mother! "

' " One's dumb, an' t'other's blind," she says. " But all the dearer me for that; and you'll lose them in the big sea." The voices justabout pierced through her; an' there was children's voices too. She stood out all she could, but she couldn't rightly stand against that. So she says: " If you can draw my sons for your job, I'll not hinder 'em. You can't ask no more of a Mother."

' She saw them liddle green lights dance an' cross till she was dizzy; she heard them liddle feet patterin' by the thousand; she heard cruel Canterbury Bells ringing to Bulverhithe, an' she heard the great Tide-wave ranging along the Wall. That was while the Pharisees was workin' a Dream to wake her two sons asleep: an' while she bit on her fingers she saw them two she'd bore come out an' pass her with never a word. She followed 'em, cryin' pitiful, to the old boat on the Wall, an' that they took an' runned down to the Sea.

' When they'd stepped mast an' sail the blind son speaks: " Mother, we're waitin' your Leave an' Good-will to take Them over." '

Tom Shoesmith threw back his head and half shut his eyes.

' Eh, me! ' he said. ' She was a fine, valiant woman, the Widow Whitgift. She stood twistin' the eends of her long hair over her fingers, an' she shook like a poplar, makin' up her mind. The Pharisees all about they hushed their children from cryin' an' they waited dumb-still. She was all their dependence. 'Thout her Leave an' Good-will they could not pass; for she was the Mother. So she shook like a asp-tree makin' up her mind. 'Last she drives the word past her teeth, an' " Go! " she says. " Go with my Leave an' Good-will."

' Then I saw—then, they say, she had to brace back same as if she was wadin' in tide-water; for the Pharisees justabout flowed past her—down the beach to the boat, I dunnamany of 'em—with their wives an' children an' valooables, all escapin' out of cruel Old England. Silver you could hear clinkin', an' liddle bundles hove down dunt on the bottom-boards, an' passels o' liddle swords an' shields raklin', an' liddle fingers an' toes scratchin' on the boatside to board her when the two sons pushed her off. That boat

she sunk lower an' lower, but all the Widow could see in it was her boys movin' hampered-like to get at the tackle. Up sail they did, an' away they went, deep as a Rye barge, away into the off-shore mistes, an' the Widow Whitgift she sat down and eased her grief till mornin' light.'

'I never heard she was all alone,' said Hobden.

'I remember now. The one called Robin he stayed with her, they tell. She was all too grievous to listen to his promises.'

'Ah! She should ha' made her bargain beforehand. I allus told my woman so!' Hobden cried.

'No. She loaned her sons for a pure love-loan, bein' as she sensed the Trouble on the Marshes, an' was simple good-willing to ease it.' Tom laughed softly. 'She done that. Yes, she done that! From Hithe to Bulver-hithe, fretty man an' maid, ailin' woman an' wailin' child, they took the advantage of the change in the thin airs just about as soon as the Pharisees flitted. Folks come out fresh an' shining all over the Marsh like snails after wet. An' that while the Widow Whitgift sat grievin' on the Wall. She might have belieft us—she might have trusted her sons would be sent back! She fussed, no bounds, when their boat come in after three days.'

'And, of course, the sons were both quite cured?' said Una.

'No-o. That would have been out o' Nature. She got 'em back as she sent 'em. The blind man he hadn't seen naught of anything, an' the dumb man nature-ally, he couldn't say aught of what he'd seen. I reckon that was why the Pharisees pitched on 'em for the ferrying job.'

'But what did you—what did Robin promise the Widow?' said Dan.

'What did he promise, now?' Tom pretended to think. 'Wasn't your woman a Whitgift, Ralph? Didn't she ever say?'

'She told me a passel o' no-sense stuff when he was born.' Hobden pointed at his son. 'There was always to be one of 'em that could see farther into a millstone than most.'

'Me! That's me!' said the Bee Boy so suddenly that they all laughed.

'I've got it now!' cried Tom, slapping his knee. 'So long as Whitgift blood lasted, Robin promised there would allers be one o' her stock that—that no Trouble 'ud lie on, no Maid 'ud sigh on, no Night could frighten, no Fright could harm, no Harm could make sin, an' no Woman could make a fool of.'

'Well, ain't that just me?' said the Bee Boy, where he sat in the silver square of the great September moon that was staring into the oast-house door.

'They was the exact words she told me when we first found he wasn't like others. But it beats me how you known 'em,' said Hobden.

'Aha! There's more under my hat besides hair!' Tom laughed and stretched himself. 'When I've seen these two young folk home, we'll make a night of old days, Ralph, with passin' old tales—eh? An' where might you live?' he said, gravely, to Dan. 'An' do you think your Pa 'ud give me a drink for takin' you there, Missy?'

They giggled so at this that they had to run out. Tom picked them both up, set one on each broad shoulder, and tramped across the ferny pasture where the cows puffed milky puffs at them in the moonlight.

'Oh, Puck! Puck! I guessed you right from when you talked about the salt. How could you ever do it?' Una cried, swinging along delighted.

'Do what?' he said, and climbed the stile by the pollard oak.

'Pretend to be Tom Shoesmith,' said Dan, and they ducked to avoid the two little ashes that grow by the bridge over the brook. Tom was almost running.

'Yes. That's my name, Mus' Dan,' he said, hurrying over the silent shining lawn, where a rabbit sat by the big white-thorn near the croquet ground. 'Here you be.' He strode into the old kitchen yard, and slid them down as Ellen came to ask questions.

'I'm helping in Mus' Spray's oast-house,' he said to her. 'No, I'm no foreigner. I knowed this country 'fore your Mother was born; an'—yes, it's dry work oasting, Miss. Thank you.'

Ellen went to get a jug, and the children went in—magicked once more by Oak, Ash, and Thorn!

A THREE-PART SONG

I'm just in love with all these three,
The Weald and the Marsh and the Down countrie;
Nor I don't know which I love the most,
The Weald or the Marsh or the white chalk coast!

I've buried my heart in a ferny hill,
Twix' a liddle low shaw an' a great high gill.
Oh hop-bine yaller and wood-smoke blue,
I reckon you'll keep her middling true!

I've loosed my mind for to out and run,
On a Marsh that was old when Kings begun;
Oh Romney Level and Brenzett reeds,
I reckon you know what my mind needs!

I've given my soul to the Southdown grass,
And sheep-bells tinkled where you pass.
Oh Firle an' Ditchling an' sails at sea,
I reckon you keep my soul for me!

THE TREASURE AND THE LAW

SONG OF THE FIFTH RIVER

When first by Eden Tree,
The Four Great Rivers ran,
To each was appointed a Man
Her Prince and Ruler to be.

But after this was ordained,
(The ancient legends tell),
There came dark Israel,
For whom no River remained.

Then He That is Wholly Just,
Said to him: ' Fling on the ground
A handful of yellow dust,
And a Fifth Great River shall run,
Mightier than these Four,
In secret the Earth around;
And Her secret evermore
Shall be shown to thee and thy Race.'

So it was said and done.
And, deep in the veins of Earth,
And, fed by a thousand springs
That comfort the market-place,
Or sap the power of Kings,
The Fifth Great River had birth,
Even as it was foretold—
The Secret River of Gold!

And Israel laid down
His sceptre and his crown,
To brood on that River bank,
Where the waters flashed and sank,
And burrowed in earth and fell,
And bided a season below;
For reason that none might know,
Save only Israel.

He is Lord of the Last—
The Fifth, most wonderful, Flood.
He hears Her thunder past
And Her Song is in his blood.
He can foresay: ' She will fall,'
For he knows which fountain dries,
Behind which desert-belt
A thousand leagues to the South.
He can foresay: ' She will rise.'
He knows what far snows melt;
Along what mountain-wall
A thousand leagues to the North.
He snuffs the coming drought
As he snuffs the coming rain,
He knows what each will bring forth,
And turns it to his gain.

A Prince without a Sword,
A Ruler without a Throne;
Israel follows his quest.
In every land a guest,
Of many lands a lord,

In no land King is he.
But the Fifth Great River keeps
The secret of Her deeps
For Israel alone,
As it was ordered to be.

NOW it was the third week in November, and the woods rang with
the noise of pheasant-shooting. No one hunted that steep, cramped country
except the village beagles, who, as often as not, escaped from their kennels
and made a day of their own. Dan and Una found a couple of them towling
round the kitchen-garden after the laundry cat. The little brutes were only
too pleased to go rabbiting, so the children ran them all along the brook
pastures and into Little Lindens farm-yard, where the old sow vanquished
them—and up to the quarry-hole, where they started a fox. He headed for
Far Wood, and there they frightened out all the pheasants, who were shelter-
ing from a big beat across the valley. Then the cruel guns began again, and
they grabbed the beagles lest they should stray and get hurt.

' I wouldn't be a pheasant—in November—for a lot,' Dan panted, as
he caught Folly by the neck. ' Why did you laugh that horrid way? '

' I didn't,' said Una, sitting on Flora, the fat lady-dog. ' Oh, look! The
silly birds are going back to their own woods instead of ours, where they
would be safe.'

'Safe till it pleased you to kill them.' An old man, so tall he was almost a giant, stepped from behind the clump of hollies by Volaterrae. The children jumped, and the dogs dropped like setters. He wore a sweeping gown of dark thick stuff, lined and edged with yellowish fur, and he bowed a bent-down bow that made them feel both proud and ashamed. Then he looked at them steadily, and they stared back without doubt or fear.

'You are not afraid?' he said, running his hands through his splendid gray beard. 'Not afraid that those men yonder'—he jerked his head towards the incessant 'pop-pop' of the guns from the lower woods—'will do you hurt?'

'We-ell'—Dan liked to be accurate, especially when he was shy—'old Hobd—a friend of mine told me that one of the beaters got peppered last week—hit in the leg, I mean. You see, Mr. Meyer will fire at rabbits. But he gave Waxy Garnett a quid—sovereign, I mean—and Waxy told Hobden he'd have stood both barrels for half the money.'

'He doesn't understand,' Una cried, watching the pale, troubled face. 'Oh, I wish—'

She had scarcely said it when Puck rustled out of the hollies and spoke to the man quickly in foreign words. Puck wore a long cloak too—the afternoon was just frosting down—and it changed his appearance altogether.

'Nay, nay!' he said at last. 'You did not understand the boy. A freeman was a little hurt, by pure mischance, at the hunting.'

'I know that mischance! What did his Lord do? Laugh and ride over him?' the old man sneered.

'It was one of your own people did the hurt, Kadmiel.' Puck's eyes twinkled maliciously. 'So he gave the freeman a piece of gold, and no more was said.'

'A Jew drew blood from a Christian and no more was said?' Kadmiel cried. 'Never! When did they torture him?'

'No man may be bound, or fined, or slain till he has been judged by his peers,' Puck insisted. 'There is but one Law in Old England for Jew or Christian—the Law that was signed at Runnymede.'

'Why, that's Magna Charta!' Dan whispered. It was one of the few history dates that he could remember. Kadmiel turned on him with a sweep and a whirr of his spicy-scented gown.

'Dost thou know of that, babe?' he cried, and lifted his hands in wonder.

'Yes,' said Dan, firmly.

> 'Magna Charta was signed by John,
> That Henry the Third put his heel upon.

And old Hobden says that if it hadn't been for her (he calls everything "her," you know), the keepers would have him clapped in Lewes Gaol all the year round.'

Again Puck translated to Kadmiel in the strange, solemn-sounding language, and at last Kadmiel laughed.

' Out of the mouths of babes do we learn,' said he. ' But tell me now, and I will not call you a babe but a Rabbi, why did the King sign the roll of the New Law at Runnymede? For he was a King.'

Dan looked sideways at his sister. It was her turn.

' Because he jolly well had to,' said Una, softly. ' The Barons made him.'

' Nay,' Kadmiel answered, shaking his head. ' You Christians always forget that gold does more than the sword. Our good King signed because he could not borrow more money from us bad Jews.' He curved his shoulders as he spoke. ' A King without gold is a snake with a broken back, and '—his nose sneered up and his eyebrows frowned down—' it is a good deed to break a snake's back. That was my work,' he cried, triumphantly, to Puck. ' Spirit of Earth, bear witness that that was my work! ' He shot up to his full towering height, and his words rang like a trumpet. He had a voice that changed its tone almost as an opal changes colour—sometimes deep and thundery, sometimes thin and waily, but always it made you listen.

' Many people can bear witness to that,' Puck answered. ' Tell these babes how it was done. Remember, Master, they do not know Doubt or Fear.'

' So I saw in their faces when we met,' said Kadmiel. ' Yet surely, surely they are taught to spit upon Jews? '

' Are they? ' said Dan, much interested. ' Where at? '

Puck fell back a pace, laughing. ' Kadmiel is thinking of King John's reign,' he explained. ' His people were badly treated then.'

' Oh, we know that,' they answered, and (it was very rude of them, but they could not help it) they stared straight at Kadmiel's mouth to see if his teeth were all there. It stuck in their lesson-memory that King John used to pull out Jews' teeth to make them lend him money.

Kadmiel understood the look and smiled bitterly.

' No. Your King never drew my teeth: I think, perhaps, I drew his. Listen! I was not born among Christians, but among Moors—in Spain— in a little white town under the mountains. Yes, the Moors are cruel, but at least their learned men dare to think. It was prophesied of me at my birth that I should be a Lawgiver to a People of a strange speech and a hard language. We Jews are always looking for the Prince and the Lawgiver to come. Why not? My people in the town (we were very few) set me apart as a child of the prophecy—the Chosen of the Chosen. We Jews dream so many dreams. You would never guess it to see us slink about the rubbish-heaps in our quarter; but at the day's end—doors shut, candles lit—aha! then we become the Chosen again.'

He paced back and forth through the wood as he talked. The rattle of the shot-guns never ceased, and the dogs whimpered a little and lay flat on the leaves.

' I was a Prince. Yes! Think of a little Prince who had never known

rough words in his own house handed over to shouting, bearded Rabbis, who pulled his ears and filliped his nose, all that he might learn—learn—learn to be King when his time came. He! Such a little Prince it was! One eye he kept on the stone-throwing Moorish boys, and the other it roved about the streets looking for his Kingdom. Yes, and he learned to cry softly when he was hunted up and down those streets. He learned to do all things without noise. He played beneath his father's table when the Great Candle was lit, and he listened as children listen to the talk of his father's friends above the table. They came across the mountains, from out of all the world, for my Prince's father was their counsellor. They came from behind the armies of Sala-ud-Din: from Rome: from Venice: from England. They stole down our alley, they tapped secretly at our door, they took off their rags, they arrayed themselves, and they talked to my father at the wine. All over the world the heathen fought each other. They brought news of these wars, and while he played beneath the table, my Prince heard these meanly-dressed ones decide between themselves how and when, and for how long King should draw sword against King, and People rise up against People. Why not? There can be no war without gold, and we Jews know how the earth's gold moves with the seasons, and the crops, and the winds; circling and looping and rising and sinking away like a river—a wonderful underground river. How should the foolish Kings know that while they fight and steal and kill? '

The children's faces showed that they knew nothing at all as, with open eyes, they trotted and turned beside the long-striding old man. He twitched his gown over his shoulders, and a square plate of gold, studded with jewels, gleamed for an instant through the fur, like a star through flying snow.

' No matter,' he said. ' But, credit me, my Prince saw peace or war decided not once, but many times, by the fall of a coin spun between a Jew from Bury and a Jewess from Alexandria, in his father's house, when the Great Candle was lit. Such power had we Jews among the Gentiles. Ah, my little Prince! Do you wonder that he learned quickly? Why not? ' He muttered to himself and went on:—

' My trade was that of a physician. When I had learned it in Spain I went to the East to find my Kingdom. Why not? A Jew is as free as a sparrow—or a dog. He goes where he is hunted. In the East I found libraries where men dared to think—schools of medicine where they dared to learn. I was diligent in my business. Therefore I stood before Kings. I have been a brother to Princes and a companion to beggars, and I have walked between the living and the dead. There was no profit in it. I did not find my Kingdom. So, in the tenth year of my travels, when I had reached the Uttermost Eastern Sea, I returned to my father's house. God had wonderfully preserved my people. None had been slain, none even wounded, and only a few scourged. I became once more a son in my father's house. Again the Great Candle was lit; again the meanly-apparelled ones tapped on our door after

dusk; and again I heard them weigh out peace and war, as they weighed out the gold on the table. But I was not rich—not very rich. Therefore, when those that had power and knowledge and wealth talked together, I sat in the shadow. Why not?

'Yet all my wanderings had shown me one sure thing, which is, that a King without money is like a spear without a head. He cannot do much harm. I said, therefore, to Elias of Bury, a great one among our people: "Why do our people lend any more to the Kings that oppress us?" "Because," said Elias, "if we refuse they stir up their people against us, and the People are tenfold more cruel than Kings. If thou doubtest, come with me to Bury in England and live as I live."

'I saw my mother's face across the candle flame, and I said, "I will come with thee to Bury. Maybe my Kingdom shall be there."

'So I sailed with Elias to the darkness and the cruelty of Bury in England, where there are no learned men. How can a man be wise if he hate? At Bury I kept his accounts for Elias, and I saw men kill Jews there by the tower. No—none laid hands on Elias. He lent money to the King, and the King's favour was about him. A King will not take the life so long as there is any gold. This King—yes, John—oppressed his people bitterly because they would not give him money. Yet his land was a good land. If he had only given it rest he might have cropped it as a Christian crops his beard. But even that little he did not know, for God had deprived him of all understanding, and had multiplied pestilence, and famine, and despair upon the people. Therefore his people turned against us Jews, who are all people's dogs. Why not? Lastly the Barons and the people rose together against the King because of his cruelties. Nay—nay—the Barons did not love the people, but they saw that if the King cut up and destroyed the common people, he would presently destroy the Barons. They joined then, as cats and pigs will join to slay a snake. I kept the accounts, and I watched all these things, for I remembered the Prophecy.

'A great gathering of Barons (to most of whom we had lent money) came to Bury, and there, after much talk and a thousand runnings-about, they made a roll of the New Laws that they would force on the King. If he swore to keep those Laws, they would allow him a little money. That was the King's God—Money—to waste. They showed us the roll of the New Laws. Why not? We had lent them money. We knew all their counsels—we Jews shivering behind our doors in Bury.' He throw out his hands suddenly. 'We did not seek to be paid all in money. We sought Power—Power—Power! That is our God in our captivity. Power to use!

'I said to Elias: "These New Laws are good. Lend no more money to the King: so long as he has money he will lie and slay the people."

'"Nay," said Elias. "I know this people. They are madly cruel. Better one King than a thousand butchers. I have lent a little money to the Barons, or they would torture us, but my most I will lend to the King. He hath promised me a place near him at Court, where my wife and I shall be safe."

' "But if the King be made to keep these New Laws," I said, " the land will have peace, and our trade will grow. If we lend he will fight again."

' "Who made thee a Lawgiver in England? " said Elias. " I know this people. Let the dogs tear one another! I will lend the King ten thousand pieces of gold, and he can fight the Barons at his pleasure."

' "There are not two thousand pieces of gold in all England this summer," I said, for I kept the accounts, and I knew how the earth's gold moved—that wonderful underground river. Elias barred home the windows, and, his hands about his mouth, he told me how, when he was trading with small wares in a French ship, he had come to the Castle of Pevensey.'

' Oh! ' said Dan. ' Pevensey again! ' and looked at Una, who nodded and skipped.

' There, after they had scattered his pack up and down the Great Hall, some young knights carried him to an upper room, and dropped him into a well in a wall, that rose and fell with the tide. They called him Joseph, and threw torches at his wet head. Why not? '

' Why, of course,' cried Dan. ' Didn't you know it was— ' Puck held up his hand to stop him, and Kadmiel, who never noticed, went on.

' When the tide dropped he thought he stood on old armour, but feeling with his toes, he raked up bar on bar of soft gold. Some wicked treasure of the old days put away, and the secret cut off by the sword. I have heard the like before.'

' So have we,' Una whispered. ' But it wasn't wicked a bit.'

' Elias took a little of the stuff with him, and thrice yearly he would return to Pevensey as a chapman, selling at no price or profit, till they suffered him to sleep in the empty room, where he would plumb and grope, and steal away a few bars. The great store of it still remained, and by long brooding he had come to look on it as his own. Yet when we thought how we should lift and convey it, we saw no way. This was before the Word of the Lord had come to me. A walled fortress possessed by Normans; in the midst a forty-foot tide-well out of which to remove secretly many horse-loads of gold! Hopeless! So Elias wept. Adah, his wife, wept too. She had hoped to stand beside the Queen's Christian tiring-maids at Court, when the King should give them that place at Court which he had promised. Why not? She was born in England—an odious woman.

' The present evil to us was that Elias, out of his strong folly, had, as it were, promised the King that he would arm him with more gold. Wherefore the King in his camp stopped his ears against the Barons and the people. Wherefore men died daily. Adah so desired her place at Court that she besought Elias to tell the King where the treasure lay, that the King might take it by force, and—they would trust to his gratitude! Why not? This Elias refused to do, for he looked on the gold as his own. They quarrelled, and they wept at the evening meal, and late in the night came one Langton—a priest, almost learned—to borrow more money for the Barons. Elias and Adah went to their chamber.'

Kadmiel laughed scornfully in his beard. The shots across the valley stopped as the shooting party changed their ground for the last beat.

' So it was I, not Elias,' he went on, quietly, ' that made terms with Langton touching the fortieth of the New Laws.'

' What terms? ' said Puck, quickly. ' The Fortieth of the Great Charter says: " To none will we sell, refuse, or deny right or justice." '

' True, but the Barons had written first: " To no free man." It cost me two hundred broad pieces of gold to change those narrow words. Langton, the priest, understood. " Jew though thou art," said he, " the change is just, and if ever Christian and Jew come to be equal in England thy people may thank thee." Then he went out stealthily, as men do who deal with Israel by night. I think he spent my gift upon his altar. Why not? I have spoken with Langton. He was such a man as I might have been if—if we Jews had been a people. But yet, in many things, a child.

' I heard Elias and Adah abovestairs quarrel, and, knowing the woman was the stronger, I saw that Elias would tell the King of the gold and that the King would continue in his stubbornness. Therefore I saw that the gold must be put away from the reach of any man. Of a sudden, the Word of the Lord came to me saying, " The Morning is come, O thou that dwellest in the land." '

Kadmiel halted, all black against the pale green sky beyond the wood— a huge robed figure, like a Moses in the picture-Bible.

' I rose. I went out, and as I shut the door on that House of Foolishness, the woman looked from the window and whispered, " I have prevailed on my husband to tell the King! " I answered, " There is no need. The Lord is with me."

' In that hour the Lord gave me full understanding of all that I must do; and His Hand covered me in my ways. First I went to London, to a physician of our people, who sold me certain drugs that I needed. You shall see why. Thence I went swiftly to Pevensey. Men fought all around me, for there were neither rulers nor judges in the abominable land. Yet when I walked by them they cried out that I was one Ahasuerus, a Jew, condemned, as they believe, to live for ever, and they fled from me everyways. Thus the Lord saved me for my work, and at Pevensey I bought me a little boat and moored it on the mud beneath the Marsh-gate of the Castle. That also God showed me.'

He was as calm as though he were speaking of some stranger, and his voice filled the little bare wood with rolling music.

' I cast '—his hand went to his breast, and again the strange jewel gleamed—' I cast the drugs which I had prepared into the common well of the Castle. Nay, I did no harm. The more we physicians know, the less do we do. Only the fool says: " I dare." I caused a blotched and itching rash to break out upon their skins, but I knew it would fade in fifteen days. I did not stretch out my hand against their life. They in the Castle thought it was the Plague, and they ran out, taking with them their very dogs.

'A Christian physician, seeing that I was a Jew and a stranger, vowed that I had brought the sickness from London. This is the one time I have ever heard a Christian leech speak truth of any disease. Thereupon the people beat me, but a merciful woman said: "Do not kill him now. Push him into our Castle with his plague, and if, as he says, it will abate on the fifteenth day, we can kill him then." Why not? They drove me across the drawbridge of the Castle, and fled back to their booths. Thus I came to be alone with the treasure.'

'But did you know this was going to happen just right?' said Una.

'My Prophecy was that I should be a Lawgiver to a People of a strange land and a hard speech. I knew I should not die. I washed my cuts. I found the tide-well in the wall, and from Sabbath to Sabbath I dove and dug there in that empty, Christian-smelling fortress. He! I spoiled the Egyptians! He! If they had only known! I drew up many good loads of gold, which I loaded by night into my boat. There had been golddust too, but that had been washed out by the tides.'

'Didn't you ever wonder who had put it there?' said Dan, stealing a glance at Puck's calm, dark face under the hood of his gown. Puck shook his head and pursed his lips.

'Often; for the gold was new to me,' Kadmiel replied. 'I know the Golds. I can judge them in the dark; but this was heavier and redder than any we deal in. Perhaps it was the very gold of Parvaim. Eh, why not? It went to my heart to heave it on to the mud, but I saw well that if the evil thing remained, or if even the hope of finding it remained, the King would not sign the New Laws, and the land would perish.'

'Oh, Marvel!' said Puck, beneath his breath, rustling in the dead leaves.

'When the boat was loaded I washed my hands seven times, and pared beneath my nails, for I would not keep one grain. I went out by the little gate where the Castle's refuse is thrown. I dared not hoist sail lest men should see me; but the Lord commanded the tide to bear me carefully, and I was far from land before the morning.'

'Weren't you afraid?' said Una.

'Why? There were no Christians in the boat. At sunrise I made my prayer, and cast the gold—all—all that gold into the deep sea! A King's ransom—no, the ransom of a People! When I had loosed hold of the last bar, the Lord commanded the tide to return me to a haven at the mouth of a river, and thence I walked across a wilderness to Lewes, where I have brethren. They opened the door to me, and they say—I had not eaten for two days—they say that I fell across the threshold, crying, "I have sunk an army with horsemen in the sea!"'

'But you hadn't,' said Una. 'Oh, yes! I see! You meant that King John might have spent it on that?'

'Even so,' said Kadmiel.

The firing broke out again close behind them. The pheasants poured

over the top of a belt of tall firs. They could see young Mr. Meyer, in his new yellow gaiters, very busy and excited at the end of the line, and they could hear the thud of the falling birds.

'But what did Elias of Bury do?' Puck demanded. 'He had promised money to the King.'

Kadmiel smiled grimly. 'I sent him word from London that the Lord was on my side. When he heard that the Plague had broken out in Pevensey, and that a Jew had been thrust into the Castle to cure it, he understood my word was true. He and Adah hurried to Lewes and asked me for an accounting. He still looked on the gold as his own. I told them where I had laid it, and I gave them full leave to pick it up. . . . Eh, well! The curses of a fool and the dust of a journey are two things no wise man can escape. . . . But I pitied Elias! The King was wroth to him because he could not lend; the Barons were wroth to him because they heard that he would have lent to the King; and Adah was wroth to him because she was an odious woman. They took ship from Lewes to Spain. That was wise!'

'And you? Did you see the signing of the Law at Runnymede?' said Puck, as Kadmiel laughed noiselessly.

'Nay. Who am I to meddle with things too high for me? I returned to Bury, and lent money on the autumn crops. Why not?'

There was a crackle overhead. A cock-pheasant that had sheered aside after being hit spattered down almost on top of them, driving up the dry leaves like a shell. Flora and Folly threw themselves at it; the children rushed forward, and when they had beaten them off and smoothed down the plumage Kadmiel had disappeared.

'Well,' said Puck, calmly, 'what did you think of it? Weland gave the Sword! The Sword gave the Treasure, and the Treasure gave the Law. It's as natural as an oak growing.'

'I don't understand. Didn't he know it was Sir Richard's old treasure?' said Dan. 'And why did Sir Richard and Brother Hugh leave it lying about? And—and—'

'Never mind,' said Una, politely. 'He'll let us come and go, and look, and know another time. Won't you, Puck?'

'Another time maybe,' Puck answered. 'Brr! It's cold—and late. I'll race you towards home!'

They hurried down into the sheltered valley. The sun had almost sunk behind Cherry Clack, the trodden ground by the cattle-gates was freezing at the edges, and the new-waked north wind blew the night on them from over the hills. They picked up their feet and flew across the browned pastures, and when they halted, panting in the steam of their own breath, the dead leaves whirled up behind them. There was Oak and Ash and Thorn enough in that year-end shower to magic away a thousand memories.

So they trotted to the brook at the bottom of the lawn, wondering why Flora and Folly had missed the quarry-hole fox.

Old Hobden was just finishing some hedge-work. They saw his white smock glimmer in the twilight where he faggoted the rubbish.

'Winter, he's come, I rackon, Mus' Dan,' he called. 'Hard times now till Heffle Cuckoo Fair. Yes, we'll all be glad to see the Old Woman let the Cuckoo out o' the basket for to start lawful Spring in England.'

They heard a crash, and a stamp and a splash of water as though a heavy old cow were crossing almost under their noses.

Hobden ran forward angrily to the ford.

'Gleason's bull again, playin' Robin all over the Farm! Oh, look, Mus' Dan—his great footmark as big as a trencher. No bounds to his impidence! He might count himself to be a man or—or Somebody—'

A voice the other side of the brook boomed:

> 'I wonder who his cloak would turn
> When Puck had led him round,
> Or where those walking fires would burn—'

Then the children went in singing 'Farewell Rewards and Fairies' at the tops of their voices. They had forgotten that they had not even said good-night to Puck.

THE CHILDREN'S SONG

Land of our Birth, we pledge to thee
Our love and toil in the years to be;
When we are grown and take our place,
As men and women with our race.

Father in Heaven who lovest all,
Oh help Thy children when they call;
That they may build from age to age,
An undefiled heritage.

Teach us to bear the yoke in youth,
With steadfastness and careful truth;
That, in our time, Thy Grace may give
The Truth whereby the Nations live.

Teach us to rule ourselves alway,
Controlled and cleanly night and day;
That we may bring, if need arise,
No maimed or worthless sacrifice.

Teach us to look in all our ends,
On Thee for judge, and not our friends;
That we, with Thee, may walk uncowed
By fear or favour of the crowd.

Teach us the Strength that cannot seek,
By deed or thought, to hurt the weak;
That, under Thee, we may possess
Man's strength to comfort man's distress.

Teach us Delight in simple things,
And Mirth that has no bitter springs;
Forgiveness free of evil done,
And Love to all men 'neath the sun!

Land of our Birth, our faith, our pride,
For whose dear sake our fathers died;
O Motherland, we pledge to thee,
Head, heart, and hand through the years to be!